963006

D1401250

PHYSICS

An Exact Science

To my daughter
VERNITA

 SCIENCE PROGRAM

SCIENCE IN EVERYDAY LIFE
Obourn, Heiss, Montgomery

BIOLOGY—A BASIC SCIENCE
Heiss, Lape

CHEMISTRY—A BASIC SCIENCE
Hogg, Alley, Bickel

PHYSICS—A BASIC SCIENCE
Burns, Verwiebe, Hazel, Van Hooft

PHYSICS—AN EXACT SCIENCE
White

PHYSICAL SCIENCE—A BASIC COURSE
Hogg, Cross, Vordenberg

EARTH SCIENCE—THE WORLD WE LIVE IN
Namowitz, Stone

PHYSICS
An Exact Science

HARVEY E. WHITE
Professor of Physics and
Director of the Lawrence Hall of Science
University of California

With the assistance of
EUGENE F. PECKMAN
Supervisor of Science, Pittsburgh, Pennsylvania
Public Schools

D. VAN NOSTRAND COMPANY, INC.
PRINCETON, NEW JERSEY
NEW YORK, N. Y.
TORONTO, CANADA
LONDON, ENGLAND

D. VAN NOSTRAND COMPANY, INC. *(Principal Office)*
120 Alexander Street, Princeton, New Jersey

D. VAN NOSTRAND COMPANY, INC.
24 West 40 Street, New York 18

D. VAN NOSTRAND COMPANY (Canada), **LTD.**
25 Hollinger Road, Toronto 16, Canada

D. VAN NOSTRAND COMPANY, LTD.
358, Kensington High Street, London W. 14

Copyright 1959 by D. Van Nostrand Company, Inc.
Published simultaneously in Canada by
D. Van Nostrand Company (Canada), Ltd.

*All rights in this book are reserved. No repro-
duction in any form of this book, in whole
or in part (except for brief quotation in critical articles or reviews), may be made without written authorization from the publishers.*

Designed by Lewis F. White

Library of Congress Card No. 59-12778
Printed in the United States of America
05634a200

Preface

THIS BOOK is designed to be used as a high-level introductory physics text in a challenging science program. It assumes that the student is being introduced for the first time to the basic principles of physics and that he or she has had a previous introduction to the simplest elements of algebra and plane geometry.

The inspiration for writing this book stemmed from the recognized need for a modern, up-to-date text that follows the same sequence as the one hundred sixty-two half-hour film lessons recorded in Pittsburgh, Pennsylvania, during the academic year 1956-57. The book is complete in itself and is designed to be entirely suitable as an introductory physics text without reference to the films. A book of laboratory exercises containing the fifty-six laboratory experiments referred to in the text is available for coordinated use, and is strongly recommended for all students whether laboratory facilities and equipment are available or not.

The text is divided into twelve units. The first five units are designed to be used for the first semester's work and are composed of fifty-one daily lessons, while the remaining seven units are designed to be used for the second semester's work and are composed of fifty-five daily lessons.

The book on laboratory exercises is unique in its treatment of experiments. Where equipment and facilities are available for any of the experiments described, the instructions in the book may be followed by the student in the laboratory, and the sample calculations that are given may be used as a student guide in the completion of a laboratory report. Where equipment or facilities are not available, the complete set of data recorded in the book may be adopted as the student's data, and the same sample calculations can be used as a guide to the completion of a laboratory report.

The increasing importance of electronics as well as atomic and nuclear physics through their application to other branches of knowledge and research has given rise to a growing demand for the inclusion of these subjects in the introductory physics course. Consequently the last twenty-one lessons of the text are devoted to these subjects.

Where the allotted time schedule for physics does not permit the utilization of all the lessons, the author suggests the omission of the subjects of Sound and/or Heat, and strongly recommends the retention of Mechanics, Electricity and Magnetism, Atomic Physics, Electronics, Quantum Optics, and Nuclear Physics.

Since most of the lessons depend upon principles, concepts, and laws presented in the preceding text and laboratory lessons, it is advisable to study the daily lessons and laboratory exercises in their assigned numerical order.

At lesson ends there are a *Summary,* highlighting the major principles discussed; *Questions,* designed to check the student's mastery and understanding of the subject matter; and *Problems,* intended to test the student's ability to apply the principles he has learned in the solution of specific problems. Some problems, as indicated by an

asterisk, are more difficult than the others, and have been included to provide a challenge to the abler student.

Sound motion picture films of 30 minutes each may be used in conjunction with any or all lessons. These films were produced through the joint cooperation of Dr. Alvin C. Eurich of the Fund for the Advancement of Education; Dr. E. A. Dimmick, Superintendent of the Pittsburgh Public Schools; Dr. Alfred W. Beattie, Superintendent of Allegheny County Schools, Pennsylvania; Mr. John F. White, General Manager of Educational Station WQED-TV; and Encyclopaedia Britannica Films Inc., of Wilmette, Illinois. The author serves as teacher in all film lessons.

Berkeley, California   HARVEY E. WHITE
June, 1959

Contents

---

* Laboratory experiments—found in separate laboratory manual, to which the italicized page numbers refer.

PROPERTIES OF MATTER

INTRODUCTION

The Parts of all homogeneal hard Bodies which fully touch one another, stick together very strongly. And for explaining how this may be, some have invented hooked Atoms, which is begging the Question. . . . I had rather infer from their Cohesion that their Particles attract one another by some Force, which in immediate Contact is exceeding strong, . . . and reaches not far from the Particles with any sensible Effect. . . . There are therefore Agents in Nature able to make the Particles of Bodies stick together by very strong Attractions. And it is the Business of experimental Philosophy to find them out.

Sir Isaac Newton, *Opticks*, 1704

← A stainless steel wire holds a gold-plated sphere that swings continuously as a pendulum in the main lobby of the General Assembly Building at the United Nations Headquarters in New York. This pendulum, as did the one in the original experiment of Jean Bernard Foucault, offers us visual proof of the rotation of the earth on its axis as the freely swinging pendulum shifts in its plane.

United Nations

Physics,
An Exact Science

PHYSICS is a natural science concerned primarily with the principles and laws governing the behavior of the inanimate world around us. As a science it is a continuous time-ordered process by which civilized man, through experimentation, reasoning, and mathematical analysis, learns more and more of the seemingly endless detail of natural phenomena.

In attempting to establish the origin of science, many historians go back in time, more than two thousand years, to the era of the great philosophers Thales, Pythagoras, Democritus, Hippocrates, Aristotle, Archimedes, Ptolemy, and their contemporaries. Others prefer to begin with Roger Bacon, Copernicus, Tycho Brahe, Kepler, William Harvey, and men of science who lived less than a thousand years ago. All of these men are considered great because in their respective lives they exhibited a keen sense of observation and they applied their powers of reasoning to the explanation of many natural phenomena. While many of the concepts they formulated showed remarkable insight, progress was relatively slow because they overlooked one all-important factor—they failed to recognize the importance of experimentation. Herein lies the secret to the rapid advancement of science in this, the twentieth century.

The two most powerful tools of modern science are (1) *the empirical method,* often called *experimental physics,* and (2) *the method of mathematical analysis,* often called *theoretical physics.* Since many people today point to physics as the most basic and, at the same time, the most exact of all the sciences, we can well expect both of these methods to find their way into this book. In the following pages, then, we will see not only the development of the experimental method through the performance of many demonstration experiments but also the application of the simplest mathematical relations to the recorded measurements made during the experiments.

It should be realized from the beginning that there are many sciences and that physics is but one of them. It is common practice to divide all of the recognized sciences into three classes: the physical sciences, the life sciences, and the social sciences. Under these headings we find, for example,

PHYSICAL SCIENCES

> Physics
> Chemistry
> Astronomy
> Geology, etc.

LIFE SCIENCES

> Biology
> Botany
> Physiology
> Paleontology, etc.

SOCIAL SCIENCES

> Political Science
> Social Science
> Economics
> Anthropology, etc.

What Is Physics? Physics is a science that involves many different subjects. These subjects may be divided and grouped under one of two headings, **Classical Physics** and **Modern Physics**. Classical physics is concerned largely with macroscopic bodies, that is, with those phenomena in which the objects involved are large and can be seen with the naked eye. Modern physics, on the other hand, is concerned primarily with the submicroscopic world, that is, with those phenomena in which the structure and the behavior of individual atoms and molecules are of prime importance.

It will be worth while, at this point, to consider briefly the various subdivisions of physics and to note the order in which they will here be studied.

CLASSICAL PHYSICS

> Mechanics
> Properties of Matter

> Heat
> Sound
> Light
> Electricity and Magnetism

MODERN PHYSICS

> Atomic Physics
> Electronics
> Quantum Optics
> Nuclear Physics

Mechanics. Mechanics is a branch of physics dealing largely with the state or motion of bodies resulting from the action of applied forces. As we study mechanics, such fundamental concepts as **speed, velocity**, and **acceleration**—as well as **force, mass, work, energy**, and **momentum**—will become familiar terms.

Properties of Matter. This is a general title applied to many and varied subjects involving the **solid, liquid**, and **gaseous** states of matter. As we delve into the subject, we will see how such practical things as the **stretching, twisting**, and **bending** of solid objects, and the **pressure, density**, and **buoyancy of liquids and gases**, can all be described in terms of simple rules and laws.

Heat. Under this heading, we will study not only the nature of heat but also the physical changes brought about by raising or lowering the temperature of a body. We will also study, for example, the principles upon which a refrigerator or a natural geyser operates, and the basis upon which an automobile, turbojet, or rocket engine performs.

Sound. Here is a practical branch of physics that should be of interest to everyone. In addition to the general subject of waves and vibrations, we will study the science of musical sounds and musical instruments, along with the transmission and speed of sound through solids, liquids, and gases, and that detection of sound which we call hearing.

Light. Visible and invisible light will be studied under many and varied conditions. The reflection, refraction, and polarization of light, as well as the optical properties of mirrors, prisms, and lenses, will be taken up in detail. Laboratory demonstrations, showing why the sky is blue and why the sun may turn yellow, orange, and red at sunset, will be explained.

Electricity and Magnetism. No one can deny the importance of these areas of physics in our lives today. We will study the principles of electric currents and circuits of various kinds, electric motors and generators, transformers, and alternating currents. In our investigation of magnetism we will study the earth's magnetic field as well as the power of electromagnets.

Atomic Physics. This is a field in which we study atoms and their external structure, electrons, protons, isotopes, X rays, and radioactivity. Much of our present day knowledge of atomic structure has been determined by studies of light sources and the wave lengths of the light they emit, called spectra.

Electronics. Any mention of the word electronics brings many devices to mind. Here we will study such things as vacuum tubes and how they work, oscillators, amplifiers, radar, television, and the photoelectric effect.

Quantum Optics. This is a subject dealing with the quantum theory of light and of its relation to atoms and their electronic structure. As strange as it may seem, atomic processes are not smooth and continuous, but go by jumps.

Nuclear Physics. As we study the atomic nucleus, nuclear energy, and atomic accelerators, we step out onto the threshold of scientific research as it is being carried on today. Among other things we will study nuclear disintegration, transmutation, and cosmic rays.

Such are the branches of that science we call physics.

Questions

1. Name the ten branches of physics to be studied in this book.

2. Name two physical sciences, two life sciences, and two social sciences.

3. Name three of the great philosophers living more than one thousand years ago.

4. What phenomena occur in civil life or in nature that you can associate directly with each of the ten subdivisions of physics?

Introduction | Lesson 2

OPTICAL ILLUSIONS

Physics as an Objective Method. It has long been known that when experiments are to be performed one cannot rely too much upon the human senses of touch, sight, hearing, etc., to make accurate observations. Methods of measurement which rely upon the senses entirely are called **subjective methods.** Methods which make use of scientific instruments are generally called **objective methods.**

In the early history of science, laws were frequently discovered by the use of subjective methods. Progress was slow, however, until such methods were replaced by objective methods using measuring instruments devised to give greater and greater precision.

It is true that many scientific discoveries have been made in the past with what we now would call the crudest of apparatus and equipment. It is the development of precision instruments and apparatus, however, which has, particularly within the last several decades, led to discoveries which are far-reaching in their theoretical implications and are of extreme practical importance to the advancement of civilization.

As an introduction to the subject of physics we will first consider a number of experiments illustrating the false impressions so easily arrived at from the use of subjective methods of observation. Although these experiments are of the nature of an entertainment, they do have more serious aspects, for they demonstrate the necessity for using objective methods in advancing science.

Subjective Methods. If someone asks you to determine the temperature of a pan of water, your first impulse, if the water is not too hot, is to use your hand or your finger tips and not to bother looking for a thermometer. To illustrate the gross inaccuracy of the touch in determining temperature, consider the three pans of water as shown in Fig. A. If the hand is first held for some little time in the pan containing **cold** water and then plunged into the **warm** water, the senses tell

cold   warm   hot

Fig. A. Experiment illustrating the uncertainty of subjective methods of measurement.

you it is hot. If, however, the hand is first held in the **hot** water and then plunged into the **warm** water, your senses tell you it is cold. Your conclusion in either case is thus influenced by your experiences immediately preceding your determination of the temperature of the middle pan. When a thermometer is used in this experiment, the same temperature will be arrived at in either case. Although this latter would be called an objective method of measurement, one still relies upon the senses to obtain a reading of the thermometer scale.

Optical Illusions. In making many scientific measurements the eye is considered as the most useful of all recording instruments. In some instances, however, the eye is not and should not be used directly in making observations, since it cannot be relied upon to observe what is really there. To illustrate how unreliable the sense of vision can be in some cases we will consider a number of examples commonly referred to as "optical illusions."

Of the hundreds of well-known optical illusions only a few of the most interesting ones will be presented here. In Fig. B is a group of six figures classified as illusions due to **lines** and **angles.** In (a), the first figure, the brim of the hat is as long as the hat is high; in (b) the diagonal lines of each parallelo-

Fig. B. Optical illusions with lines and angles.

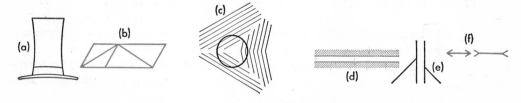

Fig. C. Which figure is tallest? Measure them.

gram are of the same length; and in (c) the perfect circle appears to be distorted. In figure (d) the two horizontal lines are parallel and straight and in (f) they are of equal length. In (e) the lower right-hand line if extended will intersect the left-hand line where it joins the vertical.

Fig. C is an example of *perspective*, an illusion suggesting depth to the picture when in reality it is flat. Actually this figure is a rectangle showing three figures of equal height. By means of slanting lines these figures are made to appear to have different heights. Experiences from early childhood have trained us to interpret the slanting lines as depth.

The next set of illusions, shown in Fig. D, are classified as *equivocal figures*. These illustrate the phenomenon of the *fluctuation* of the process of vision. In figure (a) six cubes may be seen stacked three, two, one, or seven cubes may be seen stacked two, three, two. In (b) a folded sheet of paper is seen opening either toward or away from the reader. In (c) is a flight of steps seen from above looking down, or from below looking up.

Fig. D(d) is one of the most interesting of all illusions. To fully appreciate the effect one must himself perform the experiment with a small wire cube about one inch in size. The cube is held by a small handle at one corner and viewed with one eye at a distance of from 1 to 2 ft. By the principle of fluctuation the observer next tries to make

Fig. D. Optical illusions illustrating fluctuation of the attention.

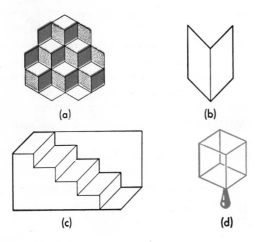

(a)

(b)

(c)

(d)

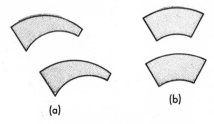

Fig. E. Optical illusions of area.

the farthest corner of the cube appear as the nearest corner. When this condition is attained, the cube upon being turned about a horizontal or vertical axis will appear to turn in the opposite direction. A little practice in the fluctuation of the visual senses is required in this experiment and it is well worth performing.

In Fig. E are two pairs of similar figures of equal area. The slanting lines at the ends make the lower figure in each case appear to be larger than the one immediately above. Such figures should be cut from white cardboard and held one above the other. When the upper figure is interchanged with the corresponding lower figure, one figure seems to grow and the other to shrink before your eyes.

In Fig. F(a) are two small squares of equal size, a white square on a black background, and a black square on a white background. When an image of this is formed on the retina of the eye, the cones and rods just beyond the white edges are stimulated by those nearby, thus causing the white image to be larger than the black one. This phenomenon is called *irradiation* or *brightness contrast*. A similar phenomenon is illustrated in Fig. F(b) where grey spots are seen at the intersections of the white lines.

Complementary Images. When the eyes are subjected to bright light for some little time, the retina seems to show tiring or *fatigue*. Furthermore, continued subjection of any part of the retina to one particular color causes only those cones sensitive to that color to tire. When the same retinal area is subsequently subjected to white light, the previously inactive cones respond more strongly than those originally stimulated and a complementary color is seen.

To observe these colored images, fix the attention on the black star in the lower right-hand corner of the field of the flag in Fig. G and keep it there for about 15 to 20 sec. Then turn the eyes toward a white wall of the room, or toward the open sky, and in one or two seconds the American flag will appear in all of its true colors. Similar effects can be observed with other color photographs.

Delayed images of this kind are always complementary in color to the original pictures, black becomes white, yellow becomes blue, green becomes magenta, magenta becomes green, etc. (For an explanation of complementary colors see Light, Lesson 12.)

The Stroboscopic Effect. When a wagon with spoked wheels is coming to a stop in moving pictures, the wheels are often noticed to stand still, then turn backward, stop, turn forward, and then stop again. This phenomenon, known as the "stroboscopic effect," is due to interrupted illumination of the moving-picture screen and can be illustrated in many ways. An interesting experiment illustrating the phenomenon is shown in Fig. H.

Fig. F. Illustrations of irradiation.

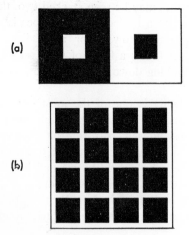

Fig. G. Fatigue images enable the above objects to appear in their natural colors.

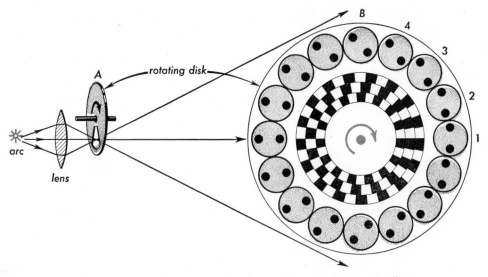

Fig. H. Experimental arrangement for demonstrating the stroboscopic effect.

Two disks are mounted on the shafts of two separate motors. The smaller disk **A** with a narrow slot is used to interrupt the light beam illuminating the larger disk. The disk **B** is white with black circles and dots arranged exactly as shown. Suppose now that disk **A** makes sixteen revolutions per second, thus illuminating disk **B** with sixteen short flashes of light per second. Suppose also that **B** makes only one revolution per second and that one flash of light comes when the disk has the position shown in the figure. Confining the attention to the circle at position (1), the two enclosed dots are one above the other. When the second flash of light appears, the circle (2) will be in position (1) and the two dots will appear to have shifted slightly clockwise. When the next flash of light comes, the circle (3) will be in position (1) and the two dots will have shifted still farther. This process continued shows that the circles will appear to stand still and the dots to rotate within them.

If the light flashes in any such experiment as the one described above are slower than 16 per second, the illuminated object will appear to flicker badly. If, however, the flashes come at an increasingly higher rate, the flicker will soon disappear entirely and the illumination will seem to be steady. The reason for this is that each retinal image is somehow retained by the vision mechanism for about one-sixteenth of a second. This is called the **persistence of vision**.

Summary

Physics is an exact science. It is a science in which objective measurements are made, using precision instruments. Repetition of an experiment produces the same results. While the eye is a remarkable instrument for observing different phenomena, optical illusions often arise, thereby demonstrating that our vision is not always reliable. Measuring instruments are more reliable than the human senses.

Questions

1. Briefly explain what is meant by the subjective method of measurement.

2. How would you measure the length of a table, using the subjective method of measurement?

3. How would you measure the temperature of a pan of water, using an objective method of measurement?

4. Briefly explain how the subjective method enters into the measurement of temperature with a thermometer.

5. What is the stroboscopic effect? Briefly explain.

6. Explain why the wheels of a wagon may appear to turn backward on a motion picture screen when the wagon is moving forward.

7. Briefly explain why motion pictures flicker when the projector runs too slowly, but do not flicker when it runs fast.

8. In what ways are any of the principles developed in this lesson involved in things happening in the world around us?

Introduction | **Lesson 3**

UNITS OF MEASUREMENT

Since physics is a science based upon exact measurement, it is essential that the student first become familiar with several of the more commonly used measuring devices and the units into which each is usually divided. Every measurement, whether it be a distance, a weight, an interval of time, or anything else, requires *two* things: first, a **number**; and second, a **unit**. One might, for example, obtain as the result of the measurement of different distances, **20 feet, 5 miles, 3 rods,** or as the result of the measurement of different weights, **6 pounds, 25 tons, 4½ ounces,** or as the result of the measurement of different time intervals, **7 hours, 26 seconds,** etc. As the result of some experiment or the reading of certain instruments one might obtain the measurements, **10.7 calories, 90 horsepower, 6 volts, 12 kilowatts,** etc. In each case the **unit** is just as essential as the **number** expressing the amount.

Although there are numerous different kinds of units, such as ergs, joules, watts, lumens, candle power, decibels, and amperes, each one can be expressed in terms of not more than three special units. These three, called **fundamental units,** are the units of **length, mass,** and **time.** All other units are called **derived units** since, as we shall see later, they can always be written as some combination of the three fundamental units.

There are in general two widely used sets of fundamental units (a) the **metric,** and (b) the **English.** Throughout the civilized world scientific observations are nearly always expressed in terms of metric units. This set employs the **standard meter** as the unit of length, the **standard kilogram** as the unit of mass, and the **second** as the unit of time.

The Standard Meter and Yard. The standard meter is a platinum-iridium bar about forty inches long which is kept in the vaults of the International Bureau of Weights and Measures near Paris, France. Three facsimiles of this bar are to be found at the United States Bureau of Standards in Washington, D. C. Each of these duplicate copies may be called an **International Prototype Meter** and is now the standard of length in the United States. From these prototypes all other measuring rods and tapes are standardized.

When the standard meter was first devised it was intended that it have a length equal to one ten-millionth part of the distance from one of the earth's poles to the equator. Although more recent measurements of the earth's dimensions have shown that the distance from pole to equator is about 10,000,880 **standard meters** the two groove marks —one on either end of the original platinum-iridium bar—are still taken to be exactly one meter apart.

The standard meter is usually divided into one hundred equal parts. Each of these parts is called the **centimeter.**

$$1 \text{ meter} = 100 \text{ centimeters}$$

or, abbreviated,

$$1 \text{ m} = 100 \text{ cm}$$

The centimeter is further divided into ten equal parts. Each of these parts is called the **millimeter.** See Fig. A.

$$1 \text{ centimeter(cm)} = 10 \text{ millimeters(mm)}$$
$$1000 \text{ millimeters(mm)} = 1 \text{ meter(m)}$$

In civil life in the United States the **yard** is used as the standard unit of length. By an act of Congress in 1866 the standard yard to be used legally in the United States was defined as 3600/3937 part of a standard meter. Since the yard is divided into thirty-six inches,

$$1 \text{ meter(m)} = 39.37 \text{ inches(in.)}$$

With twelve inches to one foot,

$$3 \text{ ft} = 1 \text{ yd}$$
$$1 \text{ ft} = 30.48 \text{ cm}$$
$$1 \text{ in.} = 2.54 \text{ cm}$$

The sizes of the inch, fractions of an inch relative to the centimeter, and millimeter, are illustrated in Fig. A.

When large distances are to be measured, it is convenient as well as customary to use large units of length. Such units are the **kilometer** in the metric system and the **mile** in the English system. One kilometer is equivalent to one thousand meters, and one mile is equivalent to five thousand two hundred and eighty feet.

$$1000 \text{ meters(m)} = 1 \text{ kilometer(km)}$$
$$1 \text{ mile(mi)} = 5280 \text{ feet(ft)}$$

The Standard Kilogram and Pound. The standard unit of mass is the **kilogram,** a block of platinum also preserved at the International Bureau of Weights and Measures near Paris. Two copies of this kilogram (which may be called International Prototype Kilograms) are kept in the vaults of the U. S. Bureau of Standards. The kilogram is divided into one thousand equal parts called **grams.**

$$1000 \text{ grams(gm)} = 1 \text{ kilogram(kg)}$$

The original intent was to base the stand-

Fig. A. Diagram comparing the centimeter scale with the inch scale.

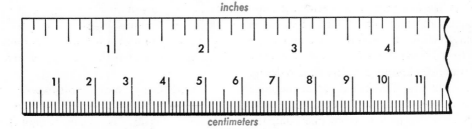

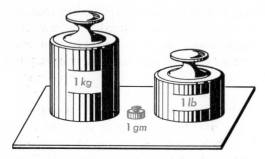

Fig. B. The mass of a standard kilogram is 2.2 times the mass of a standard pound weight.

ard kilogram upon the gram, the gram being the mass of one cubic centimeter of pure water taken at a temperature of four degrees centigrade. See Fig. B.

The standard **pound** is defined in terms of the standard kilogram by the relation that its mass shall equal 0.4536 kilogram. From this we obtain the relations

1 lb = 0.4536 kg	1 oz = 28.35 gm
1 lb = 16 oz	1 kg = 2.205 lb
1 lb = 453.6 gm	1 ton = 2000 lb

The beginning student would do well to memorize some of the above numbers and at the same time become familiar with the names of the various units.

Historical Time Pieces. Instruments for the measurement of time go back historically to the Babylonians, at least, and probably to the time of the Greeks five centuries B.C. The earliest time pieces on record were chiefly water clocks, some of very simple design and others of more elaborate design. These clocks were based upon the very elementary principle that it takes the same time for equal amounts of water to flow through a small opening. The **hour glass,** employing the same principle and using sand instead of water, is an outgrowth of the water clock and dates back to medieval times.

A water clock of moderately simple design is shown in Fig. C. Small holes at the edge of the vanes (shown in the detail diagram) allow the water to flow from one compart-

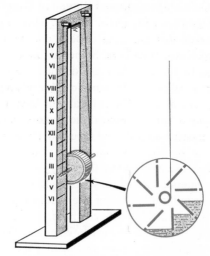

Fig. C. Diagram of an early form of water clock.

ment to the other. This permits the cylinder to turn slowly, thus unwinding the suspending cords.

The **sundial** dates back to the Chaldean astronomer Berosus, who lived about the time of Alexander the Great, 300 B.C. Today, similar instruments serve as ornaments in many of our public parks. A sundial of common design, as shown in Fig. D, consists essentially of a **pin** called a **gnomon** mounted at an angle on a circular plate called the **dial**. The gnomon is mounted in the vertical North and South plane. The edge of the gnomon is

Fig. D. Diagram of a sundial.

parallel to the earth's rotational axis and its purpose is to cast a shadow on the dial which is marked with the hours of the day. Due to the apparent yearly precessional motion of the earth's axis, small corrections must be made to the time as shown by the shadow. These corrections amounting to several minutes are usually engraved upon every sundial. The sundial on the University of California campus, for example, has the following corrections:

Jan. 10, + 17 min   May 20, + 5 min
Feb. 9, + 23 min   June 19, + 10 min
Mar. 11, + 19 min   July 19, + 15 min
Apr. 10, + 8 min   Aug. 18, + 18 min
          Sept. 17, + 4 min
          Oct. 17, − 5 min
          Nov. 16, − 6 min
          Dec. 16, + 5 min

Modern clocks depend for their regulation upon the swinging of a pendulum or the oscillation of a balance wheel. Examples of these are the grandfather clock and the modern wrist watch. Such devices will be discussed later under the heading of vibrations and waves, p. 198. Electric clocks commonly found in the city homes of today are run by tiny electric motors. The speed of these motors is controlled at the city's electric power plant by controlling the frequency of the alternating current supplied to the power lines leading to the house. The master clock at the power house is frequently a pendulum clock.

Time and the Mean Solar Day.   Three kinds of time are always recognized by astronomers: first, *sidereal time;* second, *apparent solar time;* and third, *mean solar time.* The latter is the time used in civil life. If at any given point on the earth's surface we adjust the gnomon of a sundial to lie in the North and South vertical plane, the time interval between two successive transits of the sun's shadow over the twelve o'clock mark is called the apparent solar day. For several reasons, one being that the earth's

orbit around the sun is elliptical, this interval of time varies slightly from day to day. An apparent solar day in December is about one minute longer than an apparent solar day in September. It is clear, therefore, why in this day of accurate time pieces we do not regulate our clocks to apparent solar time.

The **average** length of all apparent solar days throughout a solar year is called the **mean solar day.** This is a satisfactory time interval since it is invariable and can be kept by well regulated clocks and watches. The time interval called the **second** is defined as 1/86400 part of a mean solar day.

$$1 \text{ sec} = 1/60 \times 1/60 \times 1/24$$
$$= 1/86400 \text{ part of one day}$$

There are 365.2421 mean solar days in one solar year; that is, with respect to the sun, the earth makes 365.2421 rotations in making one complete revolution in its orbit.

For astronomical purposes a different time scale known as sidereal time is used. There is one more sidereal day in one solar year than there are mean solar days. One solar year equals 366.2421 sidereal days. The reason for the additional day is that in making one complete turn around the sun in its orbit the earth has actually made 366.2421 rotations with respect to the fixed stars. The sidereal second as ticked off by an astronomical clock is therefore slightly shorter than the second given by an ordinary clock keeping mean solar time.

Metric Units.   Nearly all scientific experiments, in the United States as well as abroad, are performed using metric units. In these units distance is usually measured in millimeters, centimeters, meters, or kilometers; mass is measured in grams or kilograms; and time is measured in seconds, minutes, or hours. In metric units the abbreviation **cgs** means **centimeter, gram, second;** and **mks** means **meter, kilogram, second.**

The English system, as already referred to, uses the foot, yard, and mile as units of length; the ounce, pound, and ton as units of force; and the second as the unit of time. We Americans inherit the English system with all of its cumbersome fractions, and because it is so firmly ingrained in our civil life, it will be a difficult task to ever change over completely to the simpler metric system. There is a strong movement today, however, advocating such a change.

The chief advantage of metric units over English units is that all units are divided into ten or one hundred parts. This enables fractional distances and masses to be expressed as decimals. Decimals, it is well known, are easier to manipulate in the addition, subtraction, multiplication, and division of two or more quantities.

Summary

All measurements in science require a number and a unit.

There are two systems of fundamental units: (a) the metric system and (b) the English system. The metric system is used most widely in science.

Length, mass, and time are called fundamental units, and all others are called derived units. The meter, kilogram, and second are fundamental units in the mks system, and the centimeter, gram, and second are fundamental units in the cgs system.

The foot, pound, and second are the common units of the English system.

The most useful conversion factor is

$$2.54 \text{ cm} = 1 \text{ in.}$$

Questions

1. What are the fundamental units in the mks system?

2. What are the fundamental units in the cgs system?

3. What is the standard kilogram? The standard meter?

4. Where are the standards of length and mass kept in the United States? What is the legal standard of length in the United States? How is the standard yard defined legally?

5. What is an apparent solar day? What is a mean solar day?

6. How many mean solar days are there in one solar year?

7. How many millimeters are there in one kilometer?

8. Upon what was the original standard meter based?

9. Upon what was the original standard kilogram based?

10. Make a list of ten fundamental units of measurements and ten derived units of measurement.

Problems

1. Find the number of centimeters in (a) 4 in. and (b) 5 ft.

2. Find the number of millimeters in (a) 10 in. and (b) 1 ft.

3. Find the number of meters in 1 mi.

4. Find the number of kilometers in 1 mi.

5. Find the number of miles in 1 km.

6. Find the number of grams mass in a weight of 1 lb.

7. Find the number of pounds weight in 1 kg mass.

8. How many seconds are there in 16.5 min?

9. How many minutes are there in 1 week?

10. Calculate the distance to the moon in meters if the distance is 239,000 mi.

Introduction | **Lesson 4**

MEASUREMENT OF DISTANCES AND ANGLES—*Laboratory*

In performing this experiment as described in the accompanying LAB-ORATORY EXERCISES you will learn how to measure the three angles of a triangle using a protractor, and the lengths of the three sides using a centimeter rule. In learning to use these simple measuring instruments you will learn how to interpolate.

SPECIAL LESSONS

. . . inasmuch as they [the Pythagoreans] saw in numbers the properties and proportions of the different kinds of harmonies, and since all other things so far as their entire nature is concerned were modelled upon numbers, whereas numbers are prior to anything else in nature,—from all this they inferred that the first elements of numbers were the first elements of all things that exist, and that the whole heaven was a harmony and a number.

Charles M. Bakewell, *Source Book in Ancient Philosophy,* Scribner's, New York, 1909, pp. 36-37.

Philosophy is written in that very great book, which continually lies open before our eyes (*I mean the Universe*); but we cannot understand it, if we do not first learn the language, and comprehend the characters in which it is written. It is written in the mathematical language, and its characters are triangles, circles and other geometrical figures, without the aid of which it is impossible to understand a word of it, without which one wanders vainly through a dark labyrinth.

Galileo Galilei, *Il Saggiatore,* Florentine Edition, 1842, p. 171.

← The key to our understanding of the world about us in the study of physics is our knowledge of mathematics. This picture shows Professor White applying a set of figures to a physical formula in one of his telecasts from "Continental Classroom."

The Slide Rule

A SLIDE RULE is a simple mechancial device used for carrying out the arithmetic processes of **multiplication** and **division**. Since slide rules are easy to use, and inexpensive ones are quite adequate for most purposes, every physics student should acquire a slide rule and learn how to use it.

The beginner should select a straight inexpensive rule about ten inches in length and one that contains four and not more than six scales. The scales most commonly used are the **A**, **B**, **C**, and **D** scales as shown in Fig. A. Note that the slide rule consists of the slide rule **body,** and two movable parts we will call the **slipstick** and the **slider.**

Significant Figures. Before learning to use a slide rule we should clearly understand the meaning of the term **significant figures.** The three lists of numbers in the right-hand column will help to illustrate its meaning.

The first significant figure of a number is the first numeral that is not zero. The last significant figure is the last numeral that is not zero.

Most slide rules are capable of handling the multiplication and division of numbers to three significant figures only. Furthermore

A Two significant figures	B Three significant figures	C Four significant figures
24	374	5279
6.9	21.5	63.08
0.37	6.05	0.1062
0.053	0.00328	0.04503
4600	546000	692700

the answers are correct to three significant figures only.

If numbers like those in column C are to be used in any slide rule calculation they should be reduced to three significant figures. These particular numbers would, therefore, be assumed to have the values 5280, 63.1, 0.106, 0.0450, and 693000 respectively. Since many of the measurements made in the science laboratory are accurate to only three significant figures, the use of a slide rule is usually, but not always, sufficient and justified.

The C and D Scales. In making your first critical examination of your slide rule note that there are four fundamental scales, and that they are marked at the left end of the

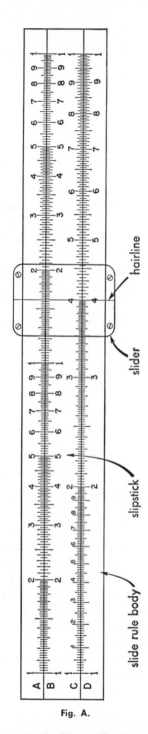

Fig. A.

will examine the entire length of these scales in three sections and see how to determine any position of the slider hairline.

Consider the left hand section of the **C** and **D** scales from the left index 1 to the principal number 2, as shown in Fig. B. Note that the interval is divided into ten divisions representing tenths, and each of these into ten divisions representing hundredths.

If the slider hairline were located in the position shown by the arrow at the left, its position would be written down as 1.14. Similarly the second arrow position represents the reading 1.37. The third arrow position appears to be half way between 1.53 and 1.54; hence we do what is called *interpolate* and write 1.535. Interpolation is a process of inserting or finding intermediate values by making a reasonable estimate as to an exact value. Since interpolation is nothing more than a good guess, the reading 1.535 is hardly better than three significant figures would indicate. Applying the interpolation process to the fourth arrow position we could write 1.950, with the understanding that the last figure 0 may not be correct.

Although a decimal point has been inserted after the first digit of each arrow position in Fig. B, it could just as readily be placed before the first digit, after the second digit, or after the third digit, etc. In other words the left index 1 can represent any of the numbers 1, 10, 100, 1000, etc. If we let this index represent 10, the right-hand number 2 will represent 20, and the arrow positions would be read as 11.4, 13.7, 15.35, and 19.50. If we let the left index represent 100, the right-hand number 2 will represent 200, and the arrow positions would read as 114, 137, 153.5, and 195.0.

Set the slider of your rule at random between the principal numbers 1 and 2, and then practice reading its position until you feel confident you are reading it correctly.

We are now ready to examine the center section of the **C** and **D** scales between the index numbers 2, 3, and 4. Note in Fig. C,

rule by **A**, **B**, **C**, and **D**. See Fig. A. Since multiplication and division are usually carried out with the two identical **C** and **D** scales, we

Fig. B.

and on your own rule, that each of the two intervals are divided into tenths, and each subdivision into fifths. In other words the smallest intervals, as marked, each represent 2/10 of a subdivision. Suppose we wanted to locate the position 2.36 on these scales. The first significant figure indicates that the position lies between 2 and 3. Set the hairline of your rule on 2. The second significant figure 3 indicates the position is between the third and fourth subdivision, while the third significant figure 6 shows it is 6/10 or 3/5 of the distance between these two subdivi-

of the arrows and be sure you can read any position of your slider hairline when it is located any place on the **C** and **D** scales.

Multiplication. *To multiply two factors carry out the four following steps: (1) Set the slider hairline on your first number on the D scale. (2) Move the slipstick so the left-hand index 1 of the C scale is exactly under the hairline. (3) Move the slider hairline to your second number on the C scale. (4) Read your answer on the D scale under the hairline.*

Fig. C.

sions. Hence the left arrow is properly located at 2.36.

Since the index numbers 3, 4, and 5 can also represent the numbers 30, 40, and 50, or 300, 400, and 500, the arrow positions could represent 23.6, 31.5, and 37.4, or 236, 315, and 374 respectively.

Finally we can examine the right-hand section of the **C** and **D** scales between the index numbers 4, 5, 6, 7, 8, 9, and 1. See Fig. D. Between each pair of numbers are ten subdivisions and each subdivision is divided into halves or 5/10. Note carefully the positions

Suppose for example you want to find the product 3 × 2. While you don't need the slide rule to find the answer, the performance of such a simple operation will clarify the method. See Fig. E. (1) Set the slider hairline on 3 of the **D** scale. (2) Move the slipstick and bring the left index 1 of the **C** scale to the hairline. (3) Move the slider to the second number 2 on the **C** scale. (4) Read the answer as 6 on the **D** scale.

A little study will show the slide rule settings for the products 30 × 20, 3 × 20, 30 × 2, 300 × 20, etc. would all be the same

Fig. D.

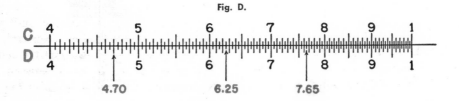

Fig. E.

as the above. The numeral 6 is the correct first numeral for all answers, but the number of zeros to be added must be determined by inspection.

Consider the procedure for obtaining the product of 24.0 × 1.5. (1) Set the slider hairline exactly on the fourth subdivision line beyond the 2 of the **D** scale. This position represents 24.0. (2) Move the left hand in-

product 24.0 × 2 is 48.0 as shown by the hairline position at the right in Fig. F.

Find the product 3.8 × 56.5. When the above steps are carried out for this product, the answer will be found to lie beyond the right hand end of the **D** scale. In such cases one moves the right hand index 1 of the **C** scale to the first number 3.8 on the **D** scale. See Fig. G. Moving the slider to the left, un-

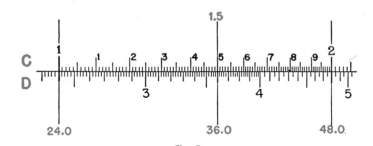

Fig. F.

dex 1 of the **C** scale to the hairline. (3) Move the slider to the fifth subdivision between 1 and 2 on the **C** scale. (4) The answer is under the hairline on the **D** scale and appears exactly at the sixth subdivision beyond 3 or 360. To locate the decimal point, inspect the two original numbers. One-and-a-half times 24 cannot be as small as 3.60 nor as large as 360. Therefore it must be 36.0. Similarly the

til the hairline is on the second number 56.5 on the **C** scale, the answer is read off the **D** scale as 215.

The Decimal Point. To find the decimal point in any problem, substitute round numbers for those appearing in the problem and determine the position of the decimal point by approximation. For example, in the last

Fig. G.

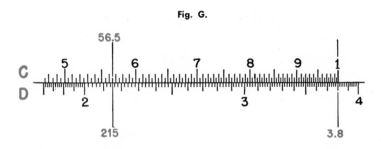

problem round off the number 3.8 to 4, and the number 56.5 to 60. The product 4 × 60 by mental arithmetic is 240, so the answer is 215 and not 21.5 or 2150.

Division. Division on the slide rule is just the reverse of multiplication.

Rule. To divide one number by the other carry out the following steps: (1) Set the slider hairline on the dividend, or numerator, on the D scale. (2) Move the slipstick until the divisor, or denominator, on the C scale lines up with the hairline. (3) The quotient, or answer, is under the C index at one end of the slipstick or the other. In simple terms, line up the numerator on the **D** scale with the denominator on the **C** scale, and the answer is under the **C** scale index.

For example, find the quotient for 6/2. (1) Set the slider hairline on 6 of the **D** scale. See Fig. E. (2) Bring the 2 of the **C** scale to the hairline. (3) The answer 2 is now under the **C** index on the **D** scale. Note that the fraction 6/2 is just upside down on the rule.

As a second example find the quotient of 215/56.5. See Fig. G. Set the hairline on 215 of the **D** scale and then line up 56.5 of the **C** scale. The answer 3.8 is on the **D** scale under the **C** index at the right. Note again that the fraction is lined up but inverted at the hairline position.

To find the decimal point in the last problem, round off the numbers and use mental arithmetic. For the number 215 write 200 and for 3.8 write 4. The quotient for 200/4 is 50. The answer, therefore, is 56.5 and not 5.65 or 565.

Square and Square Roots. To find the square of a number one multiplies that number by itself. To find the square root of a number requires the carrying out of a complicated arithmetic process. With the slide rule these operations are relatively simple.

To find the square of a number use the following rules: (1) Set the slider hairline to the number on the D scale. (2) Read the answer under the hairline on the A scale.

Inspection of Fig. A shows that directly above 2 on the **D** scale we find its square, or 4, on the **A** scale. Directly above 3 on the **D** scale is its square, or 9, on the **A** scale. Directly above 4 on the **D** scale (the position of the slider hairline shown) we find its square, or 16, on the **A** scale.

To find the square root of a number the reverse process is used: (1) Set the hairline at the number on the A scale. (2) Read the square root on the D scale under the hairline. Always use the left half of the **A** scale for numbers with an odd number of figures in front of the decimal point and the right half for those with an even number of figures before the decimal point.

In Fig. H the hairline settings are shown for finding the square roots of 4.80 and 820. The two answers are shown on the **D** scale as 2.19 and 28.6.

Fig. H.

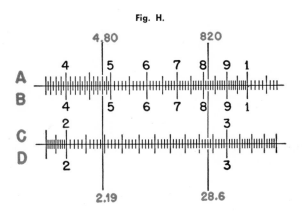

Summary

The slide rule is most frequently and conveniently used for multiplication, division, squares, and square roots. A ten-in. rule is capable of an accuracy to three significant figures. The first significant figure of a number is the first numeral that is not zero. The last significant figure is the last numeral that is not zero.

Multiplication and division are most accurately performed on the longer **C** and **D** scales, whereas squares and square roots are found by using the **A** and **D** scales.

Questions

1. Which two scales of the slide rule should be used for (a) multiplication and (b) division?

2. Which two scales of the slide rule should be used for finding (a) the squares and (b) the square roots of numbers?

3. To how many significant figures can slide rule calculations be depended upon?

4. Name the three principal parts of the slide rule.

5. Why should a long slide rule be more accurate than a shorter one?

6. Which end of the slide rule has the greatest accuracy as regards (a) significant figures and (b) percentage error? (*Note:* Can you interpolate any more accurately between 98 and 99 than between 101 and 102?)

Problems

1. Express each of the following numbers to three significant figures only: (a) 6497 (b) 38.27   (c) 0.43927   (d) 0.06008   (e) 349.8

2. Express each of the following numbers to three significant figures only: (a) 2359 (b) 64.32   (c) 0.4953   (d) 0.007647   (e) 987.7

3. Find the product of each of the following: (a) 2.5×3 (b) 2.5×3.7 (c) 1.6×5.0 (d) 6×3.5 (e) 4.7×5.8

4. Find the product of each of the following: (a) 2.7×3 (b) 3.4×2.1 (c) 2.3×2.9 (d) 5.6×3.4 (e) 4.3×8.7

5. Find the product of each of the following: (a) 3×26.4 (b) 28×35 (c) 29×17 (d) 13.5×6 (e) 17.2×21.6

6. Find the product of each of the following: (a) 2.5×17 (b) 32×1.7 (c) 19×14 (d) 26.2×1.75 (e) 23.2×9.4

7. Find the quotient of each of the following: (a) $6/5$ (b) $25/4$ (c) $38/7$ (d) $64/3$ (e) $72/2.7$

8. Find the quotient of each of the following: (a) $7/2$ (b) $32/5$ (c) $56/4.2$ (d) $26/3.4$ (e) $8.5/4.6$

9. Find the quotient of each of the following: (a) $35/6.2$ (b) $67/5.9$ (c) $325/28$ (d) $430/270$ (e) $675/780$

10. Find the quotient of each of the following: (a) 49/37 (b) 72/26 (c) 260/15 (d) 655/240 (e) 320/675

11. Find the square of each of the following: (a) 6.0 (b) 2.4 (c) 5.4 (d) 7.5 (e) 25

12. Find the square root of each of the following: (a) 25 (b) 39 (c) 65.5 (d) 420 (e) 4750

Special Lessons | **Lesson 2**

ALGEBRA AND POWERS OF TEN

Algebra. Although you have studied algebra, you may feel that you have forgotten most of it. For this reason it is well to review certain principles, even though only the very simplest manipulation of symbols will be used in the lessons that follow.

As the various subjects in physics are developed, we will see that an algebraic equation is nothing more than an abbreviated, but formal, way of expressing a principle or law and that the equation is derived from a series of experimental measurements.

Example 1. As a simple illustration of the experimental process, suppose that we have a simple platform balance of the type shown schematically in Fig. A. On one pan

Fig. A. Equal weights only will balance the scales.

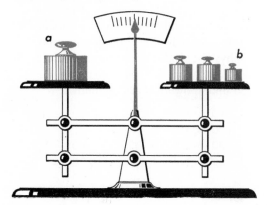

we place a 2-lb weight and on the other pan we add weights until balance is restored. Experimentally we then find **b** must have a total of 2 lb. If **a** is increased to 5 lb, **b** must be 5 lb, and if **a** is changed to 21.5 lb, **b** must be 21.5 lb. In other words we find experimentally that whatever may be the magnitude of the weight **a**, the total magnitude of **b** must be the same.

Hence we bring mathematics into the problem and write

$$a = b \qquad (1)$$

Having established this relation from many measurements, we now have confidence in this equation. We feel that if we put an unknown weight **a** on one pan and balance it with known weights on the other, Eq. (1) can be applied and we know that **a** weighs the same as **b**. The known or measured quantity **b** is on the right, and the unknown quantity **a** is on the left.

Example 2. Let us imagine having performed an experiment in which we repeatedly measured three quantities **x**, **y**, and **z** and we have established the relation

$$x = yz \qquad (2)$$

This equation says that the measurable quantity **x** is always equal to the product of two other measurable quantities, **y** and **z**. It follows, therefore, that if we do the experiment again and measure y and z, we need not measure x to find its value.

Our experimentally established Eq. (2) tells us that the unmeasured quantity x, we call the **unknown,** is always equal to the product $y \times z$.

Example 3. Suppose we have repeatedly performed a third experiment in which four quantities a, b, c, and d have been measured and we have established the following relation.

$$\frac{a}{b} = \frac{c}{d} \tag{3}$$

Now we repeat the experiment and measure b, c, and d. The quantity a becomes the unknown, and we can find its value by substituting the known quantities and carrying out the required arithmetic.

Before substituting quantities in any equation it is customary to put all known quantities on the right side of the equation and the unknown quantities on the left. For Eq. (3) this means putting b on the right side of the equation. To do this we can multiply both sides of Eq. (3) by b. We obtain

$$\frac{ab}{b} = \frac{cb}{d};$$

then

$$\frac{a}{1} = \frac{cb}{d}$$

and the desired relation becomes

$$a = \frac{cb}{d}$$

If the quantity c in Eq. (3) is the unknown, we would solve for c as follows: Multiply both sides of the equation by d and simplify.

$$\frac{ad}{b} = \frac{cd}{d}; \quad \frac{ad}{b} = \frac{c}{1}; \quad \frac{ad}{b} = c$$

Turn this last equation around and we obtain

$$c = \frac{ad}{b}$$

as the desired relation.

In similar ways we may solve Eq. (3) for b as the unknown quantity and find

$$b = \frac{ad}{c}$$

Or we can solve for d as the unknown quantity and find

$$d = \frac{bc}{a}$$

A re-examination of Eq. (3) will now show that to move any one of the four factors a, b, c, or d across the equal sign to the other side it obeys the following rule: *When any factor is moved from the denominator on one side of an equation, it goes into the numerator on the other side, and vice versa.* This last rule is a good one to memorize, for it is a short cut to any one of the four equations just derived.

These examples involve the algebraic principles of much of the mathematics we will encounter in this book, and it would be well worth while to practice carrying out these same operations using different letters for the symbols.

Abbreviated System of Numbers. In speaking of the size and shape of an object or the time interval between the occurrence of two events it is convenient to express very large numbers and very small decimals in an abbreviated form. This is done principally to conserve time and space. It is convenient for the astronomer in the study of stars and for the physicist and chemist in the study of atoms. The abbreviations in common use are based upon powers of ten as follows:

$10 = 10^1$	$1 = 10^0$
$100 = 10^2$	$0.1 = 10^{-1}$
$1000 = 10^3$	$0.01 = 10^{-2}$
$10,000 = 10^4$	$0.001 = 10^{-3}$
$100,000 = 10^5$	$0.0001 = 10^{-4}$
$1,000,000 = 10^6$	$0.00001 = 10^{-5}$

The abbreviated form on the right side of each equation is mathematically correct. For example,

$$10^3 = 10 \times 10 \times 10 = 1000$$

and

$$10^{-3} = \frac{1}{10^3} = \frac{1}{1000} = 0.001$$

In every case **the exponent is seen to give directly the number of digits the decimal point is moved from unity,** positive integers specifying the number of places the decimal point is moved to the right to make large numbers, and negative integers specifying the number of places it is moved to the left to make small decimals. To illustrate the use of this system, suppose we say that a truck weighs three million grams. This can be written

$$3,000,000 \text{ gm} = 3 \times 1,000,000 \text{ gm}$$
$$= 3 \times 10^6 \text{ gm}$$

In the abbreviated notation the mass is therefore written 3×10^6 gm. If more than one numeral occurs, any one of several abbreviations might be written. For example, in the case of large numbers,

$$840,000,000 = 84 \times 10,000,000$$
$$= 84 \times 10^7$$

or

$$840,000,000 = 8.4 \times 100,000,000$$
$$= 8.4 \times 10^8$$

In the case of small numbers, on the other hand,

$$0.0024 = 2.4 \times 10^{-3}, \text{ or } 24 \times 10^{-4}$$

To illustrate the advantages of this abbreviated notation, the mass of the **earth** and the mass of an **electron** are found by experiment to be as follows:

mass of the earth, $\quad m = 5.97 \times 10^{24}$ kg
mass of an electron, $\quad m = 9.11 \times 10^{-31}$ kg

If these are written down in complete decimal form, they would appear as follows:

mass of the earth =
$$5,970,000,000,000,000,000,000,000 \text{ kg}$$

mass of the electron =
$$0.000,000,000,000,000,000,000,000,$$
$$000,000,911 \text{ kg}$$

Multiplication and Division of Large and Small Numbers. The multiplication and division of large and small numbers in the abbreviated notation involves the addition and subtraction of exponents.

Rule 1. When a power number is changed from numerator to denominator, or vice versa, the sign of the exponent is changed. For example,

$$\frac{5}{2 \times 10^{-6}} = \frac{5 \times 10^6}{2}$$

Rule 2. When two power numbers are multiplied, their exponents are added. For example,

$$3 \times 10^5 \times 2 \times 10^4 = 3 \times 2 \times 10^{5+4}$$
$$= 6 \times 10^9$$

Again:

$$3 \times 10^{17} \times 2 \times 10^{-12} = 3 \times 2 \times 10^{17-12}$$
$$= 6 \times 10^5$$

Rule 3. When two power numbers are divided, their exponents are subtracted. For example,

$$\frac{8 \times 10^9}{2 \times 10^4} = \frac{8 \times 10^{9-4}}{2} = 4 \times 10^5$$

Again:

$$\frac{6 \times 10^{-7}}{3 \times 10^{-2}} = \frac{6 \times 10^{-7+2}}{3} = 2 \times 10^{-5}$$

Summary

Algebraic equations are nothing more than abbreviated and formal ways of expressing a principle or law, and are derived from many experimental measurements. A simple rule for transposing symbols from one side of an equation to the other is described. When any factor is moved from the denominator on one side of an equation, it goes into the numerator on the other side, and vice versa.

It is customary to transpose any algebraic equation so that the unknown quantity is on the left and all known quantities are on the right.

Large and small numbers are usually expressed in powers of ten. The exponent of any power of ten represents the number of places the decimal point is to be moved. A positive exponent signifies that the decimal point be moved to the right, while a negative exponent signifies it be moved to the left.

Questions

1. What do the symbols of an algebraic equation represent?

2. Why do we use algebra in physics?

3. Why do we express numbers in powers of ten?

4. If two numbers, expressed in powers of ten, are to be multiplied, what mathematical operation is performed on the exponents?

5. If we are to find the quotient of two numbers, each expressed in powers of ten notation, what mathematical operation is performed on the exponents?

6. If a power number is moved from the denominator to the numerator, what change takes place in the exponent?

Problems

1. The following relation between three measurable quantities—v, a, and t—has been established experimentally: $v = at$. Solve this equation for (a) a and for (b) t.

2. The following relation between three measurable quantities—v, s, and t—has been established experimentally: $s = vt$. Solve this equation for (a) v and (b) t.

3. The following relation has been established by experiment: $s = \frac{1}{2}at^2$. Solve this equation for (a) a and (b) t.

4. The following relation has been established by experiment: $v^2 = 2as$. Solve this equation for (a) a and (b) s.

5. Solve each of the following equations for x:

   (a) $\dfrac{x}{a} = \dfrac{y}{b}$ (b) $\dfrac{x}{a} = \dfrac{2y}{b}$ (c) $\dfrac{5x}{y} = \dfrac{2a}{b}$ (d) $\dfrac{a+b}{c} = \dfrac{y}{x}$

6. Solve each of the following equations for v:

   (a) $\dfrac{v}{w} = \dfrac{5s}{p}$ (b) $\dfrac{v}{p} = \dfrac{7q}{y}$ (c) $\dfrac{2s}{p} = \dfrac{v}{q}$ (d) $\dfrac{1}{a} + \dfrac{1}{b} = \dfrac{1}{v}$

7. Express each of the following numbers in powers of ten notation: (a) 6,000,000 (b) 4900   (c) 330,000   (d) 0.0095

8. Express each of the following numbers in powers of ten notation: (a) 26,000 (b) 240,000   (c) 93,000,000   (d) 0.00037

9. Solve each of the following and give the answer in powers of ten notation: (a) $5 \times 10^3 \times 10^5$ (b) $2 \times 10^6 \times 4 \times 10^7$ (c) $8 \times 10^{14} \div 2 \times 10^8$ (d) $4.2 \times 10^8 \times 2 \times 10^{-5}$

10. Solve each of the following and give the answer in powers of ten notation: (a) $4 \times 10^6 \times 3.5 \times 10^{-3}$ (b) $2.5 \times 10^{-8} \times 6 \times 10^5$ (c) $2 \times 10^7 \times 8 \times 10^8 \div 4 \times 10^5$ (d) $8 \times 10^{14} \times 2 \times 10^7 \div 10^3$

Special Lessons | Lesson 3

TRIGONOMETRY

Although you may never have studied trigonometry, you will find that the principles which will be introduced are not only simple but very useful. The word *trigonometry* means *triangle measurement.*

The Sine, Cosine, and Tangent. The measured sides and angles of a triangle are so related that any three known parts, provided at least one of them is a side, determine the size and shape of the triangle. The relations we are going to consider will all be confined to right triangles, that is, to triangles in which one angle is 90°. As a result of the following treatment we will see how it is possible to calculate the unknown sides of a right triangle from the numerical value of one known side and one of the acute angles. We will begin as we did in Introductory Lesson 4

Fig. A. The ratios between corresponding sides of similar triangles are equal.

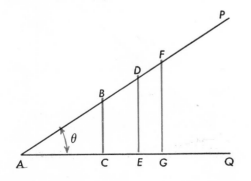

by drawing two straight lines—**AP** and **AQ**—to form any acute angle θ, as shown in Fig. A. Next we choose points like **B, D, F,** etc., anywhere along the line **AP** and drop perpendiculars to the lower line intersecting **AQ** at **C, E, G,** etc., respectively. In this way we have formed a series of right triangles, similar in shape, and all with the common angle θ.

From geometry, you may remember that the ratios of the lengths of corresponding sides of similar triangles are equal. Therefore, in abbreviated notation we may write

$$\frac{BC}{AB} = \frac{DE}{AD} = \frac{FG}{AF}$$

$$\frac{AC}{AB} = \frac{AE}{AD} = \frac{AG}{AF} \tag{1}$$

$$\frac{BC}{AC} = \frac{DE}{AE} = \frac{FG}{AG}$$

If the lengths of the sides are measured and these ratios computed, the answers will remain the same as long as the angle θ remains unchanged. Hence, for every value of an angle θ there are definite numbers that represent that angle in any right triangle.

Let **a, b,** and **c** denote the lengths of the three sides of a right triangle and θ the value of one of the acute angles as shown in Fig. B. Starting with the equalities in Eq. (1), we take the first ratio **BC/AB** and call it **the sine of** θ, the second ratio **AC/AB** and call it **the**

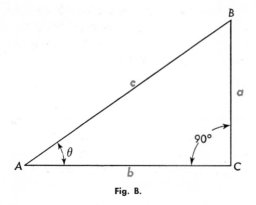

Fig. B.

cosine of θ, and finally the third ratio **BC/AC** and call it **the tangent of** θ.

In abbreviated notation these can be written

$$\sin\theta = \frac{a}{c} \qquad (2)$$

$$\cos\theta = \frac{b}{c} \qquad (3)$$

$$\tan\theta = \frac{a}{b} \qquad (4)$$

Example 1. Two lines **AP** and **AQ** make an angle of 35° with each other as shown in Fig. A. Find by graphical construction the sine, cosine, and tangent of this angle.

Solution. In graphical solutions we use a ruler and protractor and employ the method presented in Introductory Lesson 4. Two lines **AP** and **AQ** making an angle of 35° with each other are first drawn as shown in Fig. C.

Along **AP** we next measure off a fixed distance, say 5 cm, and draw a perpendicular to **AQ**. We then measure the lengths of the other two sides and find

$$a = 2.87 \text{ cm}$$
$$b = 4.10 \text{ cm}$$

along with

$$c = 5.00 \text{ cm}$$

If we now substitute these values in Eqs. (2), (3), and (4), we obtain

$$\sin 35° = \frac{2.87}{5.00} = 0.574$$

$$\cos 35° = \frac{4.10}{5.0} = 0.820$$

$$\tan 35° = \frac{2.87}{4.10} = 0.700$$

These values are to be compared with the values tabulated in Appendix I. The student would do well to repeat this construction and in so doing measure off an initial distance **c** of 8 to 10 cm. Using care, and a sharp pencil, the same values—0.574, 0.820, and 0.700— should be obtained to within two or three integers in the third significant figure.

Example 2. If one angle of a right triangle is 42° and the length of the hypotenuse is 7.0 cm, find the lengths of the other two sides. See Fig. D.

Fig. D.

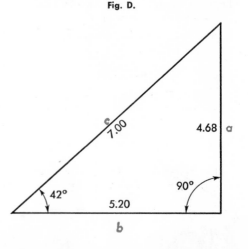

Fig. C.

Solution. The lengths of the sides a and b may be obtained graphically by using a centimeter rule and protractor drawing the triangle to scale as described in Example 1, or they may be calculated by the use of the tables of sines and cosines in the Appendix.

First we write down the sine relation from Eq. (2).

$$\sin \theta = \frac{a}{c}$$

Since $\theta = 42°$, we look in Appendix I and in the column headed sin we find opposite 42° the number 0.669. Substitute this number for $\sin \theta$ and 7.0 cm for c, and we obtain

$$0.669 = \frac{a}{7.0 \text{ cm}}$$

Now multiply both sides of the equation by 7.0 cm and obtain

$$a = 7.0 \text{ cm} \times 0.669$$

or

$$a = 4.683 \text{ cm}$$

which to three significant figures becomes

$$a = 4.68 \text{ cm}$$

To find the length of the side b we may now use either the cosine relation or the tangent relation, Eq. (3) or Eq. (4). Using the cosine relation, we write

$$\frac{b}{c} = \cos \theta$$

Before substituting, it is well to leave the unknown quantity b on the left side of the equal sign and transpose the known quantity c to the right. Multiplying both sides by c and cancelling, we obtain

$$b = c \cos \theta$$

We now look up the value for the cosine of 42° in the table in Appendix I and find cos 42° = 0.743. Substituting the known quantities, we obtain

$$b = 7.0 \text{ cm} \times 0.743 = 5.20 \text{ cm}$$

To three significant figures 5.20 cm is the length of the side b.

As a check upon these two calculated results for a and b the student should look up the tangent of 42° in Appendix I and compare the value with the ratio a/b.

Summary

Trigonometry is concerned with the relations between the lengths of the sides and the angles of triangles. The three most common relations in trigonometry are the sine, cosine, and tangent.

The sine of an angle of any right triangle is defined as the ratio of the length of the side opposite the angle to the length of the hypotenuse.

$$\sin \theta = \frac{\text{side opposite}}{\text{hypotenuse}}$$

The cosine of an angle of any right triangle is defined as the ratio of the length of the side adjacent to the angle to the length of the hypotenuse.

$$\cos \theta = \frac{\text{side adjacent}}{\text{hypotenuse}}$$

The tangent of an angle of any right triangle is defined as the ratio of the length of the side opposite the angle to the length of the adjacent side.

$$\tan \theta = \frac{\text{side opposite}}{\text{side adjacent}}$$

Questions

1. Draw a right triangle. Label the sides a, b, and c, and the angles α, β, and 90°. Write down the symbol relations for sin α, cos α, and tan α. Write down the symbol relations for sin β, cos β, and tan β.

2. If you had a ruler and a protractor, how could you find the sine, cosine, and tangent for an angle of 25°?

3. If one of the other two angles of a right triangle is known, how can you find the remaining angle?

4. If one angle of a right triangle is known and the length of hypotenuse is measured, what trigonometric relation would you use to find the length of the opposite side? Of the adjacent side?

5. If the two sides of a triangle forming an angle of 90° with each other are known, what trigonometric relations would you use to find the other two angles?

Problems

1. Find the number of degrees in each of the following angles: (a) sin $\theta = 0.375$ (b) sin $\theta = 0.839$ (c) cos $\theta = 0.788$ (d) cos $\theta = 0.242$ (e) tan $\theta = 0.649$

2. Find the number of degrees in each of the following angles: (a) sin $\theta = 0.276$ (b) sin $\theta = 0.446$ (c) cos $\theta = 0.961$ (d) cos $\theta = 0.446$ (e) tan $\theta = 2.475$

3. The hypotenuse of a right triangle is 8.5 cm long and one of the acute angles is 32°. Find, by graphical construction, the lengths of the other two sides.

4. The hypotenuse of a right triangle is 9.0 cm long and one of the acute angles is 53°. Find, by graphical construction, the lengths of the other two sides.

5. One acute angle of a right triangle is 27° and the length of the hypotenuse is 8 ft. Using trigonometry, calculate the lengths of the other two sides.

6. One acute angle of a right triangle is 55° and the length of the hypotenuse is 12 ft. Using trigonometry, calculate the lengths of the other two sides.

7. One acute angle of a right triangle is 38° and the length of the adjacent side is 8.5 cm. Using trigonometry, find the lengths of the other two sides.

8. One acute angle of a right triangle is 48° and the length of the opposite side is 15.0 cm. Using trigonometry, calculate the lengths of the other two sides.

9. If the hypotenuse of a right triangle is 20 ft long and one side is 6 ft long, (a) what are the values of the two acute angles and (b) what is the length of the other side?

10. A right triangle has sides of 3 cm, 4 cm, and 5 cm. Make a diagram to scale and measure the three angles with a protractor.

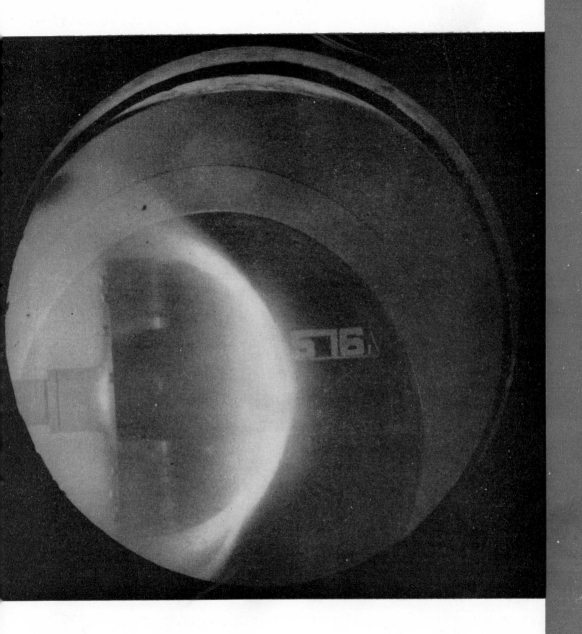

MECHANICS

Law I. Every body continues in its state of rest, or of uniform motion in a right line, unless it is compelled to change that state by forces impressed upon it.

Projectiles continue in their motions, so far as they are not retarded by the resistance of the air, or impelled downwards by the force of gravity. A top, whose parts by their cohesion are continually drawn aside from rectilinear motions, does not cease its rotation, otherwise than as it is retarded by the air. The greater bodies of the planets and comets, meeting with less resistance in freer spaces, preserve motions both progressive and circular for a much longer time.

Law II. The change in motion is proportional to the motive forces impressed, and is made in the direction of the right line in which that force is impressed.

Law III. To every action there is always opposed an equal reaction; or, the mutual actions of two bodies upon each other are always equal, and directed to contrary parts.

Sir Isaac Newton's *Mathematical Principles*, F. Cajori, ed., Andrew Motte, trans., University of California, Berkeley, 1934, p. 13.

We cannot create mechanical force, but we may help ourselves from the general storehouse of Nature. The brook and the wind, which drive our mills, the forest and the coal-bed, which supply our steam-engines and warm our rooms, are to us the bearers of a small portion of the great natural supply which we draw upon for our purposes, and the actions of which we can apply as we think fit. The possessor of a mill claims the gravity of the descending rivulet, or the living force of the moving wind, as his possession. These portions of the store of Nature are what give his property its chief value.

Hermann Helmholtz, *The Interaction of Forces*

← **Air becomes incandescent as it flows over this hemisphere-cylinder in Tunnel Hotshot at the Arnold Engineering Development Center. Test velocity was approximately Mach 16 in this run. The temperature was about 10.800° F, the flow lasting from 1/25 to 1/100 sec.**

Air Research and Development Command, USAF

Speed and Velocity

Mechanics is defined as that branch of physics dealing with the motions or states of material bodies. It is generally divided into three parts: **kinematics, dynamics, and statics.** Some of the concepts and principles to be described and classified under each of these headings are as follows:

KINEMATICS

> speed
> velocity
> acceleration
> angular velocity

DYNAMICS

> force
> impulse
> momentum
> kinetic energy

STATICS

> equilibrium
> balanced forces
> composition of forces
> resolution of forces

Kinematics is concerned with kinds of motion, dynamics with causes for changes in motion, and statics with bodies in equilibrium. As an introduction to the kinematics of motion, the elementary concepts of **speed** and **velocity** will first be taken up.

Velocity. *Velocity is defined as the rate of change of position.* Since by **change in position** of a body is meant the distance traveled, this definition of velocity can be written

$$\text{velocity} = \frac{\text{distance traveled}}{\text{time}} \quad (1)$$

As an algebraic equation

$$v = \frac{s}{t} \quad (2)$$

where **v** is the velocity, **s** the distance traveled, and **t** the elapsed time.

Change of position is illustrated in Fig. A.

Fig. A. Diagram of a body moving with constant velocity.

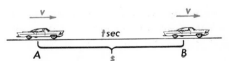

35

A car traveling with uniform velocity along a straight line passes the point **A** at one instant and the point **B** at some later instant of time. In substituting in Eq. (2) the distance traveled is **AB**, and the time interval between **A** and **B** is time **t**.

Example 1.   A man takes 2 hr to drive his car to a distant city 120 mi due east. What is his velocity?

Solution.   Here the distance traveled **s** = 120 mi, and the time interval **t** = 2 hr. The velocity therefore is

$$v = \frac{120 \text{ mi}}{2 \text{ hr}} = 60 \frac{\text{mi}}{\text{hr}} \qquad (3)$$

The answer is **60 mi/hr due east**. The units are just as important as the numbers and must be included in the answer.

If in the answer to the above example the time 1 hr in the denominator is replaced by its equivalent of 3600 sec, a velocity of 60 mi/hr becomes

$$v = 60 \frac{\text{mi}}{\text{hr}} = 60 \frac{\text{mi}}{3600 \text{ sec}} = 0.0167 \frac{\text{mi}}{\text{sec}} \quad (4)$$

If at the same time the distance 1 mi in the numerator is replaced by its equivalent of 5280 ft,

$$v = 60 \frac{\text{mi}}{\text{hr}} = 60 \frac{5280 \text{ ft}}{3600 \text{ sec}} = 88 \frac{\text{ft}}{\text{sec}} \quad (5)$$

All three of the answers above—60 mi/hr, 0.0167 mi/sec, and 88 ft/sec—are exactly equal; they are only expressed in different units. This last derived result that 60 mi/hr is equivalent to 88 ft/sec should be memorized, as it is very useful in the solving of many practical problems. A velocity of 120 mi/hr, for example, is equivalent to 2 × 88 or 176 ft/sec, while a velocity of 30 mi/hr is equivalent to ½ × 88 or 44 ft/sec.

Example 2.   A toy train running along a straight track at constant velocity requires 8 sec to travel a distance of 20 m. Find the velocity.

Solution.   Since **s** = 20 m and **t** = 8 sec, the velocity

$$v = \frac{20 \text{ m}}{8 \text{ sec}} = 2.5 \frac{\text{m}}{\text{sec}}$$

The answer is read **two point five meters per second**. To change this answer to centimeters per second the unit 1 m in the numerator is changed to 100 cm, and the answer becomes

$$v = 2.5 \frac{\text{m}}{\text{sec}} = 2.5 \frac{100 \text{ cm}}{\text{sec}} = 250 \frac{\text{cm}}{\text{sec}}$$

Distance Traveled.   If the velocity of a body is known, the distance traveled can be calculated for any given interval of time. For such problems Eq. (2) is conveniently changed by solving for **s**. Multiplying both sides of the equation by **t** does not alter the equality:

$$vt = \frac{st}{t}$$

Canceling **t**'s on the right-hand side gives **vt** = **s**, or

$$s = vt \qquad (6)$$

Example 3.   If a body moves with a velocity of 45 cm/sec, how far will it travel in 2 min?

Solution.   The distance traveled can be determined by Eq. (6).

$$s = 45 \frac{\text{cm}}{\text{sec}} \times 2 \text{ min} = 90 \frac{\text{cm min}}{\text{sec}}$$

In order to eliminate **time** units in this answer they must both be expressed in the same units. To do this, the minutes may be changed to seconds as follows:

$$s = 45 \frac{\text{cm}}{\text{sec}} \times 120 \text{ sec} = 5400 \text{ cm}$$

Note that **sec** in the numerator cancels **sec** in the denominator, leaving **cm** in the answer as the unit of length. This illustrates a common practice that should be followed in the solving of all problems. Always express like quantities in the same units.

Dividing both sides of Eq. (6) by **v** and canceling the **v**'s on the right-hand side, gives

$$t = \frac{s}{v} \qquad (7)$$

an equation for the time of travel in terms of **s** and **t**.

Example 4. If a car travels with an average velocity of 30 mi/hr, how long will it take to go 175 mi?

Solution. Using Eq. (7),

$$t = \frac{s}{v} = \frac{175 \text{ mi}}{30 \text{ mi/hr}} = 5.83 \text{ hr}$$

Vectors and Scalars. Nearly all physical measurements, whether they are made with the simplest of instruments or with the most complex of apparatus, may be classified as **vector** or **scalar** quantities.

Measurable quantities that have magnitude and direction are called vectors.

Examples of vector quantities are **displacement, velocity, acceleration,** and **force.**

Measurable quantities that have magnitude only are called scalars.

Examples of scalar quantities are **volume, area,** and **mass.**

The importance of this seemingly trivial distinction between quantities that have direction and those which do not is realized when in solving certain problems the simple process of the addition of two or more like quantities becomes necessary.

No difficulty is generally encountered with scalars since such quantities are added arithmetically. For example, in the addition of volumes, the sum of 2 gallons and 3 gallons is 5 gallons. The addition of two vectors, on the other hand, is more complicated and requires a special process called **vector addition,** which will be treated in detail in Mechanics, Lesson 5.

Speed and Velocity. The terms **speed** and **velocity** are often used synonymously. Strictly speaking, however, **speed is a scalar quantity** and **velocity is a vector quantity.** In the last section it was explained that vector quantities have magnitude and direction while scalars have magnitude only.

Speed is a term applied only to the magnitude of velocity and does not specify the direction of motion. In moving along a straight line, **speed** and **velocity** are numerically equal to each other. If, however, the speed along a curved path is constant, the velocity is not considered to be constant because of its changing direction.

When a body moves with constant speed along a straight line whose direction is specified, it is customary to speak of its **velocity.** Moving along a straight or curved path, with no reference being made to direction, it is proper to speak of its **speed.**

Table 1. Conversion Factors for Speed and Velocity

Velocity	m/sec	ft/sec	km/hr	mi/hr	Knots
1 m/sec =	1	3.281	3.600	2.240	1.940
1 ft/sec =	0.30480	1	1.0973	0.6818	0.5921
1 km/hr =	0.27778	0.9113	1	0.6214	0.5396
1 mi/hr =	0.44704	1.4667	1.6093	1	0.8684
1 knot =	0.51480	1.689	1.853	1.152	1

Example 5.   Change 30 mi/hr to kilometers per hour.

Solution.   From the table, 1 mi/hr in the left-hand column is (read across to the fourth column) equal to 1.6093 km/hr. Therefore,

$$30 \times 1.6093 = 48.279 \frac{km}{hr}$$

Dropping off the last two figures gives the answer to three significant figures as

$$30 \frac{mi}{hr} = 48.3 \frac{km}{hr}$$

The **knot** is a nautical unit of speed about 15% greater than speed in miles per hour. It is **not** correct to say the speed of a ship is 10 knots/hr; it is correct to say the speed is 10 knots.

Constant and Variable Velocity.   In mechanics it is often convenient to neglect the size and shape of a body and to consider its motion as that of a small **particle** of negligible size. For example, in describing the motion of an airplane flying between two cities it is not necessary to give a detailed description of the plane to give its position and progress. Hence, it is customary to speak of the motion of a body as the motion of particle.

If the statement is made that a particle travels 30 mi in 1 hr, it does not necessarily mean that its speed or velocity is constant. Moving due east in a straight line, the particle moved either with a **constant velocity** or with a **variable velocity.** *A constant velocity is defined as one in which equal distances are traversed in equal intervals of time and the direction is at all times that of the same straight line.* In other words, the distance traveled in any 1 sec is equal to that traveled in any other second.

A particle has a **variable velocity** when in equal intervals of time its displacements are unequal. In such cases it is customary to speak of the **average velocity.** Average velocity, $\bar{v}$, is defined by

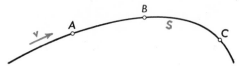

B

A

S

C

v

Fig. B. Motion along a curved path.

$$\bar{v} = \frac{s}{t} \tag{8}$$

where t is the total time required to travel the total distance s.

Curvilinear Motion.   Motion along a curved path is called curvilinear motion. When a particle moves along a curved path as shown in Fig. B, it may have a constant or variable speed. The term **speed** is used here in place of velocity since the path is not straight. A **constant speed** is defined as one in which the distances traveled in equal intervals of time are equal, the distances being measured along the curved path.

A **variable speed** means that the distances traveled in equal intervals of time are different. It follows from these definitions, by comparison with those for linear motion in the preceding section, that all of the equations in this chapter apply equally well to constant and average speed.

Instantaneous Velocity.   In describing the curvilinear motion of a particle, it sometimes becomes necessary to specify its **instantaneous velocity.** As shown in Fig. C, the instantaneous velocity of a particle at any given point in its path is obtained by drawing a tangent to the curve at the point in question. The magnitude of the instantaneous velocity is equal to the speed of the particle as it passes that point and the direction is that of the tangent to the curve at that point.

Fig. C. Arrows indicate instantaneous velocity.

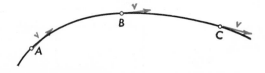

B

C

v

v

A

v

Summary

Mechanics deals with the motions or states of material bodies, and is divided into three parts:

Kinematics
Dynamics
Statics

Velocity is a vector quantity and is defined as the rate of change of position. Speed is defined in the same way but is a scalar quantity. Velocity is the distance traveled per unit of time.

Vector quantities have magnitude and direction, while scalar quantities have magnitude only.

A constant velocity is one in which equal distances are traversed in equal intervals of time and the direction is at all times that of the same straight line. Speed and velocity are both given by the relation

$$v = \frac{s}{t}$$

Questions

1. Name the three branches of mechanics. With what concepts is each to be associated?

2. Define speed and velocity. In what way are these two different?

3. What is a vector quantity? What is a scalar quantity? Give three examples of each.

4. What are the mks units of velocity and speed?

5. What are the cgs units of speed and velocity?

6. Distinguish between constant and variable velocity.

7. Define (a) constant speed, (b) constant velocity, (c) curvilinear motion, (d) variable speed, and (e) instantaneous velocity.

8. A train maintains a constant speed of 60 miles per hour as it rounds a curve. Is the velocity constant?

9. Which of the two units is the larger: (a) 1 mi/hr or 1 knot, (b) 1 km/hr or 1 mi/hr, (c) 1 mi/hr or 1 ft/sec?

10. In what ways are any of the principles developed in this lesson involved in the things happening in the world around us?

Problems

1. An airplane in a steep dive moves with a speed of 570 mi/hr. Compute its speed in (a) ft/sec, (b) km/hr, and (c) knots.

2. A ship sailing from San Francisco to Hawaii makes the trip of 2300 miles in $4\frac{1}{2}$ days. What is its average speed in (a) mi/hr, (b) km/hr, and (c) knots?

3. It takes a farmer 3 hr to walk the full length of the fence surrounding his farm one mile square. Calculate his average speed in (a) mi/hr, (b) ft/sec, and (c) cm/sec.

4. A circular racetrack is 1500 ft in diameter. A car makes 100 laps around the track in 56 min. Calculate the average speed in (a) mi/hr, (b) ft/sec, and (c) km/hr.

5. In a track-meet the 100-yd dash was won in the time of 9.4 sec. Calculate the average speed in (a) ft/sec and (b) mi/hr.

6. In the Olympic games the 100-meter dash was won in the time of 10.0 sec. Calculate the average speed in (a) ft/sec and (b) mi/hr.

7. How long will it take a ship traveling at 20 knots to go 525 mi?

8. How long will it take a ship traveling at 25 knots to go 2200 mi?

9. A world record in the 10,000 meter run was set in 1924 by P. Nurmi of Finland in the time of 30 min $6\frac{1}{2}$ sec. Calculate his average speed in (a) mi/hr and (b) ft/sec.

10. In the Olympic games of 1928 the following races were run in the respective times: (a) 100 m in $10\frac{3}{5}$ sec, (b) 200 m in $21\frac{3}{5}$ sec, (c) 400 m in $47\frac{3}{5}$ sec, (d) 800 m in 1 min $51\frac{4}{5}$ sec, (e) 1500 m in 3 min $53\frac{1}{5}$ sec, (f) 5000 m in 14 min $31\frac{1}{5}$ sec, (g) 10,000 m in 30 min $18\frac{4}{5}$ sec, and (h) 15,000 m in 46 min $49\frac{3}{5}$ sec. Calculate the average speed of each in mi/hr.

***Mechanics* | Lesson 2**

SPEED AND VELOCITY—*Laboratory*

In performing this experiment as described in the accompanying LABORATORY EXERCISES you will see how to measure the speed *of an electric train and the* velocity *of a toy automobile. The principles employed are those presented in the preceding lesson.*

***Mechanics* | Lesson 3**

ACCELERATION

Uniform Acceleration. Whenever the speed or velocity of a body changes, the motion is described as an acceleration. Acceleration is defined as ***the rate of change of velocity.*** A car "picking up speed" has a ***positive acceleration,*** while another slowing down has a ***negative acceleration.*** Standing still or moving with constant velocity, a car has no acceleration.

Consider as an illustration of accelerated motion the car shown in Fig. A. Due to a constantly acting force, exerted by the motor

Fig. A. A car undergoes constant acceleration.

through the drive wheels, this car is constantly accelerated as it moves along the straight line **AB**. As it passes **A**, it has a relatively low velocity v_0, while farther along its path at a point **B** it is moving faster and has a velocity **v**. The *initial velocity* is called v_0, and the *final velocity* is called **v**.

If the time required to go from **A** to **B** is **t**, the acceleration, by the definition given above, is schematically written:

$$\text{acceleration} = \frac{\text{final velocity} - \text{initial velocity}}{\text{time}}$$

or algebraically as

$$a = \frac{v - v_0}{t} \qquad (1)$$

Example 1. Suppose at **A**, in Fig. A, that the velocity of the car is 20 ft/sec, that at **B** it has increased to 40 ft/sec, and that it takes 4 sec to go from **A** to **B**. What is the acceleration?

Solution. By direct substitution in Eq. (1), we obtain

$$a = \frac{40 \text{ ft/sec} - 20 \text{ ft/sec}}{4 \text{ sec}}$$

$$= \frac{20 \text{ ft/sec}}{4 \text{ sec}} = 5 \frac{\text{ft}}{\text{sec sec}}$$

The answer is read **five feet per second per second** and means that the velocity increases 5 ft/sec every second of time. Initially the velocity is 20 ft/sec. An increase of 5

ft/sec means that at the end of 1 sec the velocity is 25 ft/sec, at the end of 2 sec it is 30 ft/sec, at the end of 3 sec it is 35 ft/sec, and at the end of 4 sec it is 40 ft/sec. See Fig. B. *A body is said to move with constant acceleration when its velocity changes by equal amounts each second.*

When a body is slowing down, the initial velocity is greater than the final velocity, and the acceleration, as given by Eq. (1) is negative.

Starting from Rest. When a body starting from rest undergoes a constant acceleration, the initial velocity v_0 as given in Eq. (1) is zero, i.e., $v_0 = 0$. The acceleration **a** is then given by the special equation

$$a = \frac{v}{t} \qquad (2)$$

Transposed, this takes the form

$$v = at \qquad (3)$$

Example 2. An airplane starting from rest at one end of a runway acquires its take off speed of 60 mi/hr in 8 sec. What is its acceleration?

Solution. The acceleration is obtained from Eq. (2).

$$a = \frac{60 \text{ mi/hr}}{8 \text{ sec}} = 7.5 \frac{\text{mi}}{\text{hr/sec}}$$

The answer is read **seven point five miles per hour per second.**

Remembering that 60 mi/hr is equivalent to 88 ft/sec, this same acceleration can be expressed as

$$a = \frac{88 \text{ ft/sec}}{8 \text{ sec}} = 11 \frac{\text{ft}}{\text{sec}^2}$$

read **eleven feet per second per second.**

Fig. B. Diagram of accelerated car in Example 1.

20 ft/sec   25 ft/sec   30 ft/sec   35 ft/sec   40 ft/sec

Average Velocity. While the velocity of an accelerated body is continually changing, the distance traveled in any given time t may be described in terms of its **average velocity**. The average velocity of a particle moving with constant acceleration is given by

$$\bar{v} = \frac{v + v_0}{2} \qquad (4)$$

The bar over the v indicates an average value.

For the special case of a body starting from rest, $v_0 = 0$; Eq. 4 becomes

$$\bar{v} = \frac{v}{2} \qquad (5)$$

The equation $s = vt$ already given in Mechanics, Lesson 1, p. 36, will not hold true for accelerated motion unless v is replaced by the average velocity $\bar{v}$. Thus we may write $s = \bar{v}t$, or

$$s = \frac{v}{2}t \qquad (6)$$

Example 3. A car starting from rest undergoes uniform acceleration, acquiring a speed of 100 m/sec in 8 sec. Find (a) the acceleration and (b) the distance traveled.

Solution: The given quantities are $v = 100$ m/sec and $t = 8$ sec. For the answer to part (a), use Eq. (2):

$$a = \frac{v}{t}$$

and substitute

$$a = \frac{100 \text{ m/sec}}{8 \text{ sec}} = 12.5 \frac{\text{m}}{\text{sec}^2}$$

For the answer to part (b) use Eq. (6) and substitute directly:

$$s = \frac{100 \text{ m/sec}}{2} \times 8 \text{ sec} = 400 \text{ m}$$

Derived Equations. All of the problems and experiments we will encounter in mechanics can be solved by the two basic equations derived above. Those two equations should be memorized:

$$v = at; \quad s = \frac{v}{2}t$$

Note that each equation involves only three of the quantities v, a, t, and s. Oftentimes problems arise in which the two known quantities are not in the same equation and we wish to determine, as an unknown quantity, either one of the other two. For this purpose, it is convenient to combine these two equations as follows: Solve both Eq. (3) and Eq. (6) for the time t.

$$t = \frac{v}{a}; \quad t = \frac{2s}{v}$$

Since the left-hand sides of these equations are equal, the right-hand sides are equal to each other, and we can write

$$\frac{v}{a} = \frac{2s}{v}$$

Now if we transpose, or cross multiply, we obtain

$$v^2 = 2as \qquad (7)$$

Or, if we solve both Eq. (3) and Eq. (6) for the velocity v, we obtain

$$v = at; \quad v = \frac{2s}{t}$$

Since the left-hand sides are now equal, the right-hand sides are also equal, and we can write

$$\frac{2s}{t} = at$$

Again, if we transpose, we obtain

$$s = \frac{at^2}{2}$$

or

$$s = \tfrac{1}{2}at^2 \qquad (8)$$

The equations (7) and (8) are called **derived equations.** They give no additional information to that given by Eqs. (3) and (6); they are only rearrangements of the same quantities. In their new form, however, they are more readily applied to certain types of problems and experiments. Because of their fundamental importance, all four equations will be used many times in the following chapters and, for this reason, they should be memorized.

Example 4. A plane starting at one end of a runway, undergoes an acceleration of 1.2 m/sec², for a distance of 1000 meters before taking off. Calculate the take off speed.

Solution. The given quantities are $a =$ 1.2 m/sec² and $s = 1000$ m, and the unknown quantity is v. These three factors are found in Eq. (7) only, and direct substitution gives

$$v^2 = 2 \times 1.2 \, \frac{m}{sec} \times 1000 \, m$$

$$v^2 = 2400 \, \frac{m^2}{sec^2}$$

Take the square root of both sides,

$$v = 49 \, \frac{m}{sec}$$

The take-off speed is forty-nine meters per second.

Summary

A body moving with a changing speed or velocity is said to be accelerated. Acceleration is defined as the rate of change of velocity and is given by the algebraic relation

$$a = \frac{v - v_0}{t}$$

If the moving body is speeding up, the acceleration is positive, while upon slowing down it is negative. Moving with constant velocity an object has no acceleration.

Uniform acceleration, or constant acceleration, is one in which the velocity changes by equal amounts each second.

There are four basic equations commonly used for uniformly accelerated motion. These are the kinematic equations.

$$v = at$$

$$s = \frac{v}{2} t$$

$$v^2 = 2 \, as$$

$$s = \tfrac{1}{2} \, at^2$$

Questions

1. Define (a) acceleration and (b) uniform acceleration. What is meant by negative acceleration?

2. What is meant by average velocity? If the time and distance of travel are known, how can you find the average velocity?

3. What are the mks units of acceleration? What are the cgs units? What are the English units?

4. Could a body move with a variable acceleration?

5. If a car starts from rest and moves with uniform acceleration, how do the distances traveled each second of time compare with the distance traveled the first second?

6. What is meant by (a) the initial velocity and (b) the final velocity of an accelerated body?

7. The units of acceleration involve the unit of time twice. Why is this? Can one of the units be in seconds and the other in minutes or hours?

8. Think of some project in which you could make a simple and inexpensive device for demonstrating one of the principles developed in this lesson.

Problems

1. A racing car starting from rest acquires a speed of 120 ft/sec in 9 sec. (a) What is its acceleration and (b) how far did it travel?

2. A train starting from rest acquires a speed of 30 m/sec in 2 min. (a) What is its acceleration and (b) how far did it travel?

3. A rocket starting from rest undergoes an acceleration of 0.5 m/sec^2 straight upward for 3 min, when the fuel gives out. (a) What is its final velocity and (b) how high is it above the earth?

4. A jet plane starting from rest at one end of a runway undergoes a constant acceleration of 1.6 m/sec^2 for a distance of 1200 meters before taking off. Calculate (a) the take-off speed and (b) the time required to take-off.

5. A train starts from rest and after a constant acceleration for 75 sec acquires a speed of 100 km/hr. What is its acceleration in meters per second per second?

6. A racing car starting from rest acquires a speed of 100 mi/hr in 8 sec. (a) What is its acceleration and (b) how far did it travel during this time?

7. A ball starts from rest and rolls downhill with an acceleration of 4 ft/sec^2. What will be its velocity at the end of 1 sec, 2 sec, 3 sec, and 4 sec?

8. Starting from rest, a car travels a distance of 60 ft in 2 sec. Find (a) its average velocity and (b) its acceleration.

9.* A train starting from rest travels 1 mi in 1 min. Find (a) the average velocity in ft/sec and (b) the acceleration in ft/sec^2.

10.* A car traveling at 60 mi/hr (i.e., 88 ft/sec) suddenly has its brakes applied, bringing it to rest in 4 sec. Find (a) the acceleration and (b) the distance traveled during this time.

11.* A train starting from rest acquires a speed of 60 mi/hr in 20 sec. (a) What is its acceleration in ft/sec^2? (b) What distance has it traveled?

12.* A car traveling 100 ft/sec has its brakes suddenly applied, bringing it to rest in 200 ft. Find (a) the acceleration and (b) the time to come to rest.

13.* Starting from rest, a car undergoes a constant acceleration of 2.5 m/sec^2. Find the distance traveled during (a) the first second of time and (b) the fourth second of time.

14. Starting from rest, a car maintains an acceleration of 1.5 m/sec² for 8 sec. Calculate the distance traveled during this time.

15.* A box accidentally falls from a truck traveling 30 mi/hr and slides along the ground for a distance of 100 ft. Find (a) the acceleration and (b) the time before the box comes to rest.

Mechanics | Lesson 4

ACCELERATED MOTION—*Laboratory*

In performing this experiment as described in the accompanying LAB-ORATORY EXERCISES you will make measurements on a steel ball rolling down an inclined plane. The principles involved are those of uniformly accelerated motion developed in the preceding lesson.

Mechanics | Lesson 5

COMPOSITION OF VELOCITIES

Since velocity has magnitude and direction, it is a vector quantity and, therefore, subject to the principles of vector addition.

Velocity Is a Vector Quantity. When a body moves with two velocities simultaneously, the process of vector addition is applied to find its equivalent resultant velocity. To see what is meant by **simultaneous velocities** and a **resultant velocity,** consider the following problem.

While an ocean liner is sailing eastward with a velocity of 12 mi/hr, a man walks around the deck at the rate of 5 mi/hr. The problem is to find at all times the man's velocity with respect to the water. When he walks forward in the direction of the ship's motion, his velocity of 5 mi/hr is added to the ship's velocity of 12 mi/hr to give a resultant of 17 mi/hr eastward. As the man walks aft, however, his velocity of 5 mi/hr is subtracted from the ship's velocity of 12 mi/hr to give a resultant of 7 mi/hr eastward.

Fig. A. A body undergoes two simultaneous velocities.

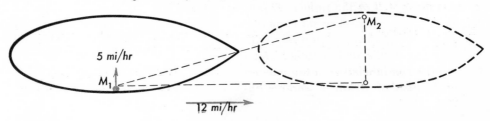

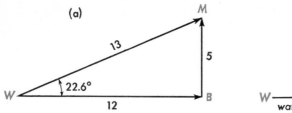

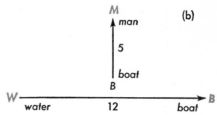

Fig. B. Vector addition of simultaneous velocities.

In the first case, the vectors are parallel and in the same direction and they add arithmetically, while in the second case they are oppositely directed and they subtract arithmetically.

When the man walks across the deck at right angles to the ship's motion, his resultant velocity is 13 mi/hr in a direction 22.6° north of east. To show how this answer is determined, a *space diagram* of the problem is given in Fig. A. The diagram at the left shows M_1 as the starting point of the man and boat, while the diagram at the right shows the position of the boat when the man reaches M_2 on the port side. The plane of the page represents the water.

The vector addition of the two velocities is shown at the left in Fig. B. The arrow **WB** is first drawn 12 units long and pointing in the direction of the boat's motion. **BM** is next drawn up from **B**, 5 units long, and pointing in the direction the man is walking on the boat. The triangle is then completed, the length of the side **WM** is measured from the graph, and the angle is measured with a protractor. The resultant **WM** = 13 mi/hr at 22.6° represents both in magnitude and direction the velocity of the man with respect to the water.

A general procedure that can be applied to all problems involving simultaneous velocities is illustrated at the right in Fig. B. Taking the above problem as an example, each vector is first drawn separately with its proper magnitude and specified direction. Each is then labeled with the moving body at the head of the arrow and the ob-

ject with reference to which it is moving at the tail. The vectors are then put together in a single diagram with like labels together, as in diagram (a).

The principles of vector addition are particularly useful when applied to the motion of a body in a medium which is itself moving. The drift of an airplane in a wind or the drift of a boat on a moving body of water are good examples.

The River-Boat Problem. A small passenger boat is capable of making 2 mi/hr in the water. The pilot heads his boat straight across a river from a point where the river is one mile wide. How far downstream will he land at the other side if the water flows at 1 mi/hr?

A space diagram for this problem is shown in Fig. C. Note how the boat, starting from the point **A** on one bank and headed originally toward the point **B** on the opposite bank, drifts along with the water and arrives at point **C**.

Following the procedure outlined above, we draw two vectors to the same scale, representing the two given velocities, and label

Fig. C. Diagram of the river-boat problem.

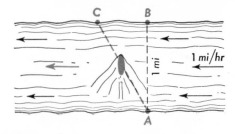

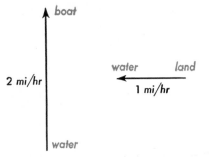

Fig. D. Velocity vectors for the river-boat problem.

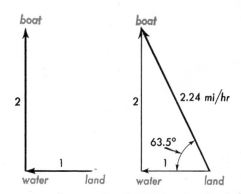

Fig. E. Composition of velocities for the river-boat problem.

them as shown in Fig. D. The two vectors are then combined with like words together, as shown at the left in Fig. E.

Connecting the two end points with a straight line, one obtains a right triangle as shown at the right. When the length of the hypotenuse is measured, it is found to be 2.24 units long. When the angle it makes with the base is measured with a protractor, it is found to be 63.5°. These represent the magnitude and direction of the velocity of the boat with respect to the shoreline or bank.

To find the distance **B** to **C** along the shore we compare the velocity vector diagram of Fig. E with the space diagram of Fig. C. Because all respective angles are equal, these

are the distances across the water and along the shore. Since the corresponding sides of two similar triangles are proportional to each other, we can write the proportionality:

$$\frac{2\ \dfrac{mi}{hr}}{1\ \dfrac{mi}{hr}} = \frac{1\ mi}{(BC)}$$

From which we find $(BC) = \frac{1}{2}$ mi. In other words, the boat makes 2.24 mi/hr along the line **AC** and arrives $\frac{1}{2}$ mi downstream at point **C.**

Summary

Velocity is a vector quantity. It has magnitude and direction. A body may move with two different velocities simultaneously. The resultant velocity of a body is the vector sum of its different velocities.

Vectors are represented by arrows. The length of the arrow is made to be proportional to the vector magnitude, and the arrowhead indicates the vector direction.

A systematic method of labeling both ends of a velocity vector is presented. Errors are often avoided by following this designation method.

Questions

1. How is it possible for a body to move with two different velocities at the same time? Explain. Give an example.

2. Give an example of a body moving with three simultaneous velocities.

3. Draw a vector to represent a car traveling eastward at 6 mi/hr. Label both ends properly.

4. Draw a vector to represent a ship sailing westward at 20 knots. Label both ends properly.

5. A plane flies 400 mi eastward in 1 hr and 20 min. Represent this velocity by a vector and label the ends properly.

6. Think of some project in which you might make a simple and inexpensive device for demonstrating one of the principles developed in this lesson.

Problems

1. An ocean liner crosses the Atlantic, sailing directly eastward at 18 mi/hr. A man walks across the deck at right angles to the ship's keel at 3 mi/hr. Make a velocity vector diagram and compute the velocity of the man with respect to the water.

2. A motor boat capable of 8 mi/hr is headed straight across a river. If the water flows at the rate of 3 mi/hr, what will be the velocity of the boat with respect to the starting point on the bank?

3. A cabin cruiser, making 10 ft/sec, heads straight across a river 1000 ft wide. If the water is flowing at 4 ft/sec, how far downstream will he land on the other side?

4.* A ship is sailing westward at 20 knots and a 15-knot wind is blowing from the north. (a) What is the velocity of the wind with respect to the ship? (b) What angle will the trail of smoke left by the funnels make with the ship's course?

5. An Indian who can paddle a canoe at 3 m/sec heads straight across a river 400 m wide. If the water flows at 1.4 m/sec, how far down the river will he land on the other side?

6.* A pilot in a plane having a cruising speed of 400 mi/hr sets his course due west. Aloft a wind is blowing from the north at 60 mi/hr. What is the velocity of the plane with respect to the ground?

7.* A pilot with a plane having a cruising speed of 200 mi/hr wishes to fly to another airport 100 mi to the north and return. A steady 50 mi/hr wind is blowing from the south. (a) What is his time flying north? (b) Flying south? (c) What is his total flying time? (d) What would be his flying time if there were no wind?

Mechanics | Lesson 6

RESOLUTION OF VELOCITIES

In the preceding lesson on **composition of velocities** we have seen how two velocities can be added together as vectors to find their **resultant** velocity. Before taking up the reverse process called the **resolution of velocities,** let us consider a type of velocity problem familiar to every airplane pilot.

The Airplane Problem. A pilot in a plane having a cruising speed of 150 mi/hr sets his course due east. Aloft, a wind of 75 mi/hr is blowing from the north. How far off his course will he be at the end of one hour? This problem involves two simultaneous velocities. The plane flies through the air

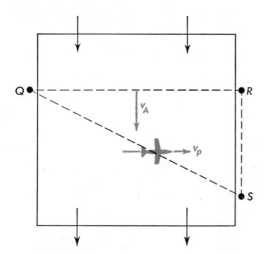

Fig. A. Space diagram for the airplane problem.

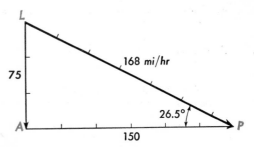

Fig. C. Vector diagram of velocities for the airplane problem.

with a velocity of 150 mi/hr and the air, thought of as a large mass, is itself moving southward. See Fig. A. Though the pilot starts from the land point **Q** and keeps the plane's nose headed directly toward the east, the plane is carried southward along the land line **QS.**

The procedure to be followed in this problem is that given in italics in the seventh paragraph of the preceding lesson. Vectors are first drawn, as shown in Fig. B. With the velocities known, each is measured off in its proper direction and to the same scale, and then labeled. The pilot and plane **P** are moving eastward at 150 mi/hr with respect to the air **A**, while the air **A** is moving southward at 75 mi/hr with respect to the land **L.**

The next step is to combine the two vectors with their like labels, the air **A** together as shown in Fig. C. The line **LP** is then drawn in with an arrowhead at **P** and the length measured with the common scale. The vector

LP of 168 represents the velocity of the plane **P** with respect to the land **L**, while the angle of 26.5°, measured from the triangle, gives the direction in which the plane is traveling with respect to the land. Fig. A shows how the plane, headed due east, and flying through the air with a speed v_p of 150 mi/hr, follows a course 26.5° south of east with a ground speed of 168 mi/hr.

To find how far off course the plane is at the end of 2 hours, we note that the space triangle **QRS** has the same angles as the vector triangle **PAL**. Since these are similar triangles, corresponding sides are proportional to each other, and we can write

$$\frac{RS}{QS} = \frac{AL}{PL}$$

Since the plane has a ground speed of 168 mi/hr, it will make twice this in 2 hrs or 336 mi. Substituting known values in the preceding equation, we obtain

$$\frac{RS}{336} = \frac{75 \text{ mi/hr}}{168 \text{ mi/hr}}$$

from which

$$RS = \frac{75 \times 336 \text{ mi}}{168} = 150 \text{ mi}$$

The plane is off course 150 mi directly south.

Components of Velocity. Many of the problems in mechanics are most easily solved by a process called the **method of components.** The method of components is applied to vector quantities only, and when applied

Fig. B. Velocity vectors for the airplane problem.

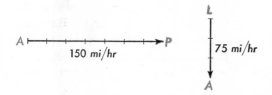

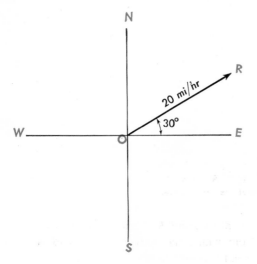

Fig. D. Velocity is a vector quantity.

The vector **OA**, when measured, is found to be 10 units long and represents the speed of the ship toward the north, while the vector **OB**, when measured, is found to be 17.3 units long and represents the speed of the ship toward the east. What this means is that the ship may be thought of as having two velocities simultaneously, a velocity of 10 mi/hr toward the north and a velocity of 17.3 mi/hr toward the east. Note that the dotted lines have lengths of 10 and 17.3 units respectively and that the vector sum of **OB** + **OA** is equal to the original vector **OR**. In other words, the **composition of velocities** refers to the combining of two velocities to find a single resultant velocity, while the resolution of a velocity refers to the breaking up of a single velocity into two velocities called **components**.

to velocities, is frequently referred to as the **resolution of velocities**.

Consider as an illustration a ship leaving New York harbor and sailing in a direction 30° north of east at a speed of 20 mi/hr. The ship's velocity can be represented by a single vector as shown in Fig. D.

We now proceed as shown in Fig. E to resolve the single velocity **OR** into two components. This is done by dropping perpendiculars to the **NS** and the **EW** lines respectively. Where the dotted lines intersect at **A** and **B**, arrowheads are drawn in, creating two vectors **OA** and **OB** at right angles to each other.

Example 1. An object is given a velocity of 50 m/sec in a direction making 40° with the **x**-axis. Resolve this velocity into two components, one along the **x**-direction and the other at right angles along the **y**-direction.

Solution. By graphical methods, we draw **x**- and **y**-axes as shown in Fig. F. The velocity vector **v** is drawn to some convenient scale 50 units long and at an angle of 40° with the **x**-axis. From the tip of this vector we draw the dotted lines parallel to the **x**- and **y**-axes

Fig. F. A velocity vector is resolved into x- and y-components.

Fig. E. A single velocity vector is resolved into two components.

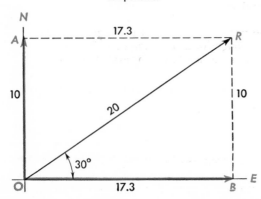

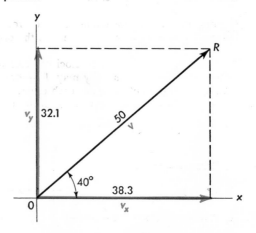

and where they cross the lines, terminate the two components v_x and v_y. Upon measuring the lengths of these two lines with our chosen scale, we find 38.3 units and 32.1 units, respectively, representing the two velocities

$$v_x = 38.3 \text{ m/sec}$$
$$v_y = 32.1 \text{ m/sec}$$

These two velocities are the components of $v = 50$ m/sec, with the subscripts denoting their x- and y-directions, respectively.

Relative Velocity. One of the principles upon which Einstein's theory of relativity is founded is that all motions are relative. A body moving with a specified velocity with respect to one frame of reference may be moving with a different velocity when referred to another. To illustrate, suppose two seaplanes leave the same island base at the same time, one flying northeast with a speed of 200 mi/hr, the other flying east with a speed of 250 mi/hr.

A vector diagram of velocities is given in Fig. G. Vector BA_1 represents the velocity of plane A_1 with respect to the base B, while vector BA_2 represents the velocity of plane A_2 with respect to the same base. For both of these vectors, the page of the book with

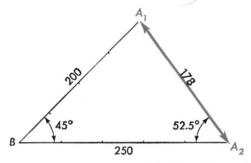

Fig. G. According to Einstein's theory of relativity all motions are relative.

the fixed point B is the frame of reference from which the velocity of A_1 and A_2 are specified.

The vector joining A_1 and A_2 represents the relative velocities of the two planes. The navigator in A_2 observes plane A_1 receding from him with a velocity of 178 mi/hr in a direction 52.5 degrees north of west, while the navigator in A_1 observes plane A_2 receding from him with a velocity of 178 mi/hr in a direction 52.5 degrees south of east.

With respect to A_2 the base B is moving west with a velocity of 250 mi/hr. With respect to A_1 the base is moving southwest with a velocity of 200 mi/hr. **All motions are relative.**

Summary

Velocity is a vector quantity. A vector has magnitude and direction, and can be resolved into two components.

Components are vector quantities, and are of such magnitudes and directions that when added together they are equivalent to the original vector.

It is customary to resolve a velocity vector into two components at right angles to each other. The motion of a body may therefore be thought of as two simultaneous motions taking place at right angles to each other. A ship sailing northeast, for example, may be thought of as sailing north and east at the same time.

Questions

1. What is meant by the resolution of velocities?

2. What are components of a vector? What are components of a velocity?

3. What is meant by relative velocity? Give an example.

4. How does the composition of velocities compare with the resolution of a velocity?

5. What is meant by relative velocity?

6. Car **A** stands still while car **B** drives away at 30 mi/hr toward the east. What is the relative velocity of **A** with respect to **B**? (Both magnitude and direction must be specified in your answer.)

7. Think of some project in which you might make a simple and inexpensive device for demonstrating one of the principles developed in this lesson.

Problems

1. A pilot in a plane cruising at 250 mi/hr, heads his plane due east. Aloft he finds a 60 mi/hr wind blowing from the south. Find his ground speed and the direction he flies.

2. A pilot in a plane cruising at 160 mi/hr heads his plane due south. Aloft he finds a 50 mi/hr wind blowing from the west. Find his ground speed and the direction he flies.

3. An object moves with a velocity of 5 m/sec along a line making an angle of 68° with the **x**-axis. Find the **x**- and **y**-components of this velocity.

4. A body has a velocity of 80 m/sec in a direction of 50° with the **x**-axis. Find the **x**- and **y**-components of this velocity.

5. A small object moves with a velocity of 65 m/sec in a direction making an angle of 20° with the **x**-axis. What are the magnitudes of the **x**- and **y**-components of this velocity?

6. An arrow is shot into the air with an initial velocity of 60 m/sec at an angle of 55° with the horizontal. Find the horizontal and vertical components of this initial velocity.

7.* A ship making 30 knots is sailing in a direction 30° north of east. What is its velocity (a) toward the north and (b) toward the east?

8.* A plane cruises at 375 mi/hr in a direction 35° south of west. What is its velocity (a) toward the south and (b) toward the west?

9.* A rocket having a velocity of 18,000 mi/hr is traveling in a direction 42° east of south. What is its velocity (a) toward the east and (b) toward the south?

Mechanics | Lesson 7

FALLING BODIES

Neglecting friction, all bodies, large and small, fall with the same acceleration. This, the law of falling bodies, is a physical paradox, for it contradicts the conclusion the average person might derive *a priori*. This is not to be wondered at, for cen-

turies ago the great philosopher Aristotle*
(384-322 B.C.) taught that heavy bodies fall
proportionately faster than lighter ones.

It took the world nearly two thousand
years to produce a challenger of Aristotle's
scientific teachings. In the year 1590 Galileo†
was pondering over the question of falling
bodies and found apparent inconsistencies
with Aristotle's teachings. He is said to have
dropped various kinds of objects from different levels of the leaning tower of Pisa and
to have timed their fall and measured their
velocities.

On one occasion Galileo is alleged to have
attracted a large crowd to the leaning tower,
where he climbed the spiral staircase to the
bell chamber at the top and there through an
open archway dropped two stones, one large
and one small. These two bodies fell side by
side and struck the ground together, thus
sounding the deathknell of an old hypothesis
and the birth of a new era in science.

Whether this particular incident is true or
not, the importance of Galileo's many authentic experiments lies not in the fact that
they demonstrated the fallacy of Aristotle's
reasoning, but that they presented to the

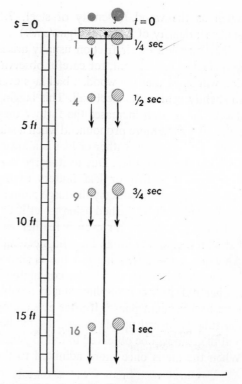

Fig. A. All bodies falling freely under the constant pull
of gravity fall a distance of 16 ft in the first second.

world a new and more reliable scientific
method, the method of experimentation.

Gravitation. The principle that all objects fall with the same acceleration can be
demonstrated in various ways. One of these
is illustrated in Fig. A where two steel balls,
one large and one small, are supported in the
groove of a wooden block 10 or 20 ft above
the ground. When the block is tipped by pulling the cord, both balls fall together and
strike the ground together. Dropped from a
height of 16 ft, the time of fall is just 1 sec.
The shaded circles in the figure show the
position of the two bodies at the end of each
quarter second.

If the balls in the experiment are replaced
by two marbles of the same size, one steel and
the other wood, they too will fall side by
side and strike the ground together. In this
case the steel marble weighs fifteen times as

* Aristotle (384-322 B.C.), famous Greek philosopher, logician, moralist, political thinker, biologist,
and founder of literary criticism, spent his early
years as a student and fellow worker with Plato.
While practically all of Aristotle's teachings concerning physical principles are now known to be
erroneous, his contributions to other fields of
knowledge have placed him high among the great
men of ancient Greece.

† Galileo Galilei (1564-1642), Italian mathematician, astronomer, and experimental physicist.
At the early age of twenty-four Galileo wrote a
treatise on the center of gravity of solids. This led
the following year to his appointment as professor
of mathematics at the University of Pisa. A rumor
that a Dutch lens grinder had observed that two
lenses used together make distant objects appear
close at hand led Galileo to construct the first
telescope. Successful telescopes of greater and
greater magnification enabled him eventually to
observe, for the first time, the mountains on the
moon, the major satellites of Jupiter, and sun-
spots. While at Pisa, Galileo carried out many experiments and public demonstrations of principles
which laid the foundations of mechanics and the
laws of projectiles and falling bodies.

much as the wood. (Density of steel, 7.6 gm/cm³; density of wood, 0.5 gm/cm³.)

The question of air friction usually arises in this latter experiment, for careful observation will show that the wooden ball lags ever so slightly behind the steel ball. This lagging due to air friction increases the farther they fall, and is even more pronounced when a still lighter object like a feather or leaf is allowed to fall at the same time. Due to its large surface area, a feather or leaf flutters to the ground, being held back by the large amount of air that must be pushed aside to let it by.

In the absence of air even a feather will fall with the acceleration of a solid steel ball. An experiment illustrating just this is shown in Fig. B. A long glass cylinder containing a feather and silver coin is connected by flexible tube to a vacuum pump. If after evacuation the tube is turned upside down, the feather and the coin will be observed to fall together. When the air is once more admitted to the

cylinder the feather will again flutter slowly to the bottom.

In the absence of air friction, all bodies fall with the same acceleration.

In the treatment of falling bodies given in the remainder of this chapter air friction is entirely neglected. The formulas presented and used in working problems are known to hold only approximately. In most practical cases, however, the calculated results are so nearly realized experimentally that corrections for air friction need only be made where the distances and velocities involved are large. A detailed discussion of the effects of air friction on falling bodies is given in Mechanics, Lesson 24, p. 95.

Free Fall. Many laboratory experiments can be performed to demonstrate the well-established laws of falling bodies. One of

Fig. C. Illustrating the distance and velocity of freely falling bodies at the end of each of the first 5 sec.

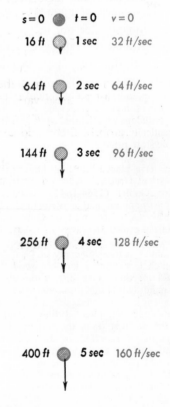

s = 0	t = 0	v = 0
16 ft	1 sec	32 ft/sec
64 ft	2 sec	64 ft/sec
144 ft	3 sec	96 ft/sec
256 ft	4 sec	128 ft/sec
400 ft	5 sec	160 ft/sec

Fig. B. In a vacuum a feather and coin fall with the same acceleration and strike the bottom together.

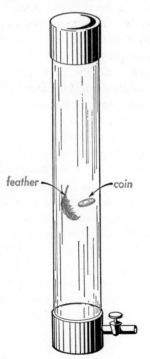

feather — — coin

these is the inclined plane experiment described in Mechanics, Lesson 4. If the angle the plane makes with the horizontal is increased, the acceleration of the ball down the plane will also increase. The velocities as well as the distances traveled will increase in the proper proportions to show that all of the equations summarized at the end of the last chapter are generally valid. This is true even for the limiting angle of 90° where the inclined plane becomes straight up and down and the steel ball falls freely under the full force of gravity.

As indicated in Fig. C, the measured distance a body falls is 16 ft in the first second; four times sixteen or 64 ft in 2 sec, nine times sixteen or 144 ft in 3 sec, etc. Inserting these distances in the equation $s = \frac{1}{2}at^2$, the constant of acceleration is computed to be $a = $ **32 ft/sec²**. If the distances are measured in centimeters, the same formula gives the equivalent acceleration as **980 cm/sec²** or **9.80 m/sec²**.

The Acceleration Due to Gravity. Experiments carried on at many points over the earth show that the acceleration due to gravity is not everywhere the same; there are slight variations. While these variations are small and are not of any consequence in most practical problems, they do exist and should be mentioned.

In general, the values of the acceleration due to gravity lie between a minimum of 32.09 ft/sec² or 9.7804 m/sec² at the equator and a maximum of 32.26 ft/sec² or 9.8321 m/sec² at the North and South poles. Referring here to the equator and the poles is only a generalization, for not all points on the equator have the same values as quoted above, nor do all points on any one latitude have the same value. Irregularities of the earth's structure give rise to minute random differences.

The International Committee on Weights and Measures has adopted as a standard or accepted value, 9.80665 m/sec² or 32.174 ft/sec². For practical purposes, however, it is customary to use the even numbered values 9.80 m/sec² and 32 ft/sec², and in formulas for free fall to use the small letter **g** in place of **a** as given in the last chapter. For freely falling bodies, then,

$$g = 9.80 \text{ m/sec}^2$$
$$g = 980 \text{ cm/sec}^2$$
$$g = 32 \text{ ft/sec}^2$$

and equations developed in Mechanics, Lesson 3, to be used are

$$v = gt \tag{1}$$

$$s = \frac{v}{2}t \tag{2}$$

$$v^2 = 2\,gs \tag{3}$$
$$s = \frac{1}{2}gt^2 \tag{4}$$

Example 1. A boy standing on a high bridge drops a stone into the water below. By looking at his watch he notes that it takes just 3 sec for the stone to fall. Calculate (a) the speed of the stone as it hits the water and (b) the height of the bridge.

Solution. To find the speed it is convenient to use Eq. (1) and substitute the known quantities **g** = 32 ft/sec² and **t** = 3 sec.

$$v = 32\,\frac{\text{ft}}{\text{sec}^2} \times 3 \text{ sec} = 96\,\frac{\text{ft}}{\text{sec}}$$

To find the height, use Eq. (2) and substitute the same quantities as follows:

$$s = \frac{1}{2} \times 32\,\frac{\text{ft}}{\text{sec}^2} \times 9 \text{ sec}^2 = 144 \text{ ft}$$

The answers are (a) the stone hits the water with a speed of 96 ft/sec and (b) the height of the bridge is 144 ft.

Summary

Neglecting friction, all bodies fall with the same uniform acceleration. For most practical purposes the acceleration due to gravity is

$$g = 9.80 \text{ m/sec}^2$$
$$g = 980 \text{ cm/sec}^2$$
$$g = 32 \text{ ft/sec}^2$$

Starting from rest a body will fall 16 ft or 4.9 m in the first second. At the end of this first second the instantaneous velocity will be 32 ft/sec or 9.8 m/sec. The kinematic equations for freely falling bodies are the following:

$$v = gt \qquad\qquad v^2 = 2\,gs$$
$$s = \frac{v}{2}\,t \qquad\qquad s = \frac{1}{2}\,gt^2$$

Questions

1. What is meant by a freely falling body?

2. Why does a leaf or feather fall more slowly than a stone?

3. If air friction were eliminated, what could you say about all falling bodies?

4. How much farther does a freely falling body fall during two seconds than it does during one second? Assume it falls from rest.

5. After falling for one second a body acquires a velocity of 32 ft/sec. How then do you account for the fact that it falls only 16 ft during that time?

6. Why do you think the velocity of a freely falling body increases continuously?

7. A paratrooper delays the opening of his parachute and soon acquires a maximum velocity of 160 mi/hr. Why is he no longer accelerated?

8. Think of some project in which you might make a simple and inexpensive device for demonstrating one of the principles developed in this lesson.

Problems

1. A workman accidentally drops a hammer while working on a tall building. If it requires 8 sec to reach the ground, (a) how high is the building and (b) with what speed does the hammer strike the ground?

2. A stone dropped into a well hits the water in 3.5 sec. (a) How deep is the well and (b) with what speed does the stone hit the water?

3. A sandbag dropped from a balloon hits the ground with a speed of 180 mi/hr. (a) How high is the balloon and (b) how long is the sandbag in falling?

4. An object falls from a bridge 225 ft above the water. (a) With what speed does it hit the water and (b) how long is it in the air?

5. A swimmer diving from a bridge acquires 4.5 sec to reach the water. (a) How high is the bridge and (b) with what speed will he hit the water?

6. A stone dropped from a tower hits the ground in 2.8 sec. (a) How high is the tower and (b) with what speed will the stone hit the ground?

7. A stone is dropped from a 100 ft tower. (a) How long will it take to hit the ground? (b) How fast will it be moving?

8. A block of lead is dropped from a tower 49 m high. (a) How long will it take to reach the ground? (b) How fast will it be moving?

9.* A stone falling from rest acquires a speed of 49 m/sec. Find (a) the height from which it was dropped and (b) the time of fall.

10. In diving from a high platform a swimmer is moving with a downward velocity of 48 ft/sec when he enters the water. Find (a) the height from which he dives and (b) the time it takes to reach the water.

Mechanics | **Lesson 8**

FALLING BODIES—*Laboratory*

In performing this experiment as described in the accompanying LAB-ORATORY EXERCISES you will make measurements on a freely falling steel ball. Using the recorded precision measurements of distance and time, and the principles developed in the preceding lesson, the accleration due to gravity is determined.

Mechanics | **Lesson 9**

NEWTON'S FIRST LAW OF MOTION

In the preceding chapter the motions of bodies have been described in terms of **speed, velocity,** and **acceleration.** The definitions of these quantities, and the laws and formulas relating to them, are classified as belonging to that branch of mechanics called "kinematics." Here in this chapter the cause of motion is to be treated. Such a treatment involves the introduction of **mass** and **force** into the equations already presented.

To Isaac Newton* goes the credit of having been the first to systematically introduce these concepts into mechanics and to formu-late the fundamental laws governing all motion. These laws constitute the fundamental principles of that branch of mechanics called "dynamics" and resolve themselves into three laws commonly referred to as "Newton's Laws of Motion."

Newton's First Law of Motion. *A body at rest or in uniform motion will remain at rest or in uniform motion unless some external force is applied to it.* This law can be

* Sir Isaac Newton (1642-1727), English physicist and mathematician, was born in England on

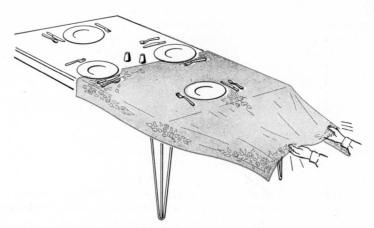

Fig. A. A tablecloth can be pulled from a table without dislodging the dishes.

demonstrated by many simple experiments. In Fig. A a tablecloth is shown in the process of being removed from under the dishes and silverware on a table without disturbing their original setting. In Fig. B a small car is shown free to move on a smooth hard track. If the track is jerked quickly to right or left, the wheels of the car will turn, but the car itself will tend to remain at rest.

Christmas Day, 1642. He obtained his education at Trinity College, Cambridge, where in 1665 he was awarded the Master of Arts degree. At just this time the prevalence of the black plague forced him into retirement at his old home in Woolsthorpe where in the two years 1665 and 1666 his genius developed. In this period he invented the calculus, discovered the composition of white light, and conceived the idea of universal gravitation. In the years that followed, he published much of his work on optics and developed his ideas on gravitation, which were published in 1687 in his "Principia." At the age of fifty he suffered from a nervous breakdown, and never again did any extensive scientific work, but devoted his time to theology. He became very absent-minded and slovenly in his personal appearance. It is needless to say, therefore, that he never married. His "Principia" is considered to be one of the greatest monuments of the human intellect. In it, Newton lays the foundations of mechanics which are broad enough to include all future developments, and these he applies to the motions of heavenly bodies under the law of gravitation. He was elected to Parliament, was president of the Royal Society for twenty-five years, and was knighted by Queen Anne in 1705. The greatness of this modest man is illustrated by a remark of his made on his deathbed, "If I have seen farther than others, it is by standing on the shoulders of giants."

In both of these experiments the dishes and the car are at rest. They tend to remain at rest because the sudden motion of the objects on which they are resting exert no large force for any appreciable length of time. Actually, the dishes and the car do move slightly due to small frictional forces between the moving parts in contact. The tendency for each body to remain at rest is due to that property, common to all material bodies, called *inertia*. *The inertia of a body may be defined as that property of a body which tends to resist a change in its state of rest or motion. Mass is defined as a quantitative measure of inertia.* In the metric system, mass is measured in grams or kilograms.

A third experiment illustrating inertia, and Newton's First Law, is illustrated in Fig. C. A small mass **M** of 1000 gm is suspended by a fine thread **A**, then pulled downward by another piece of the same thread **B**. If the

Fig. B. The smooth track can quickly be moved so as not to set the car in motion.

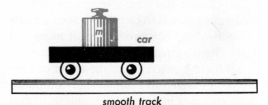

smooth track

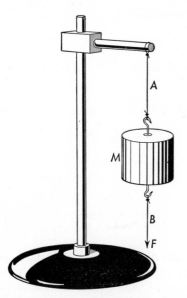

Fig. C. A slow, steady pull at F breaks the thread at A, while a quick pull at F breaks the thread at B.

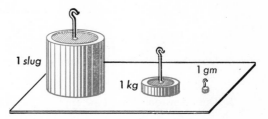

Fig. D. Units of mass are also units of inertia.

the track, Newton's First Law states that it should keep moving with the same velocity. The law, of course, neglects friction, for we know that left to itself friction will eventually bring the car to rest. The greater the friction, the sooner will it stop. The smaller the friction, the longer will it move. If friction could be entirely eliminated, the *inertia* of the car would keep it moving indefinitely with constant velocity.

force **F** is a slow, steady pull, the thread will always break at **A**; whereas if it is a sudden jerk, it will always break at **B**. In the first case the tension in the upper thread is greatest and is equivalent to the force **F** plus the weight of the mass **M**. In the second case the force **F** is momentarily very large, causing the thread to break before the mass **M** has had time to move down far enough to stretch and break the upper thread. It is the inertia of **M** that permits the very large force **F** to be momentarily applied to the lower thread only.

If the car in Fig. B is started rolling along

Inertia and Mass. Mass is a measure of inertia. In the metric system inertia and mass are measured in **grams** and **kilograms**. In the English system they are both measured in **slugs**. Fig. D is a diagram illustrating the relative size of these three units. They are shown in a hooked weight form convenient for use in experiments.

If one were to weigh these three fundamental units of mass, 1 slug would weigh 32 pounds, 1 kg would weigh 9.8 newtons, and 1 gm would weigh 980 dynes. The difference between mass and weight will be taken up in detail in Mechanics, Lesson 12.

Summary

Newton's First Law of Motion introduces the concept of inertia. Inertia is the property a body has which tends to keep it at rest if it is not moving and to keep it moving with constant velocity if it is already in motion.

Mass is a measure of inertia. Both are measured in grams, kilograms, and slugs. A body at rest or in uniform motion will remain at rest or in uniform motion unless some external force is applied to it.

Questions

1. State Newton's First Law of Motion. Give an illustration.

2. What concept does this law introduce? How is it measured?

3. Name the three fundamental units of mass and inertia. Give their respective weights.

4. Does Newton's First Law apply to the case of a car moving along a straight road at 60 mi/hr.

5. Does Newton's First Law apply to an elevator car moving upward at constant speed?

6. What is the magnitude of your own inertia? (a) In the metric mks system of units? (b) In the English system of units?

7. In what ways you can think of are the principles developed in this lesson involved in things happening in the world around us?

8. Think of some project in which you might make a simple and inexpensive device for demonstrating the principles developed in this lesson.

Mechanics | Lesson 10

PROJECTILES

Horizontal Projection. If one body falls freely from rest at the same time another is projected horizontally from the same height, the two will strike the ground simultaneously. An experimental proof of this fundamental observation may be verified by an experiment of the type diagrammed in Fig. A.

Two identical marbles **M** and **N** are sup-

Fig. A. A body dropped from rest and another projected horizontally, strike the ground at the same time.

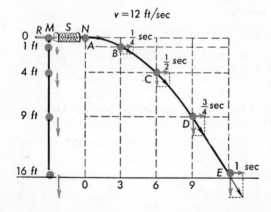

ported by a rod and trough respectively in such a way that when the compressed spring **S** is released, the rod **R** springs to the right, dropping **M** and projecting **N** horizontally. Marble **M** falling with the acceleration of gravity **g**, and marble **N** traversing the longer path **ABCDE** strike the ground at the same time. Repetition of the experiment with higher or lower projection velocities and from different heights ends always with the same result: both marbles hit the ground together.

The first conclusion that may be drawn from this experiment is that the downward acceleration of a projectile is the same as a freely falling body and takes place independent of its horizontal motion. Furthermore, an experimental measurement of *times* and *distances* shows that the horizontal velocity of projection continues unchanged and takes place independently of the vertical motion.

In other words, a projectile carries out two motions independently: (1) a constant horizontal velocity **v** and (2) a vertically downward acceleration **g**.

Projection Straight Upward. When a body is projected straight upward, its speed will rapidly diminish until at some point it comes momentarily to rest and then falls back toward the earth, acquiring again at the ground the same speed as it had upon projection. Experiment shows that the time taken to rise to the highest point of its trajectory is equal to the time taken to fall from there to the ground. This implies that the upward motions are just the same as the downward motions, but in reverse, and that the time and speed for any point along the path are given by the same equations for free fall. See Mechanics, Lesson 7.

$$v = gt \tag{1}$$

$$s = \frac{v}{2} t \tag{2}$$

$$v^2 = 2\, gs \tag{3}$$

$$s = \tfrac{1}{2}\, gt^2 \tag{4}$$

Fig. B. Neglecting air friction, the upward motion of a body is the same as the downward motion in reverse. A stone thrown upward returns to the ground with the same speed.

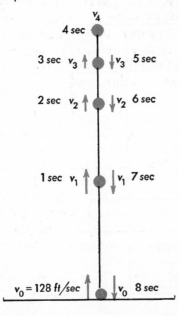

In Fig. B a particle is shown projected upward with a velocity of 128 ft/sec. After each second's time, its speed on the way up is shown to be the same as its speed at the same level on the way down. It is convenient, therefore, in solving problems on projection upward, to start at the top where the object is at rest and apply the equations for free fall.

Example 1. A ball is thrown straight upward with a speed of 128 ft/sec. Neglecting friction, find (a) the time taken to reach the top of its flight and (b) the maximum height reached.

Solution. Since the time to rise equals the time to fall, we can apply Eq. (1) for free fall. By substituting directly into the equation we obtain (a):

$$128 \, \frac{ft}{sec} = 32 \, \frac{ft}{sec^2} \times t$$

By solving for *t* and canceling units, we find

$$t = \frac{128}{32} \, sec = 4 \ sec$$

(b) By applying Eq. (4) we obtain by direct substitution

$$s = \frac{1}{2} \times 32 \, \frac{ft}{sec^2} \times (4 \ sec)^2 = 256 \ ft$$

It therefore takes 4 sec to rise to the highest point 256 ft above the ground and another 4 sec to return, or a total of 8 sec.

Projectiles. Many missiles when projected into the air follow a parabolic path. In practical cases, air friction may be considered negligible only for slowly moving objects with high densities, like a large stone, a block of metal, or a solid ball. For high-speed projectiles the air continually slows the projectile down and the path departs from a parabola somewhat in the fashion shown in Fig. C.

The interesting and important information to be obtained from a study of projectiles is the **maximum height**, the **range**, and the **time of flight**.

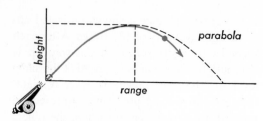

Fig. C. Projectiles tend to follow a parabolic path. Because of air friction they fall short.

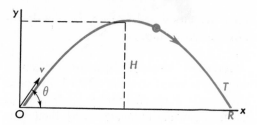

Fig. D. The range R, maximum height H, and the time of flight T of a projectile depends upon the initial velocity v and the elevation angle.

The maximum height is defined as the greatest vertical distance reached by the projectile as measured from the ground up. The range is defined as the horizontal distance from the point of projection to the point where the projectile returns again to the same level. The time of flight is defined as the time required for the projectile to again reach the level of its initial projection. Experiment shows that all three of these factors will depend upon two things: first, on the **initial velocity** of the projectile, and second, on its **angle of projection**. The latter is always measured from the horizontal and is called the **elevation angle**. See Fig. D.

If **v** is the velocity of projection and θ is the elevation angle, the maximum height **H**,

the range **R**, and the time of flight **T** are given by the formulas in Table 1.

If an object is projected with a velocity **v**, it will, neglecting air friction, rise to its maximum height in the same time it takes to fall from that height to the ground. As might be suspected from Fig. D, it will arrive at the ground with the same speed it had on projection.

To see how to apply the above equations, consider the following example.

Example 2. In the 1948 Olympic Games held in London, the 16-lb shot-put was won by Wilbur Thompson of the United States. Assuming an initial velocity of projection of

Table 1. Formulas for Projectiles

Elevation Angle θ	Maximum Height H	Range R	Time of Flight T
0°	0	0	0
15°	0.268 $v^2/8$ g	0.500 v^2/g	0.518 v/g
30°	$v^2/8$ g	0.866 v^2/g	v/g
45°	2 $v^2/8$ g	v^2/g	1.41 v/g
60°	3 $v^2/8$ g	0.866 v^2/g	1.73 v/g
75°	3.73 $v^2/8$ g	0.500 v^2/g	1.93 v/g
90°	4 $v^2/8$ g	0	2 v/g

13 m/sec and an elevation angle of 45°, find
(a) the record distance thrown and (b) the
time of flight.

Solution. The known quantities are $v =$
13 m/sec, $\theta = 45°$, and $g = 9.8$ m/sec².
Opposite $\theta = 45°$ in Table 1, we find under
the Range R the relation v^2/g. From this we
write $R = v^2/g$. Upon substituting the known
value of v and g, we write

$$R = \frac{(13 \text{ m/sec})^2}{9.8 \text{ m/sec}^2}$$

from which, upon squaring and canceling like
units, we find

$$R = \frac{169}{9.8} \text{ m} = 17.2 \text{ m}$$

Opposite $\theta = 45°$ in Table 1, we find under
Time of Flight T the relation 1.41 v/g. From
this we write $T = 1.41 \ v/g$. Again substituting known values, we write

$$T = \frac{1.41 \times 13 \text{ m/sec}}{9.8 \text{ m/sec}^2}$$

Multiplying out and canceling like units,
we obtain

$$T = 1.87 \text{ sec}$$

Summary

Neglecting air friction, the path of a projectile is a parabola. The motion of a projectile
is considered as two motions taking place simultaneously. One is a horizontal motion
with constant velocity, and the other a vertical motion under constant acceleration due
to gravity.

The vertical motion takes place according to the regular kinematic equations already
used in other lessons, and these equations can be used to derive formulas for the range,
height, and time of flight.

Neglecting air friction, a projectile has its greatest range at an elevation angle of 45° and
its greatest height at an angle of 90°. If air friction is appreciably large, a projectile will
fall short of its friction-free range.

Questions

1. When a projectile is thrown straight upward, how does its upward motion compare
   with its subsequent downward motion?

2. If a ball is thrown horizontally, what can you say about its (a) horizontal motion
   and (b) downward motion?

3. Do the horizontal and vertical motions of a projectile affect one another? (Neglect
   friction.)

4. What is meant by the elevation angle and range of a projectile?

5. At what elevation angle does a projectile acquire its (a) greatest range and (b)
   maximum height?

6. Does a 12-lb shot-put follow a parabolic path? Does a hard-driven golf ball follow
   a parabolic path?

7. How does the maximum height of a projectile compare with its range, at an elevation angle of 45°?

8. At what elevation angle will the time of flight be a maximum?

9. If the initial velocity of a projectile is doubled, how will the time of flight be affected?

10. Think of some project in which you might make a simple and inexpensive device for demonstrating the principles developed in this lesson.

Problems

1. An arrow is shot straight upward with a speed of 34.3 m/sec. Find (a) the height to which it rises and (b) the time required to return to the ground.

2. A stone is thrown vertically upward with speed of 60 mi/hr. Find (a) the height to which it rises and (b) the total time to reach the ground. (*Note:* 60 mi/hr = 88 ft/sec.)

3. A baseball is hit straight upward with a speed of 39.2 m/sec. Find (a) the maximum height reached and (b) the total time it is in the air.

4. An arrow is shot upward with a speed of 230 ft/sec. Find (a) the maximum height reached and (b) the total time of flight.

5. A mail plane in straight and level flight 300 ft above the ground releases a mail bag to be picked up on the ground. How long does it take to fall?

6. A supply plane in straight and level flight 100 meters above the ground releases a package. How long will it take to fall?

7.* A javelin is thrown with a speed of 80 ft/sec at an elevation angle of 45°. Find (a) the range, (b) the maximum height, and (c) the time of flight.

8.* A shot-put is thrown with a speed 40 ft/sec at an elevation angle of 45°. Find (a) the range, (b) the maximum height, and (c) the time of flight.

9.* An arrow is shot upward with a speed of 200 ft/sec at an elevation angle of 60°. Find (a) the range, (b) the maximum height, and (c) the time of flight.

Mechanics | Lesson 11

PROJECTILES—*Laboratory*

In performing this experiment as described in the accompanying *LAB-ORATORY EXERCISES* you will use a stream of water to observe the range and maximum height of projectiles at various elevation angles. The principles used involve those introduced in the preceding lesson.

NEWTON'S SECOND LAW OF MOTION

Newton's Second Law of Motion. Newton's First Law, concerning bodies at rest or moving with constant velocity, assumes that no forces are acting to change their state. Newton's Second Law, however, assumes that such a force is acting and describes the resulting **change in motion.** In Fig. A, for example, a small car of mass **m** is acted upon by a constant force **F.** The force is produced by the pull of gravity on the mass **M** and is transmitted to the car by a cord passing over pulleys as indicated. If the car is initially at rest, this force will start it moving; if it is already moving with a velocity v_0, the force will increase its velocity. Thus the car is accelerated.

Newton's Second Law of Motion may be stated as follows: *When a body is acted upon by a constant force, its resulting acceleration is in the direction of the applied force, and is proportional to the force and inversely proportional to the mass.*

Symbolically,

$$a \propto \frac{F}{m}$$

Fig. A. A small car being accelerated by a constant force.

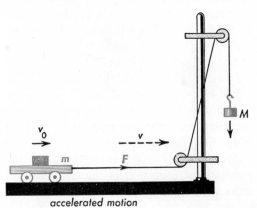

accelerated motion

This law is stated as a proportionality because it holds regardless of the units in which each of the three quantities is measured. If the units are properly chosen, an equal sign may be inserted and the law written as an equation,

$$a = \frac{F}{m}$$

By transposing **m** to the other side of the equation, the so-called "force equation" which forms the basis of so many principles in mechanics is obtained.

$$F = m \times a \qquad (1)$$
force = mass × acceleration

Example 1. Neglecting friction, what constant force will give a mass of 50 gm an acceleration of 5 cm/sec²?

Solution. By substituting directly into the force equation, Eq. (1), we obtain

$$F = 50 \text{ gm} \times 5 \frac{cm}{sec^2} = 250 \frac{gm \ cm}{sec^2}$$

The answer is a force of 250 gm cm/sec². Thus, force is not as simple a concept as it might seem at first hand; it involves all three of the fundamental units, **length, mass,** and **time.**

By definition, 1 gm cm/sec² is a unit of force called the **dyne.** According to this definition the answer to the above problem could have been written **250 dynes. The dyne is a force which, acting on a 1-gm mass, will give it an acceleration of 1 cm/sec².** In the cgs system (centimeter-gram-second system) the units of Eq. (1) become

$$1 \text{ dyne} = 1 \text{ gm} \times 1 \frac{cm}{sec^2}$$

There is a widespread preference among scientists and teachers of physics to use the kilogram and meter in place of the gram and centimeter as units of mass and length. According to the mks system (meter-kilogram-second system) unit force is called the newton in honor of Sir Isaac Newton. **The newton is defined as that force which, applied to a mass of 1 kg, will give it an acceleration of 1 m/sec².**

In the mks system of units, Eq. (1) becomes

$$1 \text{ newton} = 1 \text{ kg} \times 1 \frac{m}{\text{sec}^2} \qquad (2)$$

Example 2. Neglecting friction, what constant force in newtons will give a mass of 4 kg an acceleration of 3.8 m/sec²?

Solution. By applying the force equation, **F = ma**, we obtain

$$F = 4 \text{ kg} \times 3.8 \frac{m}{\text{sec}^2}$$

$$= 15.2 \frac{\text{kg m}}{\text{sec}^2} = 15.2 \text{ newtons}$$

The answer is a constant force of 15.2 newtons.

Dynes and **newtons** are called absolute units of force. They arise from the force equation when the fundamental units of **mass** and **time** are used as they are above.

Since 1 kg = 1000 gm, and 1 m = 100 cm,

$$1 \text{ newton} = 100{,}000 \text{ dynes}$$

The engineer seldom uses the metric system of units described above; he finds it more convenient to measure **force** in **pounds.** To apply Newton's Second Law of Motion, as expressed by the force equation **F = ma**, it is necessary to introduce a unit of mass called the **slug.** See Fig. B. **One slug is defined as that mass which, when acted upon by a force of 1 lb, is given an acceleration of 1 ft/sec².**

$$1 \text{ lb} = 1 \text{ slug} \times 1 \frac{ft}{\text{sec}^2} \qquad (3)$$

The mass of a body in slugs may be obtained by dividing the weight of that body in pounds by 32.

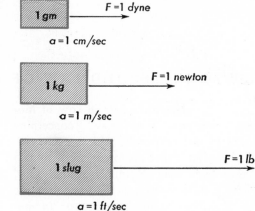

Fig. B. Unit force acting on unit mass produces unit acceleration.

Weight and Mass. When a mass **m** is allowed to fall freely, it is the constant downward force of gravity on the mass that gives rise to its constant acceleration. If Newton's Second Law is applied to this motion, see Eq. (1), the force **F** is none other than the weight **W** of the body, and the acceleration **a** is the acceleration due to gravity **g**. For falling bodies the force equation, **F = ma**, is written in different symbols.

$$W = mg \qquad (4)$$
$$\text{weight} = \text{mass} \times \text{acceleration}$$

As we have seen in the preceding chapter, **weight** and **force** have both magnitude and direction and are therefore vector quantities. Mass, on the other hand, is a scalar quantity since it has only magnitude. The distinction between **weight** and **mass** is illustrated by imagining a given body to be carried out into free space far removed from other bodies and their gravitational attraction. There, a body at rest will still have its mass but it will have no weight. That such a body has its mass would be demonstrated if another mass were to bump into it. The smaller the mass of the incoming body, the less would be the recoil of the first mass from the impact.

Weight here on the earth is due to the gravitational attraction of the earth upon a mass at its surface. In the equation **W = mg**

Fig. C. If the thread is pulled to the right, which way will the spool roll?

we may define **g** as the **weight per unit mass. W** is the **mass** times the **weight per unit mass.**

Example 3. Calculate the weight of a body having a mass of 1 kg.

Solution. By direct substitution in Eq. (4) we obtain

$$W = 1 \text{ kg} \times 9.80 \, \frac{m}{sec^2}$$

$$= 9.80 \, \frac{kg \, m}{sec^2} = 9.80 \text{ newtons}$$

Example 4. What horizontal force in pounds applied to the tongue of a small wagon weighing 176 lb will give it an acceleration of 6 ft/sec²?

Solution. By applying Newton's Second Law, Eq. (1), we obtain

$$F = \frac{176}{32} \text{ slugs} \times 6 \, \frac{ft}{sec^2}$$

$$F = 5.5 \text{ slugs} \times 6 \, \frac{ft}{sec^2} = 33 \text{ lb}$$

The answer is a constant force of 33 lb.

To illustrate how Newton's Second Law may always be relied upon, consider the following paradox. A spool of thread is placed upon the table as shown in Fig. C. With the thread leading off the underside of the spool a horizontal force **F** will cause the spool to move. Will it roll to the right and wind up the thread or will it roll to the left and unwind? The performance and explanation of this experiment are left as a problem for the student.

Summary

Newton's Second Law of Motion. When a body is acted upon by a constant force, its resulting acceleration is in the direction of the applied force and is proportional to the force and inversely proportional to the mass.

The law gives rise to the basic equation in dynamics, namely,

$$F = ma$$

In the metric system of units, forces are measured in newtons or dynes, and in the English system they are measured in pounds. Mass is measured in kilograms, grams, and slugs.

Weight and mass are different entities. Weight is a force and is due to the gravitational pull on a mass. Mass is a scalar quantity, while force is a vector quantity.

Weight and mass are related to each other by the relation

$$W = mg$$

where **g** is the acceleration due to gravity.

To find the mass of a body in slugs, its weight in pounds is divided by 32.

Questions

1. State Newton's Second Law of Motion. Write down the algebraic equation representing the law and indicate the meaning of each symbol.

2. Define or briefly explain each of the following: (a) newton, (b) dyne, and (c) slug.

3. How does the acceleration of a body depend upon the force? If the force is doubled how does the acceleration change? How does the distance traveled in one second change?

4. If the mass of a body is doubled and the force remains the same, what change takes place in the acceleration?

5. How is the weight of a body related to its mass?

6. What is the unit of mass in (a) the mks system, (b) the cgs system, and (c) the English system?

7. Which is the largest of the three forces: 1 newton, 1 dyne, 1 lb? Which is the largest: 1 lb, 10 newtons, or 2000 dynes?

8. Which way does the spool roll in Fig. C? Explain.

9. When a force is applied to a body how does the direction of the force compare with the direction of motion?

10. A 10-lb weight and 1-lb weight are dropped side by side. Since the earth pulls downward on one with a ten times greater force, why do the two have the same acceleration?

11. What would be the weight of a 1-kg mass if it were out in free space far removed from all astronomical bodies?

Problems

1. A mass of 3 kg is given an acceleration of 2.5 m/sec². Calculate the force required in (a) newtons and (b) dynes.

2. A mass of 450 gm is given an acceleration or 8 cm/sec². Find the force in (a) dynes and (b) newtons.

3. A car weighing 1600 lb has an acceleration of 2.5 ft/sec². Find the force in pounds.

4. A force of 120 lb is applied to a car weighing 2400 lb. Find (a) the mass of the car in slugs and (b) the acceleration.

5. A locomotive weighing 80 tons is capable of an acceleration of 2 ft/sec². Calculate (a) the mass of the locomotive in slugs and (b) the force it develops in pounds.

6. A midget car of mass 420 kg can accelerate at 1.2 m/sec². Find the force in newtons.

7. A force of 75 newtons acts on a mass of 22.5 kg. Find the acceleration.

8. An 8-lb weight is allowed to fall freely under the constant downward pull of gravity. Find the acceleration.

9.* A 16-ton passenger plane starting from rest at one end of a runway acquires its take-off speed of 88 ft/sec in 20 sec. Calculate (a) the acceleration and (b) the total average thrust of its propellers.

10.* A force of 50 newtons is applied to a mass of 20 kg. Find (a) the acceleration and (b) the speed acquired at the end of 5 sec.

11.* A car weighing 3200 lb is moving along a level road at a speed of 100 ft/sec. Calculate the force required to stop it in 5 sec.

Mechanics | Lesson 13 *none*

THE FORCE EQUATION—*Laboratory*

In performing this experiment as described in the accompanying LAB-ORATORY EXERCISES you will determine the accelerated motion of a toy truck. The applied force and the truck's mass are varied, and the principles of the force equation introduced in the previous lesson are applied to the results.

Mechanics | Lesson 14

NEWTON'S LAW OF GRAVITATION AND THIRD LAW OF MOTION

Newton's Law of Gravitation. Nearly everyone has heard the story of how young Isaac Newton, while sitting under an apple tree one day, was struck on the head by a falling apple. This incident set Newton to thinking about falling bodies and led him, at the early age of twenty-three, to the discovery of the law of gravitation.

It has often been said incorrectly that Newton discovered gravity. What Newton discovered was the **universal law of gravitation.**

Fig. A. Illustrating the gravitational attraction of one body of mass m_1 for another of mass m_2.

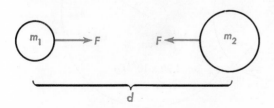

Any two bodies attract each other with a force proportional to the product of their masses and inversely proportional to the square of the distance between them.

Written in algebraic symbols,

$$F \propto \frac{m_1 m_2}{d^2}$$

As illustrated in Fig. A, **F** is the force of attraction, m_1 and m_2 are the two masses, and **d** is the distance between them. Mass m_1 pulls on m_2 with a force **F** to the left and m_2 pulls on m_1 with an equal force **F** to the right. To make an equation of this symbolism it is only necessary to replace the proportionality symbol above by an equal sign and insert a constant on either side of the equality.

$$F = G \frac{m_1 m_2}{d^2} \qquad (1)$$

Experiment shows that if F is measured in newtons, m_1 and m_2 in kilograms, and d in meters, the "Newtonian Constant of Gravitation" G has the value

$$G = 0.000,000,000,0666 \, \frac{m^3}{kg \; sec^2}$$

or in shorthand notation (see Special Lesson 2)

$$G = 6.66 \times 10^{-11} \, \frac{m^3}{kg \; sec^2} \qquad (2)$$

If F is measured in pounds, m_1 and m_2 in slugs, and d in feet,

$$G = 3.41 \times 10^{-8} \, \frac{ft^3}{slug \; sec^2} \qquad (3)$$

Example 1. Two locomotives, weighing 64 tons each, stand beside each other with their centers 10 ft apart. Calculate the gravitational attractive force between them.

Solution. First find the mass of each locomotive in slugs as follows:

$$m = \frac{64 \times 2000}{32} = 4000 \; slugs$$

Direct substitution in Eq. (1) now gives

$$F = 3.41 \times 10^{-8} \frac{4000 \times 4000}{10^2} = 0.00546 \, lb$$

This force of 0.00546 lb is extremely small and would be difficult to detect, much less measure.

If we now consider the attraction between a very large object, like the earth, and another object like our own body, the force becomes one that is quite measurable for it is none other than our own weight. It is the force that keeps all of us on the earth.

To go one step further, gravitational attraction is the force that keeps the moon in its orbit around the earth, and the earth in its orbit around the sun. Such forces have magnitudes of billions of billions of tons. See Fig. B.

If we now let m_1 represent the mass of the earth M, and m_2 represent a small mass m on earth, d becomes the earth's radius R and we can write

$$F = G \, \frac{Mm}{R^2}$$

Now if we let the mass fall freely from a few feet above the ground, its acceleration is g. By Newton's Second Law of Motion $F = mg$. Therefore,

$$mg = G \, \frac{Mm}{R^2}$$

or

$$g = \frac{GM}{R^2} \qquad (4)$$

Newton's Third Law of Motion. Of Newton's three laws of motion, the third is perhaps the least understood. This is probably due to the fact that it is seldom used in solv-

Fig. B. Gravitational attraction keeps the moon in its orbit around the earth and the earth in its orbit around the sun.

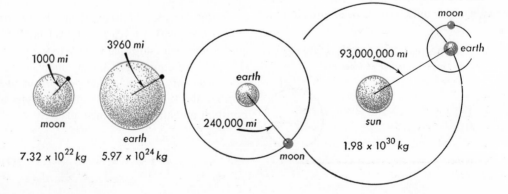

1000 mi

3960 mi

moon

earth

7.32 x 10^{22} kg   5.97 x 10^{24} kg

earth

240,000 mi

moon

93,000,000 mi

moon

earth

sun

1.98 x 10^{30} kg

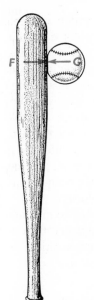

Fig. C. A bat at all times exerts a force on the ball equal in magnitude to the force the ball exerts on the bat.

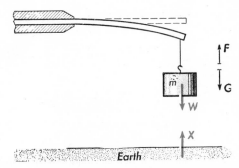

Fig. D. Illustrating Newton's Third Law of Motion. Forces always exist in pairs.

ing problems, and often when it is used it is incorrectly applied.

Newton's Third Law of Motion states that *to every action force there is an equal and opposite reaction force.*

The principle of action and reaction may be illustrated by a bat striking a ball, Fig. C. During impact the bat exerts a force **F** on the ball, and the ball exerts an equal but opposite force **G** on the bat. The force **F** being exerted on the ball gives it an acceleration to the right, while the force **G** being exerted on the bat gives it an acceleration to the left. The ball speeds up during the impact and acquires a high velocity while the bat in the same interval slows down to a lower velocity.

Consider the second example of a block hanging by a cord as illustrated in Fig. D. The weight of the block **W** is the force with which the earth pulls downward on the block, while the equal and opposite force **X** is the upward force exerted by the block on the earth.

In addition to this pair of forces, the block exerts a downward force **G** on the cord, while the cord pulls upward with the reaction force **F**. Although to many people these forces may seem confusing, it should be pointed out that

Newton himself has some difficulty in applying his third law to certain problems. The difficulty arises from trying to apply action and reaction forces to the same body when in reality they apply to different ones.

The action force and the reaction force in Newton's Third Law of Motion act on different bodies.

Whether a body is at rest or in motion, the state of that body depends upon the forces acting on it and not upon the forces it exerts on something else. So far as the body is concerned, the latter do not determine its motion.

The Train-and-Track Experiment. Another illustration of Newton's Third Law is that of a train on a track, both of which, the track as well as the train, are free to move. The drive wheels push back on the track with a force **B**, and the track pushes forward on the wheels with an equal and opposite force **F**. These two form an action and reaction pair.

In Fig. E, the track is mounted on a large wheel with its axis of rotation vertical. With the track free to move, both forces of the pair are seen to be real, the track moves backward and the train moves forward. The track moves backward because the wheels exert a force **B** upon it in that direction, and the train goes forward because the track exerts a force **F** upon it in that direction. If, when the train acquires a certain velocity, the power is shut off, the force **F** vanishes—so

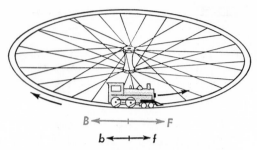

B ◄————————► F

b ◄————► f

Fig. E. Demonstration of Newton's Third Law of Motion. The train moves forward, and the track, if free to move, moves backward.

the wheels with a force **b**, and the wheels push forward on the track with an equal but opposite force **f**.

In order to keep a train moving with constant speed, a minimum force **B** great enough to overcome friction must continually be supplied to the locomotive drive wheels. The two forces acting on the train then are **F** and **b**, and these being equal and opposite have a zero resultant. There being no resultant force, there is no acceleration and the train continues to move with constant velocity.

also does **B**—and the train and track continue to move with constant speed.

In a practical case, however, the track is not only fastened down, but there is some frictional resistance to motion. Because of this friction the track pushes backward on

To start the train moving, and to maintain an acceleration, **F** must be greater than **b**. Under these conditions the acceleration, by Newton's Second Law, is

$$F - b = ma$$
$$\text{force} = \text{mass} \times \text{acceleration}$$

Summary

The universal law of gravitation was first formulated by Isaac Newton. It states that any two bodies attract each other with a force proportional to the product of their masses and inversely proportional to the square of the distance between them.

$$F = G \frac{m_1 m_2}{d^2}$$

Newton's Third Law of Motion states that to every action force there is an equal and opposite reaction force. This is the most difficult of Newton's three laws of motion to understand. It becomes clearer if one notes that the action force and reaction force act on different bodies.

Whether a body is initially at rest or in motion, its subsequent behavior depends upon the forces acting on it and not upon the forces it exerts on other bodies.

Questions

1. State Newton's Law of Gravitation. Write down the algebraic equation representing this law. Make a diagram and indicate the various factors in the equation by the proper labels.

2. Define or briefly explain (a) the acceleration due to gravity and (b) the Newtonian Constant of gravitation.

3. State Newton's Third Law of Motion. Give an example and briefly explain it in terms of the forces involved.

4. A book is at rest on a table. Make a diagram and show the two pairs of action and reaction forces involved.

5. An automobile moves along a straight and level road with constant velocity. What horizontal pairs of forces are acting here?

6. A car crashes into a stone wall. What horizontal forces are involved? Make a diagram.

7. A horse pulls a wagon along a level road. By Newton's Third Law of Motion the wagon pulls back on the horse with a force equal to the forward force of the horse on the wagon. Since these forces must always be equal and opposite, explain why the wagon ever moves at all.

8. A stone is allowed to fall freely. Neglecting air friction, what action and reaction forces are involved? What can you say about the earth's motion while the stone falls?

9. What happens to the earth's rotational motion when a heavy train starts from a station? What happens when the train stops?

10. See if you can devise a project in which you might make a simple and inexpensive device for demonstrating one of the principles in this lesson.

Problems

1.* Two metal spheres, each having a mass of 3 million kilograms, are located with their centers 4 meters apart. Calculate the force of attraction between them in newtons.

2.* The moon has a mass of 7.3×10^{22} kg, and the earth a mass of 6.0×10^{24} kg. Find the attractive force between these two bodies in newtons if their centers are 3.9×10^8 meters apart.

3. A man weighing 150 lb stands on some scales to weigh himself. What is the direction and magnitude of the force he exerts on the scale board?

4. A 20-lb stone is dropped from a bridge. What is the direction and magnitude of the force exerted by the stone on the earth?

5. A man weighing 200 lb sits in a chair. What are the directions and magnitudes of the two forces acting on him?

6. An elephant weighing 3000 lb is being lifted at constant velocity by an elevator. What are the directions and magnitudes of the two forces acting on the elephant?

Mechanics | **Lesson 15**

BALANCED AND UNBALANCED FORCES

Everyone knows that when he weighs himself, he is measuring the downward force he exerts on the foot board of the scales and that this force causes some mechanism within the scales to indicate his weight. The greater the downward force, the greater is the indicated weight. We are not interested here in the system of levers, weights, or springs within the scales, but rather with the downward force we call our **weight.**

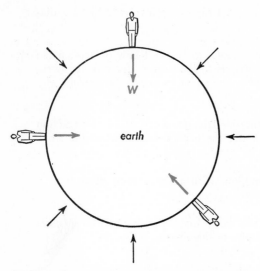

Fig. A. Weight is a force due to gravitational attraction, and gravitational force acts in the direction of a line joining the body and the center of the earth.

Weight, as explained in the last chapter, is due to the gravitational attraction of the earth for all bodies.

As illustrated in Fig. A, gravitational forces always act in the direction of a line joining the body and the center of the earth and are, therefore, perpendicular to the earth's surface at the body.

The term **force** is not confined to weight alone but to the action of any one body upon another. For example, in towing an automobile as shown in Fig. B, there are two forces acting: (1) a downward force **W** due to gravity and (2) a horizontal force **F** due to a pull on the tow line. The latter force is supplied by some external object or machine.

Regardless of the direction in which a force may act, its magnitude may be expressed in **dynes, newtons,** or **pounds.**

Fig. B. Illustrating two independent forces acting on the same body.

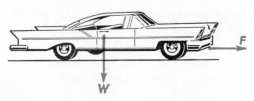

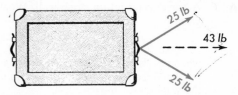

Fig. C. Two forces acting at an angle to each other are equivalent to a single force acting in a direction between them.

Forces Are Added Vectorially. Since forces have both magnitude and direction, they are vector quantities and, therefore, subject to the rules of **vector addition.** Consider the diagram in Fig. C, illustrating a heavy trunk being pulled along the floor by two ropes. With steady pulls of 25 lb each exerted in directions at 60° from each other, the trunk moves in a direction indicated by the dotted arrow.

By vector addition a resultant force can be found which, upon taking the place of the two forces shown, will produce the same motion.

When this **resultant** is determined by vector addition, it is found to have a magnitude of 43 lb and a direction making an angle of 30° with either force.

To illustrate the common methods employed in the vector addition of two forces,

Fig. D. Force diagram of two forces acting on the same body.

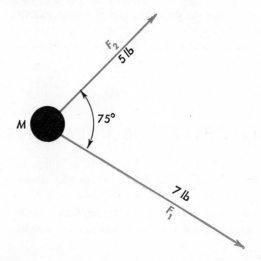

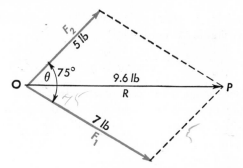

Fig. E. Illustrating the parallelogram method of vector addition.

consider the illustration shown in Fig. D, where two forces of 7 lb and 5 lb, respectively, are applied to a body at the common point **M**. In general there are two graphical methods for finding the resultant: first, the **parallelogram method;** and second, the **triangle method.**

The parallelogram method of vector addition is shown in Fig. E. First a line F_1 is drawn in the proper direction to represent the 7-lb force. The length of the line is made to be 7 cm to represent the magnitude of the force, and the arrowhead is inserted at the right end to indicate its direction. In a similar way, the line F_2 is drawn 5-cm long and in the proper direction to represent the 5-lb force.

From the head of the vector representing the 5-lb force a dotted line is drawn parallel to the 7-lb vector, and from the head of the 7-lb vector a dotted line is drawn parallel to the 5-lb vector. Starting from the origin **O**, the resultant **R** is drawn to the point **P**, where these two dotted lines intersect. Using the same scale that was used to mark off the 7-lb and 5-lb vectors, the length of **R** can be read directly as 9.6 lb, and the angle it makes with either F_1 or F_2 can be read in degrees with a protractor. In other words, the length of **R** gives the magnitude of the resultant force and the direction of **R** gives the direction of the force. As a vector equation, we write

$$\overrightarrow{F_1} + \overrightarrow{F_2} = \overrightarrow{R}$$

This resultant force, if acting on the body, will produce exactly the same effect as, and is equivalent to, the two original forces. The construction of a few vector diagrams like these, but with larger and smaller angles between the two, will show that when the forces are in the same direction, $\theta = 0$, or in opposite directions, $\theta = 180°$, the resultant **R** is equal respectively to the arithmetical sum and difference. Thus the magnitude of **R** may have any value from the arithmetic difference, 2 lb, up to the arithmetic sum, 12 lb, depending solely upon the relative directions of the two original forces.

The triangle method of vector addition, as shown in Fig. F, follows directly from the parallelogram method just described. Only half of the parallelogram need be drawn. For example, the 7-lb vector is first drawn to some scale. Second, the 5-lb vector is started at the arrowhead of the 7-lb vector and drawn in its true direction and to the same scale. The resultant is finally drawn starting at the origin **O** and ending at **P**, the second arrowhead. For convenience alone, this triangle method is to be preferred over the parallelogram method.

Conditions for Equilibrium. When one or more forces act upon a body at rest, and their resultant sum is not zero, the body will be set into motion. Under such conditions there is an **unbalanced force** acting and this force alone accounts for the acceleration. If, however, the vector sum of all the forces acting is zero, the body is in equilibrium and the body will remain at rest. To turn this statement around is to say,

Fig. F. Illustrating the triangle method of vector addition.

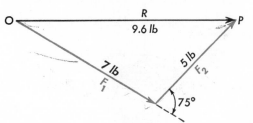

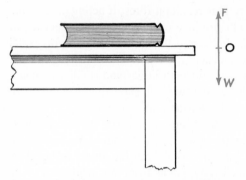

Fig. G. A book lying on a table is in equilibrium.

"Any object remaining at rest is in equilibrium, and the resultant of all forces acting upon it is zero."

If two and only two forces act upon a body in equilibrium, a little study will show that they must be equal in magnitude and opposite in direction. A book lying on the table or a lamp hanging from the ceiling are good examples of dual forces in equilibrium. See Figs. G and H.

The two forces acting on the book are **W**, the downward pull of the earth, called the **weight**, and **F**, the upward thrust of the table. Since the book is in equilibrium, the force **F** is equal in magnitude to the weight **W**.

$$\vec{F} + \vec{W} = 0$$

For the lamp the downward force, or

Fig. H. A lamp hanging from the ceiling is in equilibrium.

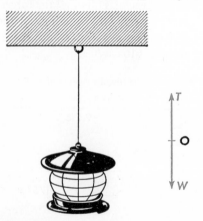

weight, is counterbalanced by the upward tension in the cord.

$$\vec{T} + \vec{W} = 0$$

Here again, the forces are equal in magnitude and opposite in direction. A body moving with constant velocity is in equilibrium: since there is no acceleration, there is no unbalanced force.

Three Forces in Equilibrium. When, as the result of the action of three forces, a body is in equilibrium, the **resultant** of all three forces must be zero. In other words, to be in equilibrium the forces, when added together as vectors, must have a result **R** = 0. With three forces such a vector diagram would have only three sides, i.e., it would be a triangle. As an illustration, consider a street light of 50 lb suspended from two points as shown in Fig. I.

The three forces acting through the common point **O** are **W**, the weight of the lamp, 50 lb acting straight downward; **F₁**, the pull of one rope at 45° up and to the left; and **F₂**, the pull of the other rope at 30° up and to the right. The force diagram is shown below and to the right.

The force **W** is first drawn downward and

Fig. I. Three forces produce equilibrium if their vector sum is zero.

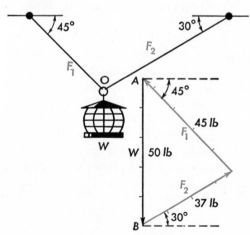

50 units long to represent 50 lb. The force F_2 is added up to the right and at 30° with the horizontal. The force F_1 is drawn in starting at **A** and 45° with the horizontal.

Where F_1 and F_2 intersect, the vectors are terminated and the arrowhead drawn as indicated. When the lengths of the two lines are measured, F_2 has a length of 37 units, representing 37 lb, and F_1 has a length of 45 units, representing 45 lb. As vectors

$$\vec{W} + \vec{F_2} + \vec{F_1} = 0$$

Summary

Force is a vector quantity. Every force has a magnitude and a direction. Two or more forces can be combined as vectors to find an equivalent force called the resultant.

There are two methods of vector addition. They are (a) the parallelogram method and (b) the triangle method. When two or more forces act on a body, their vector resultant can take the place of the forces and produce the same effect on that body.

A body at rest or moving with constant velocity is in equilibrium. To be in equilibrium the resultant of all forces acting on a body must be zero. If three forces are in equilibrium, their vectors will form a closed triangle.

If the resultant of all the forces acting on a body is not zero, the body is not in equilibrium, and it will be accelerated by that force according to the force equation

$$F = ma$$

Questions

1. Briefly describe the process of vector addition as it applies to two forces making an angle of 90° with each other.

2. What is the significance of a resultant force? What does it represent by comparison with the original forces?

3. What is the triangle method of vector addition?

4. If two forces act upon a body, what are the conditions for equilibrium?

5. If three forces act upon a body, what are the conditions for equilibrium?

6. If two forces act upon a body and it is not in equilibrium, what single force can be applied to bring it into a state of equilibrium. Explain.

7. Can you think of any examples of where the principles developed in this lesson are involved in the world around us?

8. Think of some project in which you might make a simple and inexpensive device for demonstrating one of the principles developed in this lesson.

Problems

1. Make a scale diagram of the vector addition of two forces, 3 lb and 4 lb, respectively, applied at right angles to each other. Find the resultant force (a) graphically and (b) by calculation.

2. If two forces $F_1 = 4.5$ lb and $F_2 = 6$ lb act on a body such that their directions make an angle of 90° with each other, find the magnitude of their resultant (a) graphically and (b) by calculation.

3. Two forces of 6 newtons and 8 newtons, respectively, are exerted simultaneously on the same object. If the angle between them is 60°, find by graphical construction (a) their resultant and (b) a third force that will bring the two into equilibrium.

4. Two forces of 60 newtons each make an angle of 50° with each other. Find by graphical construction (a) their resultant and (b) a third force that will produce equilibrium.

5. Two forces of 20 newtons and 30 newtons act on the same body at right angles to each other. Find, by calculation, the magnitude of their resultant. What third force acting on the body will establish equilibrium?

6. Two forces of 5 lb and 7 lb act on the same body. If the angle between them is 120°, calculate the magnitude of the resultant.

7. A canal boat is being pulled by two ropes making an angle of 45° with each other. If the forces are 150 lb and 175 lb, respectively, what is the magnitude of the resultant force?

Mechanics | Lesson 16

CONCURRENT FORCES—*Laboratory*

In performing this experiment as described in the accompanying LAB-ORATORY EXERCISES use is made of the equilibrium conditions introduced in the preceding lesson. Using spring scales and weights, coplaner forces are brought into equilibrium and the force magnitudes and directions are measured.

Mechanics | Lesson 17

RESOLUTION OF FORCES

Resolution of a Force into Components. Many of the force problems in mechanics are most easily solved by the so-called *"method of components."* To apply this method to typical problems it is necessary that we first see how a single vector may be resolved into two components. Consider as an illustration the known force **F**, making an angle of θ degrees with the **x**-axis as shown in Fig. A.

By dropping lines from **A**, perpendicular to the **x**- and **y**-axes, the component forces F_x and F_y are obtained. These two components are equivalent to the original force **F**,

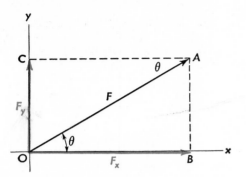

Fig. A. Illustrating the resolution of a vector into two rectangular components.

since by adding them vectorially they give **F** as a resultant.

With F_x and F_y perpendicular to each other, triangles **OAB** and **OAC** are congruent right triangles with corresponding sides equal. $F_y = BA$ and $F_x = CA$.

By trigonometry, then,

$$\frac{F_y}{F} = \sin\theta$$

$$\frac{F_x}{F} = \cos\theta \qquad (1)$$

$$\frac{F_y}{F_x} = \tan\theta$$

Since **F** and θ are usually the known quantities, the first two equations are the most useful in finding the magnitudes of force components. Transposing, they become

$$\boxed{\begin{aligned} F_y &= F \sin\theta \\ F_x &= F \cos\theta \end{aligned}} \qquad (2)$$

Example 1. A force of 750 lb is applied at an angle of 30° with the horizontal force to pull a heavy truck across a plowed field. What is the effective horizontal force?

Solution. As shown in Fig. B, the applied force **F** of 750 lb can be resolved into two components F_x and F_y. To find the magnitude of F_x we use Eq. (2) and substitute the known quantities directly.

$$F_x = 750 \text{ lb} \times \cos 30°$$

Looking up the cosine of 30° in the Appendix I, we find

$$\cos 30° = 0.866$$

Upon substitution in the above equation we obtain

$$F_x = 750 \text{ lb} \times 0.866$$
$$F_x = 649 \text{ lb}$$

The vertical component of force F_y can also be calculated, but it is not asked for.

Example 2. A force of 50 lb is applied to the handle of a 150-lb lawn roller. See Fig. C. Calculate (a) the horizontal and vertical components of this force if the handle makes an angle of 40° with the horizontal and (b) the force exerted by the roller on the ground.

Solution. The graphical solution to (a) is shown at the lower right in Fig. C. The magnitudes of the two components F_x and F_y are calculated by direct substitutions in Eq. (1).

$$F_x = 50 \text{ lb} \times \cos 40°$$
$$F_y = 50 \text{ lb} \times \sin 40°$$

Fig. B. Illustration of force components.

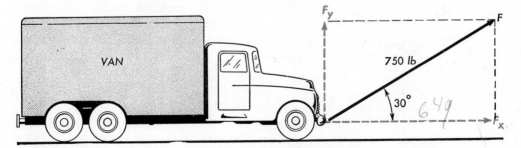

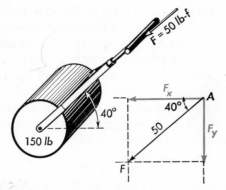

Fig. C. The force on the handle of a lawn roller is resolved into two components.

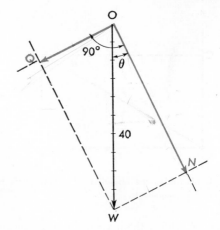

Fig. E. Resolution of the weight of the wagon into two components.

From tables of natural sines and cosines, substitution gives

$$F_x = 50 \times 0.766 = 38.3 \text{ lb}$$
$$F_y = 50 \times 0.643 = 32.1 \text{ lb}$$

The horizontal components, $F_x = 38.3$ lb, is the force causing the roller to move, while the vertical component, $F_y = 32.1$ lb, acting straight downward must be added to the weight of the roller to find the total force exerted by the roller on the ground.

$$\text{total downward force} = 150 + 32.1$$
$$= 182.1 \text{ lb}$$

Consider the following example of the resolution of a force into two rectangular components. A boy is pulling a small 40-lb wagon up a 50 per cent grade as illustrated in Fig. D. A 50 per cent grade means that for every 100 ft traveled in the horizontal direction there is a vertical rise of 50 ft. (This is not equivalent to an angle of 50°.)

Fig. D. A wagon on an inclined plane.

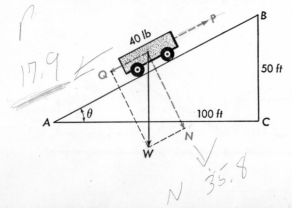

To find how hard the boy must pull on the wagon, the weight of the wagon **W** is resolved into two components, one parallel to the incline and the other perpendicular to it. As shown in diagram Fig. E, the 40-lb vector **W** is first drawn vertically downward. Two dotted lines are next drawn parallel and perpendicular to the incline, from both ends of **W**. Where these lines intersect at **Q** and **N**, the vector components **Q** and **N** are terminated. When the magnitudes of these two forces are measured, they are found to have the values **Q** = 17.9 lb and **N** = 35.8 lb. The force **N** is the force the wheels of the wagon exert against the incline and, being perpendicular to it, neither aids nor hinders the motion. To pull the wagon the boy must exert a force **P** equal to or greater than 17.9 lb, the magnitude of the component **Q** down the incline.

The Sailboat. A problem that puzzles many people, particularly those more or less familiar with sailboats, is that of sailing across the water into the wind. This phenomenon, commonly known as **tacking,** is another illustration of the resolution of a force into rectangular components.

As shown in Fig. F, the wind is from the east and the boat is headed NE. When the

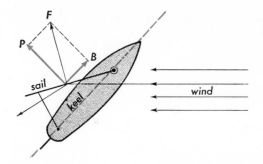

Fig. F. A boat sailing into the wind. An example of the resolution of a force F into two rectangular components P and B.

two rectangular components, one parallel and the other perpendicular to the boat, the force **B**, responsible for the boat's motion, is found.

The other component, **P**, has little effect upon the boat since it is perpendicular to the motion. It is a useless force which tends to tip the boat and move it to leeward. To prevent tipping or being pushed sideways, sailboats are equipped with a deep heavy keel. By increasing the angle between the sail and the wind, the force **F** will increase but the forward component will decrease. If the boat is headed more directly into the wind, without changing the relative position of the sail, the useful component **B** will again decrease. Most rapid progress upwind is attained when the wind and keel make an angle of 45° and the rudder is parallel to the keel.

sail is properly set, the wind, in blowing across the canvas, is deflected away in such a way that it exerts a force **F** normal to the surface as shown. By resolving this force into

Summary

A single force can be resolved into two forces called components. The vector sum of these two components is equivalent to the original force. It is customary to choose the components' directions such that they are at right angles to each other.

The reason for carrying out such a process is that the motions of bodies are more clearly analyzed and understood by studying the actions of the components.

It is frequently convenient to choose the x-axis and y-axis as directions for components. The basic equations for computing components are

$$F_x = F \cos \theta$$
$$F_y = F \sin \theta$$

Questions

1. Make a diagram showing how to resolve a single force into two components at right angles to each other.

2. Can either component of a force be larger than the original force itself if the components are at right angles to each other?

3. Imagine a car on the side of a hill with the brakes set. Show how to resolve the weight of the car into two components, one parallel to the hillside and one perpendicular to it.

4. Explain by the method of components how a sailboat can make progress through the water against the wind. Make a diagram.

5. If the ▮▮▮▮ mponents of a force are to be equal in magnitude and at right angles to each ▮▮▮▮ ngles will each make with the original force?

6. Think of some project in which you might make a simple and inexpensive device for demonstrating the principles of components.

Problems

1. Compute the magnitudes of the x- and y-components of a force of 16 lb acting in a direction making 28° with the x-axis.

2. Compute the magnitudes of the x- and y-components of a force of 25 newtons acting in a direction making 42° with the x-axis.

3. A rowboat is pulled behind a cabin cruiser by a rope inclined at an angle of 35° with the horizontal. What is the horizontal force acting on the rowboat if the tension in the rope is 45 lb?

4. The car on a 30 degree incline weighs 2.5 tons. Calculate the tension in the cable required to keep it moving with uniform speed up or down the incline.

5. A concrete bucket weighing 1500 lb is mounted on wheels and pulled up a 25° incline. Calculate the force required if the cable is parallel to the incline.

6.* A force of 10 lb is to be resolved into two forces at right angles to each other. What are the magnitudes of the components if one is twice the other.

7.* A force of 25 newtons is to be resolved into two components at right angles to each other. If one is to be 3 times the other, what are their magnitudes?

8. A long rope, making an angle of 30° with the horizontal, has the upper end tied to the top of a tree. (a) If the tension in the rope is 100 lb, what are the components of this force parallel and perpendicular to the ground? (b) Which component tends to pull the tree over?

9. A force of 50 lb is exerted in the handle of a 300-lb lawn roller. If the handles makes an angle of 30° with the horizontal, what is the total downward force on the ground?

10. One end of a rope is tied to a log and the other end to an elephant. If the rope makes an angle of 55° with the ground and a tension of 420 lb exists in the rope, what horizontal force is applied to drag the log?

Mechanics | **Lesson 18**

RESOLUTION OF FORCES—*Laboratory*

In performing this experiment as described in the accompanying *LABO-RATORY EXERCISES* you will make use of the principles of force components as treated in the preceding lesson. Part 1 employs hooked weights, cords, and pulleys on a peg board, while Part 2 employs a small toy automobile held in equilibrium on an inclined plane.

ROTATIONAL EQUILIBRIUM

We have seen in the preceding lessons how a body, acted upon by a number of forces, is in equilibrium if the vector sum of all the forces is zero. We have also seen how any force can be resolved into **x**- and **y**-components. We will begin this lesson by seeing how the conditions of equilibrium may be applied to the force components rather than to the forces themselves. To do this we simply resolve each force into **x**- and **y**-components, and then apply the conditions of equilibrium to each of the two sets of components separately.

Translational Equilibrium. In Fig. A we see three forces F_1, F_2, and F_3 acting on a body in equilibrium. If a vector diagram is made of these forces, we know that a complete triangle will be formed, and we can write

$$\vec{F_1} + \vec{F_2} + \vec{F_3} = 0 \qquad (1)$$

Indeed, if there were four, five, six, or any number of forces acting on a body, and

that body were in equilibrium, the vector sum of all the forces would have to be zero. In general then we can write

$$\Sigma \vec{F} = 0 \qquad (2)$$

where the Greek letter means **summation**, and $\Sigma \vec{F}$ means the **vector sum** of all the **F**'s. This is referred to as the **first condition of equilibrium**, or the **condition of translational equilibrium**.

In Fig. B the three forces of Fig. A have each been resolved into **x**- and **y**-components. The **x**-components of all three forces are horizontal, while the **y**-components are all vertical. We now state that the sum of all the **x**-components is zero and the sum of all the **y**-components is zero. These two statements can be written as follows:

$$\Sigma F_x = 0 \qquad (3)$$
$$\Sigma F_y = 0 \qquad (4)$$

The **x**-components of F_1 and F_3 are to the right and are said to be **positive**, while the

Fig. A. A body in equilibrium is acted upon by three forces.

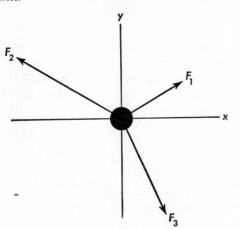

Fig. B. If a body is in equilibrium, the sum of all the x-components of force is zero, and the sum of all the y-components is zero.

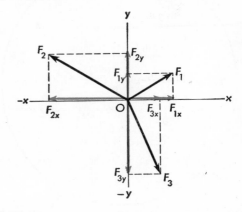

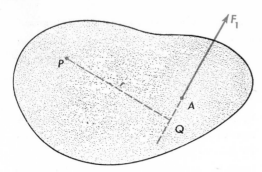

Fig. C. A single force acting on a rigid body pivoted at some point P exerts a torque $L = F_1 \times r$.

the perpendicular distance from the pivot point to the force. In Fig. C a body is shown acted upon by a torque. The force **F** is applied at the point **A**, while the body is pivoted at the point **P**. The perpendicular distance **r** is equal to the line **PQ**, and the torque **L** is given by

$$L = F_1 \times r \qquad (5)$$

If $F_1 = 5$ newtons, and $r = 3$ m,

$$L = \quad 5 \text{ newtons} \times 3 \text{ meters}$$
$$L = 15 \text{ newton meters}$$

x-component of F_2 is to the left and therefore **negative**. In other words, to have a vector sum of zero, $F_{1x} + F_{3x}$ must be just equal and opposite to F_{2x}. Similarly the sum of the upward components $F_{1y} + F_{2y}$ must be equal to the downward component F_{3y}. We see, therefore, that for a body to be in equilibrium Eqs. (3) and (4) must be satisfied. These equations too are referred to as the **first condition of equilibrium.**

Torque.   When a single force acting on a body tends to produce rotation, it is said to exert a **torque**. Torque is synonymous with **force-moment** and is defined as **the product of force times lever arm**, the lever arm being

Fig. D. Illustrating a rigid body in rotational equilibrium under the action of four torques.

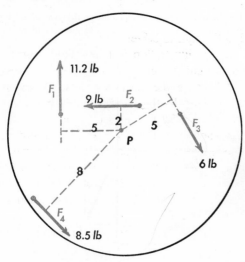

Rotational Equilibrium. Consider the rigid body in Fig. D pivoted by a pin at the point **P** and acted upon by four forces F_1, F_2, F_3, and F_4. With lever arms of 5, 2, 5, and 8 ft respectively, these four forces constitute torques L_1, L_2, L_3, and L_4. For this body to be in translational equilibrium the summation of all the forces, or the sums of all their **x**- and **y**-components, must be zero. In other words, the first condition of equilibrium must be satisfied.

To be in rotational equilibrium the summation of all the torques must be zero. This latter, the second condition of equilibrium, can be expressed symbolically as

$$\Sigma L = 0 \qquad (6)$$

It is customary to assign a positive sign to all torques acting to turn a body counterclockwise and a minus sign to all torques tending to turn it clockwise.

Let us now see how to apply the second condition of equilibrium to Fig. D. The first torque L_1 is given by the product of the force 11.2 lb and the lever arm distance 5 ft, or −56 lb ft. The minus sign indicates the torque acts in a clockwise direction. If we calculate all four torques and list them, we obtain

$$L_1 = 11.2 \times 5 = -56 \text{ lb ft}$$
$$L_2 = \quad 9 \quad \times 2 = +18 \text{ lb ft}$$
$$L_3 = \quad 6 \quad \times 5 = -30 \text{ lb ft}$$
$$L_4 = \quad 8.5 \times 8 = +68 \text{ lb ft}$$
$$\overline{\qquad \Sigma L = 0 \qquad}$$

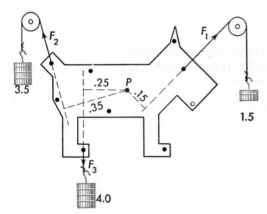

Fig. E. Demonstration experiment on rotational equilibrium.

The sum of the clockwise torques $L_1 + L_3$ = 86 lb ft is just equal to the sum of the counterclockwise torques $L_2 + L_4$. Because the sum of all the torques is zero, rotational equilibrium is assured.

Demonstration Experiment. A rigid body is defined as one whose various parts do not change their relative positions when forces are applied at different points. Actually no known bodies strictly satisfy this condition, but for practical purposes most solid bodies may be regarded as rigid.

Since a rigid body may have any size or shape, a thin piece of one-quarter-inch plywood, cut in the shape of a dog as shown in Fig. E, will be used as a demonstration experiment. Two pulleys are mounted on a pegboard, and the rigid body is pivoted free to rotate on a fixed pin P near the center. Three cords and three sets of weights are now attached to any three of the several holes drilled through the body.

Whatever weights have been selected, the dog will turn to some equilibrium position. If the pin is now removed, the dog will move as a whole to some new equilibrium position; and such a position, for example, could be the one shown in the diagram.

While the body is in this equilibrium condition, imagine the pin inserted at P and fastened to the pegboard. Such a pin cannot exert forces or torques upon the body, but it may be thought of as a pivot. Next we draw dotted lines on the dog, extending the lines of action of each of the three forces, until we can measure the lengths of the perpendicular lever arms. The lever arms shown in the diagram are in meters, and the masses are in kilograms.

Remembering that torque is given by Eq. (5) as force times lever arm, the three torques may be calculated as follows:

$$L_1 = 1.5 \times 9.8 \times 0.15$$
$$L_2 = 3.5 \times 9.8 \times 0.35$$
$$L_3 = 4.0 \times 9.8 \times 0.25$$

The products of the first two numbers give in each case the three forces in newtons. These are multiplied by the three lever arms at the right. Multiplying out and assigning a minus sign to the clockwise torque L_2, we obtain

$$
\begin{aligned}
L_1 &= +2.2 \text{ newton meters} \\
L_2 &= -12.0 \\
L_3 &= +9.8 \\
\hline
\Sigma L &= 0
\end{aligned}
$$

Since the position of P was chosen at random, we are free to relocate the pivot P anywhere in the body. Upon measuring the lengths of the lever arms to the new pivot point and calculating torques, one will again find the sum to be zero.

In the illustration just described, translational equilibrium conditions are also satisfied because the body is at rest. A vector diagram of the three forces F_1, F_2, and F_3, if drawn, will form a closed triangle. If this were not true, there would be a resultant force acting on the body and it would move in the direction of that force with an acceleration given by Newton's Second Law of Motion. Hence, both the first and second conditions of equilibrium are satisfied.

Summary

If a body is not moving in any direction, it is in translational equilibrium, and the resultant force acting upon it is zero. Similarly, if an object is not rotating, it is in rotational equilibrium and the resultant torque acting upon it is zero.

To be in translational and rotational equilibrium the following conditions must be satisfied:

$$\Sigma F = 0 \text{ (translation)}$$
$$\Sigma L = 0 \text{ (rotation)}$$

Torque L is synonymous with force-moment and is defined as the product of force times the lever arm, the lever arm being the perpendicular distance from the pivot point to the force.

It is customary to assign a negative sign to all clockwise acting torques and a positive sign to all counterclockwise torques. When applying the principles of translational equilibrium to a body, it is often convenient to resolve all forces into components and apply the principles to each set of components separately.

Questions

1. What are the conditions for translational equilibrium? If a body moves with constant velocity, is it in translational equilibrium?

2. What are the conditions for rotational equilibrium? If a body rotates with constant angular velocity, is it in rotational equilibrium?

3. Define torque. Make a diagram to show three torques acting on a body. Assign forces and lever arms to each torque. Write down the magnitude and direction of each torque.

4. Write down equations for the first and second conditions of equilibrium. Explain the meaning of each symbol.

5. A picture hangs from a nail in the wall, by a cord fastened to the two top corners of the frame. Make a diagram of the three forces acting on the picture and show the torques.

6. What examples can you think of in the world around us where the principles developed in this lesson are applicable?

7. Devise some project in which you might make a simple and inexpensive device for demonstrating one of the principles developed in this lesson.

Problems

1. A force of 6 lb is applied to a rope that is wound around the rim of a wheel 30 in. in diameter. Calculate the applied torque if the wheel is free to rotate around the center.

2. A uniform timber 8 ft long is pivoted free to turn about its center. Placed in a horizontal position a 50-lb load is placed on one end and a 20-lb load at the other. Find the resultant torque.

3. Suppose the lever arms in Fig. D were to remain unchanged, but the forces were altered as follows: $F_1 = 9$ lb, $F_2 = 4$ lb, and $F_3 = 7$ lb. To what value would F_4 have to be changed to maintain rotational equilibrium?

4. Suppose the lever arm of F_3 in Fig. D were reduced to 3 ft, and we altered the magnitude of F_4 to restore equilibrium. Find the magnitude of the new force F_4.

5. An equilateral triangle 2 ft on a side is cut from a piece of plywood. It is supported by a pivot at one corner and a 10-lb weight hangs from each of the other two corners. Make a diagram of this problem and show the magnitudes of the three forces acting on the body, as well as the two torques. Neglect the weight of the wood.

6. A sheet of metal 2 ft square is supported by a pivot at one corner. A 5-lb weight hangs from each of the two nearest corners. Make a diagram of this problem and show the magnitudes of the three forces acting on the body, as well as the two torques. Neglect the weight of the metal.

7. A uniform wooden plank 12 ft long is pivoted free to turn about its center. Placed in a horizontal position a boy weighing 100 lb is to sit on one end. (a) Where should a boy weighing 150 lb be located to produce balance?

Mechanics | Lesson 20

PARALLEL FORCES—*Laboratory*

In performing this experiment as described in the accompanying LABORATORY EXERCISES you will employ the principles of parallel forces in equilibrium. Two sets of metric weights, two platform balances, and a meter stick constitute the needed apparatus.

Mechanics | Lesson 21

CENTER OF MASS AND CENTER OF GRAVITY

In the kinematics and dynamics of motion one often neglects the size and shape of a body and speaks of the object as if it were located at a point. Of course, this is done for convenience only and is justified as long as one's interests are not centered on structural details. Under certain conditions it is found necessary to take into account the structural details and still make use of the simplest forms of Newton's laws of motion. How this is accomplished is the subject of this chapter.

Center of Mass. *The center of mass of any given body, or system of bodies, is a point such that if any plane is passed*

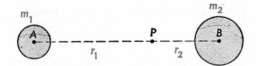

Fig. A. The center of mass of two bodies is located at some point on a line joining their centers of mass.

through it, the mass moments on one side of the plane are equal to the mass moments on the other.

Consider, for example, two spheres of mass m_1 and m_2 as shown in Fig. A. The center of mass (*abbr.* c of m) P lies on a line connecting the centers of the two bodies and in such a position that

$$m_1 \times r_1 = m_2 \times r_2 \qquad (1)$$

For a vertical plane through P, perpendicular to the plane of the page, $m_1 \times r_1$ is the mass moment of m_1, and $m_2 \times r_2$ is the mass moment of m_2. The mass moment of a body about any chosen plane is given by the mass of the body multiplied by its perpendicular distance to the plane.

Example 1. Find the c of m of two bodies $m_1 = 2$ gm, and $m_2 = 5$ gm, placed 14 cm apart.

Solution. Since the distance $r_1 + r_2 = 14$ cm, we obtain

$$r_2 = 14 - r_1$$

By substituting all known quantities in Eq. (1), we obtain

$$2 r_1 = 5(14 - r_1)$$

or

$$2 r_1 = 70 - 5 r_1$$

giving

$$7 r_1 = 70$$

or

$$r_1 = 10$$

By substituting this value of r_1 in Eq. (1), we find

$$r_2 = 4 \text{ cm}$$

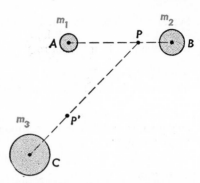

Fig. B. Illustrating the method for finding the center of mass of a three-body system.

The c of m of a three body system is found by an extension of the above principle. See Fig. B. To illustrate, two of the masses like A and B are first selected and their c of m found by use of Eq. (1). These two bodies are then treated as though they were one body located at P. With one mass $(m_1 + m_2)$ located at P and a second mass m_3 located at C, Eq. (1) is applied to find P' the resultant c of m. If a system consists of more than three bodies, the above process is continued until all masses have been included.

The c of m of all regularly shaped bodies like those shown in Fig. C is at their geometrical center. A plane passed through the center of any of these figures will divide the body into two equal parts.

Rotation about the Center of Mass. In Fig. D two masses m_1 and m_2 are shown supported at the ends of a thin rod and rotating

Fig. C. Illustrating the location of the center of mass of regularly shaped bodies.

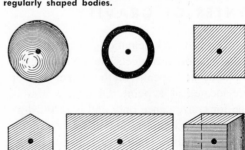

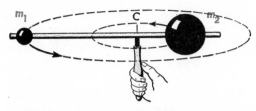

Fig. D. Illustrating the smooth rotation of two bodies around their center of mass.

smoothly around a pin through the **c of m.** If the pin is located at any other point, for example half way between the two masses, the experimenter will experience an unbalanced force on his hand, tending to make it "wobble."

Should the two-body system be thrown spinning into the air as shown in Fig. E, it will be observed to rotate about its **c of m** while the **c of m** traces out the smooth trajectory of a projectile.

The moon traverses its orbit once around the earth every four weeks. Actually the earth and the moon rotate around their common center of mass, a point on the line be-

tween their centers only 1000 mi below the earth's surface and 3000 mi from its center.

Center of Gravity. The **c of m** of the two bodies in Fig. A is the one and only point about which the two bodies will, if pivoted, balance under the earth's gravitational pull. The downward pull of the earth on m_1 is given by m_1g and the downward pull on m_2 is given by m_2g. To be in rotational equilibrium

$$m_1g \times r_1 = m_2g \times r_2 \qquad (2)$$

where each product $mg \times r$ is a force times a lever arm and is called a **force moment.** Canceling g on both sides, this relation becomes Eq. (1). Furthermore, a single upward force applied at **P**, equal in magnitude to the weight of the two bodies, will maintain equilibrium; the system will not tend to move in any direction nor will it tend to rotate.

The **c of m** is therefore a point at which all of the weight can be considered as concentrated. For this reason the **c of m** is often called the **center of gravity** (*abbr.* **c of g**).

The **c of g** of a regularly or irregularly

Fig. E. A body thrown spinning into the air rotates smoothly about its center of mass while the center of mass traces out the smooth trajectory of a projectile.

Fig. F. The center of gravity of any freely suspended object lies at or directly beneath the point of suspension.

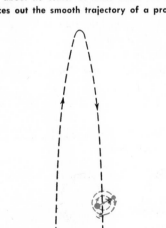

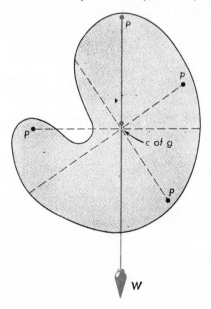

shaped body of uniform or nonuniform density can be found by suspending it from one pivot point and then another as shown in Fig. F. With each suspension from a point **P** near the periphery, the body will hang with its **c of g** directly under that point. Lines drawn along the string supporting the plumb for each suspension will all cross at the common point, the **c of g.**

If pivoted at this point and set turning, or thrown spinning into the air, the rotation will be smooth about the **c of g.** (*Note:* Because the force of gravity decreases with altitude, the **c of g** of a body is not always at exactly the same point as the **c of m.** The lower part of a mass, for example, is closer to the earth's center than the upper part and therefore has a greater weight per unit mass. For all practical purposes, however, the two terms **c of g** and **c of m** are considered synonymous.)

Summary

The concepts of center of mass and center of gravity are introduced. The center of mass is a point at which all the mass of an object may be considered as concentrated, while the center of gravity is a point at which all the weight of an object may be considered as concentrated. For practical purposes these two points are one and the same.

When a body is thrown spinning into the air, it will rotate smoothly around its center of mass. When pivoted at any fixed point, a body will hang with its center of gravity directly below that point. The basic concept of center of mass is given by the relation

$$m_1 \times r_1 = m_2 \times r_2$$

The product $m \times r$ is called mass moment.

Questions

1. Define or briefly explain each of the following: (a) mass moment, (b) center of gravity, and (c) center of mass.

2. How can one find the center of gravity of an irregularly shaped body?

3. If you have found the center of gravity of a body, how can you find the center of mass?

4. Approximately where is the center of mass of the moon and earth as a system? Of what significance is this center of mass?

5. Does the center of mass always lie somewhere within the substance of which a body is composed? Where is the center of mass of a uniform hoop?

6. In what ways are the principles developed in this lesson involved in things we can observe in the world around us?

7. Think of some project in which you might make a simple and inexpensive device for demonstrating the principles developed in this lesson.

Problems

1. Two meteorites in free space have masses of 5 kg and 9 kg, respectively. Where is their center of mass if they are 8 meters apart?

2. Two small solid spheres, with their centers 25 cm apart, have masses of 50 gm and 75 gm, respectively. Find the center of mass.

3. Two lead balls, located with their centers 24 meters apart, have masses of 3 kg and 9 kg, respectively. Find their center of mass.

4. Two masses of 5 kg and 12 kg, respectively, are located 80 cm apart. Find their center of mass.

5. Two bodies 16 lb and 21 lb, respectively, are located 3 ft apart. Find their center of gravity.

6. A uniform bar 8 m long has a mass of 4 kg. Find the center of mass if a 10-kg mass is fastened to one end.

7. A straight uniform pole 12 ft long has a weight of 30 lb. Find the center of gravity if a 20-lb mass is fastened at one end.

8. A uniform bar 6 ft long has a mass of 20 lb. Find the center of gravity if a 10-lb weight is fastened to one end and a 40-lb weight is fastened to the other.

9. A plywood board is 2 ft square and weighs 20 lb. A 5-lb weight is fastened to one corner. Find the center of gravity.

10. Two stones with masses of 2 kg and 4 kg are tied 60 cm apart at opposite ends of a wire and then thrown whirling into the air. About what point do these two rotate smoothly?

11. Five 2-kg spheres are equally spaced around the periphery of a semicircle. If the diameter is 2 m and the two end spheres are diametrically opposite each other, find their center of mass.

Mechanics | **Lesson 22**

THE SIMPLE CRANE—*Laboratory*

In performing this experiment as described in the accompanying *LABO-RATORY EXERCISES* the conditions of equilibrium are applied to the boom of a simple crane. Use is made of the principle of components as given in Mechanics, Lesson 18, and calculated force components are compared with measured forces.

EQUILIBRIUM OF RIGID BODIES

We have seen in Lesson 21 how the entire weight of a body may be considered as concentrated at a single point called its **center of gravity.** In this lesson we are going to apply this concept, along with the principles of equilibrium, to a specific problem. Although the problem itself is of no great importance, the methods by which it is solved are typical of many problems in mechanics, and it is therefore of fundamental importance.

The Crane Problem. Consider the case of a simple crane, composed of a uniform wooden timber and mounted as shown in Fig. A. Since this arrangement lends itself to being set up in the laboratory as a demonstration experiment, we will assume that the boom has a length of 4 ft and a mass of 5 lb, that a load of 6 lb is supported at the end, and that the tie rope makes an angle of 50° with the horizontal.

We now propose to find the magnitudes and direction of all the forces acting on the

Fig. A. The crane problem.

Fig. B. Isolated diagram of a crane boom showing all forces acting upon it.

boom. This is accomplished by applying the **first** and **second conditions of equilibrium.**

The first step in all such problems is to make a diagram of the rigid body itself and then to show all forces that must be acting on that body, whether their magnitudes and directions are known or not. Such an isolation diagram for the boom is shown in Fig. B.

Since the boom is uniform, its total weight of 5 lb can be assumed concentrated at the center of gravity 2 ft from either end. The other known quantities are the direction of **T**, the load of 6 lb acting straight downward at the right, and the length of the boom 4 ft.

The unknown quantities are three in number: they are (1) the magnitude of **T**, (2) the magnitude of **P**, and (3) the direction angle ϕ that **P** makes with the boom. The force **P** is the force exerted by the king post on the left end of the boom.

While there are several methods of attack on the problem, we will proceed to resolve **T** and **P** into **x**- and **y**-components, replace **T** and **P** by their respective components, and relabel the isolation diagram as shown in Fig. C. All forces are now horizontal or vertical, and we can apply the first condition of equilibrium as given in Mechanics, Lesson 19.

$$\Sigma F_x = 0 \qquad (1)$$
$$\Sigma F_y = 0 \qquad (2)$$

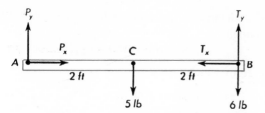

Fig. C. Isolated diagram of a crane boom showing all force components.

In the x-direction there are but two forces, P_x to the right and T_x to the left. Taking forces to the right as positive and applying Eq. (1), we obtain for the vector sum

$$P_x - T_x = 0$$

or

$$P_x = T_x \qquad (3)$$

This equation tells us that these two forces are equal in magnitude, but it does not give us their numerical value.

In the y-direction there are four forces. Taking upward forces as positive and summing them up according to Eq. (2), we obtain

$$P_y + T_y - 5 \text{ lb} - 6 \text{ lb} = 0$$

or

$$P_y + T_y = 11 \text{ lb} \qquad (4)$$

We next apply the second condition of equilibrium as explained in Mechanics, Lesson 19.

$$\Sigma L = 0 \qquad (5)$$

Since equilibrium exists, we can choose any pivot point about which to compute torques. If we select the point A, we observe that forces P_x, P_y, and T_x act in a direction through that point and have no lever arms. Having no torques about A, these forces are temporarily eliminated, and in summing up the remaining torques according to Eq. (5), we obtain

$$T_y \times 4 \text{ ft} - 6 \text{ lb} \times 4 \text{ ft} - 5 \text{ lb} \times 2 \text{ ft} = 0$$

or

$$4T_y \text{ ft} = 34 \text{ lb ft}$$

from which

$$T_y = 8.5 \text{ lb} \qquad (6)$$

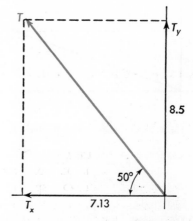

Fig. D. Force components of the tie-rope tension T.

If, in a similar way, we select B as a pivot, the forces T_y, T_x, P_x, and 6 lb have no lever arms; and applying Eq. (5), we obtain

$$5 \text{ lb} \times 2 \text{ ft} - P_y \times 4 \text{ ft} = 0$$

or

$$10 \text{ lb ft} = 4 P_y \text{ ft}$$

from which

$$P_y = 2.5 \text{ lb} \qquad (7)$$

To find the magnitude of T_x we now reconstruct a resolution diagram for the original force T as shown in Fig. D. Since we know $T_y = 8.5$ lb and the angle is 50 degrees, we can write for the lower right triangle

$$\frac{8.5 \text{ lb}}{T_x} = \tan 50°$$

Transposing, we obtain

$$T_x = \frac{8.5 \text{ lb}}{\tan 50°} \qquad (8)$$

Upon looking up tan 50° in the tables, we find 1.192, and Eq. (8) becomes

$$T_x = \frac{8.5 \text{ lb}}{1.192} = 7.13 \text{ lb}$$

By Eq. (3) we then know that

$$P_x = 7.13 \text{ lb}$$

We have now found all force components, and they are the following:

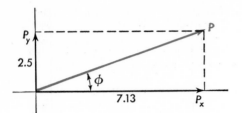

Fig. E. Force components of the force P.

$$P_x = 7.13 \text{ lb}$$
$$P_y = 2.5 \ \text{ lb}$$
$$T_x = 7.13 \text{ lb}$$
$$T_y = 8.5 \ \text{ lb}$$

Observe from these answers that half the weight of the boom, 2.5 lb, is carried by P_y, and the other half by T_y, where the 6-lb load and the 2.5 lb of the boom make 8.5 lb.

To find the original force T we apply the Pythagorean theorem for right triangles and write

$$T^2 = (7.13)^2 + (8.5)^2$$

from which

$$T = 11.1 \text{ lb}$$

We finally draw a component diagram for P, as shown in Fig. E, and again apply the

Pythagorean theorem to the lower right triangle.

$$P^2 = (7.13)^2 + (2.5)^2$$

from which*

$$P = 7.56 \text{ lb}$$

To find the angle ϕ we write

$$\tan \phi = \frac{2.5}{7.13}$$

Dividing and looking up the value in the tables, we find

$$\phi = 19°$$

All unknowns in this problem have now been determined. The forces and their directions have been computed from basic principles in mechanics, and the results are consistent with reason.

* A simplified method for finding the square root of a number to an accuracy of three figures is the following. By inspection, a guess of the square root is made to two figures. For example, if the number is 685, inspection shows that it lies between $(20)^2 = 400$ and $(30)^2 = 900$, and that a reasonable guess might be 25. The original number is then divided by 25 and gives 27.4. The average of these two numbers, 26.2, is then the square root to three figures. If greater accuracy is desired, the averaged number may be assumed to be an original guess and the process repeated.

Summary

The first and second conditions of equilibrium, along with the principles of the center of mass and center of gravity, are applied to the crane problem. Several unknown forces are determined by calculation. The results are consistent with the known forces specified originally and they may be experimentally verified.

The preliminary steps in solving this and similar problems is to make an isolation diagram of the rigid body involved and represent all known and unknown forces acting upon it. All forces are then resolved into horizontal and vertical components.

Questions

1. Make a diagram of a simple crane with the boom in a horizontal position. Show a load **W** supported at the far end and the tie rope making an angle of 60° with the horizontal.

2. Make a diagram of a simple crane with the boom making an angle of 30° with the horizontal and the tie rope making an angle of 60° with the horizontal. Show a load **W** supported at the far end.

3. Make an isolation diagram for the boom in question 1 and show all forces acting. Make a second diagram showing all forces resolved into components.

4. Make an isolation diagram for the boom in question 2 and show all forces acting. Make a second diagram showing all forces resolved into components.

5. Make a diagram of a uniform ladder leaning against a smooth wall. Make an isolation diagram showing all forces. Assume the force on the upper end is perpendicular to the wall.

6. How would you go about the task of making a small and inexpensive crane for measuring the various forces acting on the boom and calculated in this lesson?

Problems

1.* The uniform boom of a crane has a length of 10 ft and weighs 50 lb. The tie rope makes an angle of 60° with the horizontal boom, and a load of 100 lb is supported at the end. See Fig. A. Find all forces acting on the boom.

2.* A uniform pole 8 ft long and weighing 60 lb is used as the boom of a simple crane. A load of 150 lb is applied at the end. Find all the forces acting on the horizontal boom if the tie rope makes an angle of 40° with the horizontal. See Fig. A.

3. A uniform pole 16 ft long and weighing 200 lb is used as the boom of a simple crane. A load of 500 lb is supported by the far end. The boom makes an angle of 45° with the horizontal and so does the tie rope. Find the tension in the tie rope. (*Note:* Resolution of forces into components is not recommended.)

4.* A uniform ladder 10 ft long and weighing 100 lb leans against a smooth wall and makes an angle of 60° with the horizontal. Find all forces on the ladder. Assume the force of the wall on the top end of the ladder is horizontal.

5. The uniform boom of a crane has a length of 20 ft and weighs 350 lb. The boom makes an angle of 30° with the horizontal and supports a 600-lb load at the far end. Find the tension in the tie rope if it makes an angle of 60° with the horizontal.

Mechanics | **Lesson 24**

FRICTION

You will remember that Newton's Laws of Motion were introduced in earlier lessons with the provision that friction can be neglected. In this lesson we are going to study sliding friction and see how Newton's Laws of Motion can be extended to include frictional forces.

The general statement can be made that wherever you see motion there is friction. All forms of friction may be classified as one of three kinds: **sliding friction, rolling friction,** and **fluid friction.**

Sliding and rolling friction are concerned with solids, while fluid friction is concerned with liquids and gases. Generally speaking, sliding friction is greater than fluid friction

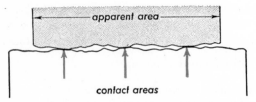

Fig. A. Illustrating the relatively small contact areas between two bodies having a much larger apparent contact area.

at low speeds, while the reverse is true at high speeds.

Sliding Friction. Whenever one body slides over another, frictional forces opposing the motion are developed between them. See Fig. B. Such forces are due largely to the atomic and molecular attractive forces at the small **contact areas**. See Fig. A. Within limits the smoothness of the surfaces does not greatly effect **f** the force of sliding friction. If the surfaces are smooth, there will be many small areas in contact; while if they are rough, there may be fewer but larger ones. It is well known that surfaces of the same material show greater friction than do surfaces of different materials. This is one of the reasons why machine bearings are often made of one metal, like bronze, while their rotating shafts are made of another, like steel.

Experiments show that to start a body sliding often requires a greater force than that needed to keep it moving. In other words **static friction**, or **starting friction**, is greater than **kinetic friction**. Once a body is moving, however, the force of sliding friction increases only slightly with increasing speed and then remains nearly constant over a moderate range of speeds.

Recent experiments, particularly with metals in contact, show that when one surface is pressed against another and sliding is brought about, the enormous pressures existing at the tiny contact areas cause a kind of welding together of the two materials. With all materials in general the atoms and molecules are so close together at the contact areas that

strong mutual attractive forces often pull microscopic bits of material from one body to the other as they move along. To start a body moving is to break these bonds instantly, while to keep it moving is to break them smoothly and continuously.

A quantitative treatment of sliding friction will here be given as the result of a simple laboratory experiment illustrated in Fig. B. In diagram (a) a block of wood of mass 500 gm is shown being pulled with uniform speed across a table top by the tangential force of a 100 gm-wt. The latter force has been arrived at by trying different loads on the hook at the right. A load greater than 100 gm will accelerate the block, while a load smaller than 100 gm will allow it to stop. Moving with constant speed, the applied force **F** is just counterbalanced by **f**, the force of sliding friction.

In diagram (b) a second block of mass 500 gm is added to make the sliding mass 1000 gm. By experiment the force required to pull the two with constant velocity is now found to be a 200 gm-wt. Should a third and then a fourth block be added successively, 300 and 400 gm-weights respectively will be

Fig. B. Sliding friction is proportional to the normal force pushing the surfaces together and independent of area of contact.

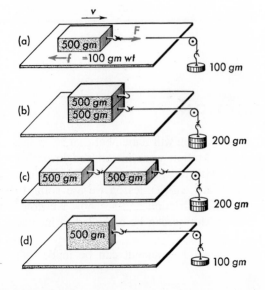

found necessary to pull them. In other words the force of sliding friction **f** is directly proportional to the total downward force **N**.

$$f \propto N \qquad (1)$$

When the two blocks in diagram (b) are connected in tandem, one behind the other as in diagram (c), the force of friction is still that of a 200 gm-wt.

Again if the single block in diagram (a) is turned on edge as in diagram (d), the force of a 100 gm-wt is just enough to slide it with constant speed. These observations, along with the results of other similar experiments, may be explained largely in terms of molecular attractive forces. In general, the total contact area where molecular attraction is effective (see Fig. A) is small compared with the total apparent area. When a greater force is applied normal to the surfaces, the contact areas increase in size and number, and the following relation is found to hold reasonably true:

The force of sliding friction is proportional to the total normal force.

Introducing the Greek letter μ as a constant of proportionality, Eq. (1) becomes

$$\boxed{f = \mu N} \qquad (2)$$

μ is called the **coefficient of sliding friction,** and is defined as the ratio

$$\mu = \frac{f}{N} \qquad (3)$$

By knowing the value of μ for a given pair

of surfaces one is able to calculate the force of friction **f** in terms of the normal force **N**. Average values of μ for a number of surfaces are given in Table 1.

Table 1. Coefficients of Sliding Friction for a Few Common Materials

(Average values for dry surfaces)

Material	μ
oak on oak..............	0.25
pine on pine.............	0.35
maple on maple..........	0.28
wood on concrete.........	0.55
smooth rubber on oak......	0.25
rubber on concrete........	0.70
metals on oak............	0.55
metals on elm............	0.20
hemp on oak.............	0.53
steel on steel.............	0.18
greased surfaces..........	0.05
iron on concrete..........	0.30
leather on metals.........	0.56
steel on babbit...........	0.14

As an illustration of the general use of the coefficient of friction consider the problem, diagramed in Fig. C.

Example 1. What force is required to pull an iron box weighing 60 lb across a smooth oak floor?

Solution. From Table 1, μ for metals on oak is 0.55. The normal force **N** is the weight

Fig. C. Sliding friction f is proportional to the normal force N pushing the surfaces together.

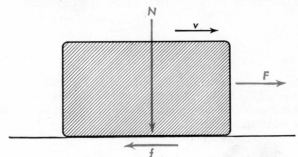

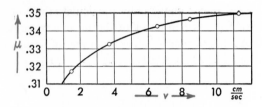

Fig. D. Experimental graph showing how the coefficient of sliding friction increases with speed, yet becomes nearly constant at relatively slow velocities.

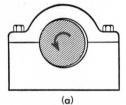 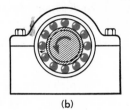

(a)   (b)

Fig. E. Sleeve bearings and ball bearings illustrate the two kinds of friction: (a) sliding friction and (b) rolling friction. (*Note: the clearance in the sleeve bearing is exaggerated.*)

of the box, or 60 lb. Substituting in Eq. (2), the force of friction is found to be

$$f = 0.55 \times 60 \text{ lb} = 33 \text{ lb}$$

The general observation that sliding friction increases with speed only slightly at low speeds and levels off to become practically constant at higher speeds is illustrated by the graph in Fig. D.

If the force **F** applied to a body is greater than that required to overcome friction **f**, the resultant force (**F** − **f**) is effective in producing acceleration. The force equation, given by Newton's Second Law of Motion as **F** = **ma**, is therefore modified by friction and becomes

$$\boxed{F - f = ma} \qquad (4)$$

resultant force = mass × acceleration

Rolling Friction. A comparison of the force required to slide a heavy box along the ground with the force required to move it on rollers shows that sliding friction is many times greater than rolling friction. It is for this reason that wheels are used on vehicles instead of runners and that ball bearings are employed in some machines in place of sleeve bearings.

A comparison of the sleeve type of bearing with a ball bearing is made in Fig. E. The rotating axle, as shown at the left, slides on the bottom of the sleeve at low speeds and climbs part way up the side as the speed increases. The purpose of lubricating such bearings with oils and greases is to keep the two metal surfaces from coming into direct contact. Properly lubricated the axle rides on a thin film of oil. In diagram (b) it may be seen how the axle rolls around on the balls with little or no possibility for sliding. The balls themselves roll in a groove called a "race."

The harder a rolling wheel or ball, and the harder the surface over which it rolls, the less is the force of rolling friction.

The same equations that hold for sliding friction also hold for rolling friction, the only difference being that the coefficients for rolling friction are exceedingly small.

$$f = \mu N \qquad (5)$$

Table 2. Coefficients of Rolling Friction

cast iron on rails..............	$\mu = 0.004$
rubber tires on concrete........	$\mu = 0.030$
ball-bearing on steel..........	$\mu = 0.002$

Summary

Sliding and rolling frictions are concerned with solids. Generally speaking, sliding friction is greater than rolling friction. For two surfaces, the ratio of the tangential force required to sustain motion, to the normal force pressing the two surfaces together, is called the coefficient of friction,

$$\mu = \frac{f}{N}$$

To apply the force equation to accelerated motion the force to overcome friction must be subtracted from the applied force to find the effective force.

$$F - f = ma$$

where F is the applied force, f is the force of friction, m is the mass and a the acceleration.

Questions

1. What is sliding friction? Rolling friction? Static friction? Kinetic friction?

2. What do recent experiments indicate as to the principal cause of sliding friction?

3. What is meant by the coefficient of sliding friction? Make a diagram to illustrate the forces involved in sliding friction.

4. Give the formula for sliding friction and explain each symbol.

5. How is the force of friction taken into account when the force equation, $F = ma$, is applied to accelerated motion?

6. If a body is already moving, and an opposing force is applied to slow it down, how should the force equation, $F = ma$, be modified to include the force of friction?

7. If a body is given a certain velocity and then released, friction would slow it down and finally bring it to rest. How would you use the force of friction to calculate the negative acceleration?

8. What everyday events can you think of in which the existence of friction is of great importance? Where is friction a nuisance?

9. What are the general methods used to reduce friction where it is not wanted?

10. What common utility devices are designed to increase friction?

11. Think of some project you might undertake and construct a simple and inexpensive device to demonstrate sliding or rolling friction.

Problems

1. A horizontal force of 38 lb is required to pull a 110-lb trunk across the floor. Find the coefficient of sliding friction.

2. A heavy box weighing 76 lb requires a horizontal force of 28 lb to pull it across the floor. What is the coefficient of sliding friction?

3. A driver, in bringing a car to a stop, skids all four tires. If the car weighs 3300 lb, what is the force of friction between the tires and the concrete pavement?

4. What horizontal force is required to pull a 120-lb pine box across a pine floor?

5. An oak box weighing 128 lb is pulled across an oak floor by a horizontal force of 46 lb. Find its acceleration. (*Note:* The mass must be in slugs.)

6. What horizontal force is required to pull a 3000-lb car with constant speed along a level concrete road?

7. A horizontal force of 36 lb is required to pull a 76-lb trunk across the floor. If 24 lb are added to the trunk, what force is required to pull it?

8. A boy exerts a horizontal force of 2 lb to pull his 20-lb sled over the snow. If a boy weighing 120 lb sits on the sled, what force must now be exerted?

9.* A 10-lb wooden box falls from a truck making 45 mi/hr (i.e., 66 ft/sec). If the coefficient of sliding friction between wood and concrete is 0.55, how far will the box slide along the pavement in coming to a stop?

COEFFICIENT OF FRICTION—*Laboratory*

This experiment is described in the accompanying LABORATORY EXERCISES. You will slide objects of various kinds down wooden boards. By measuring the angle of uniform slip in each case the coefficient of sliding friction is determined.

STREAMLINING

Fluid Friction. Friction in a gas or liquid manifests itself when the fluid is made to flow around a stationary obstacle or an object is made to move through a previously stationary fluid. Such friction is involved in the propulsion of ships through the water, and automobiles, trains, and airplanes through the air. In any discussion or treatment of fluid friction it makes no difference whether the fluid is considered as moving and the object as standing still, or vice versa. It is only necessary to specify that there is a relative motion between the two.

Experiments show that at relatively low speeds the flow of fluid around an object is smooth and regular and that fluid friction is proportional to the velocity. See Fig. A(a).

$$f = Kv \tag{1}$$

where **K** is a constant of proportionality.

If, initially, **v** = 0, frictional resistance to motion is zero and an applied force is entirely effective in producing acceleration. As the speed increases, however, friction increases proportionally so that less and less force is available for acceleration. Newton's Second Law, applied to motion through a fluid, therefore takes the same form as Eq. (4), p. 98,

$$F - Kv = ma \tag{2}$$

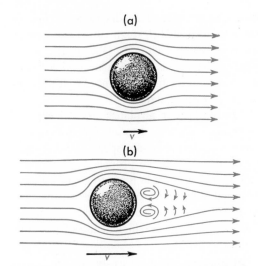

Fig. A. (a) Low-velocity fluid showing laminar flow. (b) High-velocity fluid showing turbulent flow.

where **f** has been given by Eq. (1) above. In this equation **v** and **a** represent instantaneous values of speed and acceleration.

The above equations hold only for **laminar flow,** that is, for relatively low velocities. As the speed increases, a point is reached where **turbulence** sets in and the force of friction increases rapidly and becomes proportional to the square of the velocity.

$$f \propto v^2$$

or, putting in a proportionality constant **T,**

$$f = Tv^2 \qquad (3)$$

Turbulent flow is characterized by small eddy currents that form behind the object as shown in Fig. A (b). Not only does the fluid have to move out and around the obstacle quickly, but considerable energy is taken up by the eddies. This, of course, results in greater loss of energy and therefore greater friction. When the velocity is increased still further, the eddies, instead of forming symmetrical pairs, form alternately on one side and then the other, leaving a long trail of vortex motions like those shown in Fig. B. These strings of whirlwinds or whirpools are commonly referred to as **Kármán trails.** The

existence of such trails is illustrated by the flapping of the rope on a flagpole. The waving of the flag at the top of the pole is direct evidence of the whirlwinds that follow each other alternately along the sides. As the velocity of a streamlined body approaches the velocity of sound, friction again increases rapidly, becoming proportional to the cube of the velocity: $f \propto v^3$.

Terminal Velocity. It is well known that raindrops fall with a speed that depends upon their size and not upon the height from which they fall. Starting from rest, a particle falling in a gas or a liquid increases in velocity until the retarding force of friction becomes as great as the downward force of gravity. When this condition is reached, the body is in equilibrium and falls with a constant velocity called its **terminal velocity.**

Fig. B. Eddies set up by drawing an obstacle through still water form a Kármán trail.

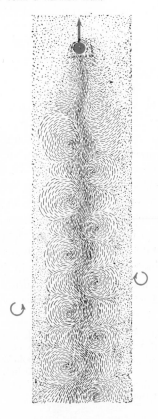

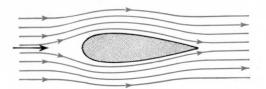

Fig. C. The flow of air around a properly shaped body may be smooth and steady.

The terminal velocity for small particles like fog drops is so low that the air stream around them is one of **laminar flow**. It was Stokes who first discovered that the terminal velocity of small particles is proportional to their weight. This relation is known as **Stokes' Law.***

For increasingly larger bodies terminal velocity increases and turbulent flow sets in to eventually be the predominating part of frictional resistance.

If a parachutist delays the opening of his chute long enough, he will attain a terminal velocity of from 130 to 150 mi/hr. At such speeds wind resistance pushes upward with a total force equal to his weight with the result that he is no longer accelerated.

Streamlining.   By shaping a body to the streamlines of the fluid through which it is moving, the retarding force of friction may be greatly reduced. This is particularly effective at high velocities where the conditions of turbulent flow would otherwise predominate.

Referring to Fig. A(b) it may be seen that by adding a tail to an object, so that its cross section has the form shown in Fig. C, the tendency to form eddy currents can be reduced and the body made to slip through the fluid with a minimum disturbance.

The experiment diagramed in Fig. D shows that a long pointed tail and a rounded or pointed nose are both effective in cutting

* Sir George G. Stokes (1819-1903), British mathematician and physicist, is well known for his fundamental contribution to hydrodynamics, diffraction, double refraction, and the polarization of light. He received the Rumford Medal in 1852 and the Copley Medal in 1893, and was at one time president of the Royal Society.

down resistance. The diagram pictures a small wind tunnel through which a stream of air is drawn by a fan **F.** Objects for which wind resistance is to be measured are suspended from a support connected at the center to a spring balance.

The bodies of airplanes, torpedoes, and ships are streamlined to cut down resistance and hence permit higher speed with the same forward thrust of the propellers. Bombs are streamlined to enable them to acquire higher terminal velocities. Automobiles, if they are to travel at high speeds, should be streamlined to make more efficient use of gasoline.

Airplanes.   The necessity for streamlining all outside structures of an airplane where high speeds must be maintained is quite clear. For land planes **solid friction** is of importance only during take-off. Once a propeller-driven plane is in the air, friction is almost entirely due to turbulent flow and is approximately proportional to the square of the velocity.

In Fig. E a streamlined plane is shown in a climb. Rising with constant velocity, the conditions of equilibrium exist and all forces acting form a closed triangle. The external forces acting on an airplane are three in number: they are **weight, thrust,** and **friction.** See Fig. F.

The weight **W** may be assumed to act vertically downward through the center of gravity of the plane. The thrust **T** is the result of the screw action of the propeller through the

Fig. D. Diagram of a tunnel used for testing the air friction of an airfoil or streamlined body.

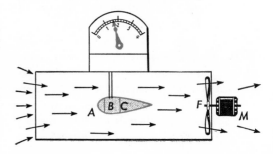

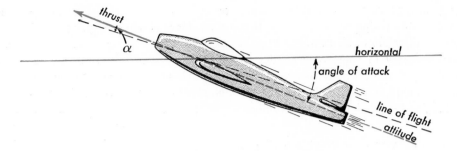

Fig. E. Diagram of a plane in a climb.

air and acts in the direction of the propeller axis. The angle between this direction, the plane's **attitude,** and the horizontal is called the **angle of attack.** The friction **f** is the resultant force of air friction on the plane and acts in a direction upward and back as shown in Fig. F(a). Note that the line of flight, the path along which the plane is flying, is not quite the same as the plane's attitude.

It is customary to resolve the frictional force into two components: one, a useful component perpendicular to the line of flight and called **lift,** and the other a hindering component parallel to the line of flight and called the **drag.**

Supersonic Velocities. The rapid development of rockets and jet propelled planes capable of acquiring and maintaining speeds

greater than the velocity of sound has increased the importance of studying high-speed air flow around bodies of different size and shape. The flow of air around missiles moving with **supersonic velocity,** that is, a velocity greater than the velocity of sound, is characterized by the existence in the air of discontinuities known as **shock waves.**

These sudden discontinuities are the result of sudden encounters of the air with an impenetrable body. At subsonic velocities the fluid is forewarned and begins its outward flow in advance of the arrival of the leading edge. With supersonic velocity, however, the fluid in front of the missile is absolutely undisturbed, while immediately behind, it is moving sideways. The sudden impulse at the nose creates a high pressure region which,

Fig. G. Shock wave produced by jet or rocket plane at supersonic velocity.

Fig. F. Force diagrams for an airplane, showing the origin of lift and drag.

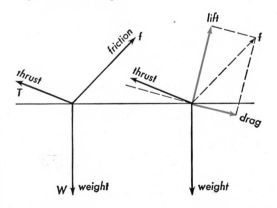

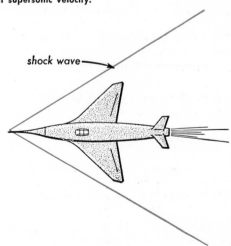

traveling outward with the velocity of sound, creates the conical-shaped shock wave that changes the direction of air flow. See Fig. G.

It is customary in supersonic studies to specify the velocity of a body relative to the velocity of sound. The ratio between these two velocities is called the **Mach Number.**

$$\text{Mach Number} = \frac{\text{velocity of body}}{\text{velocity of sound}}$$

The speed of sound in air at sea level is approximately 750 mi/hr. A missile of Mach Number 2.0 is, therefore, moving with twice the speed of sound or 1500 mi/hr.

Summary

When an object moves slowly through a fluid, the fluid medium flows around the object in smooth lines called laminar flow, and the required force to move it is proportional to the velocity. At higher speeds turbulent flow sets in, and the force to overcome friction increases to become proportional to the square of the velocity.

As a body falls through a fluid under the pull of gravity, it soon reaches its terminal velocity. Terminal velocity is attained when the upward force due to fluid friction is equal to the downward force called the weight.

The frictional force of the air on an airplane can be resolved into two components: one component is called the lift and is a useful force, while the other is called the drag and is detrimental.

When an object moves faster than sound, it sets up a shock wave. At speeds greater than the speed of sound the speed of an object is often expressed as a Mach Number.

Questions

1. Define or briefly explain each of the following: (a) laminar flow, (b) streamlined flow, and (c) turbulent flow.

2. How does fluid friction depend on velocity?

3. What is terminal velocity? What is Stokes' Law regarding small particles?

4. What is meant by streamlining a body?

5. What are Kármán trails?

6. Make a diagram of an airplane in flight. Show (a) the plane's attitude and line of flight, (b) the weight, (c) the thrust, and (d) the force of friction.

7. Make a diagram to show what is meant by the lift and drag forces on an airplane.

8. What is a shock wave? What are the conditions necessary to produce a shock wave?

9. What is meant by (a) supersonic velocity and (b) Mach Number?

10. Think of some project in which you might undertake to make a simple and inexpensive device for demonstrating laminar flow and turbulent flow.

Problems

1. The frictional force due to turbulent flow around a certain automobile traveling at 30 mi/hr is found to be 45 lb. What is the frictional force when the car is making (a) 60 mi/hr and (b) 75 mi/hr?

2. The frictional force due to turbulent flow around a certain racing car traveling at 50 mi/hr is 65 lb. What is the frictional force when the car is making (a) 150 mi/hr and (b) 160 mi/hr.

3. A paratrooper, with all his gear, weighs 250 lb when he jumps from a plane. If he delays opening his parachute and the force of friction becomes 30 lb when he is falling at 45 mi/hr, what will be his terminal velocity? Assume turbulent flow.

4. A rocket has a speed of 2250 mi/hr. What is its Mach Number?

5. A missile has a Mach Number of 3.45. What is its speed in mi/hr?

6. The frictional force on a baseball, thrown with a speed of 50 ft/sec, is .15 lb. What will be the force be when it is thrown at a speed of 120 ft/sec? Assume turbulent flow.

7. The frictional force on a golf ball traveling at 40 m/sec is 0.5 newton. What will be the force of friction when the speed is 90 m/sec? Assume turbulent flow.

8. A tennis ball having a mass of 0.05 kg has a terminal velocity of 30 m/sec when dropped from an airplane. What is the force of air friction at (a) terminal velocity and (b) at 10 m/sec?

9. Find the Mach Number of a car traveling at 60 mi/hr.

10. What is the Mach Number of a bullet traveling 1800 ft/sec?

Mechanics | **Lesson 27**

WORK AND ENERGY

There is little doubt that the most important concept in all nature is energy. It is important because it represents a fundamental entity common to all forms of matter in all parts of the known physical world. Closely associated with energy is another concept **work,** a term used in civil life to describe the expenditure of one's stored up bodily energy. Because energy is most easily described in terms of work, this latter will first be treated in detail.

Work. In its simplest mechanical form

work is defined as **the force times the distance through which the force acts.**

work = force × distance

Algebraically,

$$\boxed{\text{work} = F \times s} \qquad (1)$$

Consider the general problem of calculating the work done in lifting a mass **m** to a height **s** above the ground. See Fig. A. By Newton's Second Law of Motion (**F = ma**)

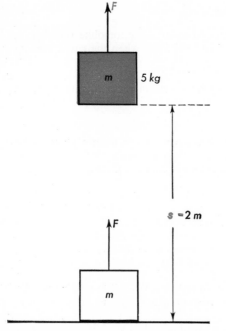

Fig. A. To raise a body vertically, work must be done against the pull due to gravity.

the force required to lift any mass **m** is equal to its own weight.

$$W = mg$$

Substitute the weight **mg** for **F** in Eq. (1),

$$\text{work done} = mg \times s \qquad (2)$$

To give numerical values assume that a mass of 5 kg is lifted vertically a distance of 2 m. By direct substitution in Eq. (2),

$$\text{work} = 5 \text{ kg} \times 9.8 \frac{m}{sec^2} \times 2 \text{ m} = 98 \frac{\text{kg m}^2}{sec^2}$$

Since **force**, in **newtons**, has the units kg m/sec², the answer can also be written

$$\text{work done} = 98 \text{ newton meters} \qquad (3)$$

Work in the **mks** system is seen to have the absolute units **kg m²/sec²**, which are equal to the derived units **newton meters**. In the **cgs** system the corresponding absolute units are **gm cm²/sec²**, which are equal to the derived units **dyne centimeters**.

In the English, or engineering, system the units of work are **foot-pounds**, abbreviated **ft-lb.**

Example 1. Find the work done in lifting a weight of 5 lb to a height of 10 ft.
Solution. By substituting directly in Eq. (1) we obtain

$$\text{work} = 5 \text{ lb} \times 10 \text{ ft} = 50 \text{ ft-lb}$$

Ergs and Joules. In the cgs system the **dyne cm** as a unit of work is called the **erg.**

$$\boxed{1 \text{ dyne cm} = 1 \text{ erg}} \qquad (4)$$

A force of 1 dyne acting through a distance of 1 cm in the same direction does 1 erg of work.

In the mks system of units, a force of **1 newton** acting through a distance of **1 m** in the same direction performs an amount of work equivalent to **1 joule.**

$$\boxed{1 \text{ newton meter} = 1 \text{ joule}} \qquad (5)$$

Since the **newton** as a unit of force $= 1$ kg $\times$ 1 m/sec² $= 1000$ gm $\times$ 100 cm/sec² $= 10^5$ dynes, the newton meter $= 10^5$ dynes $\times$ 100 cm $= 10^7$ dyne cm. In other words,

$$1 \text{ joule} = 10^7 \text{ ergs} \qquad (6)$$

The **joule** as a unit of work is, therefore, much larger than the **erg** and in many practical problems is to be preferred because of the smaller numbers involved in calculations.

Example 2. Calculate the work done in lifting a mass of 400 gm to a height of 250 cm.

Solution. The known quantities are $m = 400$ gm, $s = 250$ cm, and $g = 980$ cm/sec². By substitution in Eq. (2), we obtain

$$\text{work} = 400 \text{ gm} \times 980 \frac{cm}{sec^2} \times 250 \text{ cm}$$

$$= 98,000,000 \frac{\text{gm cm}^2}{sec^2}$$

$$\text{work} = 98,000,000 \text{ ergs}$$

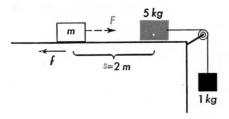

Fig. B. To slide a body along a level plane, work must be done against friction.

Work Done Against Friction.

In sliding a mass of 5 kg along a horizontal plane a distance of 2 m, the work done **will not** in general be as great as that required to lift the same mass 2 m vertically.

As shown by an example in Fig. B, the weight of a 1-kg mass is large enough to overcome friction and slide the 5-kg mass along the table. Direct substitution in Eq. (2) shows that the

$$\text{work done} = 1 \text{ kg} \times 9.8 \, \frac{m}{sec^2} \times 2 \text{ m}$$

$$= 19.6 \, \frac{kg \ m^2}{sec^2}$$

or

19.6 newton meters

This is only one-fifth as much work as that required to lift the same 5-kg mass an equal vertical distance of 2 m. See Eq. (3). By reducing the friction between the block and plane, the force **F** can be reduced still further. Such a reduction can be accomplished by

smoothing and lubricating the sliding surfaces, or better by mounting the block on wheels. Could the friction be eliminated entirely, the work done in moving any object in a horizontal direction would be practically zero, for, once started it would continue moving with constant velocity. A vertical lift, however, requires at least an amount of work equal to the weight **mg** times the height **s**.

When a force is applied to an object such that it makes an angle with the direction of motion, only the component of the force in the direction of motion is effective in doing work. This is illustrated in Fig. C where a force **F** is applied to a heavy trunk to pull it across the floor. In the right-hand diagram, **F** is shown resolved into vertical and horizontal components F_y and F_x. The upward force F_y has a lifting effect and helps to reduce friction, while the horizontal force F_x is the one that does the work. This force multiplied by the horizontal distance moved is equal to the work done.

$$\text{work done} = F_x \times s$$

Potential Energy.

Mechanical energy is divided into two categories, **potential energy** and **kinetic energy**. *A body is said to have potential energy if by virtue of its position or state it is able to do work.* Water at the

Fig. C. The force pulling a heavy trunk across a floor is resolved into components.

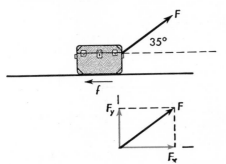

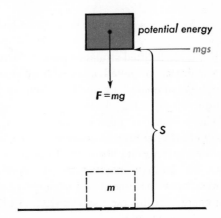

Fig. D. A body has potential energy by virtue of its position.

top of a fall or a wound clock spring is an example of an object with potential energy. The clock spring may keep a clock running for a certain length of time, and the water may, by falling, turn a paddle wheel. Potential energy is measured by the amount of work that is available. It is therefore measured in **ergs, joules,** or **foot-pounds.**

If a given mass **m** is raised to a specified height **s**, as illustrated in Fig. D, it then has potential energy **F** × **s** by virtue of its position above the ground level from which it has been lifted. The **work done** in lifting it has been stored up as potential energy in the block. This energy can be regained by dropping the mass back to the ground for in so doing it can be made to perform some kind of work. By definition

$$\boxed{\text{potential energy} = F \times s} \qquad (7)$$

or, in weight units, Eq. (2),

$$\boxed{\text{P.E.} = mg \times s}$$

Example 3. A mass of 5 kg is raised to a height of 2.5 m above the ground. Calculate its potential energy.

Solution. By substituting the known quantities in Eq. (7), we obtain

$$\text{P.E.} = 5 \text{ kg} \times 9.8 \, \frac{m}{sec^2} \times 2.5 \text{ m} = 122.5 \text{ joules}$$

If a body is lifted straight upward, carried up a staircase, or pulled up an inclined plane, the potential energy acquired is given by the **weight** × **vertical** height to which it is raised.

The meaning of **positive, zero,** or **negative potential energy** is illustrated in Fig. E. Located at any point above the **base plane** a body has positive potential energy, while at points below that line it has negative potential energy. To lift the mass **m** from **A** to **B**,

work is done and the mass acquires potential energy to the amount of **mgs₁**.

In returning from **B** to **A** the mass loses potential energy, performing **work** = **mgs₁** on some other body. Similarly in going from **A** to **C** the body loses energy and ends up at **C** with **mgs₂** less energy than it had at **A**. To raise it again to **A** an equivalent amount of work **mgs₂** will have to be done on the body.

The choosing of a **base plane** as a zero energy level is a purely arbitrary selection. In most practical applications it is customary to select the lowest point to be reached by a body as the zero level so that all displacements from there will be positive in sign. In the engineering systems of units **potential energy,** like **work,** is expressed in **foot-pounds,** i.e., **pounds** × **vertical distance in feet.**

Fig. E. Potential energy with respect to a base plane may be plus or minus.

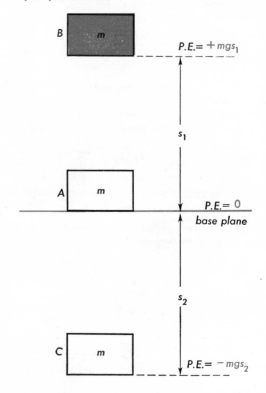

Summary

Work is defined as force times the distance through which the force acts.

In the mks units, where force is measured in newtons and distance is measured in meters, work is measured in newton meters or joules. In the cgs system of units work is measured in dyne centimeters or ergs.

In the engineering system of units, work is measured in foot pounds.

Potential energy is the energy stored in a body by virtue of its position or state, and is measured in the same units as work done.

A body may have positive potential energy or negative potential energy, depending on its position or state with respect to a predetermined zero energy level.

Questions

1. Define or briefly explain each of the following: (a) joule, (b) erg, and (c) newton meter.

2. How is work defined? In what units is work expressed? What are the English units of work?

3. What is the relation between ergs and joules? Why are joules to be preferred to ergs as units of work?

4. What is meant by potential energy? What kind of energy is stored in a wound watch spring?

5. Make a diagram and explain the difference between positive and negative potential energy.

6. Write down a formula for calculating potential energy.

7. When a force is applied to pull a trunk across a level floor, what is the work done? Is the work done stored as potential energy? If not, where is the energy?

8. Suppose a heavy box is raised to a platform by sliding it up a plank. Is all of the work done stored as potential energy? If not, explain why.

9. In what ways are the principles developed in this lesson involved in things we find in the world around us?

Problems

1. Find the work done in carrying a 100-lb sack of potatoes up three flights of stairs if the height of each flight is 12 ft.

2. An elevator car of 1500 kg is lifted from the basement of a building to the top floor, a vertical distance of 60 meters. Find the work done in joules.

3. A young man weighing 110 lb climbs to the top of a mountain 3800 ft above sea level. Find his potential energy if sea level is taken as the base plane.

4. A car of 2000 kg is pulled up an incline to a vertical height of 300 m. Find the potential energy in joules.

5. A trunk weighing 100 lb is pulled 20 ft across the floor. How much work is done if the coefficient of sliding friction is 0.50?

6. A block of ice with a mass of 20 kg slides down a plank 10 m long, making an angle of 25° with the horizontal. How much energy is lost?

7. A fallen tree weighing 2 tons is pulled through the forest by elephants for a distance of 500 ft. If the coefficient of sliding friction is 0.65, what is (a) the applied force and (b) the work done?

8. An oak box weighing 100 lb is pulled 12 ft up an oak plank by a force of 80 lb. If the plank makes an angle of 30° with the horizontal, how much energy is (a) stored as potential energy and (b) lost in overcoming friction?

Mechanics | **Lesson 28**

CENTER OF GRAVITY—*Laboratory*

This laboratory experiment is described in the accompanying LABORA- TORY EXERCISES and makes use of the principles developed in Mechanics, Les- son 21. Regular-shaped blocks of hardwood are clamped to a crossbar, and by a careful balancing process the center of mass is determined. The center of gravity of each such system is then located by suspension.

Mechanics | **Lesson 29**

ENERGY AND POWER

    In Mechanics, Lesson 27, it was stated that mechanical energy is of two kinds: *potential energy* and *kinetic energy.*

    There it was said that **a body has poten- tial energy if by virtue of its position or state it is able to do work.** In other words potential energy does not involve motion. In this lesson we will consider this second form of energy and find that it does involve mo- tion. Kinetic energy is often referred to as **energy of motion.**

    Kinetic Energy. *The kinetic energy of a moving body is defined as its ability to do work by virtue of its motion.* A car moving along the highway has kinetic energy of

Fig. A. A moving body has kinetic energy $\frac{1}{2}$ mv².

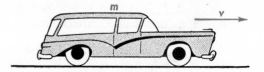

translation, and a rotating wheel on a machine has kinetic energy of rotation.

In Fig. A a car of mass m is shown moving along the road. As it moves along with a constant velocity v it possesses kinetic energy given by the formula

$$\text{K.E.} = \tfrac{1}{2}\,mv^2 \qquad (1)$$

To see how to use this formula consider the following example.

Example 1. Calculate the kinetic energy of a 20-kg mass moving with a velocity of 4 m/sec.

Solution. By direct substitution in Eq. (1) we obtain

$$\text{K.E.} = \frac{1}{2} \times 20 \text{ kg} \times \left(4 \frac{m}{\sec}\right)^2 = 160 \frac{\text{kg m}^2}{\sec^2}$$

This answer has exactly the dimensions of **work** and **potential energy,** and can be written in the same derived units.

$$\text{K.E.} = 160 \text{ joules}$$

A moving body has energy because in being brought to rest it must exert a force F on some other object, and this force acting through a distance s does work. In other words, work can be done by a moving body. Conversely, by applying a constant horizontal force F on a body of mass m for a distance s it will be given a kinetic energy $\tfrac{1}{2}\,mv^2$. See Fig. B.

$$F \times s = \tfrac{1}{2}\,mv^2 \qquad (2)$$

This is known as the "work equation." In it friction is entirely neglected, and the body is presumed to start from rest.

Fig. B. A body has kinetic energy by virtue of its motion.

$$v_0 = 0$$
$$m \quad F \xrightarrow{\quad} \qquad v \xrightarrow{\quad} \qquad F$$
$$\text{K.E.} = 0 \qquad S \qquad \text{K.E.} = \tfrac{1}{2}\,mv^2$$

Example 2. A constant horizontal force of 25 lb acts for a distance of 20 ft on a 500-lb midget racing car. If friction is neglected and the car starts from rest, (a) how much work is done and (b) what is the car's velocity?

Solution. The known quantities are $F = 25$ lb, $s = 20$ ft, and $m = 500/32$ slugs. To find the answer to (a) we use the formula

$$\text{work} = F \times s$$

By direct substitution we obtain

$$\text{work} = 25 \text{ lb} \times 20 \text{ ft}$$
$$\text{work} = 500 \text{ ft-lb}$$

(b) To find the car's velocity, we use Eq. (2). The unknown quantity v^2 is brought to the left-hand side of the equality and all other factors to the right.

$$v^2 = \frac{2(F \times s)}{m}$$

By direct substitution we obtain

$$v^2 = \frac{2 \times 500 \text{ ft-lb}}{500/32 \text{ slugs}}$$

$$v^2 = 64 \frac{\text{ft-lb}}{\text{slugs}}$$

Since slugs have the units lb sec²/ft, we may substitute and write

$$v^2 = 64 \frac{\text{ft}^2}{\sec^2}$$

and, taking the square root obtain for the velocity,

$$v = 8 \frac{\text{ft}}{\sec}$$

Power. *Power is defined as the rate of doing work, or the rate at which work is being done.*

$$\text{Power} = \frac{\text{work}}{\text{time}}$$

$$P = \frac{F \times s}{t} \qquad (3)$$

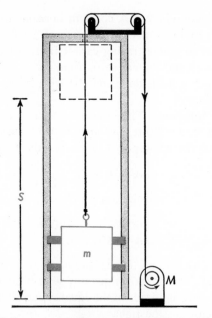

Fig. C. Demonstration of a concrete hoist. See Example 3.

Solution. This example is diagramed in Fig. C. To find the power use Eq. (3), $P = F \times s/t$.

Since the force must be in newtons, $F = mg$, on substitution we obtain

$$P = \frac{160 \text{ kg} \times 9.8 \text{ m/sec}^2 \times 30 \text{ m}}{8 \text{ sec}}$$

$$P = 5880 \frac{\text{newton meters}}{\text{sec}}$$

(a) $P = 5880 \frac{\text{joules}}{\text{sec}}$

$P = 5880 \text{ watts}$

(b) $P = 5.88 \text{ kilowatts}$

In the engineering system, with work measured in **foot-pounds,** power is expressed in **foot-pounds per second,** and in **horsepower** (*abbr.* **hp**).

$$1 \text{ hp} = 550 \text{ ft-lb/sec} \qquad (5)$$

Example 4. Find the power of an engine capable of lifting 200 lb to a height of 55 ft in 10 sec.

Solution. By direct substitution in Eq. (3) we obtain

$$P = \frac{200 \text{ lb} \times 55 \text{ ft}}{10 \text{ sec}} = 1100 \frac{\text{ft-lb}}{\text{sec}}$$

By dividing this answer by 550 to get horsepower we find

$$\frac{1100}{550} = 2 \text{ hp}$$

If 550 ft-lb/sec is changed to the metric system (1 ft = 0.305 m and 1 lb = 0.454 kg), we find

$$1 \text{ hp} = 746 \frac{\text{joules}}{\text{sec}}$$

or

$$1 \text{ hp} = 746 \text{ watts}$$

The faster a given amount of work is done the greater is the power. In other words, the smaller the time *t* in the above equation, the greater is the fraction $F \times s/t$ and the power *P*.

In the metric system, with work measured in **ergs** or **joules,** power is expressed either in **ergs per second** or in **joules per second.** One joule per second is called the **watt,** a unit of power.

$$1 \frac{\text{joule}}{\text{sec}} = 1 \text{ watt} \qquad (4)$$

The **kilowatt** is another unit of power and is equal to 1000 watts.

Example 3. A small hoist raises a 160-kg bucket of concrete to a height of 30 m in 8 sec. Find the power required in (a) joules per second and (b) in kilowatts.

Summary

By virtue of its motion a moving body has kinetic energy. This energy is given by the relation

$$\text{K.E.} = \tfrac{1}{2} mv^2$$

To set a body in motion a certain amount of work must be done. The work done is given by $F \times s$, and this is carried along as kinetic energy in the moving body

$$F \times s = \tfrac{1}{2} mv^2$$

In this, the work equation, friction has been assumed to be negligibly small. By turning this relation around one can say that a moving body with its kinetic energy $\tfrac{1}{2} mv^2$ can do an amount of work $F \times s$ in being brought to rest.

The faster any given amount of work is done, the greater is the power developed. In the mks system the watt is the unit of power. In the engineering system the unit is horse-power.

Questions

1. What are the two forms of mechanical energy? Are they measured in the same units?

2. How do you define kinetic energy? Write down the formula.

3. What is the work equation? Write it down and briefly interpret the different factors.

4. What is power? How is it defined? What does greater power do for an automobile?

5. What is the unit of power in (a) the mks system and (b) the engineering system of units?

6. What is the relation between horsepower and kilowatts? How is horsepower defined?

7. In what units should the mass of a body be expressed in calculating its kinetic energy in (a) the mks system and (b) the engineering system.

8. Think of some simple experiment you might perform to measure the kinetic energy of a toy automobile.

Problems

1. A mass of 200 kg is given a velocity of 2.5 m/sec. Find its kinetic energy in joules.

2. A mass of 5 kg is moving with a velocity of 4 m/sec. Find its kinetic energy in joules.

3. A car weighing 3200 lb is traveling along the highway with a speed of 50 ft/sec. Find its kinetic energy in ft lb. (*Note:* Mass must be in slugs.)

4. Starting from rest a 180-kg mass acquires a speed of 5 m/sec in a distance of 15 m. Find the force in newtons.

5. An elevator car weighing 1200 lb rises 100 ft in 5 sec. What is the power developed?

6. A bucket of concrete having a mass of 3000 kg is hoisted up an elevator shaft a distance of 50 m in 8 sec. Find the power in kilowatts.

7. A concrete hoist raises a 2-ton load a vertical distance of 66 ft in 8 sec. Find (a) the work done and (b) the power developed.

8. A coal elevator in a mine shaft weighs 6 tons when loaded. What is the minimum power realized by a motor that could lift this car 400 ft in one minute?

9.* An automobile weighing 3200 lb and moving with a velocity of 45 mi/hr (i.e., 66 ft/sec) is brought to rest in a distance of 200 ft. Find (a) the initial kinetic energy and (b) the average force provided by the brakes.

10. How heavy a load can a 20-hp hoist lift at a steady speed of 568 ft/min?

11. What mass can a 5 kilowatt hoist lift at a steady speed of 2 m/sec?

Mechanics | **Lesson 30**

HORSEPOWER—*Laboratory*

In performing this experiment as described in the accompanying *LABO-RATORY EXERCISES* you will determine the power of an electric motor. The power is determined in watts as well as in horsepower, and a graph is drawn of the power under different load conditions.

Mechanics | **Lesson 31**

CONSERVATION OF ENERGY

Most important of all the laws of nature is the law of the conservation of energy. While the law has been stated in almost as many different ways as there are books written on the subject, they all have in reality the same meaning. The following three examples are typical statements: (1) **in transforming energy from one form to another, energy is always conserved,** (2) **energy is never created nor destroyed,** or (3) **the sum total of all energy in the universe remains constant.**

Everyone should be aware of the fact that there are many forms of energy. To illustrate we should take a look at them.

In this lesson we are concerned with the law of conservation of energy only as it applies to the two forms of mechanical energy, **potential** and **kinetic.** The law will again be

Fig. A. Demonstration of energy transformation.

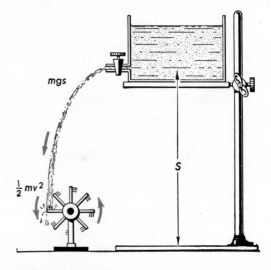

FORMS OF ENERGY

Mechanical	Light
Electrical	Atomic
Chemical	Molecular
Heat	Nuclear

encountered in connection with the other forms in the lessons on heat, electricity, and atomic structure.

As an illustration of the transformation of one form of mechanical energy into another consider the demonstration experiment shown in Fig. A.

Water in a tank escapes through an outlet pipe and falls on the blades of a paddle wheel. The water in the tank has potential energy mgh. As it falls with ever-increasing speed, that energy is converted into kinetic energy $\frac{1}{2}mv^2$. In turning the paddle wheel this energy of motion can be utilized to do mechanical work of one kind or another. On the other hand, it might well be made to turn an electric generator and convert mechanical energy into electrical. The electrical generator in turn can be connected to a toaster and convert electrical energy into heat, etc.

Consider the energy involved in a waterfall as shown in Fig. B. The water at the top of the fall has potential energy by virtue of its position above the base. As it falls over and then downward with ever increasing speed, the kinetic energy $\frac{1}{2}mv^2$ increases, while the potential energy decreases. At the bottom of the fall the potential energy approaches zero and the kinetic energy approaches its maximum value. At the top the energy was practically all potential, while near the bottom it is mostly kinetic. Assum-

ing the water to start from rest at the top and that no energy is lost in falling, the **P.E.** at the top of the falls equals the **K.E.** at the bottom.

$$\text{(P.E. at top)} = \text{(K.E. at bottom)}$$
$$F \times s = \tfrac{1}{2}mv^2 \qquad (1)$$

or

$$mgs = \tfrac{1}{2}mv^2 \qquad (2)$$

Cancel m on both sides of the equation and solve for v.

$$v^2 = 2gs$$

or

$$v = \sqrt{2gs} \qquad (3)$$

This is the special Eq. (3) derived for falling bodies in one of the preceding lessons from the laws of accelerated motion. Here the equation has been derived from the law of conservation of energy.

Example 1. A mass of 25 kg is dropped from a height of 5 m. Find the kinetic energy and velocity just as it reaches the ground.

Solution. Since the **P.E.** at the top is equivalent to the **K.E.** at the bottom,

$$\text{P.E.} = 25 \text{ kg} \times 9.8\,\frac{m}{sec^2} \times 5\text{ m}$$
$$= 1225 \text{ joules} = \text{K.E.}$$

The velocity is found by Eq. (3),

$$v = \sqrt{2 \times 9.8 \times 5} = 9.9\text{ m/sec}$$

When the falling body in the above problem is part way down, it has some **P.E.** and some **K.E.** Its total energy E is therefore of two kinds,

$$E = \tfrac{1}{2}mv^2 + mgs \qquad (4)$$

At the instant the body reaches the ground it is suddenly stopped and all of the energy is quickly transformed into heat. The transformation of mechanical energy into heat is often demonstrated in the physics laboratory by an experiment in which a quantity of lead-shot is dropped from a height of several feet and its temperature measured before and after falling. By raising the shot and drop-

Fig. B. All the available energy at the top of a waterfall is potential. At the bottom it is kinetic.

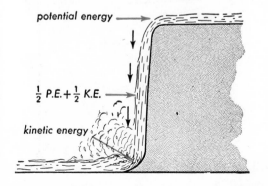

potential energy

$\frac{1}{2}$ P.E.$+\frac{1}{2}$ K.E.

kinetic energy

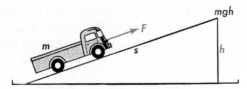

Fig. C. Conservation of energy.

ping it many times, the rise in temperature amounts to several degrees.

The Inclined Plane. Consider the demonstration experiment shown in Fig. C in which a small truck is pulled up an incline. The work done to reach the top is given by the product of force **F** times the distance **s**. By conservation of energy this must be equal to the stored up potential energy **mgh** at the top. Therefore

$$F \times s = mgh \qquad (5)$$

Now if the truck is released, it will accelerate back down the incline, thereby converting the potential energy **mgh** into kinetic energy $\frac{1}{2}mv^2$. By conservation of energy we can write

$$mgh = \tfrac{1}{2}mv^2 \qquad (6)$$

Since the **m** on both sides refers to the same mass, we can cancel out and obtain

$$gh = \tfrac{1}{2}v^2$$

or

$$v^2 = 2gh$$

from which

$$\boxed{v = \sqrt{2gh}} \qquad (7)$$

It is important to note that the velocity at the bottom of the incline depends only on the height **h**. This means that no matter how steep the incline may be, the velocity at the bottom will be the same if the height **h** is the same.

The Simple Pendulum. A similar energy treatment can be given for the swinging of a simple pendulum. At the extreme ends of each swing, see Fig. D, the bob comes momentarily to rest and the energy **E** is all potential and equal to **mgh**. At the bottom of the swing the energy **E** is all kinetic and equal to $\frac{1}{2}mv^2$.

The motion of the pendulum bob is like that of a body sliding, without friction, down an inclined plane of changing angle. The kinetic energy acquired in going down one side is just sufficient to carry it up to an equal height on the other.

The Brachistochrone. In 1696 Jean Ber-

Fig. D. Potential energy of a pendulum changes to kinetic energy and back again.

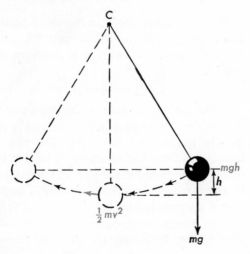

Fig. E. The brachistochrone. Which path should the ball take to reach B in the least time?

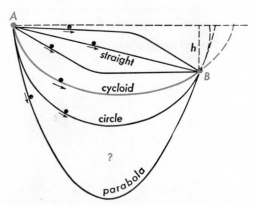

noulli addressed a letter to the mathematicians of Europe challenging them to solve within six months the following problem in mechanics. Along what path should a body move in order to descend from one point **A** to another point **B** at a lower level in the least possible time? After some months had passed Leibnitz, Jacques Bernoulli, and L'Hospital arrived at the answer. On January 29, 1697, Newton received from France a copy of the printed paper containing the problem and the following day sent the solution to the President of the Royal Society.

The curve of the shortest time, and now called the "Brachistochrome," is a cycloid. See Fig. E. The cycloid is the path traversed by a point on the rim of a wheel when it is rolled along a horizontal plane. It is interesting to note that although the cycloid is the path of least time for a body starting from rest at **A** and sliding without friction from **A** to **B**, the velocity of arrival at **B** is the same for all paths. By the law of conservation of energy this final velocity is given by Eq. (7) where **h** is the vertical height between **A** and **B.**

Summary

Energy may be transformed from any one form to another, but none is ever created or destroyed. This is the law of conservation of energy.

Confined to mechanical energy alone, we may change kinetic energy to potential energy, or vice versa, and in so doing keep the total energy constant. A body may have both kinetic and potential energy at the same time, and the sum of the two energies is called its total energy.

If the principles of conservation of energy are applied to a body falling freely from rest, the velocity attained is found to be

$$v = \sqrt{2\,gh}$$

This same relation agrees with the equations given in preceding lessons on falling bodies. A body sliding without friction down an inclined plane acquires a velocity given by the same equation.

A swinging pendulum changes in energy form between kinetic and potential energy four times every complete swing. The path of shortest time between two points at different heights is a cycloid.

Questions

1. Make a list of as many forms of energy as you can.

2. What are the two forms of mechanical energy called? Write down an equation for each.

3. A body falls from rest. What form of energy does it have (a) before it falls, (b) just before it hits the ground, and (c) halfway down?

4. Assume that a child slides without friction down a playground slide. Upon what factors does his velocity at the bottom depend? Does his velocity depend upon his weight or the length of the slide?

5. Make a diagram of a pendulum and show how its energy changes form as it swings. Where is its kinetic energy zero? Where is its potential energy a minimum, or zero?

6. Along what path should a body move in order to descend from one point **A** to another point **B** at a lower level in the least possible time?

7. Cut a disk about 2 inches in diameter from a piece of cardboard. Roll this disk along the edge of a sheet of paper and trace out the path of a point on the rim. What kind of curve is this?

8. How will the arrival speed of the marble at point **B** in Fig. E vary over the different paths?

9. In what ways are some of the principles developed in this lesson involved in the development of water power?

10. Think of some project in which you might participate in the construction of a simple and inexpensive device demonstrating the fundamental principles of conservation of energy.

Problems

1. A 5-kg stone is dropped from a height of 6 meters. Find the kinetic energy just before it strikes the ground.

2. A 16-lb stone falls from a height of 25 ft. Find its kinetic energy just before it strikes the ground.

3. A 2-kg mass is raised to a height of 5 meters and then dropped. Find (a) the potential energy acquired at its highest point and (b) the maximum velocity acquired in falling.

4. An 8-lb weight is raised to a height of 40 ft and then dropped. Find (a) the potential energy acquired at its highest point and (b) the maximum velocity acquired in falling.

5. A 10-kg box slides for 6 meters down a 30° incline. Neglecting friction, calculate (a) the velocity acquired and (b) the kinetic energy.

6. A boy weighing 64 lb slides for 20 ft down a slide inclined 30° with the horizontal. Neglecting friction, what is (a) his velocity and (b) his kinetic energy when he reaches the bottom of the slide?

7. A simple pendulum 1-m long has a 1-kg bob. If the bob is raised until the string is horizontal and then released, find (a) the potential energy before release and (b) the maximum velocity acquired as it swings.

8. A 5-kg mass is raised to a height of 16 meters and then dropped. Find (a) the potential energy at the top, (b) the time of fall, and (c) the maximum velocity acquired.

9. Four hundred joules of energy are expended in projecting a 5-kg mass straight upward. What is (a) its initial velocity and (b) its maximum height reached?

10. A 2-kg mass is to be projected upward with a velocity of 10 m/sec. Find (a) the energy required and (b) the maximum height reached. Employ energy principles only.

CONSERVATION OF MOMENTUM

When two or more bodies collide with each other, momentum is conserved. The law of conservation of momentum applies to all collision phenomena and states that *the total momentum before impact equals the total momentum after impact.* Consider as an example the "head-on" encounter of two balls as shown in Fig. A. Before impact the mass m_1 is moving with a velocity u_1 and has a momentum m_1u_1, while m_2 is moving with a velocity u_2 and has a momentum m_2u_2. The total momentum before impact is therefore equal to the sum of the two momenta, $m_1u_1 + m_2u_2$.

By similar reasoning it is clear that after impact, m_1 and m_2, with their new velocities v_1 and v_2 have a total momentum $m_1v_1 + m_2v_2$. The law of conservation of momentum requires that

$$m_1u_1 + m_2u_2 = m_1v_1 + m_2v_2 \quad (1)$$

momentum before impact =

momentum after impact

Fig. A. The total momentum of two bodies before impact is equal to the total momentum after impact.

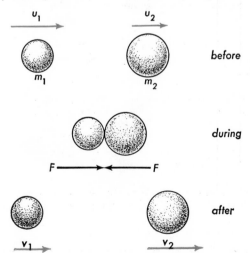

During impact two equal but opposite forces are set up between the bodies, one the force exerted by m_1 on m_2 and the other the force exerted by m_2 on m_1. These two equal but opposite forces are an action and reaction pair explained by Newton's Third Law of Motion. Each force acts for the same short interval of time giving equal impulses Ft to both bodies. By Newton's Second Law, as expressed by the impulse equation $Ft = mv - mv_0$, equal impulses produce equal changes in momentum. One body gains as much momentum as the other loses. In other words, the total momentum remains constant.

Example 1. An ivory ball of mass 5 gm moving with a velocity of 20 cm/sec collides with another ivory ball of mass 10 gm moving in the same direction along the same line with a velocity of 10 cm/sec. After impact the first mass is still moving in the same direction but with a velocity of only 8 cm/sec. Calculate the velocity of the second mass after impact. Apply Eq. (1).

Solution. By direct substitution in Eq. (1),

$$(5 \times 20) + (10 \times 10) = (5 \times 8) + (10 \times v_2)$$
$$200 = 40 + 10 v_2$$
$$10 v_2 = 160 \quad v_2 = 16 \text{ cm/sec}$$

After impact the second mass has a velocity of 16 cm/sec.

If in the above example the total kinetic energy after impact is calculated and compared with the total kinetic energy before impact, the two will not be found equal. Employing the equation $K.E. = \frac{1}{2} mv^2$,

$$K.E. = \frac{1}{2}(5 \times 20^2) + \frac{1}{2}(10 \times 10^2)$$
$$= 1500 \text{ ergs, before impact}$$
$$K.E. = \frac{1}{2}(5 \times 8^2) + \frac{1}{2}(10 \times 16^2)$$
$$= 1440 \text{ ergs, after impact}$$

The difference in energy, to the amount of 60 ergs, has disappeared as mechanical energy and gone into heat. During impact both masses were slightly deformed in shape due to the mutually acting forces and a small amount of heat was generated internally. This heat goes to raise the temperature of the two colliding bodies. It is only by including this heat energy of 60 ergs with the mechanical energy after impact that makes it possible to retain the law of conservation of energy.

This is just another way of stating that collisions in general are not perfectly elastic. If they were perfectly elastic, conservation of mechanical energy would hold as well as conservation of momentum. Perfectly elastic collisions are known to occur between the **ultra-microscopic** atoms and molecules of a gas but not with the **macroscopic** bodies encountered in every day life. The more inelastic the colliding bodies the more energy is transformed into heat. A treatment of elasticity and its application to collision problems will be given in Lesson 3 on Properties of Matter.

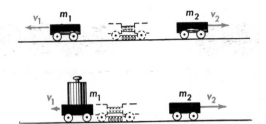

Fig. B. Conservation of momentum demonstration experiments.

It is important to note from the discussion above, that **for all impact problems whether perfectly elastic or not, the law of conservation of momentum should be applied.**

Experiments. An interesting experiment illustrating conservation of momentum is shown in Fig. B. Two small cars of equal mass, $m_1 = m_2$, are tied together with a compressed spring between them. When the cord tie is burned with a match, releasing the spring, the two cars fly apart with equal velocities. Before the spring is released the cars are at rest and the total momentum is zero. After the spring is released, the total momen-

Fig. C. Experiment with a light and heavy pendulum. Illustrating the law of conservation of momentum.

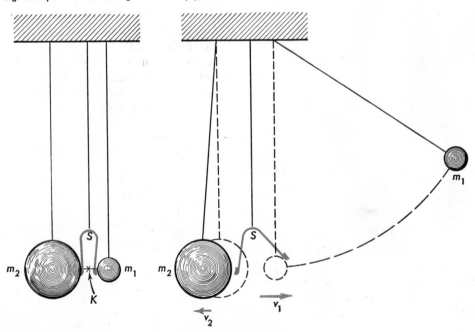

Fig. D. Experiment with the duckpin balls illustrating the law of conservation of momentum.

tum is still zero since the two velocities are oppositely directed. Momentum being a vector quantity,

$$m_1v_1 + m_2v_2 = 0 \qquad (2)$$

With motions to the right taken as positive, v_2 is positive and v_1 negative, and the two momenta cancel.

If the experiment above is repeated with one of the cars heavily loaded as shown in diagram (b), the two fly apart as before but with unequal velocities. The lighter mass moves away with a high velocity while the heavier mass recoils with a low velocity. The product $m_1 \times v_1$, however, is equal in magnitude to the product $m_2 \times v_2$, and the sum of the two momenta is zero.

Example 2. A 60 kg shell is shot with an initial velocity of 500 m/sec from a gun having a mass of 2000 kg. What is the initial velocity with which the gun recoils?

Solution. Applying Eq. (2) and substituting directly the known quantities,

60 kg × 500 m/sec + 2000 kg × v_2 = 0
30,000 kg m/sec + 2000 v_2 kg = 0

$$v_2 = \frac{30,000 \text{ kg m/sec}}{-2000 \text{ kg}} = -15 \text{ m/sec}$$

The gun recoils with a velocity of 15 m/sec.

An experiment illustrating the recoil velocity of a heavy mass like that in example 1 is shown by two pendulums in Fig. C. A U-shaped spring, compressed and tied with a cord **K**, rests against a heavy iron ball m_2 and a small wooden ball m_1. When the cord **K** is burned through by a lighted match, the spring is released and the two masses fly apart with equal but opposite momenta. The small mass acquires a high velocity and

swings up to a considerable height while the large mass is barely perceived to move.

Another interesting experiment illustrating conservation of momentum may be performed with eight or nine duckpin balls and a grooved board as shown in Fig. D. When one ball is rolled up to the others, it will be stopped by collision with the end ball, and the ball on the opposite end will roll out with almost the same speed. If two balls are rolled up, as indicated in the diagram, two will roll out on the other end, and if three are rolled up, three will roll out, etc. Glass or steel marbles work best in this experiment as they are highly elastic; however, duckpin balls or billiard balls produce a more spectacular effect.

Question. When two balls are rolled up to collide with the others, why doesn't just one ball roll off on the other side with twice the velocity, thus conserving momentum?

Answer. The answer to this question involves the conservation of energy as well as momentum. If only one ball came off with twice the velocity to conserve momentum, its kinetic energy would be twice the energy available from the two incident balls.

The propelling force of a jet plane or

Fig. E. Conservation of momentum accounts for the forward thrust on a rocket plane or missile.

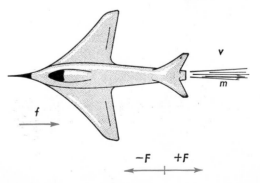

rocket is derived from the principle of momentum. See Fig. E.

As the gases are burned within the combustion chambers of the engine, they exert a large forward force $-F$ on the plane and an equal and opposite force $+F$ on the exhausting gases. As a result of the backward force the gases acquire a very high velocity v and a momentum mv. Flying at constant speed, the forward thrust $-F$ just balances the frictional resistance f of the air. To relate the thrust with the exhaust gas momentum we write down the force equation:

$$F = ma$$

For uniformly accelerated motion we also have

$$v = at$$

or

$$a = v/t$$

Direct substitution in the force equation gives

$$F = m\frac{v}{t}$$

or

$$Ft = mv \qquad (3)$$

To apply this, the **impulse equation**, to the jet or rocket engine, m represents the mass of gas exhausted in any chosen number of seconds t. The impulse $F \times t$ exerted on the gases is just equal and opposite to the impulse $-F \times t$ exerted on the plane.

Summary

When one body collides with another, the law of conservation of momentum applies, and not the conservation of mechanical energy. The total momentum of all bodies in collision is the same before and after impact.

During the impact of two bodies, equal and oppositely directed forces are involved. While the two equal forces act on different bodies, the total mechanical energy after impact is always less than the total mechanical energy before impact. Because bodies are not perfectly elastic, some energy is converted into heat.

When a shell is fired from a gun its momentum, as it leaves the gun barrel, is equal to the recoil momentum of the gun.

The force acting upon a body, multiplied by the time over which it acts, is called the impulse. As a result of an impulse Ft, momentum mv may be imparted to a body.

Questions

1. State the law of conservation of momentum as it applies to a head-on collision of two bodies.

2. Is the total kinetic energy before the impact of two bodies the same as the total energy after impact? Explain.

3. When a shell is fired from a large gun what can you say about the momentum of the shell? The gun?

4. What is the total momentum of a gun before a shell is fired? Immediately after it is fired?

5. A man in a heavy boat pulls on a rowboat by means of a rope. What can you say about the momentum of each boat? Which will have the greatest speed?

6. Define impulse and write down the impulse equation. What are the units of impulse in the mks system? What are the units of momentum?

7. How does conservation of momentum apply to a rocket? Will a rocket work in a vacuum, or must it have air to push on?

8. If one freight car is at rest and another bumps into it, and the two lock together, will conservation of momentum apply?

9. Think of some project in which you might make a simple, inexpensive device for demonstrating the principles of conservation of momentum.

Problems

1. Moving with a velocity of 30 m/sec, a steel ball of 10-kg mass collides with another steel ball of 20-kg mass moving in the same direction along the same line with a velocity of 15 m/sec. After impact the first ball is moving in the same direction with a velocity of 14 m/sec. Calculate the velocity of the second ball after impact.

2. A gun weighing 500 lb fires a 4-oz shell with a muzzle velocity of 2000 ft/sec. If the gun is free to move, what is the recoil velocity?

3. A gun weighing 1600 lb is mounted on wheels. It fires a 20-lb shell horizontally with a muzzle velocity of 1800 ft/sec. What is the gun's recoil velocity?

4. A 6-kg mass moving with a constant speed of 3 m/sec overtakes and bumps into a 3-kg mass moving in the same direction with a constant velocity of 1 m/sec. If after impact the 3-kg mass has a velocity of 2.8 m/sec, calculate (a) the velocity of the 6-kg mass and (b) the energy lost in the form of heat.

5.* A 400-gm block of wood lying on a fence post is hit by a rifle bullet of 25-gm mass. If the bullet enters the block with a velocity of 600 m/sec and leaves the other side with a velocity of 200 m/sec, find the recoil velocity of the block.

6.* A 30-gm bullet moving with a velocity of 600 m/sec enters and becomes embedded in a block of wood weighing 3.6 kg. With what velocity will the block recoil if it was at rest before the impact?

7. A gun weighing 1200 lb fires a 4-oz shell with a muzzle velocity of 2000 ft/sec. If the gun is free to move, what is its recoil velocity?

8.* A 5-kg block of wood hangs as a pendulum by a long string. When a 15-gm bullet is fired at close range into the block and becomes embedded there, the block swings to a height of 20 cm above its rest position. Find (a) the recoil speed of the block and (b) the muzzle velocity of the bullet.

ENERGY AND MOMENTUM—Laboratory

In performing this experiment as described in the accompanying LABO-RATORY EXERCISES you will employ the principles of impulse and momentum presented in the previous lesson. A large iron weight is dropped from a fixed height and, by successive impacts, a large nail is driven into a block of wood. A plotted graph of the measurements indicates the hardness of the wood at various depths.

LEVERS

The great philosopher Archimedes* once said, "Give me a place to stand on and I will move the earth." In making this boast Archimedes was undoubtedly referring

* Archimedes (287-212 B.C.), Greek mathematician and inventor, was born at Syracuse in Sicily. He was the son of Pheidias, an astronomer, and was on intimate terms with, if not a relative of, Hiero, king of Syracuse. Of the many stories or legends told of him and King Hiero, the one of the lever is perhaps the most famous. Having made the claim "Give me a place to stand on and I will move the earth," King Hiero summoned him for an explanation. He is said to have set one end of a lever to a ship that was just ready to be launched and King Hiero himself, upon pushing lightly upon the other end, moved the ship into the water.

Another time King Hiero, suspecting that his goldsmith had not made his crown of pure gold, as instructed, gave Archimedes the task of learning the truth without harming the crown. Just when he felt he would have to tell the king it couldn't be done, Archimedes stepped into the bath and noticed how the water ran over the edge. Springing from the bath he ran naked through the streets shouting "Eureka." To find the volume of the metal had stumped him, but now he knew that by submerging the crown in a vessel previously filled with water, the volume of the overflow water would equal the volume of metal. Knowing the actual weight of the crown and its volume, he calculated the density and found it to be less than the density of pure gold. A confession from the goldsmith confirmed the king's suspicions and Archimedes experimental observations.

to the principle of the lever. It must have been common knowledge at the time of Archimedes that when some heavy object had to be lifted or a huge stone had to be loosed from the ground, a long straight pole could be used to do it.

Levers. There are in reality three classes of levers, and these are shown in their simplest form in Fig. A. In each illustration **P** is the **fulcrum,** or **axis,** about which the lever is made to pivot, **W** is the **weight** or **load** to be lifted, and **F** is the **applied force** or **effort.** The distance r_1 is called the lever arm of the load, and the distance r_2 the lever arm of the applied force.

The lever arm of any force is defined as the perpendicular distance between the force direction and the fulcrum. The moment of a force is defined as the product of **force times lever arm.**

$$\text{moment} = \text{force} \times \text{lever arm} \qquad (1)$$

To operate a lever, force **F** of a certain magnitude must be applied to maintain equilibrium or balance, and then the force increased ever so slightly to cause motion and lift the weight **W.** To maintain equilibrium

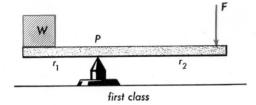

first class

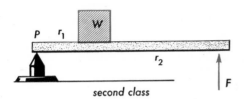

second class

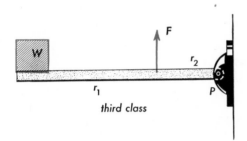

third class

Fig. A. Illustrating the three classes of levers commonly used for lifting heavy objects.

the moments of both forces must counterbalance each other. In other words the moment of the force tending to produce a clockwise rotation must equal the moment of the force tending to produce a counterclockwise rotation.

clockwise moment = counterclockwise moment

For each of the three classes of levers in Fig. A,

$$W \times r_1 = F \times r_2 \qquad (2)$$

Example 1. How great a load can be lifted by a lever of the first class if the force applied is 150 lb? Assume the lever to be 10 ft long with the fulcrum 2 ft from the load.

Solution. Referring to Fig. A(a) and Eq. (2),

$$W \times 2 = 150 \times 8$$

or

$$W = \frac{150 \times 8}{2} = 600 \text{ lb}$$

It will be noted that the closer W is to the fulcrum P the greater will be the load that can be lifted by any given force F. This is undoubtedly what Archimedes had in mind when he said, "Give me a place to stand on and I will move the earth."

Diagrams of three common devices are shown in Fig. B illustrating the three classes of levers. In the wheel and axle of diagram (a) the horizontal line **APB** represents a lever of the first class with **P** as a fulcrum, **AP** as one lever arm, and **PB** as the other. The weight **W** is lifted by one rope wound around the axle, while the smaller force **F** is applied to another rope wrapped around the wheel.

Fig. B. Illustrating devices employing the principles of levers.

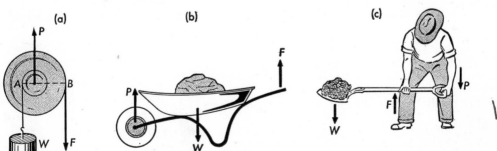

The wheelbarrow in diagram (b) employs a lever of the second class with the pivot **P** at the wheel. The heavily loaded barrow is lifted to a rolling position by applying a smaller force **F** at the handles.

The loaded shovel in diagram (c) illustrates a lever of the third class, the fulcrum being located in the man's left hand.

Cog wheels in a machine, a crank shaft in an engine, and pulley wheels in a block and tackle are additional examples involving levers of the first class.

Summary

All levers can be classified under one of the three following classes: first class, second class, or third class.

The principles of all levers are the same and are given by the relation

$$W \times r_1 = F \times r_2$$

where the product on the left is the force moment of the load to be moved and the product on the right is the force moment of the applied force.

The moment of a force is the product of the force and the perpendicular distance from its line of action to the fulcrum.

Questions

1. Make a diagram of a first-class lever. Show how a claw hammer pulling nails employs the principle of a first-class lever.

2. Make a diagram of a second-class lever. Make a diagram of a nut cracker and explain wherein the principle of the second-class lever is involved.

3. Make a diagram of a third-class lever. Give an example of some practical application of the principle.

4. What class of lever action is involved in each of the following: (a) scissors, (b) pliers, (c) tongs, (d) wheelbarrow, (e) oars in a rowboat, and (f) sweeping with a broom?

5. Make a diagram of a second-class lever and explain how to calculate the clockwise moment and the counterclockwise moment.

6. What class of lever is involved in the forearm? Where is the applied force, and where is the load to be lifted?

7. What class of lever is involved in the pedaling of a bicycle?

8. What practical utility devices can you think of that employ levers of one kind or another?

Problems

1. A pole 5 m long is used as a second-class lever to lift a mass of 600 kg. Where must the load be placed if the maximum applied force available is 750 newtons?

2. A plank 16 ft long is used as a first-class lever to lift a 1200-lb load. Where must the pivot be located if the applied force is 130 lb?

3. A bar 2.50 m long is used as a lever of the second class to lift a mass of 50 kg. Where must the weight be suspended if the applied force is 39.2 newtons?

4. A mass of 5 kg is lifted by a lever of the third class. Where should a force of 215.6 newtons be applied if the lever is 100 cm long?

5. A pole 4 m long is used as a second-class lever to lift a 155-kg mass. If this load is located 75 cm from the pivot, what force must be applied at the far end?

6. A wheel and axle have radii of 45 cm and 10 cm, respectively. What force on the wheel cord will raise a 60-kg mass fastened to the axle cord?

7. What force must be applied to the handles of a wheelbarrow if the handles are 4 ft from the axle of the wheel, and the 200-lb load to be lifted is 18 in. in from the axle?

8. A screw driver is used as a first-class lever to pry the lid from a tin can. If the distance between the tip of the lid and the rim of the can is 8 mm and the applied force of 15 newtons is 20 cm from the rim, what force is applied to the lid?

9. An oarlock is 28 in. from the handle of a 10-ft oar. If a force of 35 lb is used on each of two oars, what will be the force acting to move the boat through the water? (Assume pivots at tip of oar blades.)

Mechanics | **Lesson 35**

LEVERS—*Laboratory*

In performing this experiment as described in the accompanying *LABO-RATORY EXERCISES* you will apply the principles of moments to all three classes of levers. The equipment required is simple and inexpensive and is readily assembled.

Mechanics | **Lesson 36**

ANATOMICAL MECHANICS

In the preceding lessons we have seen that to obtain a solution to many problems in mechanics, it is customary to neglect certain minor details like the weight of a beam or the friction in a bearing in order to simplify a problem and arrive at some approximate yet practical numerical answer.

Although complicated, the general principles of muscle function in animals as well as in living human beings may also be simplified in much the same way by neglecting certain minor parts. As a result of such simplification the bones of the body and the muscles that move them form the compression and tension members respectively of mechanical systems already classified as levers. It is,

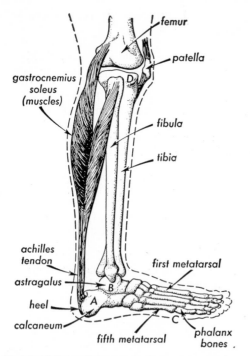

Fig. A. Skeleton diagram of the lower leg and foot showing the muscles and tendon used in rising on tiptoe.

therefore, the purpose of this chapter to show in what way some of the principles of mechanics may be found in and applied to the human anatomy.

Mechanics of the Foot. An elementary example of anatomical mechanics is found in an analysis of foot movement. See Fig. A. In the flexion and extension of the whole foot the ankle acts as a hinge or pivot about which rotation in a vertical plane takes place. The top of the *astragalus* is like a ball fitting into and free to turn in the socket formed by the ends of the *fibula* and *tibia* bones of the leg.

When a person attempts to rise on tiptoe, the strong muscles, the *gastrocnemius* and *soleus* forming the calf of the leg, act as prime movers. A sufficient tightening of these muscles causes the heel to rise, and the foot to bend at **C** where the *phalanx* of the toes join the *metatarsals*.

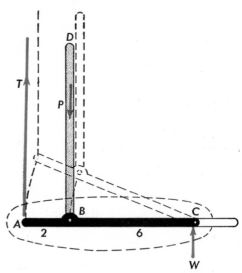

Fig. B. Schematic diagram showing the mechanical principle of the human foot when rising on tiptoe.

A simple space diagram shown in Fig. B illustrates how rising on tiptoe involves the simplest type of lever action with a fixed pivot at **C**. The horizontal member **AC** represents the foot skeleton from **A** to **C** in Fig. A, and the vertical member **BD** the leg skeleton from **B** to **D** supporting the body. To calculate the tension required of the muscles and the load to be carried by the leg bones, the foot member **A** to **C** is isolated as a rigid body and all forces acting upon it taken into account.

There are three forces acting on the isolated member: (a) an upward force at **A** due to tension in the muscles, (b) a downward force at **B** due to the leg bones, and (c) an upward force at **C** due to the floor. As a problem let it be assumed that a person weighing 150 lb *stands on one foot* and then rises on tiptoe. Assign the dimensions of 2 in. for **AB** and 6 in. for **BC**, and calculate the tension force **T** and the compression force **P** as follows:

By taking moments about **A**, the counterclockwise torque is **W** × 8 in. and the clockwise torque **P** × 2 in.

Equate torques, as in conditions of equilibrium.

$$P \times 2 \text{ in.} = W \times 8 \text{ in.}$$

Substitute $W = 150$ lb and solve for P.

$$P = \frac{150 \text{ lb} \times 8 \text{ in.}}{2 \text{ in.}} = 600 \text{ lb}$$

Take moments about B and equate.

$$T \times 2 \text{ in.} = W \times 6 \text{ in.}$$

Substitute and solve for T.

$$T = \frac{150 \text{ lb} \times 6 \text{ in.}}{2 \text{ in.}} = 450 \text{ lb}$$

As a check it is observed that the total upward force $W + T$ of 600 lb equals the total downward force P of 600 lb.

It should be pointed out that tension is produced by a contraction of the large part or "belly" of a muscle and not by the narrow section called the *tendon*.

Mechanics of the Lower Jaw.   The *mandible,* or lower "jawbone," is a large, strong, horseshoe shaped bone, forming the lower third of the facial skeleton. See Fig. C. A pair of **condyles** at the ends fit into sockets one on either side of the skull just in front of the auditory canal and act as hinges about which the lower jaw pivots.

The *masseter,* or "chewing muscle," is one of the strongest muscles in the body. As illus-

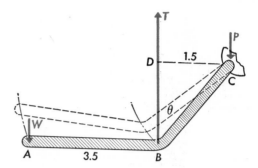

Fig. D. Schematic diagram showing the mechanics involved in chewing.

trated in the figure, it is located in the back part of the side of the face. Originating on the lower margin of the **zygoma,** the masseter passes downward to where it terminates on the lower edge of the **ramus** of the mandible.

The action of the two masseters, one on either side of the face, is such as to lift the lower jaw and at the same time draw it slightly forward. In principle this is a lever action with a pivot at C, an upward force at B, and a load force at A introduced when chewing takes place between the teeth of the upper and lower jaws.

A schematic diagram of the lever action is shown at the right in Fig. D, with selected values of the dimensions given in inches. When the lever is isolated as a rigid body all of the acting forces, due to symmetry, are reduced to three, W, T, and P. To calculate the magnitudes of these forces at least one of them must be known.

As a problem let it be assumed that the lower jaw, in chewing with the front teeth, is able to exert a measured force of 20 lb. To calculate the tension T exerted by the two masseters, the point C is assumed as pivot, and torques equated as follows:

$$W \times 5 \text{ in.} = T \times 1.5 \text{ in.}$$

Inserting $W = 20$ lb and solving for T,

$$T = \frac{20 \text{ lb} \times 5 \text{ in.}}{1.5 \text{ in.}} = 66.7 \text{ lb}$$

Fig. C. Diagram of the human skull.

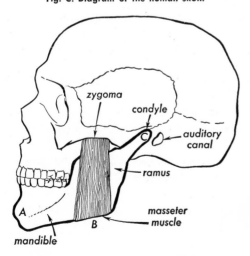

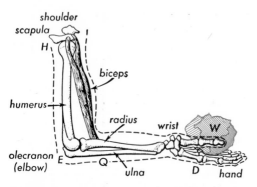

Fig. E. Skeleton diagram of the arm and hand showing the bicep used in lifting a load W.

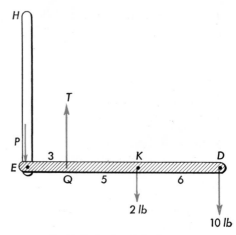

Fig. F. Mechanics of the forearm.

Equating downward forces to upward forces,

$$P + W = T$$

from which

$$P = T - W = 66.7 - 20 = 46.7 \text{ lb}$$

Each masseter therefore exerts one half of 66.7 lb, or 33.35 lb, while the condyles each press against their sockets with a force of one-half of 46.7 lb, or 23.35 lb.

The Biceps. The above procedure of solution will be applied to the muscle problem involved in the flexion of the lower arm. In Fig. E a skeleton of the forearm is shown in a horizontal position supporting a stone in the palm of the hand. With a pivot point at the elbow joint the forearm and hand form a compression member like the boom of a crane, while the **biceps** assuming the duty of prime mover in any flexor movement, become the tension member.

The biceps originate on the **scapula** or shoulder from where they pass downward and forward to terminate on the **radius** near the elbow.

A schematic diagram of this force problem is shown in Fig. F: the vertical member (**EH**) represents the **humerus;** the horizontal member (**ED**), 14 in. in length, the forearm and hand; and the tension member (**T**), the biceps. A weight of 10 lb is assumed held in the hand, while the weight of the forearm and hand is taken to be 2 lb and applied at the center of mass 8 in. from the elbow.

The problem to be solved resolves itself into one of calculating (a) the upward force **T** exerted by the biceps and (b) the downward force **P** exerted by the humerus on the elbow. The solution of this problem will be left as an exercise for the student. See problem 7.

Summary

The principles of mechanics are applied to the human body. Many such applications are simplified by applying the principles of the lever. The bones of the body withstand enormous compressional forces, while the muscles and tendons withstand large tension forces.

In rising on tiptoe the foot becomes the lever, the applied force arises in the large gastrocnemius and soleus muscles of the lower extremity, and the compressional forces are sustained by the tibia and fibula.

The lower jawbone, the mandible, is involved in chewing, and the large masseter muscle is the prime mover. When chewing, the mandible pivots at the condyles, and the action is that of a third-class lever.

The forearm operates as a third-class lever. The biceps act as prime movers and, with a pivot at the elbow, exert forces many times those acquired in the hands.

Questions

1. Make a diagram of the lever system of the foot when one rises on tiptoes. What muscles apply the required force? What large tendon is involved? Where is the pivot? What class lever is this?

2. Make a diagram of the lower jaw as a lever. What muscles are involved in producing the primary force? Where is the pivot? What class lever is involved?

3. Make a diagram of the lever action involved with the forearm horizontal and the upper arm vertical. With a weight in the palm of the hand, what large muscles are brought into play? With the lower arm as a lever, where is the pivot? What class lever is this?

4. Which is the larger of the two forces brought into action in rising on tiptoe: the tension force due to the muscles or the compressional force in the bones?

5. Which is the larger of the two forces brought into action in chewing: the muscle tension or the pivot force?

6. With the forearm in the position shown in Fig. E, which force is the larger, the tension in the biceps, or the load lifted by the hand?

7. Think of some project in which you might make a simple and inexpensive device for demonstrating any of the principles developed in this lesson.

Problems

1. If the greatest load a 150-lb man can lift and still rise on his tiptoes while holding it is 250 lb, what is the corresponding muscle tension he can exert through each Achilles' tendon? Referring to Fig. B, assume **AB** = 1.75 in. and **AC** = 8.75 in.

2. In applying the brake pedal of a truck a man exerts a force of 20 lb with the ball of his right foot. If the dimensions of his foot are **AB** = 1.45 in. and **AC** = 6.25 in. (see Fig. B), find (a) the tension in the Achilles' tendon and (b) the compressional force on the calcaneum.

3. A man weighing 175 lb and carrying a 100-lb bag rises on tiptoes. Calculate (a) the downward force on the astragalus of each foot and (b) the tension in each Achilles' tendon if the dimensions of each foot (see Fig. B) are **AB** = 1.45 in. and **BC** = 5.7 in.

4. A 120-lb boy pedals a bicycle. When he puts all of his weight on the ball of one foot, what is the tension in the Achilles' tendon? The dimensions of his foot are **AB** = 1.38 in. and **AC** = 7.42 in. (See Fig. B.)

5. In biting down to crack a nut with his front teeth a man exerts a force of 22 lb. Calculate the tension in the masseter muscles if the mandible has the following dimensions (see Fig. D): **AB** = 9 cm, **BC** = 6.6 cm, and θ = 48°.

6. If each masseter muscle of a man is capable of exerting a maximum force of 65 lb, calculate the maximum force he can exert by his front teeth if the mandible has the following dimensions (see Fig. D): **AB** = 3.6 in., **BC** = 2.5 in., and θ = 52°.

7. Solve the problem as it is stated in the last paragraph of this lesson (see Fig. F.)

8. If the heaviest load a strong man can lift in his one hand in the median position shown in Fig. E is 25 kg, what is the required tension in the biceps? Assume the distance **EQ** = 6.0 cm and the distance **ED** = 36 cm. Neglect the weight of the forearm.

9. If a man can lift a 40-lb weight in one hand in the median position of Fig. E, what is the tension exerted by his biceps? Assume **EQ** = 2.5 in. and **ED** = 15 in. Neglect the weight of the forearm.

Mechanics | Lesson 37

MACHINES

All contrivances connected with machine installations that utilize natural sources of energy may be classified in three groups: (1) *prime movers*, (2) *machines*, and (3) *utility devices*. To the first group belong all such devices as manpower, horsepower, electric motors, water turbines, steam turbines, gas engines, diesel engines, etc. To the second group belong such mechanisms as levers, pulley wheels, gears, belts, and cams, as well as combinations of them, while to the third group belong such end products as airplane and ship propellers, car and locomotive drive wheels, tractor and tank tracks, clock and watch hands, etc.

From the above definitions, therefore, a mechanical machine constitutes a device wherein mechanical energy is applied at one point and mechanical energy in a more useful form is delivered at another.

The Lever. The lever as described in detail in Mechanics, Lesson 34, is one of the

simplest of all mechanical devices that may rightfully be called a machine. By applying a downward force at one end of a lever, as shown in Fig. A, a heavy load may be lifted at the other. The principle of the lever requires that the moment on one side of the fulcrum **P** be equal to the moment on the other side.

$$W \times r_1 = F \times r_2 \qquad (1)$$

When the two moments are exactly equal, the lever is in equilibrium, that is, all parts are at rest or moving with uniform speed. If the lever is at rest, then, neglecting friction, any small additional force added to **F** will produce the necessary lifting motion.

Mechanical Advantage. *The mechanical advantage of a machine may be defined as the ratio of the output force deliv-*

Fig. B. A lever is classified as a machine.

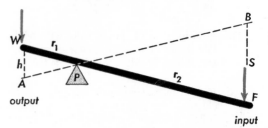

Fig. A. A lever of the first class.

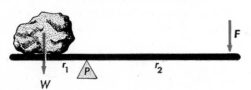

ered by the machine to the input force applied by the prime mover. With a simple machine like the lever, in Fig. B, **W** represents the **output force** and **F** represents the **input force**, and the mechanical advantage (*abbr.* **M.A.**) is given by

$$\text{M.A.} = \frac{W}{F} \qquad (2)$$

By transposing Eq. (1) the mechanical advantage is also expressed as the ratio of the lever arms.

$$\text{M.A.} = \frac{W}{F} = \frac{r_2}{r_1} \qquad (3)$$

Suppose for example that a man weighing 150 lb wishes to lift a heavy stone weighing 1500 lb by means of a lever. The mechanical advantage required of the lever must therefore be

$$\text{M.A.} = \tfrac{1500}{150} = 10$$

Eq. (3) shows that to obtain this mechanical advantage the lever arm r_2 must be 10 times as long as r_1. Although 1500 lb can be lifted by the application of a force only one-tenth as large, energy relations show that the operator is not getting "something for nothing." The law of conservation of energy requires that the work done by the machine be no greater than the work done on the machine. As illustrated in the diagram, the work done on the machine by the operator is equal to the product of **force** × **distance, F × s**, while the work done by the machine is equal to the product of **weight** × **distance, W × h.**

By conservation of energy

$$W \times h = F \times s \qquad (4)$$
$$\text{output} \qquad \text{input}$$

Transposing gives

$$\frac{W}{F} = \frac{s}{h} \qquad (5)$$

which shows that the mechanical advantage, defined as the ratio of the forces **W/F**, is

also given by the inverse ratio of the distances, **s/h.**

Efficiency. In arriving at the above relations for the mechanical advantage, it was assumed that the lever, as a machine, operates without friction. As a practical matter such ideal conditions are desirable but never actually attained. It is customary in engineering practice to neglect friction at first by applying the above equations and then to make corrections where necessary by taking into account the efficiency of the machine.

Friction in a machine is not always a desirable feature, for by its presence energy is continually wasted in all moving parts by being transformed into heat. By the law of conservation of energy,

input work = output work + wasted energy

The efficiency of a machine is defined as the ratio of output work to input work.

$$\text{efficiency} = \frac{\text{output work}}{\text{input work}} \qquad (6)$$

This ratio is always less than unity and is usually multiplied by 100 to express the efficiency in per cent.

$$\text{per cent efficiency} = \frac{\text{output}}{\text{input}} \times 100 \qquad (7)$$

The smaller the energy lost through friction the greater is the efficiency of a machine and the nearer is the efficiency to 100%. In all cases where friction is assumed to be so small that it can be neglected, the efficiency is taken to be 100% and the mechanical advantage is given by Eqs. (2), (3), and (5).

If friction is appreciably large and must be taken into account when making calculations, the mechanical advantage is still given by Eq. (2), but not by the ratio of the lever arms r_2/r_1, or the distances moved **s/h.**

Wheel and Axle. The wheel and axle is a simple machine involving the principle of

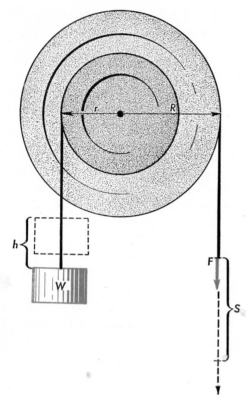

Fig. C. Wheel and axle.

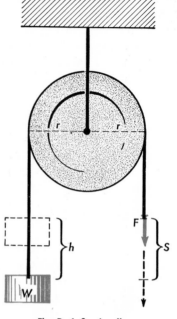

Fig. D. A fixed pulley.

$$\frac{W}{F} = \frac{2\,\pi R}{2\,\pi r} = \frac{R}{r} \qquad (9)$$

the lever. As shown in Fig. C, a heavy load **W** is lifted by a rope wrapped around an axle of radius **r** by pulling down on another rope wrapped around an attached wheel of larger radius **R**. By exerting the force **F** through a distance **s** the load **W** is lifted a distance **h**. Neglecting friction, the input work **F** × **s** is equal to the output work **W** × **h**.

In one revolution of the wheel the force **F** moves down a distance **s** equal to the circumference of the wheel **2** πR, and the load **W** moves up a distance **h** equal to the circumference of the axle **2** πr. By conservation of energy

$$W \times 2\,\pi r = F \times 2\,\pi R \qquad (8)$$
$$\text{output} \qquad\qquad \text{input}$$

Transposing **F** to the left side of the equation and **2** πr to the right, the mechanical advantage **W/F** is given by

Pulleys. The action of a pulley is the same as that of a lever having equal arms. Singly, pulleys may be used in one of two ways, either as **a fixed pulley** or as **a movable pulley**. In Fig. D a fixed pulley is shown being used to lift a load **W** by means of an applied force **F**. With the pivot at the center of the pulley the two forces have equal arms, each equal to the radius **r**. Having equal arms, the forces, neglecting friction, must be equal, and the theoretical mechanical advantage is unity.

Although a mechanical advantage of unity obtained with a fixed pulley may be looked upon as no mechanical advantage at all, it often happens that a downward force is more conveniently applied to lift a body than is an equal upward force.

A movable pulley, on the other hand, see Fig. E, has a mechanical advantage of 2. To move the load **W** upward a distance **h**, both of the supporting cords must be shortened by

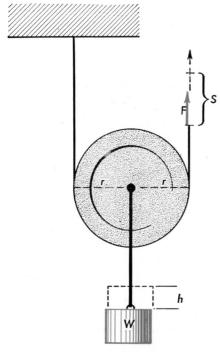

Fig. E. A movable pulley.

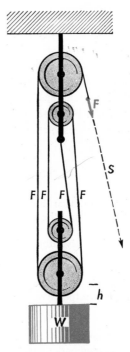

Fig. F. A block and tackle.

this same amount. To take up the slack the force **F** must move up a distance **s** = **2 h.** By energy conservation

$$W \times h = F \times (2\,h)$$
$$\text{output} \qquad \text{input}$$

from which the mechanical advantage **M.A.** = **W/F** = 2.

Block and Tackle. The block and tackle is a contrivance with a large mechanical advantage, employing the use of any number of movable and fixed pulleys. One form is shown in Fig. F. The pulleys, it is noted, are in two blocks with two pulleys or sheaves in each block. The fixed end of the rope is attached to the lower end of the upper block and after passing around each pulley, as shown, goes to the prime mover.

In some blocks the pulleys are all of the same size and mounted side by side, while in others they are of different size and mounted one below the other as shown. Re-

gardless of size, the function of each pulley is simply to reverse the direction of the force **F** so that the same tension exists throughout the supporting rope.

Neglecting friction in the pulleys and the weight of the rope, the tension in each of the four sections of rope holding up the lower block and weight **W** in the diagram is equal to **F.** For the block and weight to be in equilibrium, therefore, the total upward force 4 **F** must be equal to the downward force **W.** This gives for the mechanical advantage,

$$\text{M.A.} = W/F = 4$$

The same result is derived from energy considerations as follows. In raising the load **W** a height **h,** each of the four ropes supporting it must be shortened by this amount, and hence the prime mover must exert the force **F** through a distance **s** = 4 **h.** Since **F** × **s** = **W** × **h,** the mechanical advantage **W/F** = **s/h** = 4.

In general, the mechanical advantage of any block and tackle is given by the number of parallel ropes supporting the load. The load **W** includes the weight of the lower block.

M.A. = number of supporting ropes   (10)

The above relations give only the theoretical mechanical advantages of pulleys and blocks and tackles. Because of friction such mechanical advantages are never realized, and the efficiency is less than 100%. To determine the efficiency and the actual mechanical advantage, weights can be applied as loads, and the actual force required to operate the machine can be measured. The latter is readily performed as an experiment by the use of weights for both **W** and **F**, and establishing equilibrium.

Summary

A machine is a device that forms the connecting link between a source of energy called the prime mover and the useful and applied end product called the utility device.

The mechanical advantage of a machine is defined as the ratio of the output force delivered by the machine to the input force applied by the prime mover.

The efficiency is defined as the ratio of the output work to the input work. Largely because of friction the output work is always less than input work and the efficiency is less than 100%.

No matter how simple or complex a machine may be, its unit parts will contain one or more of the elementary devices: levers, pulleys, wheel and axles, cog wheels, sprocket wheels, chains, and belts.

Questions

1. What is meant by the mechanical advantage of a machine? What is meant by efficiency?

2. If a lever has a mechanical advantage of 5, what can you say about (a) the forces involved and (b) the lever arms?

3. If the efficiency of a machine is 90 percent, what can you say about (a) the work done and (b) the forces involved?

4. What class of lever principle is involved in a wheel and axle?

5. Assuming 100 percent efficiency, what is the mechanical advantage of (a) a fixed pulley and (b) a movable pulley?

6. What is a block and tackle? How are they used to lift heavy loads?

7. How can you determine the mechanical advantage of a block and tackle by looking at the ropes?

8. How could you measure the mechanical advantage of a block and tackle rig? How could you measure the efficiency?

9. Work out the plans for a project in which you would construct a simple and inexpensive device for demonstrating the mechanical advantage of a machine involving two levers.

Problems

1. A wheel and axle have diameters of 18 in. and 1.5 in., respectively. (a) What is the mechanical advantage? (b) What force is required to lift a load of 600 lb?

2. A farmer raises a bucket of water weighing 45 lb from the bottom of a well. To do this he has the rope wound around a 10-in. diameter wooden drum, and a crank with its handle 18 in. from the center of rotation. Find (a) the mechanical advantage and (b) the required force on the handle.

3. A horizontal force of 50 lb is applied to the top of an automobile tire of one of the wheels of the automobile stuck in the mud. (a) What is the effective force on the automobile? (b) What is the mechanical advantage?

4. In a garage a block and tackle is used to lift a 360-lb motor out of a car. If the upper and lower blocks each contain four sheaves and one end of the rope is connected to the upper block, (a) what is the mechanical advantage? (b) What force must be applied? (Neglect friction.)

5. Two pulley wheels with diameters of 3 in. and 10 in. are mounted fast on the same shaft. Power from a motor is supplied to a belt passing around the larger pulley and a machine is belted to the smaller pulley. (a) What are the relative speeds of the two belts and (b) what is the mechanical advantage? (Assume no friction.)

6.* A block and tackle is used to pull tree stumps out of the ground. Each block contains three pulleys. One block should be fastened to the tree stump and the other to the anchor. (a) To which of the two blocks should the rope be fastened to obtain the greatest mechanical advantage? Make a diagram. (b) If a force of 100 lb is applied to the free end of the rope, and the efficiency is 50%, what force is applied to the stump?

7.* A painter hoists himself up the side of a tall building by a block and tackle having two pulleys in the upper block and one in the lower block. The man and his equipment weigh 180 lb. What is the tension in the rope? (*Note:* The man himself does the pulling.)

Mechanics | **Lesson 38**

BALLISTICS—*Laboratory*

In performing this laboratory experiment as described in the accompanying LABORATORY EXERCISES you will apply the principles of momentum and impulse to the firing of a 22-rifle. From measurements on the height of a recoiling block of wood the muzzle velocity of several different shells is determined.

CIRCULAR MOTION

Angular Speed. The speed with which a body rotates is called its **angular speed** or **frequency of rotation.** Either of these terms refers to the number of complete revolutions a body makes in unit time and is designated by the letter **f.**

| f = number of revolutions per second | (1) |

A flywheel, for example, might be said to have an angular speed of 10 revolutions per second (*abbr.* 10 rps). This is equivalent to an angular speed of 600 revolutions per minute (*abbr.* 600 rpm), and to an angular speed of 36,000 revolutions per hour (*abbr.* 36,000 rph).

Consider a body of mass **m** fastened to the end of a string and whirling in a circle of radius **r.** See Fig. A. Since **v**, the speed of the body along its path, is defined as the distance traveled per unit time, the relation between **v** and **f** is given by

$$v = 2\pi rf \qquad (2)$$

For formulating the laws of mechanics it will be found convenient to express all rotation in radians and not in degrees or revolutions. **The radian is a unit of angular measure** just as the centimeter is a unit of linear measure. It is defined as the angle subtended by the arc of a circle whose length is equal to the radius of the same circle. Re-

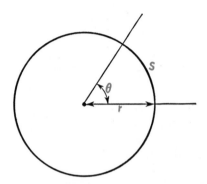

Fig. B. The radian is a unit of angular measure. When the arc s equals the radius r, the angle e equals one radian.

ferring to Fig. B the distance **s** measured along the arc is equal to the radius **r**, and the angle $\theta = 1$ **radian.**

Since the entire circumference of a circle is just 2π times the radius **r**, there are 2π radians in one complete circle.

| 2π radians = 360° |

Since $\pi = 3.1416$,

$$1 \text{ radian} = \frac{360°}{6.283} = 57.3°$$

It follows from the above relations that the angle θ in radians between any two points on the circumference of a circle is given by **s**, the length of the arc between the two points, divided by the radius **r.** In words,

$$\text{angle in radians} = \frac{\text{arc length}}{\text{radius}}$$

or, in algebraic symbols,

$$\theta = \frac{s}{r} \qquad (3)$$

The reason for measuring angles in radians

Fig. A. A mass m moving in a circle of radius r with a uniform speed v.

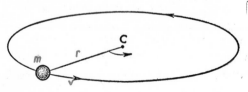

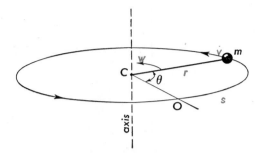

Fig. C. Illustrating circular motion.

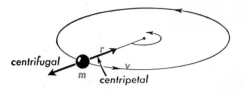

Fig. D. A mass *m* moving in a circle experiences an acceleration toward the center.

is that it simplifies all formulas for rotary motion. As an illustration consider the speed of a stone being whirled on the end of a string as shown in Fig. C. The angular velocity of the motion is defined as the angle turned through divided by the elapsed time.

$$\text{angular velocity} = \frac{\text{angle turned through}}{\text{time}}$$

In algebraic symbols,

$$\omega = \frac{\theta}{t} \qquad (4)$$

and is to be compared with the corresponding definition of linear velocity,

$$v = \frac{s}{t} \qquad (5)$$

Angular velocity ω corresponds to linear velocity v, and angular displacement θ corresponds to linear displacement s. With θ measured in radians and t in seconds, the angular velocity ω has the units of radians per seconds (*abbr.* rad/sec).

As a problem, suppose a stone, when it is whirled on the end of a string 50 cm long, makes 8 complete revolutions in 2 sec, and we wish to find the angular velocity in radians per second. To employ Eq. (4) the angle θ is first calculated as follows. Since 1 revolution $= 2\pi$ radians, 8 revolutions are equivalent to

$$\theta = 2\pi \times 8 = 50.2 \text{ rad}$$

Substitution in Eq. (4) gives

$$\omega = \frac{\theta}{t} = \frac{50.2 \text{ rad}}{2 \text{ sec}} = 25.1 \frac{\text{rad}}{\text{sec}}$$

Centripetal Force. When a stone is whirling on the end of a string there is an inward force exerted by the string on the ball. This force is called the **centripetal force**. By Newton's Third Law of Motion the ball exerts an equal but opposite force on the string. This is called the **centrifugal force**. Both forces are illustrated in Fig. D. Since the only force acting on the ball is inward, the ball is not in equilibrium but is being continually accelerated in the direction of the force, i.e., toward the center.

This appears to be a physical paradox, for here is a body moving with constant speed in a circle and yet being accelerated toward the center of the circle without getting any closer to it. If the string were to break suddenly, the ball would fly off on a tangent to the circle and move with constant velocity according to Newton's First Law.

To obtain a clearer picture of centripetal force and acceleration toward the center, motion in a circle as illustrated in Fig. E is to be compared with the motion of a projectile accelerated downward by the pull of gravity as described in Mechanics, Lesson 10. Because of the earth's attraction of all bodies, a projectile is continually accelerated downward away from the straight line of its original projection. In circular motion the mass is continually accelerated toward the center, always at right angles to its instantaneous velocity and away from any straight-

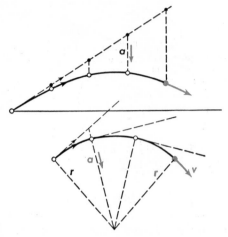

Fig. E. A diagram comparing circular motion to that of a projectile.

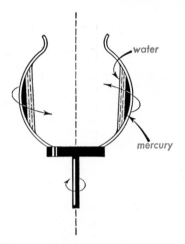

Fig. F. Mercury and water rotate in a dish, the water is inside the mercury. Centripetal force, like gravitational force, is greater for the more dense substance.

line-tangent along which it would travel if suddenly released.

The acceleration of a body toward the center of the circle in which it is moving is called the **centripetal acceleration** and is given by the relation

$$a = \frac{v^2}{r} \tag{6}$$

Centripetal force is defined as that constant force which acting continuously at right angles to the motion of a particle causes it to move in a circle with constant speed. Since by Newton's Second Law of Motion, **F = ma**, centripetal force is given by

$$F = m\frac{v^2}{r} \tag{7}$$

Example 1. A mass of 5 kg is moving with a speed of 6 m/sec in a circle of 2 m radius. Find the centripetal force.

Solution. The known quantities can be substituted directly into Eq. (7).

$$F = 5 \text{ kg} \frac{(6 \text{ m/sec})^2}{2 \text{ m}} = 90 \frac{\text{kg m}}{\text{sec}^2}$$

or

$$F = 90 \text{ newtons}$$

Experiments Demonstrating Centripetal Force. Many interesting experiments can be performed to illustrate centripetal force. In Fig. F mercury and water have been placed in a dish and the dish set rotating rapidly about a vertical axis. From Eq. (7) it is observed that **r** and **v** will be the same for both water and mercury and that **m** is different. Since mercury is 13.6 times heavier than an equal volume of water, the required centripetal force **F** must be 13.6 times greater for mercury. The mercury therefore takes the outermost position in the dish.

Although the earth is often said to be spherical, it is in reality an oblate spheroid, i.e., a slightly flattened sphere. Accurate measurements show that the earth's diameter is 28 mi greater through the equator than it is through the poles. The cause for this flattening is illustrated in Fig. G by two circular metal strips. Diagram (a) shows the strips round when at rest while (b) shows the flattening due to rapid rotation. The flattening of the earth is due to its own rotation of **2** π radians every 24 hr. It is the enormous size of the earth and its lack of greater rigidity that makes it behave as though it were soft and semiplastic.

The opening of the loop in a lariat as

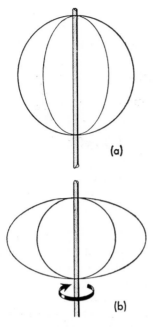

(a)

(b)

Fig. G. The flattening of the earth is due to its rotation about the polar axis.

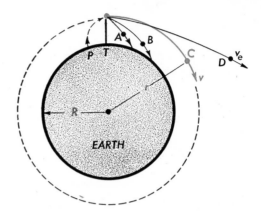

Fig. I. Illustrating the principles of rocket launching of earth satellites.

whirled and thrown by a cowboy is due to centripetal force. See Fig. H. Due to rotation each small section of the rope, acting as an individual mass **m**, tends to fly off on a tangent and thus get as far from the center of rotation as possible. The average distance from the center of all sections of the rope is a maximum when the loop takes the form of a circle rotating about an axis perpendicular to the plane of the loop.

Fig. H. A lariat takes a circular form because each small part tries to fly off on a tangent, thus getting as far from the center as possible. Centripetal force is responsible for keeping it in a circle.

Earth Satellites.   To understand the basic principles of a satellite propelled into an orbit around the earth by a rocket-launching process, consider the schematic diagram of Fig. I. Here we visualize a tower **T** reaching out beyond the earth's atmosphere and projectiles being fired in a horizontal direction at different velocities.

Projectile **A**, with its low initial velocity, follows a nearly parabolic path and falls to the ground a relatively short distance away. Projectile **B**, with its somewhat higher velocity, is also accelerated toward the earth's center but with considerably increased range.

Projectile **C**, with its higher velocity of almost 18,000 mi/hr, is also accelerated toward the earth's center, but it follows a curved path, keeping its distance from the center unchanged.

If **g** is the acceleration due to gravity at the earth's surface, Newton's Law of Gravitation says that the acceleration farther away is inversely proportional to the square of the distance. Calling this distance **r**, we can write

$$g_r = g \left(\frac{R}{r} \right)^2 \qquad (8)$$

This acceleration toward the earth's center is none other than the required centripetal acceleration of Eq. (6),

$$g_r = \frac{v^2}{r}$$

Upon equating the right sides of these equations, we obtain

$$g \frac{R^2}{r^2} = \frac{v^2}{r}$$

Upon canceling r on both sides, we find

$$g \frac{R^2}{r} = v^2$$

To move in a circular orbit a satellite must therefore have a velocity given by

$$v = \sqrt{g \frac{R^2}{r}} \qquad (9)$$

To put a satellite into orbit from the earth's surface the rocket takes off in a vertical direction from a point P in Fig. I. As the rocket's speed increases, guidance controls turn it gradually so that at the moment the fuel in the last stage is exhausted it has proper orbit speed and direction. The required precision with which this is done is extremely difficult to obtain.

Example 1. If the earth's radius is 6360 km, what horizontal speed must be imparted to a satellite to cause it to orbit in a circle 800 km (about 500 mi) above the earth's surface?

Solution. Since the acceleration due to gravity $g = 9.8$ m/sec², direct substitution in Eq. (9) gives

$$v = \sqrt{\frac{9.8 \times (6{,}360{,}000)^2}{7{,}160{,}000} \frac{m^2}{sec^2}}$$

$$v = \sqrt{55.4 \times 10^6 \frac{m^2}{sec^2}}$$

$$v = 7450 \frac{m}{sec}$$

This is equivalent to 16,700 mi/hr.

Escape Velocity. To escape from the earth's gravitational influence a projectile D in Fig. I must be given an initial velocity specified by this equation:

$$v_e = \sqrt{2g \frac{R^2}{r}} \qquad (10)$$

where v_e is called the **escape velocity**. At the earth's surface where $r = R$ this equation gives

$$v_e = 11{,}200 \frac{m}{sec}$$

which is about 25,000 mi/hr. By escape one means that the missile leaves the earth so far it is beyond a gravitational attraction that will bring it back again.

Summary

Angular measure in mechanics is most conveniently measured in radians rather than in degrees or revolutions. In so doing, all the equations of motion for rotation and translation have the same forms.

There are 2π radians in one complete circle, and angular velocity is measured in radians per second. An object moving along a circular path with constant speed has an acceleration toward the center given by

$$a = \frac{v^2}{r}$$

The force required to keep the object moving along its circular path is given by

$$F = m \frac{v^2}{r}$$

This centripetal force is always directed toward the center of the circle.

The flattening of the earth and the opening of the loop of a lariat are attributed to centripetal forces.

To "go into orbit" an earth satellite must be given a sufficiently high velocity **v** to make its centripetal acceleration v^2/r equal to the acceleration due to gravity g_r.

Questions

1. Define or briefly explain the meaning of each of the following: (a) radian, (b) centripetal acceleration, (c) centripetal force, (d) centrifugal force, and (e) angular velocity.

2. How many degrees are in one radian? How many radians are in 360°?

3. If you know the speed of rotation in revolutions per second, how do you find the angular velocity in radians per second?

4. How does one explain the fact that the diameter of the earth is 28 miles shorter through the poles than through the equator?

5. Can you explain how each link of a fast-rotating circular loop of chain obtains its required centripetal force to keep it moving in a circle? Is such a chain under tension when it is rotating?

6. Explain how an orbiting satellite can be continuously accelerated toward the earth and still maintain the same distance from the earth's center.

7. Devise some simple and inexpensive device for demonstrating centripetal and centrifugal forces.

Problems

1. An emery wheel rotates with a speed of 6000 rpm. What is the speed in (a) rps and (b) radians per second?

2. The engine of an automobile revolves with an angular speed of 4200 rpm. What is the speed of the rim of the attached flywheel if it is 1 ft in diameter?

3. A stone at the end of a string 50 cm long is whirled in a circle with a speed of 31.4 m/sec. Calculate the angular speed.

4. A mass of 2 kg is fastened to the end of a wire 40 cm long and whirled in a circle with an angular speed of 720 rpm. (a) Calculate the speed of the 2-kg mass. (b) Find the centripetal force.

5. A small lead weight of 2 lb is fastened to one end of a fine wire and whirled in a circle of 4-ft radius with a speed of 32 ft/sec. Find the centripetal force.

6. A mass of 50 gm is tied to one end of a string and whirled in a circle of 1-m radius with a speed of 12 m/sec. Calculate the centripetal force in newtons.

7. A weight of 2 lb is whirled at 60 rpm in a horizontal circle at the end of a cord 5 ft long. Neglecting gravity, what is the tension in the cord?

8.* A 3200-lb car making 60 mi/hr rounds a curve of 1000-ft radius. What is (a) the angular speed in rad/sec, (b) the centripetal acceleration, and (c) the centripetal force?

9.* A boy weighing 128 lb sits on the floor of a merry-go-round 20 ft from the center. If the coefficient of friction is 0.5, at what angular speed will he start to slide?

10.* A motorcycle and rider making 72 km/hr round a curve of 100-m radius. (a) What is the centripetal acceleration? (b) At what angle will they lean from the vertical?

11. A pail held at arm's length is swung overhead in a circle of 1-m radius. What is the minimum speed at the top to assure that no water spills out?

12.* Calculate the speed of a satellite launched into a circular orbit 100 miles above the earth's surface. Assume the earth's radius to be 4000 miles.

13.* What is the speed of an earth satellite launched into a circular orbit 1000 miles above the earth's surface? Assume the earth's radius to be 4000 miles.

14.* Find the escape velocity of a space missile as it leaves a point 500 miles above the earth's surface.

15.* What is the escape velocity required of a space ship if no more fuel is burned after it reaches an altitude of 1000 miles?

Mechanics | **Lesson 40**

CENTRIPETAL FORCE—*Laboratory*

This laboratory experiment is described in the accompanying LABORA-TORY EXERCISES and involves a special piece of apparatus. A known mass, attached to the end of a spring, is whirled in a circle. The centripetal force is then calculated from the measured rotational speed, and compared with the static force required to stretch the spring by the same amount.

Mechanics | **Lesson 41**

DYNAMICS OF ROTATION

When a rigid body is acted upon by a unbalanced torque, it is set into rotation. Free to turn about an axis, such a body increases in angular velocity acquiring, when the torque ceases to act, some final speed. See Fig. A.

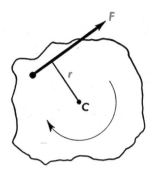

Fig. A. A rigid body is acted upon by a torque, F × r.

Angular Acceleration. Just as the acceleration of a body in linear motion is defined as the rate of change of velocity, so *the angular acceleration of a body in rotation is defined as the rate of change of angular velocity.*

By comparison these two definitions are expressed the same mathematically.

$$a = \frac{v - v_0}{t} \qquad \alpha = \frac{\omega - \omega_0}{t}$$

linear   angular

The angular acceleration α is analogous to the linear acceleration a, while the initial angular velocity ω_0 is analogous to v_0, and the final angular velocity ω is analogous to v.

If objects start from rest, these two defining equations reduce to

$$a = \frac{v}{t} \qquad \alpha = \frac{\omega}{t} \qquad (1)$$

linear   angular

Upon transferring t to the other side of each equation, we obtain

$$v = at \qquad \omega = \alpha t \qquad (2)$$

linear   angular

A similar comparison between linear velocity and angular velocity is to be noted in the equations

$$v = \frac{s}{t} \qquad \omega = \frac{\theta}{t} \qquad (3)$$

linear   angular

The following example will illustrate the meaning of, as well as an application of, the above angular formulas.

Example 1. A flywheel starting from rest acquires a speed of 240 rpm in 10 sec. Find the angular acceleration.

Solution. The final velocity in radians per second is calculated by use of Eq. (3). Since there are 2π radians in 1 revolution

$$\omega = \frac{2\pi \times 240}{60} = 25.1 \frac{rad}{sec}$$

To find the angular acceleration, use Eq. (1).

$$\alpha = \frac{25.1 \ rad/sec}{10 \ sec} = 2.51 \frac{rad}{sec^2}$$

This is read two point five one radians per second per second.

It is clear from the above formulas that the quantities **s**, **v**, and **a** in the linear equations have only to be replaced by the corresponding angular quantities θ, ω, and α to obtain the angular equations. This direct correspondence is the result of using the radian as a unit of angular measure and holds throughout all of the formulas in mechanics.

The relation between linear quantities measured around any given circle to the angular quantities describing the same motion are shown in Fig. B and given by the following interrelations.

$s = r\theta$	(4)
$v = r\omega$	(5)
$a = r\alpha$	(6)

Kinematics of Rotation. The term kinematics of rotation refers to a quantitative description of motion such as that given above.

Fig. B. A wheel free to rotate about its center is given an angular acceleration.

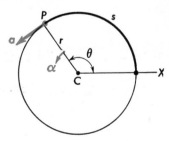

To complete the customary set of formulas for circular motion we need only write down the four linear equations used so many times in the preceding lessons and their rotational counterparts as follows:

$v = at$	$\omega = \alpha t$	(7)
$s = \dfrac{v}{2}\,t$	$\theta = \dfrac{\omega}{2}\,t$	(8)
$v^2 = 2\,as$	$\omega^2 = 2\,\alpha\theta$	(9)
$s = \frac{1}{2}\,at^2$	$\theta = \frac{1}{2}\,\alpha t^2$	(10)

Example 2. An automobile engine starting from rest is given an angular acceleration of 20 rad/sec² for 10 sec. Find (a) the angular velocity acquired, (b) the total angle turned through, and (c) the total number of revolutions.

Solution. The given quantities are $\alpha =$ 20 rad/sec, and $t = 10$ sec. To find the angular velocity ω, use Eq. (7).

(a) $\qquad \omega = 20\,\dfrac{rad}{sec^2} \times 10\ sec = 200\,\dfrac{rad}{sec}$

To find the angle θ use Eq. (8) or Eq. (10). Using Eq. (8), we find

(b) $\qquad \theta = \dfrac{200\ rad/sec}{2} \times 10\ sec$

$\qquad \theta = 1000\ rad$

To find the number of revolutions, divide by 2π

(c) $\qquad \theta = \dfrac{1000\ rad}{2\pi} = 159\ rev$

Dynamics of Rotation. In the treatment of angular acceleration given in the preceding sections of this lesson, neither the torques causing the acceleration nor the mass of the rotating body entered into the calculations. When these two factors are introduced into the equations, the treatment is referred to as the **dynamics of rotation.**

When a specified torque is applied to a body free to rotate about some axis, the angular acceleration produced depends not only

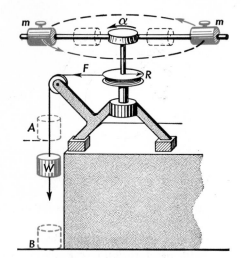

Fig. C. An experimental demonstration of moment of inertia.

upon the size and shape of the body but also upon the distribution of the mass with respect to the axis of rotation.

To see how these factors are taken into account, consider the simplest kind of an example, namely, two identical masses m on a crossbar and free to rotate about a vertical axis as shown in Fig. C. The cord wrapped around the drum R and passing over a pulley to the weight W gives rise to a constant force F and hence a constant torque to angularly accelerate the system.

When the masses are clamped at equal distances from and half way out on the arms, the angular acceleraton is relatively large, and the weight W exerting the constant torque L quickly drops from A to B. When the masses m are moved to the outer ends of the arms where their distance r is doubled, the angular acceleration is reduced to $\frac{1}{4}$ and the weight W takes 2 times as long to go from A to B.

We see by this experiment that under the action of a constant torque the angular acceleration depends upon the distribution of the mass with respect to the axis of rotation. This is not analogous to linear motion since a constant force F applied to a mass m will produce a constant acceleration a independent of the shape of the body. To retain the

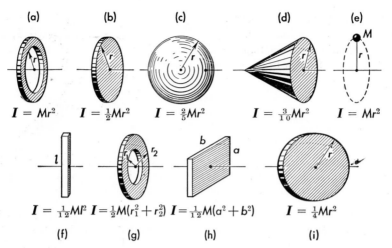

$I = Mr^2$ $I = \frac{1}{2}Mr^2$ $I = \frac{2}{5}Mr^2$ $I = \frac{3}{10}Mr^2$ $I = Mr^2$

$I = \frac{1}{12}Ml^2$ $I = \frac{1}{2}M(r_1^2 + r_2^2)$ $I = \frac{1}{12}M(a^2 + b^2)$ $I = \frac{1}{4}Mr^2$

(a)   (b)   (c)   (d)   (e)

(f)   (g)   (h)   (i)

Fig. D. Formulas for the moment of inertia of certain regularly shaped bodies.

similarity between linear and rotational formulas we write

$$\boxed{\begin{array}{cc} F = ma & L = I\alpha \\ \text{linear} & \text{angular} \end{array}} \quad (11)$$

and thereby introduce a new quantity I called the **moment of inertia**. The moment of inertia I in rotary motion takes the shape and mass into account and is analogous to m in the force equation.

Moment of Inertia. The true moments of inertia of a number of regular shaped solid bodies are given in Fig. D. Diagram (a) represents a thin ring or hoop of radius r, (b) a disk of uniform density, (c) a solid sphere with an axis through the center, etc.

Two common moments of inertia not given in the figure are

spherical shell, very thin—around any diameter,

$$I = \frac{2}{3} Mr^2$$

uniform ring—around any diameter,

$$I = \frac{1}{4} M(r_1^2 + r_2^2)$$

Kinetic Energy of Rotation. When a body is in a state of rotation, it possesses kinetic energy. It possesses this energy because in being brought to rest it may be made to do work. To calculate the amount of energy stored up in a rotating body, an equation analogous to the linear equation is used.

$$\boxed{\begin{array}{cc} \text{K.E.} = \frac{1}{2} mv^2 & \text{K.E.} = \frac{1}{2} I\omega^2 \\ \text{linear} & \text{angular} \end{array}} \quad (12)$$

As might well be expected, the moment of inertia I enters into the rotational energy.

Example. A large grindstone with a mass of 20 kg and radius 50 cm is rotating with an angular speed of 300 rpm. Calculate its kinetic energy.

Solution. The given quantities are $\omega = 300$ rpm and $M = 20$ kg. To use Eq. (12) we must first calculate I and then ω. From diagram (b) in Fig. D we find

$$I = \frac{1}{2} Mr^2$$
$$I = \frac{1}{2} 20 \text{ kg} \times (.5 \text{ m})^2$$
$$I = 2.5 \text{ kg m}^2$$

Dividing 300 rpm by 60 we obtain an angular velocity $\omega = 5$ rps. Multiplying by 2π, we find $\omega = 31.4$ rad/sec. Using Eq. (12), we can now substitute, to find

$$\text{K.E.} = \frac{1}{2} I\omega^2$$
$$\text{K.E.} = \frac{1}{2} 2.5 \text{ kg m}^2 \times (31.4 \text{ rad/sec})^2$$
$$\text{K.E.} = 1230 \frac{\text{kg m}^2}{\text{sec}^2}$$
$$\text{K.E.} = 1230 \text{ joules}$$

Summary

The dynamic equations for rotation are identical in form to the dynamic equations for motion along a straight line. In all rotational equations

s becomes θ

v becomes ω

a becomes α

m becomes I

F becomes L

The one complication that arises in rotational motion is that of I, the moment of inertia. While the change in shape of a given body or system of bodies does not change its total mass, its moment of inertia about the axis of rotation can change greatly.

The moment of inertia of a body depends upon the mass as well as upon the distribution of the mass with respect to the axis of rotation. A rotating body has kinetic energy $\frac{1}{2} I \omega^2$.

Questions

1. Define angular acceleration. What are the units of angular acceleration in the mks system?

2. What is meant by the kinematics of rotation? By the dynamics of rotation?

3. Newton's Second Law of Motion is generally represented by the force equation $F = ma$. What is the rotational counterpart?

4. What is the meaning of moment of inertia? What determines the moment of inertia of a body? To what property does it correspond in linear motion?

5. What is the formula for the kinetic energy of a rotating body? What are the units of rotational kinetic energy in the mks system? What are the units of linear motion?

6. Without altering its mass, how can the moment of inertia of a body be increased? How can it be decreased?

7. A uniform disk, a solid ball, and a metal hoop all have the same mass and diameter. Which one has the largest moment of inertia? Which one has the smallest?

8. Think of some simple inexpensive device you could make for demonstrating some of the principles introduced in this lesson.

Problems

1. Starting from rest the large flywheel of a steam engine acquires a speed of 450 rpm in one minute. Find the angular acceleration in rad/sec².

2. An automobile engine is idling at 300 rpm. Upon acceleration it acquires a speed of 3000 rpm in 2 sec. Calculate (a) the angular acceleration and (b) the angle turned through during the acceleration.

3. An emery wheel one foot in diameter in making 3600 rpm. Find (a) the tangential velocity of a point on the rim, and (b) the distance traveled in 5 sec by a point midway between the rim and center.

4. Starting from rest a grindstone acquires a speed of 1200 rpm in 5 sec. Find (a) the angular acceleration, and (b) the total number of revolutions.

5. Calculate the moment of inertia of an emery wheel that has a mass of 4 kg and a diameter of 40 cm.

6. A uniform solid ball has a mass of 6 kg and a diameter of 30 cm. Calculate (a) its moment of inertia and (b) its kinetic energy if rotating about an axis through its center at 6 rps.

7. A uniform ring of 5-kg mass has an internal diameter of 16 cm and an external diameter of 20 cm. Find its moment of inertia.

8. A uniform rod 50 cm long has a mass of 1 kg. Find its moment of inertia about an axis through its center.

9. A uniform disk of 1-m radius and 5-kg mass rotates about its center at 5 rad/sec. Calculate its kinetic energy.

10.* A solid ball with a mass of 100 kg and radius 50 cm rotates about an axis through its center at 4 rps. Find its kinetic energy in joules.

11.* An emery wheel 30 cm in diameter and 2-kg mass rotates at 3000 rpm. Find (a) its moment of inertia and (b) its kinetic energy.

Mechanics | **Lesson 42**

CONSERVATION OF ANGULAR MOMENTUM

In our previous lessons on rotating bodies we have seen that by expressing all angles in radian measure, rather than in degrees, the various formulas for angular motion became identical in form with the corresponding linear formulas. It is the purpose of this lesson to extend our study of the mechanics of rotation to include angular momentum.

Angular Momentum. We have seen that when a constant force **F** is applied to a mass **m** for a period of time **t**, the velocity **v** it acquires is given by the impulse equation

$$Ft = mv \qquad (1)$$

A comparison of such motion with its rotational counterpart is shown in Fig. A. If we

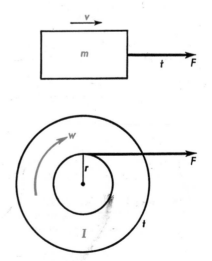

Fig. A. Comparison of linear motion with rotational motion.

replace the linear symbols in Eq. (1) by those for rotational motion, we obtain

$$Lt = I\omega \qquad (2)$$

where ω is the angular velocity, I is the moment of inertia, and L is the torque given by $F \times r$. In linear motion Ft is the impulse and mv the momentum. In rotational motion Lt is the angular impulse and $I\omega$ the angular momentum.

Example 1. The wheel of a grindstone (see Fig. A) has applied at its axle, 2 cm in radius, a constant tangential force of 600 newtons. Find the angular momentum acquired at the end of 8 sec.

Solution. Begin by calculating the torque L.

$$L = F \times r$$
$$L = 600 \times 0.02$$
$$L = 12 \text{ newton meters}$$

By direct substitution in Eq. (2) we finally obtain

$$Lt = 12 \times 8 = I\omega$$
$$I\omega = 96 \text{ newton m sec}$$

Consider the case of a mass m on the end of a string, rotating in a circle as shown in Fig. B. The moment of inertia of this mass is given by Mr^2. (See Fig. D, diagram (e), p. 147.)

$$I = Mr^2$$

Fig. B. A ball of mass m whirling in a circle at the end of a string has an angular momentum mvr.

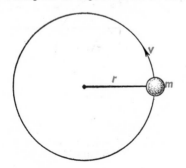

In a previous lesson we have also seen that the angular velocity ω is given by v/r

$$\omega = \frac{v}{r}$$

Therefore, the angular momentum $I\omega$ of this special case is given by

$$I\omega = Mr^2 \times \frac{v}{r} \qquad (3)$$

$$I\omega = Mvr \qquad (3)$$

Conservation of Angular Momentum. Just as there is a law of conservation of momentum for bodies moving in a straight line, so also is there a law of conservation of angular momentum for bodies in rotation. This law can best be illustrated by an experiment as shown in Fig. C.

Fig. C. Experimental demonstration of the conservation of angular momentum.

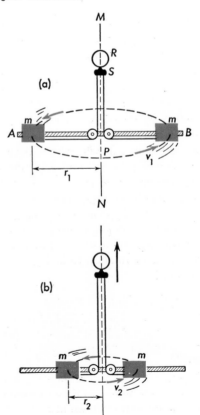

Two equal masses **m** are mounted on a rod **AB** capable of rotation about a vertical axis **MN**. Cords fastened to each mass and leading over pulleys at **P** to the ring **R** enable the radial distance to be changed from r_1 in (a) to r_2 in (b) by simply pulling up on the ring **R**. The swivel **S** prevents the cords from twisting.

When the system is first set rotating as in (a) with an angular velocity ω_1, the angular momentum of each mass is $I_1\omega_1$. On pulling up on the ring **R** the radius decreases to r_2 and the angular velocity ω_2 increases. Conservation of angular momentum requires that, for each mass **m**,

$$I_1\omega_1 = I_2\omega_2 \qquad (4)$$

Since this particular demonstration involves masses rotating as shown in Fig. B, Eq. (3) can be invoked and we can write

$$Mv_1r_1 = Mv_2r_2 \qquad (5)$$

Conservation of angular momentum therefore requires the product of these three quantities to remain constant. We can readily see, therefore, that if **r** decreases, **v** must increase, while if **r** increases, **v** must decrease.

Gyroscopic Stability. If a balanced gyroscope wheel is mounted in gimbal rings as shown in Fig. D, it will, when set spinning at high speed, exhibit a property called "gyroscopic stability." When the gyro is picked up and carried about, the base can be turned in any direction without altering the direction of the spin axis relative to the earth. In other words, the plane of the gyro wheel seems to have assumed a rigidity in space.

To change the direction of the "spin axis" a torque must be exerted upon it. It is the function of the gimbal ring mounting to allow the base support to be turned in any way without exerting any torque whatever upon the wheel.

Newton's First Law of Motion, involving the inertia of a body, has its rotational counterpart in the above experiment.

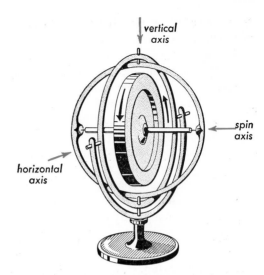

Fig. D. Gyroscope mounted in gimbal rings for demonstrating gyroscopic stability.

A body in rotation about some fixed axis will continue to rotate about that same axis with constant speed unless it is acted upon by an unbalanced torque.

An interesting experiment illustrating the same principle is diagramed in Fig. E. An observer stands on a turntable with weights in each hand. With arms fully extended horizontally he is first set rotating slowly. Upon drawing the hands and weights in toward the chest as shown, the angular speed is considerably increased. This experiment is best appreciated by the turning observer who feels

Fig. E. Experiments illustrating conservation of angular momentum.

himself speeded up by what seems to be a mysterious force.

The kinetic energy of rotation in each of these two experiments increases as the masses are pulled in closer to the center of rotation. This increase is due to the fact that work, equal to force times distance, must be done to pull them in.

This principle is used by expert figure skaters on the ice. They start into a whirl with their arms, and perhaps one leg extended, and then upon drawing the arms and leg in they obtain a greatly increased angular speed.

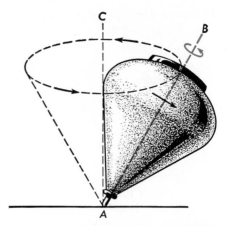

Fig. F. A spinning top precesses around a vertical axis.

The Spinning Top. A common top, set spinning like the one shown in Fig. F, is a good illustration of angular momentum. It is but one of the many forms of gyroscopes. Spinning about its axis the top precesses about its peg or pivot point, the line **AB** describing an inverted cone about the vertical line **AC**. If when looking down from above, such a top is spinning in a clockwise direction the precession is clockwise; spinning counterclockwise the precession is counterclockwise.

Summary

All rotating bodies have angular momentum, which is given by the product of the moment of inertia by the angular velocity.

If while a body is in rotation, any or all of its parts alter their positions in any way relative to the axis of revolution, and no external torques are brought into action, the total angular momentum will remain unchanged.

A spinning top is one form of gyroscope. Because of the gravitational force on a top or gyroscope it will precess around a vertical axis. If no external torques are applied to a freely rotating body, it will not precess but, following Newton's First Law of Motion, it will continue rotating about the same axis with constant angular speed.

Moment of inertia is a quantitative measure of rotational inertia.

Questions

1. State the law of conservation of angular momentum. How is angular momentum determined? Upon what two factors does it depend?

2. What is an angular impulse?

3. Under what conditions does the law of conservation of angular momentum apply? Does it apply to the motion of the moon around the earth?

4. What is inertia? What is rotational inertia? Since mass is a quantitative measure of inertia, what quantity is a measure of rotational inertia?

5. What is a gyroscope? Should a gyroscope have a large moment of inertia? If so, why?

6. Why should the wheel of a gyroscope be well balanced?

7. What is precession? Where is it observed?

8. Two equal weights are tied to the ends of a string and a bowknot tied in the string. Shortly after the two are thrown spinning into the air the bowknot comes untied. What happens to the angular velocity and the angular momentum?

9. Devise some simple and inexpensive device you could make to demonstrate conservation of angular momentum.

Problems

1. A 4-lb ball at the end of a wire 5 ft long is whirled in a circle with a speed of 20 ft/sec. Calculate its (a) moment of inertia and (b) angular momentum.

2. A 500-gm stone at the end of a string 50 cm long is whirled in a circle with a speed of 3 m/sec. Calculate its angular momentum.

3. A 4-kg mass is fastened to the end of a thin wire 3 m long and whirled in a circle with an angular speed of 4 rps. Calculate its angular momentum.

4.* A solid ball of mass 5 kg and diameter 20 cm is rotating about an axis through its center. If the angular speed is 5 rps, find the angular momentum.

5.* An emery wheel in the form of a disk has a mass of 4 kg and a diameter of 30 cm. If it is turning at 1200 rpm, what is its angular momentum?

6.* A 10-kg solid ball, with a 30-cm diameter, rotates around an axis through its center at 5000 rad/sec. Find the angular momentum.

7.* The rotating parts of an automobile motor have a moment of inertia equivalent to that of a uniform disk 1 ft in diameter and weighing 64 lb. (a) What is its moment of inertia in slugs ft²? (b) Find its angular momentum when rotating at 6000 rpm.

Mechanics | **Lesson 43**

MOMENT OF INERTIA—*Laboratory*

This laboratory experiment is described in the accompanying *LABORA-TORY EXERCISES* and is aimed at the experimental determination of the moments of inertia of several regularly shaped bodies. The apparatus is simple and is inexpensively constructed in any average school or home shop.

ATOMIC THEORY OF MATTER

In dealing with the physical properties of matter it is convenient to divide substances into three forms or states: (1) **the solid state,** (2) **the liquid state,** and (3) **the gaseous state.** Most substances may be made to take on any one of these three forms simply by altering the temperature.

The atomic theory of matter assumes that all matter in the universe is made up of ultramicroscopic particles called atoms and that these are at all times in a rapid state of motion. The nature of this motion and its activity depends upon the temperature and the state of the matter in question, as well as upon the kinds of atoms of which it is composed.

Kinds of Atoms. Although there are thousands of different substances known to the scientific world they all, when broken down into their smallest component parts, are found to be composed of one or more kinds of atoms. A substance which contains atoms of one kind only is called an **element,** while those containing more than one kind are called **compounds** or **mixtures.** Iron, aluminum, platinum, mercury, hydrogen, and helium are examples of elements; whereas water, salt, brass, wood, and air are examples of compounds and mixtures.

The technical names and chemical abbreviations of a few of the more commonly known elements are given in Table 1. A complete table of the nearly one hundred known elements is given in the Appendix.

With each element it is customary to associate two numbers: one is called the **atomic number,** the other the **atomic weight.** The atomic number, given at the left in the tables, specifies the position that element always occupies with respect to all the others, while

Table 1. Some of the Chemical Elements

Atomic No.	Element	Symbol	Atomic Weight
1	hydrogen	H	1.0078
2	helium	He	4.004
3	lithium	Li	6.940
4	beryllium	Be	9.02
6	carbon	C	12.01
7	nitrogen	N	14.01
8	oxygen	O	16.000
10	neon	Ne	20.183
13	aluminum	Al	26.97
26	iron	Fe	55.84
50	tin	Sn	118.70
78	platinum	Pt	195.23
79	gold	Au	197.2
80	mercury	Hg	200.61
82	lead	Pb	207.18
88	radium	Ra	225.95
92	uranium	U	238.17
94	plutonium	Pu	239.18

the atomic weight on the right gives the average weight of one atom of that element relative to the average weight of an oxygen atom as sixteen. On this basis the atom of the lightest known element, hydrogen, has an average weight of approximately unity.

Atomic weights increase with increasing atomic number, the four exceptions being 18-argon, 28-nickel, 53-iodine, and 91-protoactinium.

To illustrate the minuteness of individual atoms, the actual masses in grams and approximate diameters in centimeters of the lightest element, hydrogen, and the very heavy element, plutonium, are as follows:

$$1. \text{ hydrogen} \begin{cases} \text{mass} = 1.66 \times 10^{-24} \text{ gm} \\ \text{diameter} = 1 \times 10^{-8} \text{ cm} \end{cases}$$

94. plutonium $\begin{cases} \text{mass} = 3.9 \times 10^{-22} \text{ gm} \\ \text{diameter} = 6 \times 10^{-8} \text{ cm} \end{cases}$

The actual mass of any atom in grams can be obtained by multiplying the atomic weight of that element by the unit atomic mass 1.66×10^{-24} gm.

Although the intricate structure of each atom plays an important part in its physical and chemical behavior, we will neglect this detailed structure for the time being and think only of each atom as being a tiny sphere-like particle with a very small mass. Later in other lessons where it is pertinent to do so the structure of individual atoms will be considered in detail.

Molecules. One of the most important properties of atoms is their ability to act upon one another at a distance. Some atoms, when they come close together, attract each other, while others exhibit a force of repulsion. When, at the close approach of two or more atoms, attraction occurs, the atoms may combine to form a molecule. Once a molecule has formed it will move about and behave as a unit particle under various physical conditions.

Molecules in general may contain almost any number of atoms. Those having but one atom are called **monatomic molecules,** those with two are called **diatomic molecules,** and those with three **triatomic molecules.** In the free state of a gas some atoms, like helium, neon, and krypton, prefer to exist alone; whereas others, like hydrogen, nitrogen, and oxygen prefer to combine and move about in pairs.

Examples of monatomic molecules are helium (He), neon (Ne), and krypton (Kr); of diatomic molecules are hydrogen (H_2), nitrogen (N_2), oxygen (O_2), and carbon monoxide (CO); and of triatomic molecules are ozone (O_3), carbon dioxide (CO_2), water (H_2O), and hydro-cyanic acid (HCN). See Fig. A. Besides these simplest atomic aggregates there are molecules known to contain many atoms. Along with triatomic molecules they are called polyatomic molecules.

It is clear from the diagrams in Fig. A that the atoms of a molecule may be of the same

Fig. A. Schematic diagrams of a few common molecules. First Row. Helium, neon, hydrogen, nitrogen, oxygen, carbon monoxide, hydrochloric acid. Second Row. Ozone, carbon dioxide, water, hydrocyanic acid. Third Row. Methane, acetylene, benzine, methyl alcohol, ethyl alcohol.

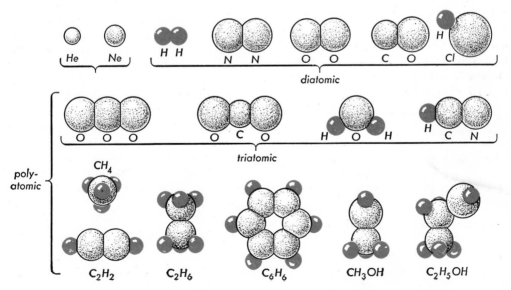

Fig. B. The forces between atoms in a molecule behave like springs.

kind or different. The question as to why some atoms cling together in pairs and others do not is a subject involving the structure of the atoms themselves. If the individual atoms of a molecule are brought much closer together than their normal separation, they repel each other and are pushed apart. If they are pulled farther apart, the forces become attractive, pulling them together. In other words, they act as though they were connected by springs as shown in Fig. B. Pushed closer together or pulled farther apart, they tend to move back to some equilibrium distance. In terms of energy they occupy a position of **minimum potential energy.** To push them closer together or to separate them requires work.

At large distances all atomic forces become very weak so that if by some means or other the atoms of a molecule are pulled far enough apart they become completely separated as free atoms. A graph of the forces between atoms is shown in Fig. C. The horizontal scale giving the distance *r* between atoms will be slightly different for different atoms, but the equilibrium position **E** is approximately 3×10^{-10} meters.

Fig. C. Typical graph of the force between the two atoms of a diatomic molecule.

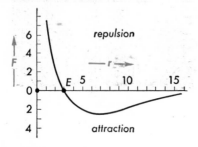

Molecular Weight. The molecular weight of a substance is defined as the sum of the atomic weights of the atoms which make up one molecule of that substance. A carbon dioxide molecule, for example, has two oxygen atoms of weight 16 and one carbon atom of weight 12. The molecular weight of carbon dioxide is therefore $16 + 16 + 12 = 44$. Similarly the molecular weight of nitrogen is 28, oxygen is 32, and helium is 4. To find the mass of a molecule in grams, its molecular weight should be multiplied by unit atomic mass 1.66×10^{-24} gm.

Three States of Matter. As already stated, matter may exist in three states: (1) the solid state, (2) the liquid state, and (3) the gaseous state. If a solid is heated sufficiently, it can be made to melt or liquefy, and by continued heating can be boiled or vaporized. As a vapor it is in the gaseous state. If, on the other hand, a gas is cooled sufficiently, it will condense and become a liquid. The continued cooling of a liquid will cause it to solidify or freeze. In the case of water, nature performs all these changes of state: ice is melted to become water, and water is vaporized to become steam; water vapor or clouds condense to become rain, and rain freezes to become ice or hail. Although it may sometimes require extreme heat or extreme cold, all substances can be transformed from any one state to another.

Brownian Motion. Although no one has ever observed directly the random motions of molecules, it is possible to observe in a microscope the resultant recoils of larger particles under their continual bombardment. The effect was first discovered in 1827 by Robert Brown, a British botanist, who observed the irregular but lifelike motions of small particles suspended in a liquid. These microscopic particles appear to be continually agitated and make a succession of quick jumps first one way and then another. Such

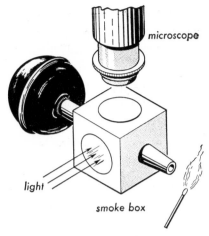

Fig. D. Experimental arrangement for observing the Brownian motion of smoke particles.

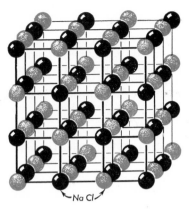

Fig. E. Atomic model for sodium chloride (NaCl is common table salt).

motions are called Brownian movements, after the name of their discoverer.

One method of observing Brownian motion in a gas is illustrated in Fig. D. Smoke from the tip of a match, just extinguished, is drawn into a small box by squeezing and releasing the rubber bulb. A strong beam of light from an arc light, entering the box through a glass lens in the side, illuminates the smoke particles, enabling them to be seen from above with a high power microscope. The tiny smoke particles appear as bright starlike points darting first one way then another.

The Solid State. As the temperature of a liquid is lowered, the molecular activity decreases. This permits the atoms to pack a little more closely together and accounts for the slight contraction of a liquid on cooling, and conversely for its expansion on heating. As they come closer and closer together, the tendency of each atom to wander through the liquid decreases. If the temperature is lowered still further, a point is ultimately reached where the liquid freezes and becomes a solid.

In the solid state each atom is confined to a definite small space between neighboring atoms. This is illustrated in Fig. E by an atomic model of an ultramicroscopic crystal. The model illustrates a cubic lattice, a simple type of structure in which the atoms take positions at the corners of cubes. Common table salt with its two kinds of atoms, sodium and chlorine, always forms such a cubic lattice, the individual atoms alternating in kind in each of the three directions, Na, Cl, Na, Cl. Na, etc.

Actual photographs of two crystals shown in Fig. F clearly show the tendency for substances to take on regular forms upon solidifying. Quartz is composed of silicon and oxygen, while calcite is composed of calcium, carbon, and oxygen.

Fig. F. Natural crystals of quartz and calcite.

Summary

All matter is said to exist in one of three states: solid, liquid, and gas. There are some one hundred known kinds of atoms called elements. Atoms may be combined into molecules, called compounds or mixtures.

Elements are generally listed according to their atomic number and atomic weight. With but few exceptions, increasing atomic number is accompanied by increasing atomic weight.

Molecules may be classified as monatomic, diatomic, triatomic, or polyatomic.

Under a microscope small particles can be seen dancing about as the result of recoiling from molecular impacts. This is called Brownian motion.

In the solid state, atoms take on regular and systematic arrays. This is called crystal structure.

Oftentimes lattice arrays of the solid are partially retained in the liquid state.

Questions

1. What are the three states of matter? How do these states differ from each other? Which, in general, is the most compact?

2. How many known elements are there? What constitutes an element?

3. What is meant by (a) atomic number and (b) atomic weight?

4. Give an example of a (a) monatomic molecule, (b) diatomic molecule, (c) triatomic molecule, and (d) polyatomic molecule.

5. What general treatment of most solids will change their state to the liquid or gas?

6. What is Brownian motion? How is it observed?

7. What can you say about the arrangement of atoms in a solid, like iron? In a solid like common table salt?

8. How could you set up an experiment to demonstrate the forces between the atoms of a linear triatomic molecule? If you were to push the outer atoms of a molecule toward each other and suddenly release them, what kind of motion do you think would ensue?

PROPERTIES
OF MATTER

Proposition 7. *A solid heavier than a fluid will, if placed in it, descend to the bottom of the fluid, and the solid will, when weighed in the fluid, be lighter than its true weight by the weight of the fluid displaced.*

Archimedes, *On Floating Bodies, Book I*

Proposition 1. *If a solid lighter than a fluid be at rest in it, the weight of the solid will be to that of the same volume of the fluid as the immersed portion of the solid is to the whole.*

Archimedes, *On Floating Bodies, Book II*

Or take a Wire string of twenty, or thirty, or forty foot long, and fasten the upper part thereof to a nail, and to the other end fasten a Scale to receive the weights: Then with a pair of Compasses take the distance of the bottom of the scale from the ground or floor underneath, and set down the said distance, then put in weights into the said scale in the same manner as in the former trials, and measure the several stretchings of the said string, and set them down. Then compare the several stretchings of the said string, and you will find that they will always bear the same proportions one to the other that the weights do that made them.

Robert Hooke, *POTENTIA RESTITUTIVA, or Spring*, London, 1678.

← The elasticity and toughness of plastic used in the making of safety glass is demonstrated by the impact of a man's arm. Various materials encountered in our daily living possess properties which have made them suitable for their special use.

Libby-Owen-Ford Glass Company

Elasticity

I N THE FOLLOWING treatment of elasticity the **gram** and **kilogram** are frequently treated as units of force. Such usage is justified since the actual applied forces are directly proportional to the masses that produce them.

$$W \propto m$$

We therefore introduce the **gram weight** and **kilogram weight** (*abbr.* gm-wt and kg-wt) as units of force.

One kilogram weight is defined as a force equivalent in magnitude to the downward pull of the earth on a one kilogram mass.

$$W = mg$$

One gram weight is defined as a force equivalent in magnitude to the downward pull of the earth on a one gram mass.

Fig. A. Experiment illustrating Hooke's law.

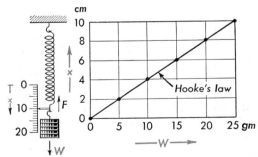

Stretching of a Spring. If a vertically mounted rod, wire, or spring is supported rigidly at its upper end and weights are added to its lower end, the amount by which it is stretched is found to be proportional to the weight applied. This is known as **Hooke's Law.** The stretching of a spring is illustrated in Fig. A. Due to an added weight **W** the spring is stretched a distance **x**. If a second equal weight is added, the total distance stretched will be twice that for the first one. If a third weight is added, the total distance stretched will be three times that for the first one, etc. This is illustrated by the graph shown at the right in Fig. A. Each value of **x** is plotted vertically and the corresponding loads **W** are plotted horizontally.

More specifically, when the first 10 gram weight is added the stretch or elongation is 2 cm. With two 10 gram weights the total elongation is 4 cm, and with three weights **x** = 6 cm, etc. A continuation of this shows, as does the graph at the right in Fig. A, that each 10 gram weight produces an added elongation of 2 cm. To make an equation of this we write

$$W = kx \qquad (1)$$

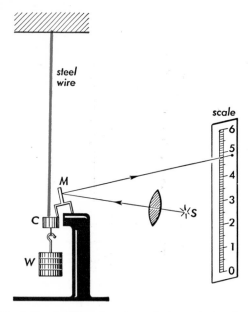

Fig. B. The stretching of a wire under increasing tension can be measured by an *optical lever.*

der to check Hooke's law, resort to some method of measuring extremely small changes in length. This is frequently done by means of a device known as the optical lever. As shown by the experiment diagramed in Fig. B, a beam of light is reflected from a small mirror **M** mounted on a small three-legged stool, two legs of which rest on a stationary platform, as shown, and the third on a small clamp **C** at the lower end of the wire. As the wire stretches under an added weight **W**, the mirror tips back and the light beam is reflected up a measurable amount on the distant scale.

Like the stretching of a spring described in the preceding section, the stretching of a wire obeys Hooke's law. The amount stretched is directly proportional to the force applied and is illustrated by the straight part of the graph **AP** in Fig. C. If the weights are removed, the wire will return to its original length. If weights are continually added, the forces applied will eventually become too great, and Hooke's law will no longer hold as the elongation will increase too rapidly. This is the region **EP** on the graph. Carried too far in this direction, the wire will break. The point **E** at which Hooke's law ceases to hold is called the *elastic limit*. If the wire is stretched beyond this point it will be permanently stretched and will not return to its original length when the weights are removed.

where **k** is a constant and equal in this experiment to 5. Each value of **x** multiplied by 5 gives the corresponding weight **W**. When the spring in Fig. A is stretched a distance **x** the spring itself exerts an upward force **F** equal but opposite in direction to **W**. For the spring, then,

$$F = -kx \qquad (2)$$

The minus sign indicates that **x** and **F** are in opposite directions. This equation is often referred to as Hooke's law.*

The Stretching of a Wire. Because a wire or rod will not stretch very far before reaching the breaking point, one must, in or-

* Robert Hooke (1635-1703), English experimental physicist known principally for his contributions to the wave theory of light, universal gravitation, and atmospheric pressure. He originated many physical ideas but perfected few of them. Hooke's scientific achievements would undoubtedly have received greater acclaim had his efforts been confined to fewer subjects. He had an irritable temper, and made many virulent attacks on Newton and other men of science, claiming that work published by them was due to him.

Fig. C. A graph of the stretching of a wire showing Hooke's law, the elastic limit, and the breaking point.

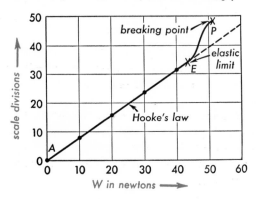

Stress and Strain. When a force of any magnitude is applied to a solid body, the body becomes distorted. Whether the distortion is large or small, some portion of the body is moved with respect to some neighboring portion. As a result of this displacement atomic forces of attraction or repulsion set up restoring forces which resist the alteration and tend to restore the body to its original shape. The greater the applied force the greater will be the deformation, thereby setting up greater atomic restoring forces acting to bring about equilibrium.

It is common engineering practice to describe the restoring forces in a distorted body as a **stress** and to give to this term the quantitative definition of **force per unit area**. The actual deformation of the body produced by an applied force involves a change in geometrical form called **strain**. Strain is defined as a quantitative measure of deformation.

Hooke's Law. Hooke's law, as described above for the stretching of a spring or wire, applies equally well to other types of deformation. In general, Hooke's law states that **stress is proportional to strain.** The stress set up within an elastic body is proportional to the strain caused by the applied load.

$$\text{stress} \propto \text{strain.} \qquad (3)$$

To make an equation of this a proportionality constant **K** is introduced:

$$\text{stress} = K \text{ strain}$$

Transposing,

$$K = \frac{\text{stress}}{\text{strain}} \qquad (4)$$

The constant **K** has a value characteristic of the material of the elastic body and is called the **modulus of elasticity.**

Young's Modulus. Consider the experiment, diagramed in Fig. B, where a wire or rod is clamped at one end and a load is applied at the other. Let **l** represent the wire's original length, **A** its cross-sectional area, and

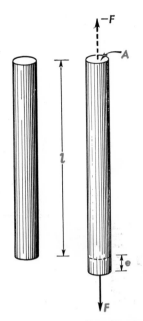

Fig. D. Young's modulus for the stretching of a wire or rod is given by Fl/Ae.

e the elongation produced by the applied load **F.** See Fig. D.

By definition, stress is the force per unit area, and strain is the elongation per unit length.

$$\text{stress} = \frac{F}{A} \qquad (5)$$

$$\text{strain} = \frac{e}{l} \qquad (6)$$

When these defining equations are substituted in Eq. (4) the modulus of elasticity **K** is called **Young's modulus,** written as **Y**, and is given by

$$Y = \frac{F/A}{e/l}$$

* Thomas Young (1773-1829), English scientist. Born of a Quaker family, young Thomas had read the Bible twice through at the age of four and at fourteen could speak seven languages. He studied medicine in London, Edinburgh, Göttingen, and Cambridge and at twenty-eight was appointed professor of physics at the Royal Institution. Young is best known for his experiments proving the wave theory of light, but he also made valuable contributions to mechanics, medicine, and to the mechanism of sight and vision. He was one of the first to decipher successfully Egyptian hieroglyphic inscriptions.

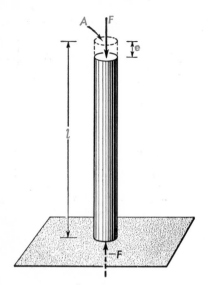

Fig. E. Young's modulus for the compression of a rod is given by Fl/Ae.

or

$$Y = \frac{Fl}{Ae} \qquad (7)$$

Young's modulus **Y** is a very practical constant, for if its value is known for any given material, the amount of stretch produced in any size of wire or rod of that material can be calculated. Careful laboratory experiments have established such values for many common substances. (See Table 1.)

Example 1. A copper wire 3 m long and 2 sq mm in cross-sectional area hangs from the ceiling. What will be its elongation if a 2-kg mass is suspended from the lower end?

Solution. Transpose Eq. (7) to solve for **e**, and substitute known dimensions and

Young's modulus for copper from Table 1.

$$e = \frac{Fl}{AY} = \frac{2000 \text{ gm} \times 980 \text{ cm/sec}^2 \times 300 \text{ cm}}{0.02 \text{ cm}^2 \times 12.5 \times 10^{11} \text{ dynes/cm}^2}$$

$$= 0.0235 \text{ cm}$$

Care must be taken in solving such problems as this to express the force **F** in the same units as the force in the modulus.

Table 1. Young's Modulus

Material	Dynes/ sq cm		Lb/ sq in.	
aluminum........	7	$\times 10^{11}$	10.2	$\times 10^6$
brass..........	9.02	"	13.09	"
copper.........	12.5	"	18.0	"
iron..........	21.0	"	30.0	"
steel (mild).......	19.2	"	27.9	"
tendon (human)....	1.6	"	2.3	"
muscle (human)....	0.009	"	0.013	"
bone (tension).....	22	"	32	"
bone (compression)	22	"	32	"
nerve..........	0.1850	"	0.2680	"
vein...........	0.0085	"	0.0123	"
artery.........	0.0005	"	0.0007	"

Compression. When a load **F** is applied to the ends of a rod to compress it as shown in Fig. E, the decrease in length is the same in amount as the elongation it would acquire when the same load is applied as a tension. In other words, Hooke's law applies to compression, the values of Young's modulus for stretching are valid, and the above Eq. (7) can be used for all calculations within the elastic limit.

Summary

When a rod or wire is put under tension, it stretches by an amount proportional to the applied force. Similarly, under pressure it will be compressed by an amount proportional to the force. This is known as Hooke's law and is generally expressed by the equation

$$F = -kx$$

The minus sign indicates that the amount of stretch or compression **x** and the restoring force **F** are in opposite directions.

If a wire or rod is stretched too far, it will go beyond its elastic limit and be permanently elongated.

Young's modulus is a constant that represents the ratio of stress to strain in the stretching of a solid. Stress is defined as the force per unit area, and strain as the elongation per unit length.

Questions

1. What is Hooke's law as applied to a spring? As applied to the stretching of a rod or wire?

2. Draw a graph representing the stretching of a wire and indicate the elastic limit. If the wire is stretched beyond the elastic limit, what would the graph look like as the load is gradually removed?

3. What is Young's modulus? What is stress? What is strain? Write down an equation for each.

4. Who was Thomas Young? For what is he known in science?

5. If the same force is applied to one wire that is twice as long as another, how will elongations compare?

6. If the lengths of two copper wires are the same but one has twice the diameter of the other, how will their elongations compare under the same force?

7. How would you go about experimentally determining Young's modulus for a brass wire? How could you use a lever to determine the very small elongations under the different loads? You may wish to do this as a project.

Problems

1. A steel coil spring 12 in. long is stretched to a total length of 18 in. by a load of 30 lb. What would be its length if stretched by a 7.5-lb load?

2. A bronze coil spring 25 cm long is stretched to a length of 28 cm when a mass of 75 gm is fastened to the lower end. Find the length of the spring when 5 gm more is added to the lower end.

3. A force of 45 lb stretches a coil spring 5 in. What force will compress the same spring 1.5 in.?

4.* An iron wire 3 m long and cross-sectional area 0.01 cm² is subjected to a tension of 5 kg. Calculate its elongation.

5.* A brass wire 2.5 m long and 2 mm in diameter hangs from the ceiling. If a mass of 2 kg is suspended from the lower end, what will be the elongation?

6.* A copper wire 6 m long and 0.01 cm² in cross-sectional area hangs from the ceiling. If a mass of 4.0 kg hanging from the lower end stretches the wire 0.2 cm, what is the value of Young's modulus?

7.* Find the elongation of a tendon 5 cm long and 0.4 cm in diameter if put under a tension of 2000 newtons.

8.* An artery has a length of 10 cm and a cross-sectional area of 0.30 cm². Find the elongation under a tension of 50 newtons.

HOOKE'S LAW—*Laboratory*

This laboratory experiment is described in the accompanying *LABORA-TORY EXERCISES*, and its purpose is to determine Young's modulus for an unknown steel wire. By means of a long, delicate mechanical lever the small elongations of the wire are accurately determined.

BENDING, TWISTING, AND BOUNCING

Bending. When a rod or beam is subjected to a force tending to bend it, the amount of bending is proportional to the force applied. This is illustrated in Fig. A, where a uniform board is shown supported at both ends and a downward force **F** is shown exerted at the middle.

If we use known weights for the applied force, and for the different loads we measure the bending displacement **d**, we will find that **d** is directly proportional to **F**. Such measurements for a piece of pine ¾ in. by 3 in. by 4 ft are easily made and may be plotted to form a graph as shown in Fig. B. The fact that the graph is a straight line is a good demonstration that Hooke's law applies to this form of bending, and that

$$d \propto F$$

Fig. A. The bending of a beam follows Hooke's law.

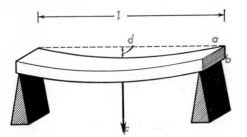

From theoretical considerations the actual relation between **d** and **F** is given by the equation

$$d = \frac{Fl^3}{4\,Yab^3} \tag{1}$$

where **a** is the beam width, **b** is its thickness, **l** is its length, and **Y** is Young's modulus.

To see how stretching and compressing enter into the bending of a beam, imagine the beam divided up into layers as shown in Fig. C. In bending, the lower layers are stretched by varying amounts, while the upper layers are compressed.

Fig. B. Illustrating Hooke's law for bending.

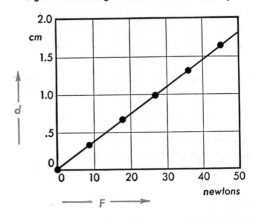

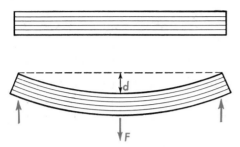

Fig. C. The bending of a beam involves stretching and compressing of different parts.

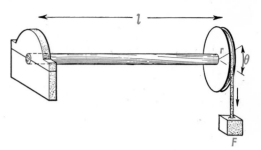

Fig. E. The twisting of a rod obeys Hooke's law.

The bending of a beam, clamped at one end as shown in Fig. D, also follows Hooke's law. The bending displacement **d** is directly proportional to the applied bending force **F** and the two are related by the formula

$$d = \frac{4\ Fl^3}{Yab^3} \qquad (2)$$

Torsion. A detailed knowledge of torsional stresses and strains has considerable practical application in engineering design. When a rod or bar is clamped at one end and a torque is applied at the other, it is twisted as illustrated in Fig. E. Within the elastic limit the angular displacement θ is proportional to the applied torque **L** and is given by

$$\theta = k\frac{Ll}{D^4} \qquad (3)$$

where **D** is the rod diameter.

Again if one makes measurements on any given rod and plots a graph of θ against **L**, a straight line is the result.

Eq. (3) agrees with the experimental observation that if the length **l** of a rod is doubled, the same torque will double the angle θ.

Fig. D. The bending of a springboard obeys Hooke's law.

By doubling the rod diameter **D** on the other hand the angle θ is decreased sixteenfold. (*Note:* $2^4 = 16$.)

Fig. F illustrates an application of torsional stress in the profession of orthodontics. **Orthodontia,** or **dental orthopedics,** is that branch of dentistry dealing principally with the straightening of teeth. In one technique it is customary to fit each tooth with a wide metal band containing an arch bracket. Each bracket has a rectangular slot into which a square arch wire is tied.

To produce a rotation of tooth **A** as indicated at the right, a permanent twist has been put into the square arch wire between that tooth and its neighbor. A torsional stress is thereby produced, and over a period of several weeks the stress is gradually relieved by the turning of the tooth. The possible movement of the roots of teeth through the mandible as well as the upper jawbone in any direction is well known to every dentist.

Impact of Elastic Bodies. When two bodies collide with each other, the law of con-

Fig. F. Illustrating an application of torsional stress to the straightening of teeth by the Orthodontist.

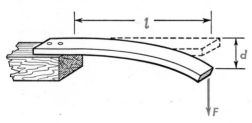

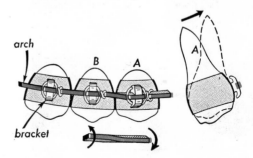

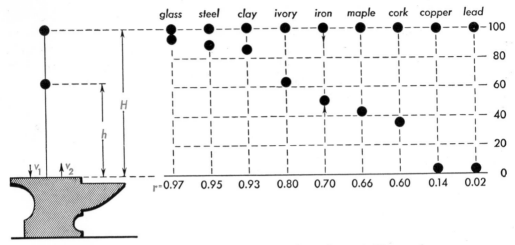

Fig. G. The bouncing marble experiment illustrating the resilience of different substances.

servation of momentum states that *the total momentum before impact is equal to the total momentum after impact.* This law is not sufficient, however, to determine what the individual velocities of each of the two bodies will be. Different kinds of material behave differently at impact and will move apart with different velocities. As an illustration, consider the experiment diagramed in Fig. G.

Spheres of different substances are dropped successively, all from the same height, onto the smooth top surface of a large

anvil and allowed to bounce to their various heights. Contrary to one's preconceived ideas of elasticity, a glass or steel marble will bounce to a greater height than will a ball made of the best Pará or India rubber. A lead ball or marble, on the other hand, hardly bounces at all.

In this particular experiment the two bodies in collision are the marble and the anvil. Because of its very great mass the recoiling velocity of the anvil is negligibly small.

As illustrations of the compression of a

Fig. H. Photographs of (a) the impact between a golf club and ball and (b) the impact between a tennis racket and ball. (*After Edgerton*)

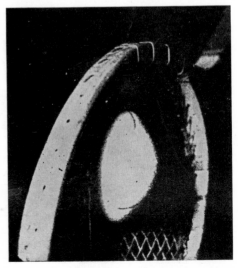

solid when in collision with another solid, note the deformation of the two balls in Fig. H. These are instantaneous photographs of (a) a golf ball being struck by a golf club and (b) a tennis ball being struck by a tennis racket. They illustrate what is called the *resilience* of matter. *Resilience is defined as the ability of a body to undergo a compression, or rapid deformation, without the development of permanent deformation.* Resilience is the opposite of brittleness.

Coefficient of Restitution. *The coefficient of restitution is defined as a number expressing the ratio of the velocity with which two bodies separate after collision to the velocity of their approach before collision.*

$$r = \frac{\text{velocity of separation}}{\text{velocity of approach}} \qquad (4)$$

or, as a formula,

$$r = \frac{v_2}{v_1} \qquad (5)$$

Values of the constant r for different substances may be obtained from the above de-

scribed experiment by determining the velocity v_1 of a marble just before it strikes the anvil and the velocity v_2 just as it leaves on rebound. Rather than measure these velocities directly it is more convenient to make use of the laws of falling bodies and to calculate the velocities from the height to which the marbles are carried. Since $v = \sqrt{2\,gs}$ for falling bodies, $\sqrt{2\,gH}$ can be written for v_1 and $\sqrt{2\,gh}$ for v_2, to give

$$r = \frac{\sqrt{2\,gh}}{\sqrt{2\,gH}}$$

$$r = \sqrt{\frac{h}{H}} \qquad (6)$$

As illustrated in Fig. G, H is the height from which a marble falls and h is the height to which it rebounds. For a very elastic substance, like glass or steel, colliding with steel, r has a value of 0.95 or better, whereas for a very inelastic substance, like lead, colliding with steel, r is extremely small. It is seen from Eq. (4) that the smallest value r can have is zero, whereas the largest value is unity.

Summary

When a rod or beam is subjected to a force tending to bend it or twist it, the amount of bending or twisting obeys Hooke's law by being proportional to the applied force.

The bending of a beam, whether it is clamped or pivoted at one or both ends, obeys Young's modulus. This is apparent when it is realized that in bending a beam the material is compressed on the inner side of the curve and is stretched on the outer side.

When two bodies collide with each other, their subsequent motions not only obey the law of conservation of momentum but depend upon the elastic properties of the material of which they are composed.

These elastic properties are determined by the coefficient of restitution, a number defined as the ratio of the velocity with which two bodies separate after collision to the velocity of their approach before collision.

Of all common materials, glass and steel exhibit the greatest elasticity.

Questions

1. What basic relation is observed in the bending of a beam or rod? What is the law?

2. How does the bending of a beam or rod depend upon (a) the applied force, (b) the length, (c) the width, and (d) the thickness?

3. What basic relation is observed in the twisting of a uniform rod? What is the law?

4. How does the twisting of a round rod depend upon (a) the applied torque, (b) the length, and (c) the diameter?

5. What is the technical meaning of the coefficient of restitution? What is resilience?

6. How is restitution most easily demonstrated? How is the coefficient of restitution measured?

7. What are the lowest and highest possible values for the coefficient? Name a substance which under average impact velocities has (a) a very small coefficient and (b) a very high coefficient.

8. If you wanted to determine the coefficient of restitution by bouncing a marble on the smooth flat surface of an anvil, how would you determine the two heights h and H with high precision?

Problems

1. The two ends of a 12-ft oak plank rest on supports. A man weighing 190 lb, standing at the center, depresses the plank 4 in. If a second man weighing 150 lb joins him there, what is the depression?

2. A boy weighing 80 lb depresses the end of a diving board 3 in. by standing at the very end. How much would the board be bent by a man weighing 250 lb?

3. The free end of a diving board at the edge of a swimming pool is 18 in. above the water. If a man weighing 160 lb, standing on the end of the board, bends it to within 6 in. of the water, how heavy a person will bend it to within 4 in. of the water?

4. An ivory ball is dropped from a height of 72 in. onto the smooth surface of a heavy anvil. To what height will it bounce if the coefficient of restitution is 0.60?

5. A porcelain ball is dropped from a height of 3 ft onto the smooth top of a steel anvil and is found to bounce to a height of 9 in. Calculate the coefficient of restitution.

6. A solid steel marble is dropped from a height of 4 m onto the smooth flat surface of an anvil. Calculate the height to which it will bounce.

7. A glass marble is dropped from a height of 28 in. onto a smooth, heavy steel anvil as shown in Fig. G. Calculate the height to which it will bounce.

8. A golf ball when dropped from a height of 4 ft and allowed to hit a concrete pavement bounces to a height of 2.5 ft. Calculate the coefficient of restitution.

9.* The free end of a springboard at the edge of a swimming pool is 2 ft above the water. How close to the water will the board come if a 200-lb man stands on the end of the board? Assume the board to be 1 ft wide, 2.0 in. thick, and 16 ft long. Young's modulus is 1.4×10^7 lb/in.^{2}

10.* An ivory ball with a mass of 200 gm, moving with a speed of 300 cm/sec, collides head-on with another ivory ball of the same mass and size, at rest. If the coefficient of restitution is 0.65, find the velocity of each ball after collision.

Properties of Matter | Lesson 4

PRESSURE IN LIQUIDS

Properties of solids, like bending and twisting, do not exist in liquids. Liquids, however, can be put under compression and, if placed in a thoroughly cleaned vessel or container, can be subjected to very high tensions. Although these properties are of considerable interest, they have not proved to be of much practical importance. There are physical properties of liquids, on the other hand, which are considered to be of general importance. These are pressure, buoyancy, surface tension, and capillarity.

Pressure. It is essential in the following treatment of the properties of liquids to introduce the concept of *pressure* as contrasted with the meaning of *total force*. *Pressure is defined as the force per unit of area.* Written in the form of an equation,

$$pressure = \frac{total\ force}{area}$$

$$P = \frac{F}{A} \tag{1}$$

As an illustration of the distinction between pressure and total force, consider the two aluminum metal blocks in Fig. A. Block (a) stands on one end where the area is 200 sq. in., while block (b) stands on one edge where the area is 400 sq in. Weighing 1000 lb, each block separately exerts the same downward force. Standing on end as in (a), the downward pressure is given by Eq. (1) as

$$pressure = \frac{1000\ lb}{200\ in.^2} = 5\ \frac{lb}{in.^2}$$

This is read **5 pounds per square inch.** Standing on edge as in (b), on the other hand, the pressure is only one half as great.

$$pressure = \frac{1000\ lb}{400\ in.^2} = 2.5\ \frac{lb}{in.^2}$$

Over each square inch in the first case there is a downward force equivalent to 5 lb, while in the second case there is only 2.5 lb. The pressure in (a) is, therefore, twice as great as the pressure in (b), but the total downward force is the same.

Transposing **A** to the other side of Eq. (1) gives

$$F = P \times A \tag{2}$$

Total force equals pressure times area.

Liquid Pressure. It is frequently necessary to determine the pressure at various depths within a liquid as well as the pressure

Fig. A. A block standing on end exerts a greater pressure than when it is lying on its side.

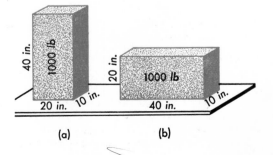

(a)   (b)

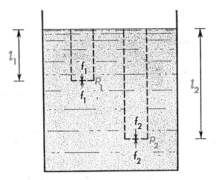

Fig. B. The pressure exerted by a liquid depends upon the depth.

on the bottom and sides of any containing vessel. The rule regarding pressure states that **the magnitude of the pressure at any depth is equal to the weight of a column of liquid of unit cross section reaching from that point to the top of the liquid.**

At a depth of l_1, as illustrated in Fig. B, the pressure p_1 is given by the weight of a column of liquid 1 sq cm in cross section and l_1 centimeters in height. At a greater depth of l_2, the pressure p_2 is given by the weight of a column of liquid 1 sq cm in cross section and l_2 centimeters in height.

Fig. C. Experimental demonstration of pressure within a liquid.

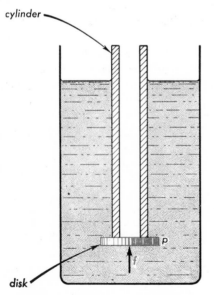

This can be demonstrated with a glass cylinder and a thin lightweight disk as shown in Fig. C. With water surrounding the empty cylinder the force **f**, pushing up, holds the disk tightly against the end. If the cylinder is gradually filled with water, an increasing downward force is exerted on the disk. Just as the water inside reaches the level of the water outside, the disk drops from the end of the cylinder, showing that the downward force and upward force at that point and at that instant become equal. We can conclude from this experiment that not only is the pressure at any given point in a liquid given by the weight of the liquid above it but that the pressure at one point is equal to the pressure at any other point at the same level.

Pressure in a liquid is defined as the normal force exerted by the liquid per unit area.

Pressure is usually measured in **pounds**

Fig. D. Experimental demonstration of equal pressures in all directions.

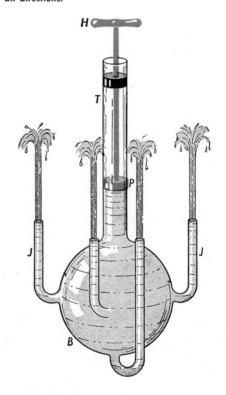

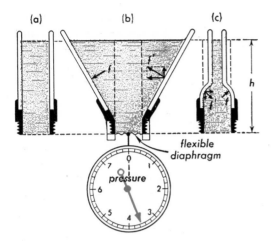

(a)   (b)   (c)

flexible
diaphragm

pressure

Fig. E. Demonstration with Pascal's vases.

per square inch, dynes per square centimeter, or newtons per square meter.

Pressure Acts in All Directions. In a liquid at rest, the force exerted by the liquid upon any surface is perpendicular to the surface. At any given point the force exerted on an element of surface is independent of the orientation of that surface. This can be illustrated in many ways. For example, in Fig. D a hollow steel ball **B**, filled with water, is connected at the top by a metal tube **T**. By pushing down on the handle **H** the plunger **P** forces water out of the several metal tubes **J** leading from the sides and the bottom of the ball. Equal force in all directions is indicated by the water jets all coming to the same height as drawn.

Pressure on a Surface. Because of pressure, the force **f** exerted by a liquid at rest is perpendicular to the wall with which the liquid is in contact. As a proof suppose the force were not perpendicular but at some angle to the surface. Such a force could be resolved into two components, one normal and the other tangent to the surface. But, the tangent component cannot exist, for if it did the wall would exert an equal and opposite force on the liquid and the liquid would move. Since the liquid is assumed to be at

rest, the force **f** must be normal to the surface.

The vessels shown in Fig. E are known as Pascal's vases.* Three glass vessels of different shape but the same height have screw-in metal bases that fit into the same pressure meter shown at the lower center. The three vases are inserted one after the other and filled with water to the same height **h**. Even though the amount of water is greatly different in each vase the pressure, as measured by the meter, is the same.

The experimental fact that the small amount of water in vessel (c) can exert the same downward force as the large amount in vessel (b) may be considered as a verification of equal pressure. Let **f** represent the force of the water on unit area of the wall and **f′** the equal and opposite force of the wall on the water. The latter is shown resolved into vertical and horizontal components. The vertical component in (b) is upward and supplies the additional force needed to support the extra amount of water, while in (c) the vertical component is downward and supplies the additional force equivalent to the missing column of water above.

Pressure Transmission, Pascal's Principle. Any change of pressure in an enclosed fluid is transmitted undiminished to all parts of the fluid. A practical application of this principle is to be found in hydraulic systems where a force is applied on one part of the liquid and some load is moved at another. Consider as an illustration the hydraulic press illustrated in Fig. F.

Two pistons, one large and one small and connected by a pipe, are filled with a liquid. When a force **F** is applied to the smaller pis-

* Blaise Pascal (1623-1662), French religious philosopher, physicist and mathematician. Noted principally for his discoveries in pure mathematics, and for his experiments with the barometer. His experiments and his treatise on the equilibrium of fluids entitle him to rank with Galileo and Stevinus as one of the founders of the science of hydrostatics and hydrodynamics.

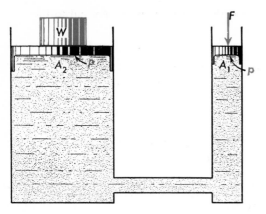

Fig. F. Illustrating the principles of the hydraulic press.

Since pressure is defined as force per unit area, $p = F/A_1$ for the smaller piston while $p = W/A_2$ for the larger. Since these pressures are equal,

$$\frac{W}{A_2} = \frac{F}{A_1}$$

from which

$$W = \frac{A_2}{A_1} F \qquad (3)$$

ton, the increased pressure p created immediately underneath the piston of area A_1 is transmitted undiminished to the larger piston of area A_2.

Should the larger piston of such a press have ten times the area of the smaller, a load ten times that of the applied force may be lifted. Such a system, therefore, has a mechanical advantage equal to the ratio of the piston areas, A_2/A_1.

Summary

Pressure is defined as the force per unit area. In mks units pressure is given in newtons/m², and in engineering units in lb/in.²

Pressure at any depth within a liquid is given by the weight of a column of liquid of unit cross section reaching from that depth point to the top free surface of the liquid. Pressure has no direction and is not a vector quantity.

Pressure at any point within a liquid acts in all directions. The pressure on any flat surface area gives rise to a force that is always perpendicular to the surface.

Pascal's principle states that any change of pressure in an enclosed fluid is transmitted undiminished to all parts of the fluid. This is the principle of the hydraulic press.

Questions

1. How is pressure defined? What are the units of pressure in the mks system? In the engineering system?

2. How can the pressure at any depth within a liquid be calculated? Is pressure a force? Is pressure a vector quantity?

3. If you know the pressure on a flat surface within a liquid, how can you determine the force exerted on a given area of the surface?

4. What do Pascal's vases demonstrate? How can you explain the equal forces exerted on the bottom surface area of each vase?

5. State Pascal's principle. What practical application makes use of the principle?

6. Can you think of any place where Pascal's principle is made use of in most American-made cars?

7. What simple and inexpensive device could you make to demonstrate that the pressure at any given depth within a liquid is the same in all directions?

Problems

1. A concrete block 2 ft wide, 3 ft long, and 1 ft high weighs 1080 lb. Find the pressure it exerts on the ground in (a) lb/ft^2 and (b) lb/in^2.

2. A solid block of sandstone 12 cm wide, 20 cm long, and 10 cm high has a mass of 5 kg. Find the pressure it exerts on the ground in newtons per square meter.

3. A solid block of limestone 75 cm wide, 160 cm long, and 120 cm high has a mass of 3900 kg. Find the pressure it exerts on the ground in newtons per square meter.

4. The water pressure on the bottom of a tank is 10 lb/in^2. What is the total force on the bottom if the area is 20 ft^2?

5. The water pressure on the bottom of a tank is 20 lb/in^2. Find the total force on the bottom if the area is 5 ft^2.

6. The areas of the pistons in a hydraulic press are 1600 $in.^2$ and 4 $in.^2$, respectively. What force on the smaller piston is required to lift a 2-ton automobile by the larger piston?

7.* What minimum diameter could the cylinder of an hydraulic press have if it is to lift a 2-ton car with an applied liquid pressure of 40 $lb/in.^2$?

8. If one cubic inch of water weighs 0.036 lb, find the pressure at a depth of 10 ft below the surface in a tank of water.

9. If one cubic inch of mercury weighs 0.50 lb, what will be the pressure at a depth of 2 ft below the surface in a vessel of mercury?

10.* If one cubic centimeter of water has a mass of 1 gm, find the pressure at a depth of 5 meters in a tank of water.

Properties of Matter | **Lesson 5**

PRESSURE IN LIQUIDS—*Laboratory*

In performing this laboratory experiment as described in the accompanying *LABORATORY EXERCISES* you will measure the pressure within a vessel of water at different depths. The apparatus used is readily constructed from common laboratory equipment.

ARCHIMEDES' PRINCIPLE

Archimedes' Principle.* Archimedes' principle states that *a body floating or submerged in a liquid is buoyed up by a force equal to the weight of the liquid displaced.* For example, if a block of wood is floating in water, as shown in Fig. A, the buoyant force **F** holding the block up is equal to the weight of the water displaced (shaded area). When the block is first placed in the water it sinks until the buoyant force **F** becomes great enough to equalize the downward force, the weight of the block **W**.

An experimental demonstration of the truth of Archimedes' principle is shown in Fig. B. A small cylindrical cup containing a close fitting solid metal cylinder is accurately balanced by a set of weights on an equal-arm balance. No change in balance occurs when in diagram (b) the cylinder has been removed from the cup and suspended from a hook underneath. In diagram (c) a beaker of water has been raised until the cylinder is completely submerged. Balance is now de-

*See footnote on Archimedes in Mechanics, Lesson 34.

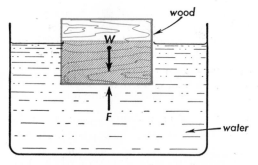

Fig. A. A block of wood lowered into the water sinks until the buoyant force of the water equals the weight of the block.

stroyed because of the upward buoyant force of the water on the cylinder.

If Archimedes' principle is correct, the buoyant force is equal to the weight of a volume of water exactly equal to the volume of the cylinder. A slow addition of water to the cup in diagram (d) shows that at the very instant the cup becomes filled, exact balance of the beam is restored. The restoring of balance confirms the principle.

Measurement of Density. One of the

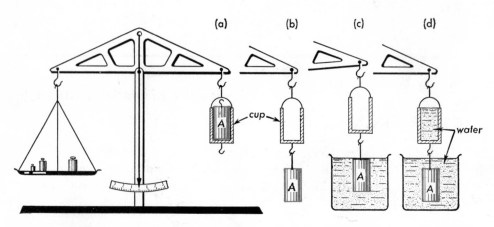

Fig. B. Illustrating the four steps in an experiment demonstrating Archimedes' principle.

2.54

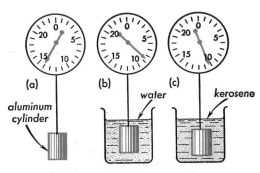

(a)　(b)　(c)

water　kerosene

aluminum
cylinder

Fig. C. The buoyant effect of liquids may be used as a means of determining the density of solids or liquids.

many ways of measuring the density of solids or liquids is by the use of Archimedes' principle. An experiment in which the density of a solid (aluminum) and of a liquid (kerosene) may be determined is shown in Fig. C. A solid aluminum cylinder is weighed with spring scales (a) in air, (b) in water, and (c) in kerosene.

Diagram (a) gives directly the mass of the cylinder as 1400 gm. When submerged in water the scales indicate a mass of only 880 gm. The difference $1400 - 880 = 520$ gm multiplied by g is the buoyant force and therefore the weight of the displaced fluid. But since the density of water is equal to 1 gm/cm³, 520 gm of water will have a volume of 520 cm³. Therefore 520 cm³ is the volume of the cylinder.

By definition we say that the density of any body of matter is given by

$$\rho = \frac{M}{V} \tag{1}$$

Having found both M and V for the aluminum cylinder, the density of aluminum is

$$\rho = \frac{M}{V} = \frac{1400 \text{ gm}}{520 \text{ cm}^3} = 2.7 \frac{\text{gm}}{\text{cm}^3}$$

Submerged in kerosene, the cylinder weighs 1040 gm-wt, indicating a buoyant force $1400 - 1040 = 360$ gm-wt. Since the cylinder displaces its volume 520 cm³ of liquid, and this liquid weighs 360 gm-wt, the density of the kerosene is

$$\rho = \frac{M}{V} = \frac{360 \text{ gm}}{520 \text{ cm}^3} = 0.69 \frac{\text{gm}}{\text{cm}^3}$$

The densities and weight densities of a few common substances are given in Table 1.

Hydrometers. The densities of liquids are measured by the buoyant force they exert on a floating body called an hydrometer. One form of hydrometer is employed by gas station attendants to measure the density of the acid in car storage batteries. The acid density in a battery is a direct measure of the amount of stored electrical energy it contains.

The battery hydrometer shown in Fig. D consists of a hollow glass tube with a weight

Fig. D. Diagram of a typical hydrometer used for measuring the density of the acid in a storage battery cell.

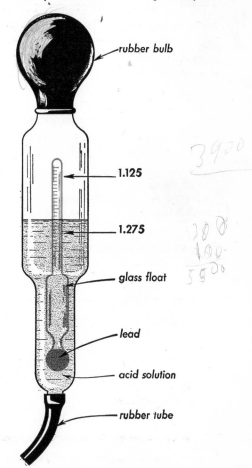

rubber bulb

1.125

1.275

glass float

lead

acid solution

rubber tube

Table 1. Densities and Weight-Densities of a Few Materials

Material	ρ (gm/cm³)	ρ_w (lb/ft³)
aluminum............	2.7	169
brass...............	8.5	530
copper..............	8.9	556
diamond............	3.5	218
gold................	19.3	1205
iron................	7.5	468
lead................	11.4	712
osmium.............	22.5	1405
platinum............	21.5	1342
silver...............	10.5	655
maple wood.........	~0.7	44
glass...............	~2.6	162

at the bottom and a graduated stem at the top. For convenience the glass float is enclosed in a larger glass tube with a rubber bulb at the top and a short rubber tube at the bottom. The density of the battery liquid is measured by inserting the rubber tube through the vent in the top of the cell and drawing up a small sample of the solution into the main glass tube. Having a constant mass **M**, the hydrometer tube sinks until it displaces its own weight in liquid; the more dense the liquid, the higher it floats. A suitable scale on the stem is one that is calibrated directly in gm/cm³. For a fully charged battery the hydrometer will float high, the liquid lever indicating 1.275 gm/cm³, whereas if it is completely discharged it will sink to a low level, indicating a density of about 1.125 gm/cm³.

Hydrometers for measuring very slight differences of density and with a high degree of accuracy have a large float and very thin stem, while those designed for greater ranges of density with less accuracy have a smaller float and thicker stem.

Summary

According to Archimedes' principle, and in conformity with experimental observations of the most precise nature, a body wholly or partially submerged in a liquid is buoyed up by a force equal to the weight of the liquid displaced.

By weighing an object in air and then again when it is submerged in water the density of the object can be determined. All metals, as well as most other solid materials, have densities and weight densities greater than that of water. Woods in general have a density less than 1 gm/cm³ and therefore float on water.

The densities of liquids are easily and quickly determined by means of a hydrometer. Such instruments are based in principle upon Archimedes' principle.

Questions

1. State Archimedes' principle. Why will a block of wood float on water? Why will a solid block of metal sink?

2. How does the weight of a block of metal in air compare with its apparent weight submerged in water?

3. Why can a ship made entirely of steel float on water when a solid steel sphere will sink?

4. What is the apparent weight of a block of wood floating on water?

5. How can one find the density of an irregular shaped body like a stone? How can one find the density of a liquid using Archimedes' principle?

2 54
4,5,3,1

6. What is a hydrometer? Upon what principle is it based? What practical uses do you think they have?

7. What element has the greatest density? What is the weight density of gold? Could you lift a solid gold sphere 6 in. in diameter?

Problems

1. A stone weighed in air is found to have a mass of 2360 gm. When weighed in water it has an apparent mass of 1720 gm. Find its density.

2. A block of metal weighed in air is found to have a mass of 274 gm. When weighed in water it has an apparent mass of 242 gm. Find its density.

3. A 15-lb stone has an apparent mass of 12 lb when weighed in water. Find its weight-density. The weight-density of water is 62.4 lb/ft^3.

4. An iron casting has a mass of 36 kg in air. What will be its apparent mass when weighed in water if it has a density of 7.5 gm/cm^3.

5. An ivory ball weighed in air has a mass of 280 gm. When weighed in water, its apparent mass is 132 gm; and weighed in oil, its apparent mass is 193 gm. Find (a) the density of ivory and (b) the density of the oil.

6. When weighed in air a solid metal casting has a mass of 772 gm. When weighed in water its mass is 732 gm. (a) What is the density of the metal and (b) what is the metal? (See Table 1.)

7. A metal cylinder weighs 12.0 lb in air and 10.6 lb when submerged in water. What is the weight density of the metal?

8.* A solid brass cylinder weighs 6 lb in air and 5.4 lb when submerged in a liquid. Find the weight density of the liquid.

9.* A stone weighs 2.70 kg-wt in air, 2.20 kg-wt in water, and 2.40 kg-wt in oil. Find the density of (a) the stone and (b) the oil.

10. A crown supposedly made of pure gold has a mass of 1.65 kg when weighed in air and an apparent mass of 1.47 kg when weighed in water. What is its density? Is it pure gold? Could it be copper plated with gold?

Properties of Matter | Lesson 7

DENSITY AND WEIGHT-
DENSITY—*Laboratory*

In performing this experiment as described in the accompanying LABO-RATORY EXERCISES you will make use of Archimedes' principle and, by weighing objects in air and submerged in water, determine their densities and weight densities.

SURFACE TENSION

Adhesion and Cohesion. All matter is composed of atoms and molecules of one kind or another. As already stated in Mechanics, Lesson 44, these ultramicroscopic particles attract each other with forces which depend upon the kinds of atoms or molecules involved and upon the distance between them. The closer two atoms or molecules are together, the greater is the attractive force between them. The attractive force between different kinds of molecules is called *adhesion,* and the attractive force between two like kinds of molecules is called *cohesion.*

Although the force of attraction between two molecules is extremely small, the combined attraction of billions of molecules contained within a very small bit of matter is astonishingly great. A steel cable 1 in. in diameter, for example, will support a maximum load of 25 or more tons without breaking. This is a direct measure of the cohesive forces between hundreds of billions of atoms.

The difference between adhesion and cohesion can be demonstrated by an experiment diagramed in Fig. A. A glass plate **G** is supported by one arm of a beam balance. The plate, after being balanced by weights on the left-hand scale pan, is brought into contact with the surface of water as shown. Addi-

tional weights are next added at **W** until the plate breaks free from the water surface. Upon examining the glass, water is found clinging to the under surface, showing that the break came between water molecules only. The adhesive forces between glass and water molecules therefore exceed the cohesive forces between water molecules. The weight added in the experiment is therefore a measure of the cohesive forces between water molecules.

If mercury is substituted for the water in the above experiment and the glass plate pulled away from the mercury surface, the added weights will measure adhesion, the force of attraction between glass and mercury molecules. This is shown by the fact that no mercury clings to the bottom of the glass plate. Thus the cohesion between mercury molecules is greater than the adhesion between mercury and glass.

Surface Tension. The cohesion of molecules gives rise in liquids to a phenomenon called surface tension. According to this aspect of molecular attraction, the surface of a liquid acts at all times as though it has a thin membrane stretched over it and that this membrane is under tension and trying to contract. It is for this reason that fogdrops, raindrops, soap bubbles, etc., assume a spherical shape as they fall through the air. (For any

Fig. A. Experiment illustrating the forces of adhesion between glass and water.

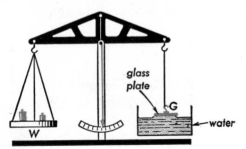

glass plate

G

water

Fig. B. Demonstration of the spheroidal state.

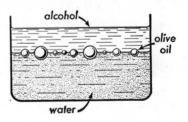

alcohol

olive oil

water

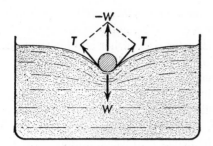

Fig. C. A steel needle can float by itself on water.

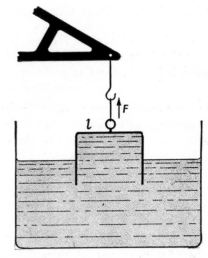

Fig. D. Wire loop for measuring surface tension.

specified volume of matter a sphere has a smaller surface area than any other geometrical figure.)

An experiment designed to illustrate the spheroidal state of a liquid drop is shown in Fig. B on page 180. Alcohol and water are poured carefully into a glass vessel where they form a separation boundary, the water with its greater density going to the bottom. Olive oil, which is not soluble in either water or alcohol, is then dropped into the liquid. The drops quickly take on a spherical form and, due to their intermediate density, settle slowly to the boundary level where they remain suspended.

A second illustration of surface tension is the floating needle experiment. A common sewing needle lowered horizontally to the surface of water in an open dish will be found to float as shown in Fig. C. (If the needle is first drawn through the fingers, a thin film of grease is deposited on the surface, making it easier to float. The adhesion between water and grease is very weak.) For the needle to break through the surface, water molecules must be pulled apart. Rather than do this the surface becomes depressed until the upward buoyant force $-W$ is equal in magnitude to W, the weight of the needle. See Archimedes' principle, p. 176. Surface tension T keeps the film intact.

Surface tension in the laboratory is usually measured by an arrangement illustrated in Fig. D. A small wire frame of length l is dipped into water and then pulled slowly out. As a result of both cohesion and adhe-

sion, a thin film of water is formed in the frame. This film pulls down by a force which can be measured by balancing the frame from the arm of a beam balance. Weights are slowly added to the other scale pan until the film breaks. The maximum weight added before breaking the film measures directly

Fig. E. The rise of water in capillary tubes is due to adhesion, cohesion, and surface tension.

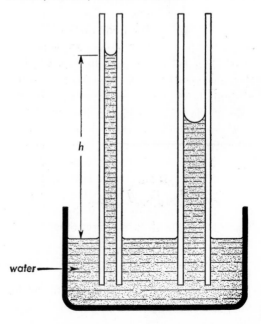

water

the cohesive forces of the water film, the surface tension.

The coefficient of surface tension is defined as the force of contraction across a line of unit length, the line and the force being perpendicular to each other, both lying in the plane of the liquid surface. If **F** is the maximum force applied in the above experiment and **l** is the length of the wire frame, the surface tension **T** is given by

$$T = \frac{F}{2l} \qquad (1)$$

The factor **2** enters because there are two surfaces to a thin film, thus making the effective length of the surface to **2 l.**

Table 1. The Coefficient of Surface Tension of a Few Liquids

(T in dynes/cm)

Liquid	0°C	20°C	50°C
acetone........	26.3	23.7	19.9
alcohol........	24.0	22.3	19.8
benzine.......	31.5	28.9	25.0
mercury.......	508	480	445
water.........	75.6	72.7	67.9

Capillarity. When a long glass tube is placed in a dish of water as illustrated in Fig. E, the water rises in the tube until it reaches a certain height and then stops. The finer the bore of the tube the higher the water rises.

Water rises in capillary tubes because the adhesive forces of glass for water are greater than the cohesive forces of water. When a fine-bore tube is first placed in water, the glass walls immediately above the edge of the water attract molecules to it by adhesion. These molecules in turn attract other nearby

molecules, pulling them up by cohesion. This process continues, filling up the space below as the water rises higher and higher. Surface tension, the result of cohesion, prevents any of the water from dropping back. The water continues to rise until surface tension is equalized by the weight of the liquid in the tube.

The height **h** to which a liquid will rise in a capillary tube is given by the following formula:

$$h = \frac{2T}{r\rho g} \qquad (2)$$

In the cgs system of units **T** is the surface tension measured in dynes per centimeter length, **r** is the radius of the bore in cm, ρ is the density of the liquid in gm/cm³, and **g** is the acceleration due to gravity and equal to 980 cm/sec².

Surface tension is largely responsible for the rise of sap in trees. Carefully performed experiments show that water, by surface tension, can be raised to heights of one hundred feet or more.

Example 1. One end of a capillary tube is placed in a dish of water. Assuming the surface tension to be 70 dynes/cm and the diameter of the tube to be 1 millimeter, find the height of rise.

Solution. By direct substitution in Eq. (2) we obtain

$$h = \frac{2 \times 70}{0.05 \times 1 \times 980} = 2.86 \text{ cm}$$

In cases where the cohesive forces of a liquid are greater than the adhesive forces, a liquid column in a capillary tube is depressed. Mercury in a glass capillary is a good example.

Summary

The attractive force between different kinds of molecules is called adhesion, and the attractive force between like kinds of molecules is called cohesion.

Cohesion gives rise to the surface property and behavior of a liquid called surface tension. Because the surface of a liquid behaves as though it were a stretched sheet of elastic material like rubber, small drops of liquid tend to form spheres.

The coefficient of surface tension is the force per unit length that acts across lines drawn in the surface of the liquid. A liquid like water rises in glass capillary tubes because the adhesive forces of glass for water are greater than the cohesive forces of water.

Questions

1. What is the difference between adhesion and cohesion? How do the cohesive forces of mercury molecules compare with their adhesive forces for glass?

2. How do the cohesive forces of water molecules compare with their adhesive forces for glass?

3. What is surface tension? What is the spheroidal state? Why do small drops of a liquid take the shape of spheres?

4. Why can a steel needle or razor blade float on water? What holds the steel body up?

5. Define the coefficient of surface tension. How does surface tension change with temperature? Which has the greater coefficient, mercury or water? What would this difference have to do with the rigidity of water and mercury drops of the same size?

6. What is capillarity? Why does water rise in a glass capillary tube?

7. Upon what does the height of the water column in a capillary tube depend? Does the thickness of the glass walls of the tube affect the height?

8. Where in nature do you think capillarity plays an important role in the functioning of animate and inanimate objects?

9. When a glass tube is placed in mercury the liquid is depressed rather than raised. Why do you think this should be so?

Problems

1. A U-shaped wire having a length of 2.5 cm is lowered into water at 0°C. What force is required to break the film as the wire is slowly lifted from the water as shown in Fig. D?

2. Draw a graph from the values of T given in Table 1 for water and from it determine the coefficient of surface tension of water at 15°C and at 30°C?

3. A U-shaped wire 3.6 cm long requires a force of 180 dynes to pull it out of liquid benzine and break the film as shown in Fig. D. (a) What is the coefficient of surface tension? (b) What is the temperature?

4. A glass capillary tube has an internal diameter of 0.2 mm. How high will the water rise in this tube if its lower end is placed in water at 20°C?

5. Water at 50°C is found to rise to a height of 10 cm in a glass capillary tube. What is the diameter of the bore?

6. A U-shaped wire having a length of 4.5 cm is lowered into benzine at 20°C. What force is required to break the film that forms as the wire is slowly lifted from the liquid as shown in Fig. D?

7. One end of a glass tube with an internal diameter of 0.25 mm is dipped in alcohol at 20°C. How high will the liquid rise in the tube?

8. If water at 20°C rises to a height of one meter in a glass tube, what is the diameter of the bore?

9. If water at a temperature of 50°C rises to a height of 25 cm in a glass capillary tube, what is the diameter of the bore?

10. If water at a temperature of 80°C rises to a height of 10 cm in a glass capillary tube, what is the diameter of the bore? (Extrapolate the values from the graph drawn in problem 2.)

Properties of Matter | **Lesson 9**

THE ATMOSPHERE

The Earth's Atmosphere. We on the earth's surface, although little conscious of the fact, are submerged in a great sea of air called the atmosphere. This air, which to the earth is the most common of all gases, is really a mixture of well-known gases: about 77% nitrogen, 21% oxygen, and 1% argon. The remaining 1% includes small quantities of such gases as carbon dioxide, hydrogen, neon, krypton, helium, ozone, and xenon.

Being most dense at sea level (see Fig. A), the atmosphere extends upward to a height of from fifty to several hundred miles. The apparent uncertainty as to the exact height of the atmosphere is not real, for the air gets thinner and thinner the higher one goes and finally thins out into interstellar space. Observations show that even interstellar space, which is often referred to as the most perfect vacuum, contains a small but definite amount of matter in the gaseous state: about one molecule per cubic centimeter.

Living as most of us do near sea level, we are constantly subjected to an enormous pressure due to the weight of the air above us. Unbelievable as it may seem, the air exerts a pressure of close to 15 lb for every square inch of surface. This, the atmospheric pressure, is given by the weight of a column of air 1 sq in. in cross-section and reaching from sea level to the top of the atmosphere.

Fig. A. Illustration of the air surrounding the earth. The height is exaggerated to bring out the decrease in density with altitude. (If drawn to scale, the earth's atmosphere would form a layer much thinner than the line shown here representing the earth's surface.)

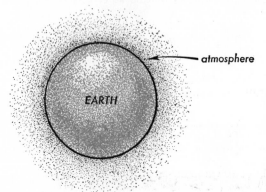

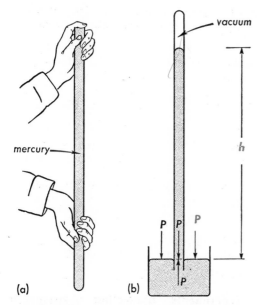

Fig. B. Torricelli's experiment. The making of a mercury barometer.

The Mercury Barometer. A barometer is a device for measuring the atmospheric pressure. There are in common use today two kinds of barometers—the **mercury barome-**

ter and the **aneroid barometer.** The mercury barometer was invented by the Italian physicist, Evangelista Torricelli, some three hundred years ago. Torricelli's experiment is illustrated in Fig. B. A long glass tube is filled with mercury and the finger placed over one end as shown in diagram (a). This tube is then inverted and with the open end in a dish of mercury the finger is removed as in diagram (b). At the instant the finger is removed the mercury level drops in the tube to a height **h** as shown. The mercury drops until the pressure due to its own weight inside the tube (at the level **P**) is equal to the atmospheric pressure outside.

At sea level the height at which the mercury column stands is about 76 cm or 30 in. This height will be the same regardless of the diameter of the tube or the length of the vacuum space at the top. Torricelli's experiment shows that a column of air 1 sq cm in cross section and reaching to the top of the atmosphere is equal in weight to a column of mercury of the same cross section and 76 cm high.

Fig. C. Schematic diagram and cross section of an aneroid barometer.

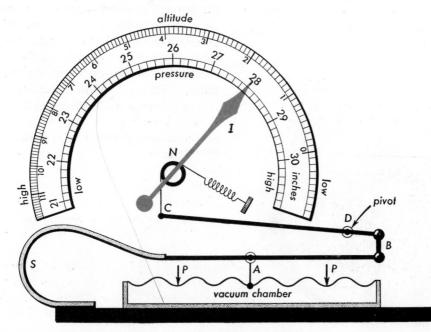

The height of the mercury in a barometer measures directly the atmospheric pressure. Instead of specifying the pressure in lb/in.² or in dynes/cm², it is customary to give the height of the mercury column in inches or centimeters.

If a barometer were made to employ water in place of mercury, the barometer tube would have to be at least 13.6 times as high, or 1034 cm. This is equivalent to about 34 ft. Such an instrument would be too cumbersome to be of much practical value.

The Aneroid Barometer. The desirability of a small portable pressure measuring instrument has led to the development of the aneroid barometer. This device is frequently used as an altimeter and barometer combined. A cross-section diagram of such an instrument is shown in Fig. C, and a photograph is reproduced in Fig. D. A small flat metal box, evacuated and with a flexible top, is attached at **A** to a multiplying system of levers. The end of the lever system is connected to a small cable **C** which is wrapped around a spindle **N** carrying a pointer **I**. If the atmospheric pressure **P** increases, the

Fig. D. Aneroid barometer used for measuring atmospheric pressure.

flexible boxtop is pushed down at **A.** This lowers the end of the lever system at **B** and, with a pivot at **D**, raises the point **C.** The cable winds up on the spindle **N**, turning the pointer **I** to the right to a scale reading of higher pressure. The scale of the aneroid is calibrated by a standard mercury barometer so the pressure is always given in centimeters or inches of mercury.

Since the atmospheric pressure decreases as one goes to higher altitudes, a barometer is often used to determine elevation. As a matter of fact, aneroid barometers are frequently made with an altitude scale attached. Such instruments, called **altimeters,** are to be found on the instrument panel of every airplane and dirigible.

Experiments Illustrating Atmospheric Pressure. Normal atmospheric pressure of 15 lb/in.² does not ordinarily impress a person as being very great. Taken over a considerable area, however, such a pressure gives rise to a tremendous force.

An experiment illustrating atmospheric pressure is diagramed in Fig. E. In diagram (a) a thin sheet of rubber is first tied over the top end of a jar. When this is done the air pressure inside is the same as that outside. If now the inside force, upward on the rubber, is removed by means of a vacuum pump, the outside force pushes the rubber down inside as shown in diagram (b).

The principles of breathing in the human

Fig. E. Experiments illustrating the magnitude of atmospheric pressure.

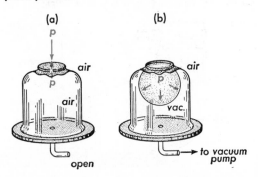

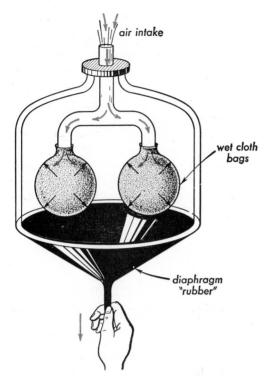

air intake

wet cloth
bags

diaphragm
"rubber"

Fig. F. Experimental demonstration of the principles of breathing by the human body.

inverted cylinder and piston. By pumping out the air from the cylinder chamber, the atmospheric pressure lifts the piston and accompanying heavy weights **W.** With a circular piston only 5 in. in diameter a total weight of 295 lb can be lifted. The second diagram represents the drinking of water from a glass by means of a straw. The water is not drawn up through the straw; it is pushed up from the outside. Suction at the top end of the straw removes the air, and hence the pressure at that point, and the atmospheric pressure at the liquid surface in the glass pushes the water up the straw and into the mouth. This is similar in its action to a siphon.

The Magdeburg Hemispheres. In the year 1654 Otto von Guericke performed before the Emperor Ferdinand III, at Regensburg, the celebrated experiment of the "Magdeburg hemispheres." Two copper hemispheres, about 22 in. in diameter, were placed together to form a sphere as shown in Fig. H. A ring of leather soaked in oil and wax was set between them to make an airtight joint. When the sphere was evacuated, two teams, consisting of eight horses each, were unable to pull the hemispheres apart. This is not to be wondered at for the force required to pull them apart is easily calculated and amounts to nearly three tons.

body are demonstrated in Fig. F. Muscular contraction in pulling down on the **diaphragm** creates a low pressure around the lungs and atmospheric pressure pushes air into the lungs. Retraction of the diaphragm raises the pressure and compresses the lungs, forcing air and carbon dioxide out.

Two additional experiments are illustrated in Fig. G. The first diagram represents an

Fig. H. The Magdeburg hemisphere designed by Otto von Guericke.

Fig. G. Experiments illustrating the presence of atmospheric pressure and its action in all directions.

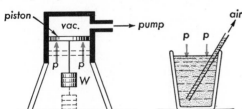

piston

vac.

pump

air

p   p

p   p

W

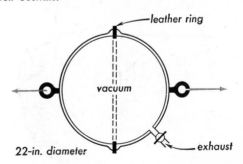

leather ring

vacuum

22-in. diameter

exhaust

Summary

Because of the fact that air has weight, the atmosphere around and above us exerts a pressure. Atmospheric pressure is measured by means of a mercury barometer. Aneroid barometers are mechanical devices for measuring atmospheric pressure, and they are easily transported.

Atmospheric pressure at sea level is approximately 15 lb/in². Such pressures give rise to enormous forces on surfaces of relatively small area. The Magdeburg hemispheres are good examples of this.

There is no such thing as suction. Soda water rises in a straw, for example, because of pressure differences between the ends. Atmospheric pressure pushes the liquid up.

Because atmospheric pressure decreases with increasing altitude, aneroid barometers are often calibrated to give altitude. Such instruments are called altimeters and are used in airplanes.

Questions

1. What is a mercury barometer? About how tall are they? What do they measure?

2. What is the approximate height of the mercury column in a barometer at sea level (a) in centimeters and (b) in inches?

3. What is an aneroid barometer? Why are they preferred to a mercury barometer?

4. What is an altimeter? What are the principles upon which they operate?

5. What was the Magdeburg hemisphere experiment? How large were the hemispheres? How can one calculate the force required to pull the hemispheres apart?

6. If a flat plate were placed over the open side of one hemisphere of the kind shown in Fig. H and the air removed from inside, how would you calculate the force required to pull the plate off? How would this force compare with that of pulling the two hemispheres apart?

7. Make a schematic diagram of our lungs and explain how the air is forced in and out as we breathe.

8. Since there is no such thing as suction, how is it that soda water can be brought up into one's mouth with a straw?

Problems

1. A hollow glass sphere 8 inches in diameter is evacuated. Calculate the total inward force on the outside surface under standard atmospheric pressure of 15 lb/in². (*Note:* The area of a sphere is $4\pi r^2$.)

2. A circular screen of a TV picture tube is 20 in. in diameter. With the tube thoroughly evacuated and standard atmospheric pressure outside, what is the total inward force on the screen? Assume the screen to be flat.

3. Magdeburg hemispheres, with an internal diameter of 4 in., are put together and thoroughly evacuated. What minimum force will pull them apart under normal atmospheric pressure?

4. One Magdeburg hemisphere, 2 ft in diameter, has a thick glass plate placed over the opening and then evacuated. Calculate the total inward force on the glass plate.

5. If a cylindrical tin can 8 cm in diameter and 10 cm tall were thoroughly evacuated, what would be the force on each end?

6. If a barometer contains water in place of mercury, how high will the water column be at sea level?

7. Magdeburg hemispheres with an internal diameter of 10 cm are put together and thoroughly evacuated. What minimum force (in newtons) will pull them apart at sea level?

8. The cylinder and piston in Fig. G have an internal diameter of 6 in. What maximum load can be lifted by the piston as the cylinder is evacuated? Assume atmospheric pressure to be 15 lb/in².

9. A cylindrical pipe 20 in. in diameter has flat brass plates on the ends. If the pipe is thoroughly evacuated, find the total inward force exerted by the outside air on each plate.

10. If a tin can 10 cm in diameter were thoroughly evacuated, what would be the force on each end (in newtons) tending to collapse it?

Properties of Matter | **Lesson 10**

DENSITY OF AIR—*Laboratory*

This experiment is described in the accompanying LABORATORY EXERCISES and is devoted to the weighing of a measured volume of air. From the mass and volume the density can be computed.

Properties of Matter | **Lesson 11**

FLUIDS IN MOTION

The term fluid applies to any substance capable of flowing and includes gases as well as liquids. Since all fluids have mass, Newton's Second Law of Motion implies that unbalanced forces are required to set them in motion. As a matter of practical interest we will consider the various means by which such forces are obtained, how they are applied to fluids, and what factors control the resultant motion. In these discussions the student would do well to keep in mind the fact that liquids are practically incompressible.

Velocity Through an Orifice. Many city water supply systems store water in reser-

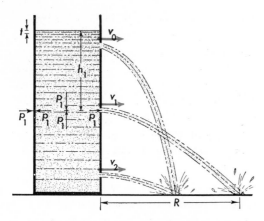

Fig. A. The velocity of efflux through a hole in the side of a vessel of water increases with depth.

in motion is gravity acting through the liquid as pressure. We have already seen how the pressure at any given depth is the same in all directions. At a depth h_1 (see Fig. A), the liquid exerts a pressure p_1 against the walls and the walls exert an equal and opposite pressure against the liquid.

The instant an opening is made in the side of the vessel the wall pressure is destroyed at that point and the liquid pressure inside pushes the liquid directly in front of the hole, giving it an acceleration outward and normal to the plane of the opening. To find the velocity of escape, consider the potential energy of the liquid body in the vessel when the hole is first opened and then a short time later when a small amount of liquid has escaped, dropping the surface level a distance *t*.

voirs on some hilltop or in a nearby water tower, and from these run the water through pipes into the houses, stores, and factories in and around the city. Such an arrangement is called a **gravity system.**

When a hole is opened in the side of a vessel containing a liquid, the velocity of flow through the orifice increases with depth. Here the unbalanced force setting the liquid

As far as energy is concerned the change is the same as though the top layer of water had been lowered a distance **h** and its potential energy **mgh** converted into kinetic energy $\frac{1}{2}$ **mv**^{2} in the emergent stream. By conservation of energy,

Fig. B. Flow of water through a pipe showing the velocity head h_v, friction head h_f, and the pressure head h_p.

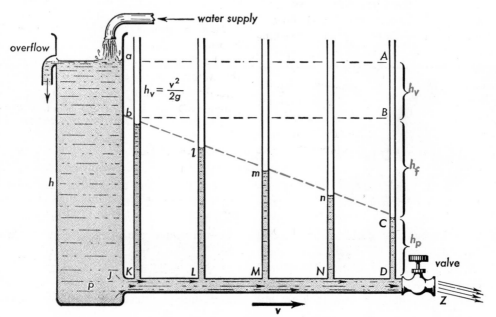

$$mgh = \tfrac{1}{2} mv^2 \qquad (1)$$

Since **m** is the same on both sides it may be canceled, giving

$$v = \sqrt{2\,gh} \qquad (2)$$

the same as the law of falling bodies.

The velocity of efflux at any depth h is equivalent to the velocity acquired by free fall from the same height.

This relation, first discovered by Torricelli, is known as **Torricelli's theorem.***

Flow Through a Pipe. One of the factors determining the flow of water, oil, or gas through a pipe, or the flow of blood through the arteries and veins of the body, is the resistance to flow offered by the confining walls. Consider the experiment shown in Fig. B in which water from a vertical tank at the left is made to flow through a horizontal glass tube at the bottom. The pressure at five equally spaced points along the tube is measured by vertical standpipes, and the velocity of flow is controlled by the valve at the right. By means of a "water supply" and "overflow" pipe the water level in the tank is maintained at a constant level, thus assuring a constant pressure and hence a steady flow.

With the valve closed, the water "seeking its own level" soon brings all standpipes to the same level **aA**. Their heights thereby indicate equal pressures at all points along the pipe **K** to **D**. When the valve is partially opened and a steady flow is attained, the water in each pipe drops to different levels similar to those shown. The more the valve is opened, the more rapid is the flow and the steeper is the straight line **blmnC**.

Since at all times the heights of columns **bK**, **lL**, **mM**, **nN**, and **CD** measure the pressures at the points **K**, **L**, **M**, **N**, and **D**, respec-

tively, the straight line **bC** indicates a smooth and uniform drop in pressure all along the pipe from **K** to **D**. Such a drop in pressure, designated h_f in the figure, is due to **fluid friction** in the pipe and is called the **friction head**. By measuring the friction head for different rates of flow, a comparison of the results will show that h_f is proportional to the square of the velocity. This may be expressed as an equation

$$h_f = Kv^2 \qquad (3)$$

where **K** is the proportionality constant.

At extremely low velocities which are seldom realized, the friction head is proportional to **v**.

The pronounced drop in level from **a** in the tank to **b** in the first standpipe measures the drop in pressure at **K** where the water is practically at rest in the tank and is then speeded up to a velocity **v** upon entering the pipe. Just as in Torricelli's theorem, the drop in potential energy from **a** to **b** is converted into kinetic energy in the stream, and by Eq. (2)

$$h_v = \frac{v^2}{2\,g} \qquad (4)$$

Here h_v equals **ab** and is the **velocity head.**

The final pressure at the point **D** where the water is being drawn from the pipe is directly measured by the height of the liquid column **CD**, and is called the **pressure head** h_p.

Viscosity of Liquids. If a thick syrup or heavy oil is subjected to pressure and made

* Evangelista Torricelli (1608-1647), Italian physicist and mathematician and disciple of Galileo. He is most noted for his scientific articles on fluid motion, on the theory of projectiles, and on geometrical optics.

Fig. C. The water in a river flows fastest at the top surface.

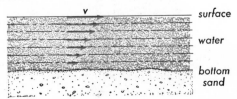

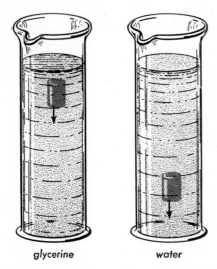

glycerine   water

Fig. D. The rate at which a weight settles in a fluid is a measure of viscosity.

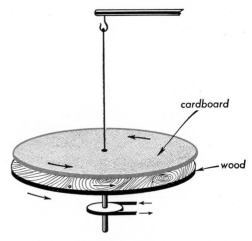

cardboard

wood

Fig. E. Because of the viscosity of the air the cardboard dish is carried around by the rotating disk below.

to flow through a pipe, the rate of flow will not be so great as when gasoline or water is sent through the same pipe under the same total pressure. This difference in rate of flow is due to an internal fluid resistance called viscosity. In some ways viscosity resembles the friction between solids and in other respects it is quite different.

Consider the slow steady flow of water over the sandy bed of a river or stream. See Fig. C. Flow measurements show that the speed is a maximum at the top surface and decreases with depth, becoming approximately zero at the bottom.

If we imagine the water divided into thin layers as indicated, it will be seen that the motion is such that the layers are sliding over one another. Because of the interlocking forces between molecules, the sandy river bed tends to keep the bottom layer from moving at all, the bottom layer in turn tends to

hold back the second layer, this second layer tends to hold back the third, etc.

Since the division into layers is an arbitrary one, we see that all the way up through the liquid there must be frictional forces tending to resist relative motion. The greater the resistance to motion, the greater is the viscosity.

A simple demonstration of the effect of viscosity on the flow of a liquid around an obstacle is given in Fig. D. Two identical weights are dropped simultaneously, one into water and one into glycerine. In water the weight settles quickly, but in glycerine the descent is very slow.

A demonstration of the viscosity of gases is illustrated in Fig. E. A cardboard disk suspended at its center by a thread is placed close to but not touching a wooden disk. When the latter is set into rapid rotation, the cardboard disk begins to rotate in the same direction and gradually picks up speed.

Summary

The velocity of escape of a liquid through a hole in the side of a liquid tank is equivalent to the velocity acquired by free fall from the liquid surface to the opening. This is known as Torricelli's theorem

$$v = \sqrt{2\,gh}$$

Friction arising from the flow of a liquid through a pipe gives rise to a decrease in pressure along the pipe. The change in pressure is called the friction head and is proportional to the square of the velocity

$$h_f = Kv^2$$

The height h is called the velocity head and is the liquid height required to set the liquid mass into motion

$$h_v = \frac{v^2}{2g}$$

Internal friction in a fluid is called viscosity. Because of the interlocking forces between molecules, layers near the confining channel walls move with lower velocities, thereby giving rise to continual distortions in the fluid. The forces act to oppose the distortion and to dissipate energy.

Questions

1. What is a fluid? What is an orifice? What fluids are readily compressible? What fluids are very nearly incompressible?

2. What determines the velocity of escape of a liquid through an orifice? What is Torricelli's theorem? Write down the equation.

3. What is meant by the velocity head for water flowing through a pipe? What is the friction head? How does the velocity head vary with the velocity of the liquid? How does the friction head vary?

4. What is viscosity? Name two liquids having high viscosity and two liquids with low viscosity.

5. Where in a water pipe is the velocity highest? Where is the velocity lowest?

6. In which liquid, oil or water, will a stone sink the most rapidly?

7. Do gases qualify as fluids? Do gases have viscosity? How could you demonstrate the viscosity of a gas?

8. If a freely suspended pendulum is set swinging, why will it slow down and stop? Would it stop more quickly if submerged in oil?

Problems

1. A water tank develops a hole in the side 2.5 meters below the water surface. Find the velocity of efflux?

2. A farmer's milk can develops a hole in the side 40 cm below the liquid level inside. Find the escape velocity of the milk.

3. A cylindrical tank 20 ft high and full of water develops a hole in its side 16 ft below the top. Find the velocity of the water flowing through the orifice. 32 F.

4. At what speed will the velocity head of a stream of water be equal to 15 cm of mercury?

5. A cylindrical tank 8 m high and full of water has a horizontal pipe connected near the bottom and running into a house. If water flows through the pipe at 2 m/sec, what is the velocity head?

6. A cylindrical tank 80 ft high and full of water develops a hole in its side 16 ft below the top. How far from the base of the tank will the emerging water strike the ground? See Fig. A.

7.* Water flowing with a velocity of 2 m/sec in a pipe 4 cm² in cross section enters a short section of pipe having a cross section of 1 cm². Calculate (a) the velocity in the smaller pipe. Find the velocity head in (b) the larger pipe and (c) the smaller pipe.

8.* Water flowing with a velocity of 1 m/sec in a pipe 3 cm in diameter enters a section having a diameter of only 1 cm. Find (a) the velocity in the second pipe, (b) the velocity head in the larger pipe, and (c) the velocity head in the smaller pipe.

Properties of Matter | **Lesson 12**

FLUID FRICTION—*Laboratory*

This experiment is described in the accompanying LABORATORY EXERCISES. Water in a reservoir is sent through a horizontal glass pipe. Pressure differences along the pipe are determined from standpipes, and the velocity heads and friction heads are determined from various measurements.

Properties of Matter | **Lesson 13**

. BERNOULLI'S PRINCIPLE

When a river runs through broad open country, the water runs slowly; but when it comes to a narrow rocky gorge, its velocity increases many fold. Similarly, when a gas or liquid flowing through a pipe comes to a narrow constricted section, the velocity increases as it enters the constriction and decreases again as it leaves the other end. This is illustrated by an experiment diagramed in Fig. A.

The arrangement is the same as in the preceding lesson, Fig. A, except that the horizontal flow pipe contains a short section **DE** having only half the cross-sectional area as elsewhere. When the valve is opened and a condition of steady flow exists, the water in the standpipes will have dropped from **sr** to new levels like **a**, **b**, **d**, etc., as shown. It is to be noted that, as the water enters the constriction at **C**, the velocity of flow increases and the pressure drops from **c** to **l**. Farther along where it leaves the narrow tube at **F**, the velocity decreases and the pressure rises from **f** to **k**.

This illustrates Bernoulli's principle which may be stated as follows:

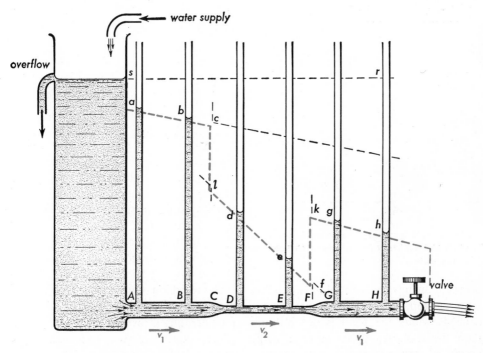

Fig. A. Where the velocity of a fluid increases, the pressure drops, and where the velocity of a fluid decreases, the pressure rises.

Where the velocity of a fluid is high the pressure is low, and where the velocity of a fluid is low the pressure is high.

Experiments Illustrating Bernoulli's Theorem. Bernoulli's theorem is often referred to as a physical paradox and is the basis of many interesting phenomena. A number of experiments involving this principle will be described. In the first illustration (a) in Fig. B a blast of air from a nozzle is blown between two sheets of cardboard suspended about 3 in. apart by cords. Instead of being

Fig. B. Demonstrations of Bernoulli's principle.

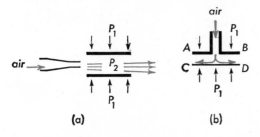

(a)　　　　　　　　(b)

blown apart, as one might expect, they come together. The reason for this action is that, between the two sheets where the velocity of the air is high, the pressure p_2 is low. On the two outside surfaces where the air is not moving, the pressure p_1 (atmospheric pressure) is high and pushes the two sheets together.

In the second diagram (b) air is blown through a hole in the center of a disk **AB** as shown. When a piece of paper **CD** is placed close to the opening, it is not blown away but is drawn toward the disk. Where the velocity of air between the disk and paper is high, the pressure is low; and the higher pressure p_1 on the underside of the paper pushes it up against the disk.

One often hears it said that, during a certain windstorm, tornado, or hurricane, the roofs of one or more houses were blown off without otherwise damaging the house. This is not as freakish an accident as one might think, for there is a simple explanation. A

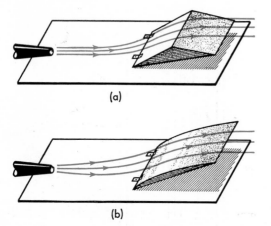

(a)

(b)

Fig. C. Experiments illustrating the lifting forces on a roof and an airfoil when a fast stream of air is blown over the top surface.

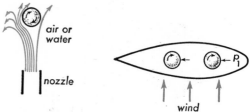

Fig. E. Demonstrations involving Bernoulli's principle.

high wind blowing over the roof creates a low pressure on top, and the atmospheric pressure inside where the wind is not blowing lifts off the roof. An excellent experiment illustrating the phenomenon is shown in Fig. C. A jet of compressed air is blown over the surface of a board on which is located a balsa wood model of a house roof or an airplane wing, hinged at one edge.

Diagram (a) in Fig. D represents a common form of perfume atomizer. Squeezing the bulb sends a stream of air through the central tube, creating a low pressure p_2 inside. Atmospheric pressure p_1 on the liquid surface pushes liquid up the stem to be blown out the right-hand tube with the air stream.

Most of the baseballs thrown by a pitcher are curves, some up or down and others in or out, i.e., to right or left. This is an art, accomplished by throwing the ball so that it spins rapidly about some particular axis. To produce a downward curve, i.e., a **drop ball,**

Fig. D. Demonstrations involving Bernoulli's principle.

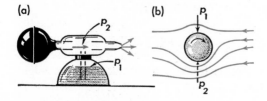

(a)   (b)

the ball is given a top spin as shown in diagram (b). Here instead of having the ball moving to the right we can imagine the ball standing still, but spinning, and the air to be moving from right to left.

At the top surface where the wind and ball are moving in opposite directions, the air is slowed down by friction, giving rise to a high-pressure region. On the underside the surface moving with the wind keeps the velocity high, thus creating a low-pressure region. The resultant downward force thus causes the ball to drop faster than usual.

If a small Ping-pong ball is placed in a vertical stream of air or water, it will rise to a given height above the nozzle and stay at that level, spinning and bobbing around without falling. If the ball goes to one side as illustrated in Fig. E, the fluid going by on the left side causes the ball to spin as shown. The velocity being high on the left means a low pressure. The higher pressure on the right where the velocity is low pushes the ball back into the stream.

The same principle has been applied to the historical **Flettner rotor ship** which, instead of using sails, employed two tall, rotating cylinders, motor driven. As shown by the top-view diagram, Fig. E, a wind from broadside the ship produces a forward force. Such a ship, carrying a cargo, crossed the Atlantic twice not many years ago. Although the trips were successful, the uncertainty of a strong wind makes shipping with such boats unreliable.

The Lift of an Airplane Wing. The major part of the lift of an airplane wing is due

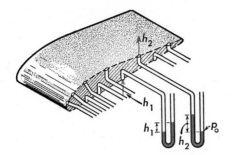

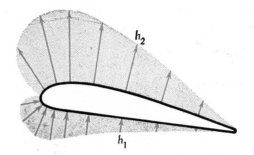

Fig. F. Experimental arrangement of mercury manometers showing how the air pressure can be measured at various points over the surface of an airfoil.

Fig. G. Diagram of an airfoil showing pressure differences over the surfaces.

to the top surface. This discovery has been made in laboratory wind tunnels by setting up sections of airfoils in fast moving currents of air and measuring the pressure at various regions of the surface with pressure gauges. Fig. F shows how this can be done with mercury manometers connected by long tubes to small openings on the top and bottom surfaces.

When the air is still, all manometer tubes show equal heights in their two arms and normal atmospheric pressure p_0 exists at all points inside the hollow wing as well as outside. When the air stream is set in motion,

manometers connected to the top surface show a drop from atmospheric pressure while those connected below show a rise. Since atmospheric pressure on the outside surfaces was previously counterbalanced at all points by the atmospheric pressure inside the hollow wing, the manometer readings h_1 and h_2 give directly the resultant pressures on the two wing coverings.

A graphical representation of the manometer pressures is shown in Fig. G. Note the very large effect of the upper surface as compared with the lower surface, particularly near the leading edge.

Summary

Bernoulli's theorem involves liquid pressure under steady flow in a nonviscous incompressible fluid. Although no liquid fulfills these conditions perfectly, water comes close to it.

In simple words, the theorem states that where the velocity of a fluid is high the pressure is low, and where the velocity of a fluid is low the pressure is high. This is somewhat of a paradox but one that is verified by experiment.

The lift of an airplane wing, an atomizer, and a curving baseball are explained by Bernoulli's theorem.

Questions

1. What is Bernoulli's theorem? To what kind of fluids does it apply?

2. Why does a baseball curve when it is thrown with a spin? What direction must the ball spin in order to curve "out" for a right-handed batter? Make a diagram.

3. How does a Ping-pong ball stay on top of a vertical water jet? Make a diagram and explain how Bernoulli's theorem is involved.

4. Which of the two surfaces, upper or lower, gives rise to the greatest lifting force on an airplane wing?

5. What was the Flettner rotor ship? For what purpose was it built? Was it successful? Was it practical?

6. Why is the roof of a house easily blown off in a windstorm or tornado? Explain. Make a diagram.

7. How does an atomizer work? What brings the liquid up the stem? Make a diagram and explain.

8. Briefly outline some project you might carry out to demonstrate Bernoulli's theorem or its application.

Properties of Matter | **Lesson 14**

VIBRATIONS AND WAVES

Simple Harmonic Motion. Most solid objects in nature are set into vibration when struck a sudden blow. Any motion, simple or complex, which repeats itself in equal intervals of time is called **periodic motion**. There are many examples in everyday life which give rise to a special kind of periodic motion called **simple harmonic motion**. The swinging of the clock pendulum, the turning of the balance wheel of a watch, or the vibration of a tuning fork are good examples of such motions. The term simple harmonic motion applies to these because each can be described in terms of one of the simplest known types of periodic motion, namely, **uniform circular motion**.

Simple harmonic motion is defined as the projection on any diameter of a point moving in a circle with uniform speed. This is illustrated in Fig. A. The point **p** moves around the circle of radius **r** with uniform speed **v**. If at every instant a perpendicular is drawn from **p** to the diameter **AB**, the intercept **P** will move with simple harmonic motion. Moving back and forth along the straight line **AB**, the velocity v_x is continually changing. At the center point **C** it has its greatest velocity, while at **A** and **B** it is momentarily at rest. Starting from either end of its path the velocity increases until it reaches **C**; from there it slows down again, coming to rest at the opposite end of its path.

The amplitude r of any simple harmonic motion is defined as the maximum value of the displacement x, and the period is defined as the time required to make one complete vibration.

Fig. A. Diagram illustrating simple harmonic motion along a straight line.

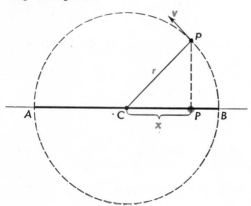

If a vibration starts at **A**, it is not completed until the point moves across to **B** and back again to **A**. If it starts from **C** and moves to **B** and back to **C**, only half a vibration has been completed. The amplitude **r** is usually measured in centimeters and the period **T** in seconds.

The frequency of any harmonic motion is defined as the number of complete vibrations per second. For example, if a particular vibrating object completes one vibration in one-half second (the period $T = \frac{1}{2}$ sec), then it will make two complete vibrations in 1 sec (the frequency $n = 2$ vib/sec). If again a body completes one vibration in one tenth of a second, $T = 1/10$ sec, it will make ten vibrations in 1 sec, $n = 10$ vib/sec. In other words, **n** and **T** are reciprocals of each other.

$$period = \frac{1}{frequency} \qquad (1)$$

In algebraic symbolism,

$$T = \frac{1}{n} \qquad (2)$$

The Spring Pendulum. Two kinds of pendulums are shown in Fig. B. The first consists of a mass **m** fastened securely to the lower end of a coil spring. If the mass is raised to the point **A** as shown, and released, the mass will move up and down with simple harmonic motion and with an amplitude **a**.

Fig. B. Two types of spring pendulums.

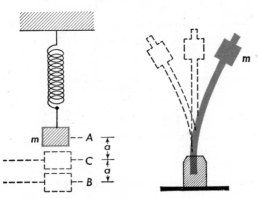

The second pendulum consists of a mass **m** attached securely to a leaf spring. Pulled to one side or the other, it too will vibrate with a definite frequency and period. The period **T** of both of these spring pendulums is given by the formula

$$T = 2\pi\sqrt{\frac{m}{k}} \qquad (3)$$

where **k** is the spring constant given by Hooke's law.

$$F = -kx$$

See Properties of Matter, Lesson 1, Eq. (2). The stiffer the spring, the larger is the spring constant **k** and the shorter is the period **T**.

The Simple Pendulum. A simple pendulum consists of a mass **m**, called the **bob**, fastened to one end of a lightweight cord, wire, or rod, and free to swing about a pivot point **P** as shown in Fig. C.

When such a pendulum is set swinging in an arc that is relatively short, its period **T** is given by the following formula

$$T = 2\pi\sqrt{\frac{l}{g}} \qquad (4)$$

Fig. C. To double the period of a simple pendulum the length must be increased fourfold.

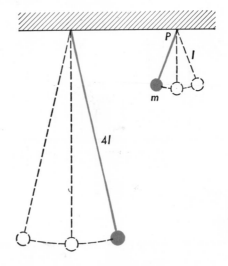

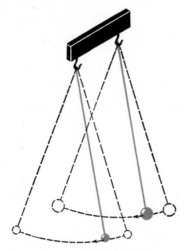

Fig. D. Two simple pendulums of the same length but different mass have the same period of vibration.

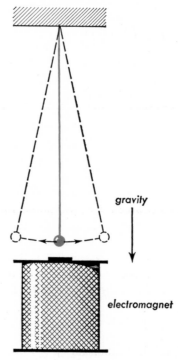

Fig. E. An increase in gravitational attraction, like the downward pull of the magnet, will shorten the period of a simple pendulum.

The length of the pendulum *l* is the distance from the pivot **P** to the center of mass of the bob, and **g** is the acceleration due to gravity. The fact that the mass of the bob does not appear in Eq. (4) signifies that pendulums of equal length but different mass have the same period. See Fig. D.

The effect of the acceleration of gravity **g** on the period is illustrated in Fig. E. If the pull of gravity could be increased, the period of all pendulums would decrease, that is, they would swing faster. If gravity could be decreased, the periods would be greater, that is, they would swing more slowly. In the diagram the pull of gravity is imitated by means of an electromagnet. When the magnet is turned on it pulls down on the iron bob and makes it swing more quickly.

Transverse Waves. The motion of any

Fig. F. Diagram of a wave machine for demonstrating transverse waves.

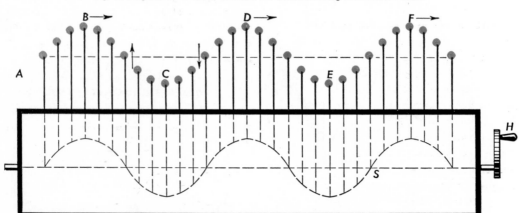

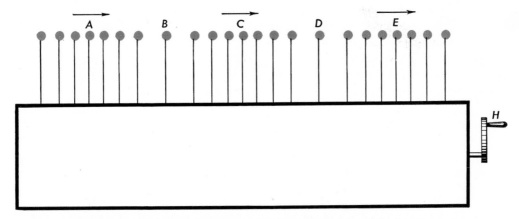

Fig. G. Diagram of a wave machine for demonstrating longitudinal waves.

material object may be considered as a source of waves. A board striking the water, the snap of a finger, or a bowed violin string are examples of this.

Transverse waves are those in which each particle vibrates along a line perpendicular to the direction of propagation. Along any one line of travel all particles are vibrating in one plane only. Such waves are illustrated in Fig. F by means of a wave machine designed for this purpose. As the handle **H** is turned one way or the other, the small round balls at the top move up and down with simple harmonic motion. As they move up and down, each along its own line, the wave form **ABCDEF** will move to the right or to the left. Light is an example of transverse wave motion.

Longitudinal Waves. Longitudinal waves are those in which the vibrations of the particles are along straight lines parallel to the direction of propagation. This type of wave is illustrated in Fig. G by another wave machine. As the handle is turned, each small ball moves horizontally and in the plane of the page with simple harmonic motion. In so doing the regions of rarefaction **B** and **D** and the regions of condensation **A**, **C**, and **E** move to the right, always keeping their same relative distances.

Sound waves in air are examples of longi-

tudinal waves. Each air molecule vibrates back and forth about some equilibrium position as the wave train passes by.

Wave Length. When a vibrating object sends out waves through a homogeneous medium, the waves travel with constant velocity. If the source vibrates with simple harmonic motion and waves are transverse, they have the general appearance of the waves shown in Fig. H. *The wave length is defined as the distance between two similar points of any two consecutive waves* and is represented by the Greek letter lamba λ. The distance between two consecutive wave crests, for example, is equal to one wave length.

The amplitude of a wave is defined as the maximum value of the displacement. This is illustrated by **r** in Fig. H, the amplitude of the waves being proportional to the amplitude of the source. *The frequency of a train of waves is defined as the number of waves passing any given point per second.* This is equal to the frequency of the source

Fig. H. Illustrating the factors concerning waves and wave motion.

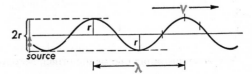

and is usually designated by **n.** It is customary to express frequency in **vibrations per second** or in **cycles per second.**

$$V = n\lambda \qquad (5)$$

From the definitions of velocity, frequency, and wave length the following very simple relation exists between them:

The length of one wave λ times the number of waves per second **n** equals the total distance traveled in 1 sec **V.**

Summary

Most solid objects in nature are set into vibration when struck a sudden blow. Most vibrations may be described as simple harmonic motion. SHM may be defined as the projection on a diameter of a point moving on a circle with uniform speed.

The period **T** and frequency **n** of any vibrating object are reciprocals of each other. The vibration period of a mass on the end of a spring depends upon the mass **m** and the spring constant **k,** and does not depend upon the amplitude.

The period and frequency of a simple pendulum depend only upon the length of the pendulum and the acceleration due to gravity. If the amplitude is not too large, the frequency will not change with amplitude.

Waves travel through a medium with a velocity given by the wave equation $V = n\lambda$. The wave length λ is the distance between like points on consecutive waves, **n** is the frequency, and **V** is the velocity or speed.

Questions

1. What is periodic motion? What is simple harmonic motion? Why are we interested in such motions?

2. What is amplitude? What is meant by the frequency of a simple harmonic motion? What is the period of vibration? What is the relation between period and frequency?

3. Upon what factors does the vibration frequency of a spring depend? Does the frequency change with amplitude?

4. Upon what two factors does the frequency of a simple pendulum depend? Does the frequency change with amplitude? How can you double the period of a simple pendulum?

5. What are transverse waves? How can you demonstrate transverse waves?

6. What are longitudinal waves? Are such waves found in nature? Give an example.

7. What is meant by wave length? What is the amplitude of a wave?

8. What three factors are involved in the general wave equation? Write down the equation?

9. Think of some project in which you might make a simple and inexpensive device for demonstrating one of the principles developed in this lesson.

Problems

1. A steel spring vibrates with a frequency of 260 vib/sec. Find the period.

2. A strip of bronze clamped at one end vibrates with a period of 0.0125 sec. Find its frequency.

3. (a) Find the period of a simple pendulum 20 m long. (b) What is its frequency?

4. Find the length in meters and inches, of a "seconds pendulum." A seconds pendulum is one for which the period is one second.

5. Find the period and frequency of a pendulum 1 m long.

6. What length pendulum in meters will have a frequency of 10 vib/sec?

7. A tuning fork with a frequency of 500 vib/sec sends out sound waves having a wave length of 27 in. Find the speed of the waves.

8. Transverse waves, traveling along a stretched cord with a speed of 50 ft/sec, have a wave length of 2.5 in. Calculate the frequency.

9. A tuning fork of frequency 250 vib/sec sends out sound waves with a speed of 355 m/sec. Find the wave length.

10.* A mass of 50 gm hangs from the lower end of a coil spring. (a) What will be its period of vibration if the spring constant is 2000 dynes/cm? (b) What is the frequency?

11.* A 16-lb weight hangs from the end of a coil spring. (a) What will be its period of vibration if the spring constant is 4 lb/in.? (b) What is the frequency?

12.* A mass of 1 kg hanging from the lower end of a spring stretches it 1 cm. What period and frequency will this system have when set into vibration?

13.* A 32-lb weight supported at the end of a coil spring stretches it 6 in. What period and frequency will this system have when it is set into vibration?

Properties of Matter | **Lesson 15**

THE PENDULUM—*Laboratory*

In performing this experiment as described in the accompanying LABO- RATORY EXERCISES you will measure the vibration frequencies of coil springs and simple pendulums. These measured frequencies are compared with those calcu- lated from measured spring constants and pendulum lengths.

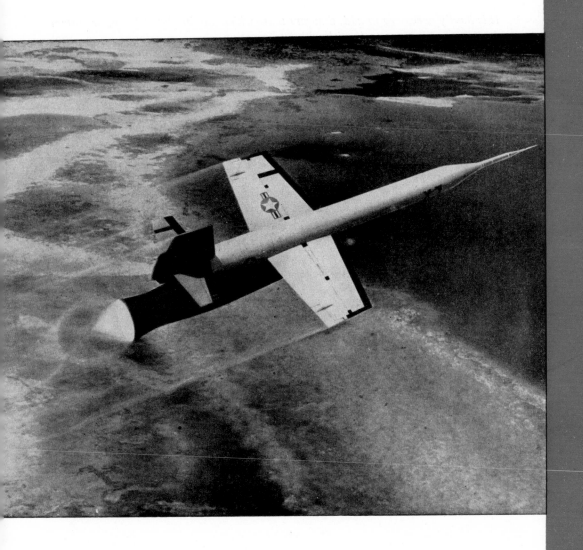

HEAT

It is hardly necessary to add, that any thing which any insulated *body, or system of bodies, can continue to furnish* without limitation, *cannot possibly be a* material substance: *and it appears to me to be extremely difficult, if not quite impossible, to form any distinct idea of any thing, capable of being excited, and communicated, in the manner the heat was excited and communicated in these experiments, except it be MOTION.*

> Lord Rumford—*An Experimental Inquiry Concerning the Source of the Heat Which Is Excited by Friction*

Heat is nothing but motive power, or rather motion which has changed form. It is a motion of the particles of bodies. Wherever there is destruction of motive power, there is, at the same time, production of heat in an amount precisely proportional to the quantity of motive power which has been destroyed. Reciprocally, wherever there is destruction of heat, there is the production of motive power.

One might then propose as a general thesis, that motive power is a constant quantity in nature, that it is never, properly speaking, produced or destroyed. In truth, it changes form, that is to say it produces now one kind of movement, now another; but it is never annihilated.

> Sadi Carnot—from his notebook

← **An artist's conception of the experimental X-7A in flight. The rocket engine is based on a flow of fuel and air being directed and ignited through exhaust pipes, the thrust coming from the momentum exerted on the burned gases.**

> **Lockheed Missiles and Space Division**
> **Lockheed Aircraft Corporation**

Temperature and Expansion

TEMPERATURE is only relative and, like *time,* is difficult to define in terms of the simplest concepts. The word *temperature* means intensity of heat and may be defined as a number on a scale.

Thermometers. The first authentic record of a thermometer dates back to the time of Galileo. Galileo's thermometer, as illustrated in Fig. A, consists of a narrow glass tube with an opening at one end and a bulb at the other. The open end of the tube is filled with colored water and inverted in a dish of water. When the temperature of the surrounding air rises, the air within the bulb expands, forcing the water down the tube. If the bulb is cooled, the air inside contracts, drawing the water up. (To be exact, atmospheric pressure outside pushes the water up.) A scale attached to the narrow tube can be calibrated to any temperature scale, low temperatures at the top and high temperatures at the bottom.

Of the many forms of temperature measuring devices, the mercury thermometer is the most common. See Fig. B. A mercury thermometer consists of a narrow glass tube (called a capillary), the bottom end being sealed to a small bulb and the top end being closed. The bulb and part of the capillary

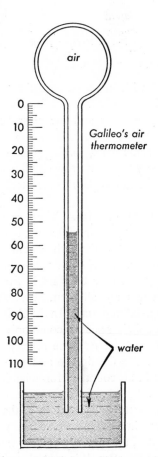

Fig. A. Air on heating expands and pushes the water down in the tube. On cooling, the air contracts and the water rises.

207

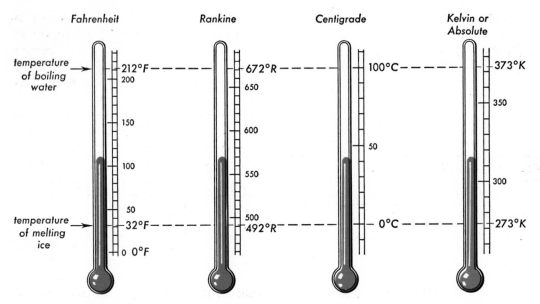

Fig. B. Mercury thermometers illustrating the four common temperature scales.

are filled with mercury, and the remaining section is evacuated. When the temperature rises, the mercury and the glass bulb both expand. The mercury, however, expands more than the glass, forcing a small part of the mercury up the narrow capillary. A scale is engraved on the glass to read temperature.

Temperature Scales. There are in general use today four different temperature scales. These are the Fahrenheit, Rankine, Centigrade, and Kelvin, or Absolute. Each scale is shown by a diagram in Fig. B. The thermometers are all identically made, but each has a different scale. In the United States the Fahrenheit scale is commonly used in civil life, and the Rankine scale is used by engineers. The Centigrade and Kelvin scales are used in all countries for scientific measurements.

To calibrate a thermometer, the bulb is first placed in a mixture of ice and water and the height of the mercury column marked on the side of the stem. It is next placed in steam just above boiling water and again marked. These two marks then determine two fixed

points in Fig. B for whatever scale is to be used.

Between the temperatures of melting ice and boiling water there are 180° on the Fahrenheit and Rankine scales, as compared with 100° on the Centigrade and Kelvin scales. The ratio of these numbers is 9:5. This comparison shows that a temperature rise of 9°F, or 9°R, is equivalent to a rise of only 5°C, or 5°K.

The lowest temperature ever reached is approximately −273.16°C, or −459.69°F. For theoretical reasons, which will be given later, this is the lowest temperature that can ever be attained. The Kelvin and Rankine scales start with the lowest possible temperature as **absolute zero.** On the basis of the Centigrade and Fahrenheit scale divisions, this locates the freezing point of water, to the nearest whole number, at 273°K or 492°R, and the boiling point at 373°K or 672°R.

It is frequently necessary to change temperature readings from one temperature scale to another. Rather than develop formulas for such changes it is more convenient to work

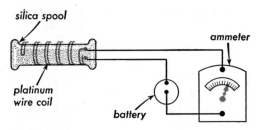

Fig. C. Electrical-resistance thermometer showing connections between the platinum wire coil, the battery, and the ammeter.

out the simple mathematical steps by the inspection of a diagram like Fig. B.

For example a change from 0°C to 100°C is equivalent to a change from 32°F to 212°F. Consequently

100 C degrees = 180 F degrees

or

5 C degrees = 9 F degrees

Therefore,

0°C = 32°F, 5°C = 41°F, 10°C = 50°F, 15°C = 59°F, etc.

Electrical Thermometers. If very low or very high temperatures are to be measured, other than mercury thermometers must be employed.

A diagram of an **electrical thermometer** is shown in Fig. C. A fine piece of platinum wire is wound around a small spool made of silica. The ends of this wire are connected to a battery and an ammeter. The purpose of the battery is to supply the electric current and the ammeter is to determine its exact value. When the temperature of a hot body like a furnace is to be measured, the spool of platinum wire is placed inside the furnace and the battery and ammeter outside. A rise in temperature causes the resistance of the platinum wire to increase, and the current, therefore, to decrease. When the platinum wire reaches the temperature of the furnace, its resistance reaches a constant value and the ammeter pointer indicates a steady current. In many cases the ammeter scale is calibrated to give the temperature in degrees.

Another form of electrical thermometer, called a **thermocouple,** is illustrated in Fig. D. This temperature recording device is based upon a principle, discovered in 1821 by Seebeck, known as the **thermo-electric effect.** Two pieces of wire, one copper and one iron, are joined together at the ends to form a complete loop. When one junction is heated and the other kept cool, an electric current flows around the loop in the direction indicated by the arrows. The greater the difference in temperature between the two junctions the greater is the electric current.

Fig. E represents a thermocouple connected by wires to an ammeter. If the junction of the thermocouple is first placed in

Fig. D. A thermocouple.

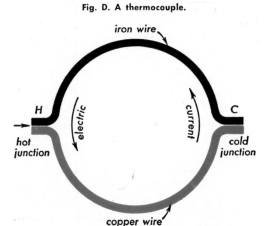

copper wire

Fig. E. A thermocouple thermometer circuit diagram.

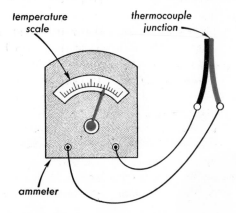

melting ice and then in boiling water, the two scale readings of the ammeter can be marked 0°C and 100°C at the appropriate points. This calibrates the instrument, making of it a direct reading thermometer.

Thermocouples are not always made of copper and iron as shown in Fig. D. Any two different metals when brought into contact will exhibit a thermo-electric effect. Some combinations of two metals, however, produce larger currents than others. For very high temperature measurements platinum and platinum-iridium alloys are used, owing to their very high melting point temperatures.

Thermal Expansion of Solids. In general, when an object is heated—whether it be a solid, liquid, or gas—it expands. There are but a few known exceptions to this. The expansion of a solid with a rise in temperature can be demonstrated by heating a long wire and measuring its over-all elongation. One experimental arrangement for demonstrating this is shown in Fig. F. An iron wire about 2 m in length is fastened to a hook **A** at one end and to a weight **W** at the other.

Fig. F. Demonstration of thermal expansion.

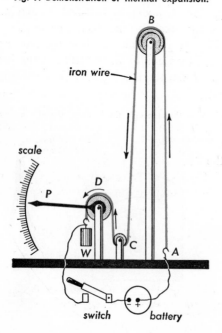

Between these two points the wire passes over three pulleys **B**, **C**, and **D**. The wire is heated by connecting it to a battery and sending an electric current through it from end to end.

As the wire is heated and lengthens, the weight slowly falls, thus turning the pulleys as well as the pointer **P**. When the current is turned off by opening the switch, the wire cools and at the same time contracts to its original length.

Not all substances expand by the same amount when heated through the same difference in temperature. It is common practice to describe the expansion of any solid by specifying its linear coefficient of thermal expansion.

The ratio of the change in length per degree Centigrade to the original length of a substance is called the linear coefficient of thermal expansion.

$$\alpha = \frac{e}{l(t_2 - t_1)} \tag{1}$$

where **e** is the change in length, **l** is the original length, and $t_2 - t_1$ is the change in temperature.

A list of a few common metals with their known values of α are given in Table 1.

Table 1. Linear Coefficients
of Thermal Expansion

Material	α per °C
aluminum	25×10^{-6}
brass	18×10^{-6}
copper	17×10^{-6}
glass (soda)	17×10^{-6}
glass (pyrex)	3×10^{-6}
gold	14×10^{-6}
iron	11×10^{-6}
lead	29×10^{-6}
nickel	13×10^{-6}
platinum	9×10^{-6}
quartz	0.4×10^{-6}
silver	18×10^{-6}
steel (common)	8×10^{-6}

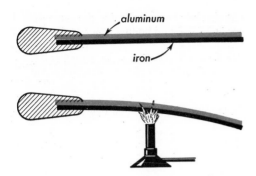

Fig. G. A bimetallic strip bends when heated.

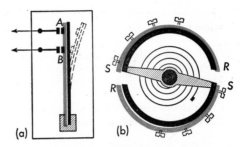

Fig. H. Devices using bimetallic strips: (a) balance wheel of a watch and (b) thermostat.

Since the values of α are known for most materials in common use, the expansion **e** is usually the unknown quantity. Solving Eq. (1) for **e**, we find

$$e = \alpha l(t_2 - t_1) \qquad (2)$$

Example 1. A steel rod is ground and polished to a length of 10 cm when the room temperature is 25°C. What will be its length when the temperature is raised to 300°C?

Solution. In Table 1 we find $\alpha = 8.0 \times 10^{-6}$ per °C. By direct substitution in Eq. (2), we obtain,

$$e = 8.0 \times 10^{-6} \times 10 \times (300 - 25)$$
$$e = 22000 \times 10^{-6} = 0.022 \text{ cm}$$

The rod therefore lengthens by 0.022 cm to give an over-all length of 10.022 cm.

It should be noted that if the length of the rod has been 10 ft the elongation would have been 0.022 ft. In other words **e** and **l** are always in the same units.

Differential Expansion. In the previous section it was stated that all substances do not expand alike. Some metals like brass and aluminum expand twice as much as others, like iron and platinum.

This difference in expansion is demonstrated by the heating of a bimetallic strip as shown in Fig. G. Two thin strips of different metal are placed side by side and welded together over their entire length. When heated, one metal expands more than the other, causing the strip to bend. The hotter it becomes the more it bends. When it cools down to its original temperature, the strip becomes straight again; and if cooled still further, it bends in the opposite direction.

Differential expansion as shown by this experiment finds many practical applications in industry. Bimetallic strips are used, for example, in the making of balance wheels for fine watches and in thermostats for refrigerators, hot water heaters, and car radiators. When on a hot day the spokes of the balance of a watch expand, they shift the weight of the rim farther from the center, causing the balance wheel to oscillate more slowly. By making the rim of the wheel of two bimetallic strips this can be compensated for as shown in Fig. H. With a rise in temperature the ends of the spokes **S** move out and the free ends **R** of the bimetallic strips bend in closer to the axis of rotation. One expansion compensates the other, keeping the watch running at the same rate.

Summary

There are many kinds of thermometers and several temperature scales. Mercury thermometers are the most common and are based upon the principle that mercury expands with a rise in temperature.

The Kelvin, or Absolute, temperature scale starts at absolute zero, and using the same division units as the Centigrade scale, finds melting ice at 273°K and boiling water at 373°K.

Mechanical engineers make extensive use of the Rankine temperature scale, which starts at absolute zero. Using the same division units as the Fahrenheit scale, the Rankine scale finds melting ice at 492°R and boiling water at 672°R.

Five degrees on the Absolute or Centigrade scales are equivalent to nine degrees on the Rankine or Fahrenheit scales.

The electrical resistance thermometer and the thermocouple are used to measure high as well as low temperatures.

Most solids expand on heating and contract on cooling. Different materials expand different amounts, however, and use is made of such differences in bimetallic strips.

The expansion of materials with a rise in temperature is usually specified by a constant called the linear coefficient of thermal expansion.

Questions

1. What are the names of the four temperature scales?

2. At what temperature does ice melt on each of the four temperature scales? At what temperature does water boil?

3. How many degrees are there between the freezing and boiling points of water on each of the four temperature scales?

4. What is an electrical resistance thermometer? What is it used for? What physical property changes with temperature? Where does the electric current come from?

5. What is a thermocouple? Is a battery used to supply the electric current? What metals are used for very high temperature measurements?

6. If you had a mercury thermometer without a scale, how could you make a Centigrade scale for it? A Fahrenheit scale?

7. What is meant by thermal expansion? What is meant by differential expansion?

8. What is a bimetallic strip? What are they used for?

9. How is the thermal expansion of materials generally specified? Define the linear coefficient of thermal expansion? Of what practical use is this constant?

10. What simple and inexpensive device could you make to illustrate one of the principles presented in this lesson? What materials would you need and where would you get them?

11. Could you use the property of thermal expansion to make an accurate thermometer?

Problems

1. What temperature on the Centigrade scale is equivalent to the following: (a) 50°F, (b) 77°F, (c) 95°F?

2. What temperature on the Absolute or Kelvin scale is equivalent to the following: (a) 50°C, (b) −40°C, (c) −40°F?

3. What temperature on the Fahrenheit scale is equivalent to the following: (a) 76°C, (b) 110°C, (c) 32°C, and (d) 40°R?

4. A standard gauge block, made of silver, is exactly 4.000 cm long at 25°C. Calculate its length when the temperature is 60°C.

5. The standard platinum meter bar at the Bureau of Standards is exactly calibrated at 27°C. Find the distance between the end marks when the temperature is 52°C.

6. The iron rails used in building cross-country railroads are 60 ft in length. If at the time they are nailed into place the temperature is 40°C, how large will the gaps be-tween rails be when the temperature drops to −40°C?

7.* A gold strip is made into a ring whose outside diameter is 2.0 cm at 25°C. Find the diameter when the temperature is raised to 75°C.

8.* The iron rim of a wagon wheel has an internal diameter of 1.0 m when the tempera-ture is 150°C. What is its diameter when it cools off to 25°C?

9.* A hole is drilled in a block of copper and reamed to a diameter of 3.60 cm when the temperature is 30°C. What is the diameter when heated to a temperature of 80°C?

10.* A steel tape measure 100 ft long is standardized to be used at 72°F. What will be its error in length when used at a temperature of 0°F?

Heat | Lesson 2

THERMAL EXPANSION—*Laboratory*

In performing this experiment as described in the accompanying LABO-RATORY EXERCISES you will measure the lengths of several different metal rods at room temperature and again at the temperature of steam. The coefficients of thermal expansion are calculated from the recorded data.

Heat | Lesson 3

HEAT CAPACITY AND CHANGE OF STATE

According to the kinetic theory of matter, the individual atoms of which all sub-stances are made are in a state of rapid mo-tion. As a body is heated to a higher tempera-ture, this atomic motion increases and the body expands. As a body cools, the atomic motions decrease and the body shrinks. That heat is a form of energy and is due to the

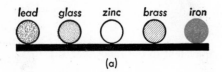

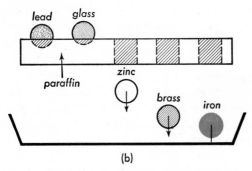

Fig. A. Experiment demonstrating the different heat capacities of different substances of the same size.

kinetic energy of molecular motion was first proposed by Count Rumford the latter part of the eighteenth century.*

The Calorie. The difference between temperature and quantity of heat is well illustrated by the following experiment. See Fig. A. Five marbles, all of the same size but made of different materials, are heated in boiling water to a temperature of 100°C. At a given instant they are all placed on a sheet of paraffin about 0.5 cm thick and permitted to melt their way through. The iron and brass marbles are observed to drop through first, but the lead and glass marbles never do. This illustrates the fact that the heat content of the iron and brass, even though raised to the same temperature as the others, is consid-

* Benjamin Thompson was born in Rumford, New Hampshire, in 1753. He spent most of his adult life in Germany, where, among other things, he managed an artillery factory. From his observations about the heat developed in boring cannon, he was able to show that heat is not a pervading fluid, but a form of internal energy of the atoms or molecules forming the substance. His own expression was that heat was a mode of motion of these particles. For these and other services, the Emperor chose to appoint him to the German nobility, and Thompson chose the name of his birthplace, Rumford, as his title.

erably greater than the heat content of the glass and lead.

In order to determine the exact heat capacity of a substance, we must first define the **calorie** and the **British thermal unit.**

The quantity of heat required to raise the temperature of 1 gm of water 1°C is called the calorie (abbr. cal).

The quantity of heat required to raise the temperature of 1 lb of water 1°F is called the British thermal unit (abbr. BTU).

The ratio between these two units is readily computed and found to be

$$1 \text{ BTU} = 252 \text{ cal} \qquad (1)$$

Once the calorie or the BTU is defined, the amount of heat required to raise any amount of water from one temperature to another may be calculated by simply multiplying the mass of water by the temperature rise. For example, to raise 25 gm of water from 10°C to 50°C requires $25 \times 40 = 1000$ cal, or to raise 6 lb of water from 32°F to 60°F requires $6 \times 28 = 168$ BTU.

While 1 cal of heat will raise 1 gm of water 1°C, a different number of calories will be required to raise the temperature of 1 gm of some other substance 1°C. For example, to raise 1 gm of iron 1°C requires only one tenth of a calorie, while to raise 1 gm of lead 1°C requires only one thirtieth of a calorie. In other words, the thermal capacities of equal masses of different materials have different values.

The thermal capacity of a substance is defined as the number of calories required to raise 1 gm of that substance through 1° C in the cgs system or the amount of heat to raise 1 lb 1°F in the engineering system.

The ratio between the thermal capacity of a substance and the thermal capacity of water is called specific heat.

Numerically **specific heat** has the same value as **thermal capacity;** being a ratio, however, it is like **specific gravity** and has no units.

The specific heats or thermal capacities of a few common substances are given in Table 1.

Table 1. Specific Heats

	c
aluminum............	0.220
brass...............	0.092
copper.............	0.093
glass..............	0.160
gold...............	0.031
glycerine...........	0.60
ice................	0.50
iron...............	0.105
lead...............	0.031
mercury............	0.033
silver.............	0.056
zinc...............	0.092

To illustrate the use of this table, consider the calculation of the heat content of the marbles used in the foregoing experiment. The measured mass of each marble is given in the second column of Table 2 and the corresponding thermal capacity in the next column. The product of these two quantities gives the values shown in the fourth column; they represent the amount of heat required to raise that marble 1°C. Since all marbles

Table 2. Results of Marble Demonstration

Marble	m (gm)	c	H for 1°C	H for 80°C
lead	45	.031	1.39	111
glass	10	.160	1.60	128
zinc	24	.092	2.20	176
brass	30	.092	2.76	221
iron	28	.105	2.94	235

were raised from room temperature 20°C to the boiling point of water, 100°C, the values in the fourth column have been multiplied by the rise in temperature 80°C to obtain the total heat values in the last column.

These numbers clearly indicate that in this experiment iron and brass should melt through the paraffin first: they have available within them the largest amounts of stored thermal energy, 235 and 221 calories, respectively.

The definition of thermal capacity and the calculation of total heat content may be summarized by a generally useful formula of the following form,

$$H = m\,c\,(t_2 - t_1) \qquad (2)$$

H represents the total amount of heat in calories or BTU, *m* the mass of the body to which it is added, *c* is the thermal capacity, and $t_2 - t_1$ is the rise in temperature.

Change of State. The continuous addition of heat to a solid or liquid mass will eventually bring about a change of state. The general behavior of many substances can be illustrated by a detailed description of the changes that occur with the most common of all liquids, water. If a block of ice at a temperature of −50°C is placed in a pan and put on a stove to heat, its temperature will rise slowly until it reaches 0°C.

At 0°C the temperature stops rising and the ice begins to melt. More and more ice is melted as heat is continually added, and not until it has all turned to water does the temperature begin to rise. As the water becomes hotter and hotter, it eventually reaches a temperature of 100°C, when vigorous boiling sets in. Here again the temperature stops rising, and as heat is added, more and more water is boiled away to become steam. Finally when all has become steam at 100°C, the temperature begins to rise once more.

All of these changes of temperature and changes of state are shown by a graph in Fig.

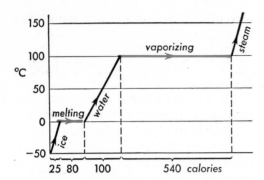

Fig. B. Heat-temperature graph for one gram of ice starting at —50°C. Illustrating the latent heat of fusion and vaporization.

B. The horizontal sections represent changes of state without change in temperature, while the slanted sections on either side represent changes in temperature without abrupt changes in state.

Melting Point. *The melting point is defined as the temperature at which a substance under normal atmospheric pressure changes from the solid to the liquid state, or vice versa.* Every substance has its own melting point, which for water is at 0°C. As shown by a few common substances listed in Table 3, some substances melt at very low temperatures while others require extremely high temperatures.

Recent studies of the atomic structure of certain liquids show that at temperatures approaching the freezing point the lattice formation assumed by the individual atoms is essentially that of the solid state, whereas others show no such resemblance or similarity right up to the freezing temperature.

Boiling Point. *The boiling point is defined as the temperature at which a sub-*

stance, under normal atmospheric pressure, changes from the liquid to the vapor state, or vice versa. These temperatures too are listed in Table 3. A knowledge of melting and

Table 3. The Melting and Boiling Points for a Few Common Substances

Substance	Melting Point °C	Boiling Point °C
air...................	−212	−191
aluminum.............	658	1800
copper...............	1080	2310
gold.................	1063	2500
helium...............	−271	−268
hydrogen.............	−259	−252
iron.................	1530	2450
lead.................	327	1525
mercury..............	−39	357
nitrogen.............	−210	−195
oxygen...............	−219	−184
platinum.............	1760	3910
silicon..............	1420	3500
silver...............	962	1955
sulfur dioxide........	−75	−10
tin..................	232	2270
tungsten.............	3400	5830
water...............	0	100

boiling points is of considerable practical importance. Solid carbon dioxide, liquid air, liquid hydrogen, and liquid helium are used as refrigerants for cooling, whereas metals like tungsten and platinum are used in furnaces designed for the heating of bodies to very high temperatures.

Summary

According to the kinetic theory of matter a rising temperature results in more rapid motions of atoms and molecules and usually results in expansion. Heat is a form of energy and is measured in calories or British thermal units.

The quantity of heat required to raise the temperature of 1 gm of water 1°C is called the calorie.

The quantity of heat required to raise the temperature of 1 lb of water 1°F is called the British thermal unit.

The thermal capacity of a substance is defined as the number of calories required to raise 1 gm of a substance through 1°C. The ratio between the thermal capacity of a substance and the thermal capacity of water is called the specific heat.

The specific heat of water is 1.00, while the specific heats of most substances are considerably smaller. The general formula for the heat content of a body is given by

$$H = mc(t_2 - t_1)$$

Heat is required to change the state of a substance even though its temperature remains constant. The temperatures at which substances melt or boil under normal atmospheric pressure are called their melting and boiling points, respectively.

Questions

1. What is the kinetic theory of matter? What happens when a solid is heated and then cooled?

2. What is a calorie? What is a British thermal unit? Which is the larger?

3. What is the thermal capacity of a substance? What are the units of thermal capacity in the cgs system?

4. What is the specific heat of a substance? What are the units of specific heat?

5. What is the general formula for finding the total heat content of a substance? In what units should each factor be specified?

6. How does one cause the change of state of matter? Will the addition of heat to a body always raise its temperature?

7. What is meant by the boiling point? What is meant by the melting point?

8. What is the melting point of lead? What is the boiling point of lead? What are the melting and boiling points of oxygen?

9. How could you determine the melting point of tin? Could you use a mercury thermometer? (Glass melts at about 450°C.)

Problems

1. How many calories are required to raise the temperature of 5 kg of water from 25°C to 100°C?

2. How many BTU are required to raise the temperature of 35 lb of water from the freezing point to the boiling point?

3. How many calories are required to heat 500 gm of aluminum from 27°C to 152°C?

4. Find the number of calories required to raise the temperature of 2 kg of iron from 24°C to 184°C.

5. A copper cup weighing 200 gm contains 600 gm of water, all at 20°C. How many calories are required to raise their temperature to 100°C?

6. An aluminum cup of mass 180 gm contains 400 gm of water, all at 25°C. How many calories are required to raise their temperature to 100°C?

7. A 2-kg block of iron is placed in a copper cup of mass 100 gm and containing 500 gm of water, all at 25°C. How much heat is required to raise the temperature to 100°C?

8. A 1000-gm gold bar is placed in an aluminum cup of mass 200 gm containing 600 gm of water, all at 30°C. How much heat is required to raise the temperature to 100°C?

9.* A 2 kg block of iron at 100°C is dropped into 750 gm of water contained in a 325-gm copper calorimeter cup. If the initial temperature of the water is 12°C, what will be its final temperature?

Heat | Lesson 4

HEAT TRANSFER

There are numerous methods by which heat may be transmitted from one place to another. Some of these methods are slow and round about, while others are very fast and straight to the point. A careful study of all known methods has led to the realization that there are but three general types of heat transfer. These are **conduction, convection,** and **radiation.** Conduction is a slow process by which heat is transmitted through a substance by molecular activity. Convection is a more rapid process involving the motion of heated matter itself from one place to another. Radiation of heat from one place to another takes place in the same manner and with the same speed as light, 186,000 mi/sec.

Conduction. Not all bodies are good conductors of heat. Metals like copper and silver are much better for this purpose than are other substances like wood, glass, paper, and water. The ability of a given substance to conduct heat is called its **thermal conductivity.**

The relative conductivities of different substances can be illustrated by an experiment performed as follows: Similar rods of six different metals—copper, aluminum, brass, tin, german silver, and lead—are coated with a special yellow paint and arranged as shown in Fig. A. The rods, mounted in rubber corks, project through holes in a metal tube where their lower ends are heated to 100°C by steam passing through the tube. As the heat travels slowly up each rod the yellow paint turns to red. After 5 or 10 min the height to which the paint has turned color is approximately as shown by the stippled areas in the figure. Of these six metals, copper is observed to be the best conductor and lead the poorest.

In order to heat an object it is customary to bring it into contact with some other body at a higher temperature. A pan of water, for

Fig. A. Experiment illustrating the relative heat conductivities of six different metals: copper, aluminum, brass, tin, german silver, and lead.

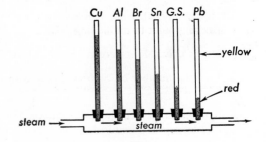

example, is generally heated by placing it over an open flame. The combustion of natural gas first sets the gas molecules into a rapid state of motion. These molecules striking the bottom of the pan set the molecules of the metal into rapid vibration. They in turn strike other metal molecules, thus transferring the motion through to the other side. This is called heat conduction. The metal molecules set the first layer of water molecules moving and they in turn set others moving. Thus molecular motion, called heat, has been given to the body of water.

Laboratory experiments show that the amount of heat flowing through a rod is proportional to the time, the cross-sectional area, and the difference in temperature between the ends, and is inversely proportional to the length.

Using appropriate symbols for each of these factors and inserting a proportionality constant, the following equation is set up:

$$H = k \frac{A(t_2 - t_1)}{L} T \qquad (1)$$

H is the amount of heat flowing through the body of length L and cross section A, k is the thermal conductivity, T is the time interval of flow, t_2 is the temperature of the hot end, and t_1 is the temperature of the cold end. It is quite clear to almost everyone that if the temperature difference $t_2 - t_1$ or the area A is increased (see Fig. B), the amount of heat passing through is increased. It is not as obvious, however, that an increase in the length L causes a decrease in heat flow, or that a decrease in length produces an increase. This latter will be illustrated by two experiments.

Fig. B. Illustrating the various measurable factors involved in the flow of heat through a body by conduction.

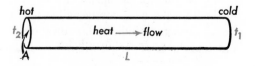

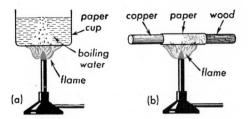

Fig. C. Illustrating the conduction of heat through paper.

Although paper is a poor conductor, the flow of heat through it can be made very great by increasing A, the cross-sectional area, and decreasing L, the distance it has to flow. Diagram (a) in Fig. C, illustrates thermal conductivity by the boiling of water in a paper cup. Although the gas flame plays directly against the surface of the paper, the cup will not burn. The reason for this is that the heat from the lower surface of the paper is conducted through to the water fast enough to keep the temperature of the paper from rising too high. If the paper is thick, the lower surface will burn. Strange as it may seem, the thinner the paper, the less is the chance of burning.

In diagram (b) of Fig. C, a thin piece of paper is wrapped once around a rod made half of wood and half of copper. When the flame is brought up as shown, the paper burns only where it is in contact with the wood and not at all where it is in contact with the copper. Copper, being a good conductor, carries the heat into the interior of the metal and away from the metal surface. Since wood is a poor conductor, it cannot conduct the heat away from the surface fast enough, and the paper heats up and soon burns.

The thermal conductivities of a few common substances are given in Table 1.

The number k is the quantity of heat in calories that in 1 sec will pass through a 1 cc cube when two opposite faces are maintained at 1°C difference in temperature. Knowing the value of k for a given substance, it is possible to calculate, by means of Eq. (1), the amount of heat flowing through any sized object made of that same substance.

Table 1. Thermal Conductivities
(k, in cal cm/sec cm^2 C$^\circ$)

Substance	k
silver........................	0.97
copper.......................	0.92
aluminum....................	0.50
brass........................	0.26
iron.........................	0.16
lead.........................	0.08
german silver................	0.10
mercury.....................	0.02
tile.........................	0.002
glass........................	0.0025
water.......................	0.0014
wood........................	0.0005
paper.......................	0.0003
felt.........................	0.00004

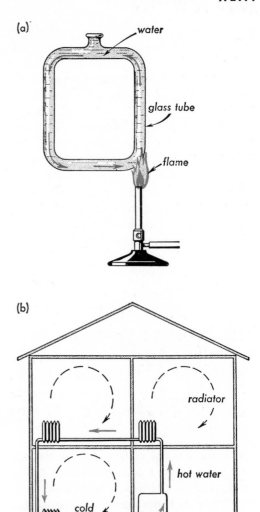

(a) water

glass tube

flame

(b)

radiator

hot water

cold

heater

Fig. E. Illustrations of heat convection by the circulation of water in a pipe and air in a room.

Example. One end of an aluminum rod 40 cm long and 5 cm^2 in cross section is maintained at a temperature of 100°C and the other end at 20°C. Find the amount of heat that will flow through the rod in 2 min.

Solution. Substitution in Eq. (1) gives

$$H = 0.50 \frac{5(100 - 20)}{40} 120 = 600 \text{ cal} \quad (2)$$

Convection. Why is it that a poor conductor of heat like water can be heated so quickly when it is placed in a pan over a hot fire? It is due to the second method of heat transfer known as **convection.** Water on the bottom of a pan is heated first. Because of a rise in temperature it expands. Being lighter than the cold water above, it then rises to the top, permitting cold water to come to the bot-

tom from the sides. This action sets up a flow of water called a **convection current.** See Fig. D. Convection currents thus keep the water stirred up as it heats.

Convection currents set up by the heating of a vessel of water are illustrated in Fig. E (a). A glass tube in the shape of a letter O is filled with water and then heated at one of the lower corners as indicated. A drop of ink admitted at the top opening will mix with the

Fig. D. Convection currents in a pan of water being heated over a stove burner.

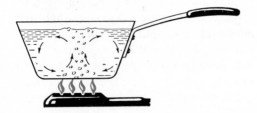

water and quickly flow around the tube in a counterclockwise direction. This circulation is the basis of the hot-water heating systems used in some houses. As illustrated in diagram (b), hot water from a supply tank in a lower room or basement rises and flows through several radiators, only to return, somewhat cooled, to the tank, where it is reheated.

Similar to this in its action is the hot-air heating system used in some houses. Air heated in a furnace in the basement rises through an outlet in or near the floor as shown in Fig. F. Rising up one side of the room this air travels across the ceiling, down the other side, and across the floor to return to the furnace by another opening.

Convection results from differences in density and pressure because hot gases and liquids expand on heating.

Convection currents in the atmosphere are quite noticeable and account for the wind. Along the sea coast cool air from over the ocean comes as a sea breeze due to convection. The sun's rays are absorbed more readily by the land than they are by water, and the warmed air over the land rises, while cooler air from the ocean comes in to take its place.

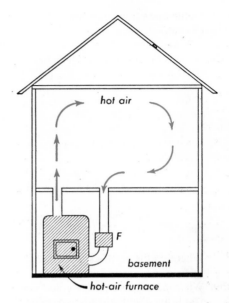

Fig. F. Convection hot-air currents set up by heating.

At night the land cools quickly by radiation back toward the cold sky, and soon the air over the water is the warmer and, rising, causes a reversal in air movement. The wind blows from the land to the sea. These air currents are readily observed by smoke from a fire built on the seashore. During the day the smoke blows inland and at night it blows seaward.

Summary

The transfer of heat from one point to another is accomplished in three ways: conduction, convection, and radiation.

Conduction of heat is a slow process by which increased atomic and molecular vibrations are transmitted from one to another by collision.

The ability to conduct heat varies widely between substances. Metals, in general, are good conductors, while nonmetals are poor conductors.

Convection of heat is more rapid than conduction and is accomplished by the actual transport of a hot gas or liquid from one point to another. Because hot gasses and liquids expand on heating, convection results from differences in density and pressure.

Questions

1. What is meant by heat transfer? What are the methods of heat transfer?

2. Name three substances that are good thermal conductors. Name three poor conductors of heat.

3. What is the process by which heat is conducted through a solid? Is this a rapid method of heat transfer?

4. Upon what factors does the amount of heat conducted through a rod depend? Write down the formula.

5. What is convection? Is convection a more rapid method of heat transfer than conduction? Why?

6. What causes heated air or water to undergo convection?

7. Although water is a poor conductor of heat, a pan of water is quickly heated on a hot plate or burner. Why? Is conduction involved here? Is convection involved?

8. Where on the earth's surface should one find the air currents rising most rapidly?

9. What inexpensive device could you devise for demonstrating convection? How could you bring about forced convection?

Problems

1. One end of a copper rod 20 cm long and having a cross-sectional area of 4 cm^2 is maintained at 20°C, and the other end at 50°C. How much heat will flow through the rod in 5 min?

2. A brass rod is 20 cm long and has a cross-sectional area of 2 cm^2. How much heat will flow through this rod in 4 min if one end is maintained at 25°C and the other end at 100°C?

3. A silver rod, with a cross-sectional area of 5 cm^2, is 25 cm long. If one end is maintained at 0°C and the other end at 250°C, how much heat will flow through in 10 min?

4. The bottom of a copper boiler is 1 mm thick and has a cross-sectional area of 400 cm^2. If the upper surface is maintained at 80°C and the lower surface at 82°C, how much heat will flow through in 2 min?

5. The bottom of an aluminum pan is 2 mm thick and has an area of 500 cm^2. If the upper surface is maintained at 90°C and the lower surface at 91.5°C, how much heat will flow through in 5 min?

6. A large glass window pane 2 m by 3 m is 5 mm thick. If the snow outside maintains the outer surface at 0°C and the heat of the room maintains the inner surface at 15°C, how much heat will be conducted out in 1 hr?

7.* The wooden handle of a frying pan is 2.5 cm in diameter and 15 cm long. If the pan temperature is 400°C and the free end of the handle is kept at 40°C, how much heat will flow through in 1 min?

SPECIFIC HEAT—*Laboratory*

In performing this experiment as described in the associated book LAB-ORATORY EXERCISES you will determine the specific heat of the element lead by using the principles of calorimetry. The procedure involves weighing, tempera-true measurements, and the application of the principle Heat Lost = Heat Gained.

RADIANT HEAT

When the sun comes over the horizon in the early morning, the heat can be felt as soon as the sun becomes visible. This heat, called radiant heat or radiation, travels with the speed of light, 186,000 mi/sec.

Radiant heat is but one of the many forms of energy and is readily detected by means of a radiometer, thermocouple, thermister, thermometer, etc. A Crooke's radiometer, shown in Fig. A, will often be found in a jewelry store window. In daylight or under a bright light the little pinwheel made of very thin mica, will be found spinning around as if by perpetual motion.

Each vane of such a radiometer is shiny on one face, and blackened on the other. The black faces absorb more radiant energy than

Fig. A. A Crooke's radiometer.

the polished surfaces and heat the adjacent air. The faster recoiling air molecules therefore exert a larger force on the blackened sides driving it around.

Should a radiometer be so highly evacuated that little air remains inside the vessel, light waves in bouncing off the polished surfaces will exert twice the force they do in being absorbed on the blackened side and the pinwheel will spin the other way.

Radiant heat rays, like visible light, are electromagnetic waves and have all the general properties known to visible light. The essential difference between the two is that heat waves, sometimes called **infrared rays,** are not visible to the human eye.

A demonstration of the reflection of infrared rays is diagramed in Fig. B. A candle flame acting as a source at **F** emits light and heat rays in all directions. Of these rays only the ones traveling toward the concave mirror M_1 are reflected into a parallel beam. Arriving at the second concave mirror M_2, these rays are again reflected, being brought together to a focus on the exposed junctions of a thermopile **T**. As the junctions of the thermopile warm up, an electric current is produced, causing the ammeter pointer **P** to move to the right. When the candle is removed, the pointer returns to zero.

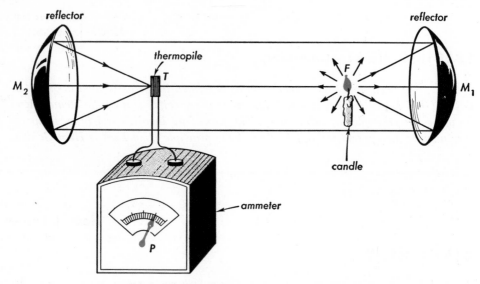

Fig. B. Reflection of heat rays by concave mirrors.

A practical example of heat radiation is to be found in every home where a fireplace is used as a means of heating. Contrary to most beliefs, the heat entering a room from a fireplace is practically all in the form of infrared rays originating in the flames, the coals, and the stone or brick walls. The air that is heated within the fireplace does not enter the room but is carried up the chimney as a convection current. See Fig. C. This rising current of air draws fresh air into the room

Fig. C. A fireplace heats a room by radiation from the flame, the coals, and the stove walls. Convection currents set up a draft and carry warm air and smoke out the chimney.

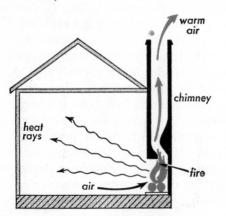

and into the fire, thus supplying fresh oxygen to the burning wood or coal.

A Dewar-flask, or **thermos bottle,** is an example of a practical device in which the conduction, convection, and radiation of heat are reduced as much as possible. As shown by the cross-section diagram in Fig. D, a thermos bottle consists of a double-walled glass vessel silvered on the inside. The purpose of the silvering is to reflect all radiant heat attempting to enter or leave the vessel. The space between the walls is highly evacuated to prevent convection, and the glass, being a poor conductor, minimizes conduction through the walls of the neck. With the exception of the vacuum space between walls, a calorimeter of the type commonly used in laboratories is similar to a Dewar-flask.

A new type of heating system for public buildings and private dwellings has recently been developed. Known to engineers as **panel heating,** this system heats the walls of the rooms by hot air or water pipes that run through them. Even though the windows are open on the coldest days, radiant heat keeps the occupants warm.

Emission and Absorption. The rate at

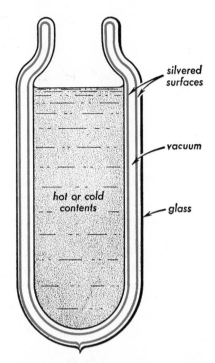

Fig. D. The Dewar-flask, or "thermos bottle," minimizes conduction by using glass, convection by evacuating, and radiation by silvering.

painted with a dull black paint, while the two on the right are chrome plated.

Gradually the mercury levels on the left change more and more in the direction shown, while those on the right change very little. The black surfaces are good radiators and good absorbers, warming the air in box **A** and driving the left-hand mercury level down. The polished surfaces are poor radiators and poor absorbers, and the air in box **B** warms up ever so little.

Black Body Radiation. The relation between the radiant heat **E** emitted by a body and its temperature was first made through the extensive laboratory experiments of Josef Stefan. The same law was later derived from theoretical considerations by Ludwig Boltzmann, and is now known as the **Stefan-Boltzmann law.**

$$E = kT^4$$

which a body radiates or absorbs heat depends not only upon the absolute temperature but also upon the nature of the exposed surfaces as well.

Objects that are good emitters of heat are also good absorbers of the same kind of radiation.

This is known as **Kirchhoff's Law of Radiation.** A body whose surface is blackened is an excellent emitter as well as an excellent absorber. If the same body is chromium plated, it becomes a poor emitter and a poor absorber.

A good demonstration of Kirchhoff's law is shown in Fig. E. Two airtight metal boxes **A** and **B** are connected by small hose connections to two glass U-tubes containing mercury. All mercury surfaces are first adjusted to the same level. A third metal box containing boiling water is now inserted between and equidistant from the other two as shown. The two adjacent surfaces on the left are

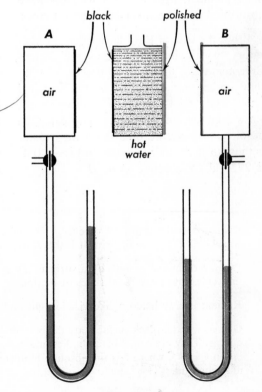

Fig. E. Apparatus for demonstrating Kirchhoff's Law of Radiation.

Here **E** represents the energy radiated per second by a body at an absolute temperature **T**, and **k** is a proportionality constant. The law applies only to so-called "black bodies."

A black body is defined as one which absorbs all of the radiant heat that falls upon it.

Such a perfect absorber would also be a perfect emitter.

If **E** represents the heat in calories radiated per second per square centimeter of a black body, then **k** $= 1.36 \times 10^{-12}$. If **E** is measured in ergs/cm^2 sec, then **k** $= 5.7 \times 10^{-5}$.

The best laboratory approach to a black body is a hole in a blackened box. Practically all heat entering such a hole would be absorbed inside. Black velvet cloth or a surface painted dull with lampblack will absorb about 97% of the radiant heat falling on it, and may for many purposes be considered a black body. Polished metal surfaces, however, are far from being black bodies; they absorb only about 6% of the incident energy and reflect the remainder. Most other substances have absorption ratios between these two extremes.

Prevost's Law of Heat Exchange. Laboratory experiments, as well as the Stefan-Boltzmann law, show that all bodies, whether they are hot or cold, radiate heat. The words "hot" and "cold" are only relative terms, since even ice radiates heat. The greater the absolute temperature of a body the greater is the rate at which it radiates, and ice at 0°C is 273° above absolute zero.

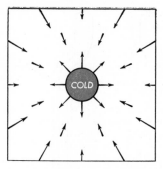

Fig. F. A cold body warms up to room temperature.

If a cold block of metal is brought into a warm room, it radiates heat to the walls of the room and the walls of the room radiate heat to the block. Because the walls are at a higher temperature, they give more heat per second to the block than the block gives up in return. See Fig. F. Due to this unequal exchange of heat, the temperature of the cold block rises until it comes to the same temperature as the room, at which time it radiates and absorbs at exactly the same rate.

Prevost's Law of Heat Exchange states that a body at the temperature of its surroundings is radiating and receiving heat at equal rates.

When a person stands near a fireplace, he feels warm because his body receives more heat from the fire than it emits. If he stands next to a cold window, he feels chilly because he radiates more heat than he absorbs. The side of his body facing the window gets noticeably colder than the other.

Summary

Radiation is the transport of energy by means of invisible electromagnetic waves that travel with the speed of light. It is therefore much faster than conduction and convection.

When radiant energy falls on a surface, much of it is absorbed by setting the atoms and molecules into more rapid states of motion.

Radiant energy behaves like visible light and is reflected from mirrorlike surfaces.

Objects with jet-black surfaces are the best absorbers as well as the best emitters of radiant energy. They are called black bodies and radiate an amount of energy **E** given by the relation **E** $= kT^4$, where **T** is the absolute temperature of the surface and **k** is a proportionality constant.

All objects, hot or cold, radiate heat energy. The higher the temperature the more they radiate per second.

Questions

1. What is radiant heat? How fast does it travel? Can it travel through a vacuum?

2. How are conduction, convection, and radiation involved in the proper operation of a fireplace?

3. How are the three methods of heat transfer reduced in the construction of a thermos bottle?

4. What is the Stefan-Boltzmann law? What is a "black body"?

5. What is Kirchhoff's law? How can the law be demonstrated? What kind of clothes would be the coolest on a hot sunny day?

6. What is Prevost's law of heat exchange? Does ice radiate heat? Why will a hot piece of iron cool off to room temperature but not cool below room temperature?

7. What kind of surface should a stove have if it is to radiate a maximum amount of heat? Why should it not be chromium plated and polished?

8. What inexpensive device could you make to demonstrate one of the principles given in this lesson?

Problems

1. How many calories of heat are radiated from 1 cm² of the surface of a dull black stove in 1 min if the temperature is 500°K?

2. How much heat is radiated by a dull black stove in 1 min if the total exposed area is 0.5 m² and the surface is 700°K?

3. How many calories of heat are radiated in 1 sec from a black body surface with an area of 5 cm² and a temperature of 327°C?

4. A solid copper ball 10 cm in diameter is coated with lamp black and heated to a temperature of 727°C. How many calories of heat are radiated from this sphere per second? (*Note:* The area of a sphere is $4 \pi r^2$.)

5. An iron ball 2 cm in diameter is coated with lampblack and heated to a temperature of 1027°C. How many calories of heat are radiated from this sphere per minute?

6.* A blackened iron ball with a surface area of 10 cm² and temperature of 727°C is placed in a box whose walls are blackened and which has a temperature of 227°C. Find the net loss of energy in calories per second from the ball.

HEAT OF FUSION—*Laboratory*

In performing this experiment as described in the accompanying LABO-RATORY EXERCISES you will apply the principles of calorimetry to measure the calories of heat consumed to melt a quantity of ice. The latent heat of fusion can be determined from the recorded data.

CHANGE OF STATE

Expansion and Contraction on Fusion. When molten metal of one kind or another is poured into a mold for casting, the metal may contract or expand on solidifying and then, on cooling down to room temperature, contract or expand according to its coefficient of thermal expansion. Cast iron, for example, is a substance which, on solidifying, expands slightly but then, on cooling down to room temperature, contracts about 1% of its length. It is therefore well suited to casting since slight expansion on solidifying aids in the reproduction of every detail in the mold. To allow for shrinkage in cooling, however, an increase of ⅛ in. per ft must be introduced in the wood pattern used in making the mold.

Fig. A. When the water inside the bomb freezes, the expansion bursts the cast-iron walls.

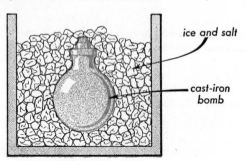

ice and salt

cast-iron bomb

An experiment illustrating the enormous expansion forces of freezing water is diagramed in Fig. A. A small cast-iron bomb, about 2 in. in diameter and ⅛ in. thick is completely filled with water at a temperature close to 0°C. After the threaded iron plug is screwed in tightly, the bomb is packed in a freezing mixture of cracked ice and salt. After some minutes the water freezes as it explodes the bomb with a dull thud.

This experiment shows that by exerting large pressures on cold water, its necessary expansion on freezing can be held back until a temperature lower than 0°C is reached.

Regelation. If two small blocks of ice are held in opposite hands and two of their relatively flat surfaces pressed tightly together, they will upon release be stuck together. The explanation is that where contact is made between the blocks, high pressure at localized spots lowers the melting point sufficiently to melt the ice. In order to melt, the ice must acquire heat (80 cal/gm) and this it gets by conduction from the nearby ice. The water then flows to one side and, returning the heat it had taken away from the nearby ice, freezes, sealing the blocks together. This is a process called **regelation**. The same process explains why snow when

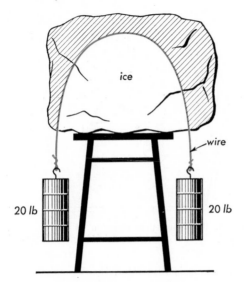

Fig. B. Ice melts under pressure, allowing the wire to work its way through.

squeezed in the hands, sticks together to form well packed snowballs.

Glaciers are well known to seemingly "flow" around hard jutting rocks as they move slowly down a rocky ravine. The ice melts under the pressure it receives from a rock on one side, and the water flowing down and around to the open gap on the other side freezes again to go on as if the rock were never there.

A simple laboratory experiment demonstrating this principle is shown in Fig. B. A small wire with heavy weights attached is hung over a block of ice and allowed to remain for some time. Slowly the wire is observed to melt its way through the ice. On completion of the cut the block of ice is still in one piece, the gap made by the wire having frozen shut. The high pressure under the wire melts the ice, and the water flows around to the other side where it freezes again.

Cooling by Evaporation. When water is left in an open dish, it slowly evaporates, i.e., it goes spontaneously into the gaseous state. Evaporation therefore is a free expansion, and expansion is always accompanied by

cooling. This phenomenon of cooling by evaporation, which is so important from the standpoint of its many commercial applications, is explained by the kinetic theory of matter.

Because of the random motions of the molecules of a liquid, some molecules obtain, momentarily, a very high velocity. If a molecule at the surface is given a high velocity in an upward direction, it may escape into the air above. Some of these escaped molecules soon find their way back into the liquid by chance collisions with air molecules from above the surface, but many of them do not. See Fig. C. The sporadic escape of molecules may be speeded up by blowing air across the surface. The air carries the newly escaped molecules away before they have a chance to return to the liquid.

By virtue of the high speed of the molecules escaping from a liquid surface, considerably more than the average kinetic energy is carried away with them. A lowering of the average kinetic energy of the remaining liquid molecules means a lowering of the temperature. The more rapid the evaporation, therefore, the faster will be the cooling. This is strikingly demonstrated by pouring a small amount of ether or alcohol on the finger. Either of these liquids, and particularly ether, evaporates very rapidly, cooling the surface of the finger quickly. Ether is often used in this way by surgeons, in place of an anesthetic, to freeze local spots of the body before beginning a minor operation.

Cooling by evaporation can be demon-

Fig. C. Evaporation of water from an open dish is due to the rapid motion of the water molecules and their occasional escape into the air space above.

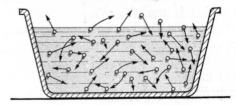

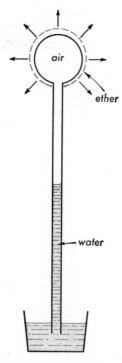

Fig. D. Experiment demonstrating the cooling effect produced by the evaporation of ether.

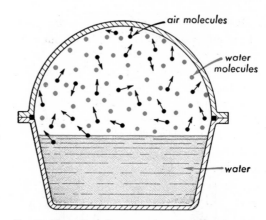

Fig. E. Illustrating the saturation of air with water vapor.

sure. This is illustrated by the values given in Table 1. The temperature of the air is given in one column and the maximum amount of water that can exist in the vapor state in a cubic meter of air is given in the other.

Table 1. Mass of Water Vapor in One Cubic Meter of Saturated Air

Temperature	Water Vapor
0°C or 32°F	4.8 gm
5°C " 41°F	6.8 gm
10°C " 50°F	9.3 gm
15°C " 59°F	12.7 gm
20°C " 68°F	17.1 gm
25°C " 77°F	22.8 gm
30°C " 86°F	30.0 gm
35°C " 95°F	39.2 gm

strated to a large group by pouring a small quantity of ether over the bulb of an air thermometer as shown in Fig. D. Because of the cooling of the glass bulb the air inside contracts, drawing more water up into the stem of the thermometer.

Humidity. When water molecules escape by evaporation from the free surface of a liquid, they mix with the air molecules above. If the space above the liquid surface is enclosed, as shown in Fig. E, this mixture cannot escape. Under these circumstances the water will continue to evaporate until the air above becomes saturated with water vapor, that is, until it can hold no more. When this condition is reached, as many free water molecules will be returning to the liquid every second as there are water molecules escaping.

The maximum amount of water the air can hold in the vapor state depends upon the temperature and very little upon the air pres-

It is clearly seen from the table that the hotter the air the greater is the amount of water it can hold in the vapor state.

The atmosphere which we might term free air is not always saturated with water vapor. If it contains very little or no water vapor, we say the air is dry; if it contains a great deal, we say it is damp.

The quantity of water vapor present in 1 m³ of air is called the absolute humidity.

It is, therefore, a measure of the dampness of the air. Absolute humidity is measured by the number of grams of water vapor present in 1 m³ of air. For example, the absolute humidity might be said to be 14 gm/m³.

It is customary in speaking of the dampness of air, not to specify the absolute humidity but the **relative humidity.** *The ratio of the quantity of water vapor actually present in any volume of air to the quantity required to saturate the same volume of air at the same temperature is called the relative humidity.*

To illustrate this, suppose the air at the present time contains 5.7 gm/m³ of water vapor and the temperature is 25°C. If the air were saturated at this temperature (see Table 1), it would contain 22.8 gm/m³. Therefore the

$$\text{relative humidity} = \frac{5.7}{22.8} = 0.25 \qquad (1)$$

It is customary to express such answers in per cent and say that the relative humidity in this case is 25%.

If air which is saturated with water vapor is cooled to a lower temperature, some of the water vapor may condense to the liquid state. These are the conditions under which rain and fogdrops are formed. The reason for this condensation is that at the lower temperature and equilibrium conditions less water can exist in the vapor state and still saturate the air. If the air cools without the formation of rain or fog, the air takes on an unstable state in which it is supersaturated.

The Dew Point. When the temperature of a glass of water is slowly cooled, a temperature is reached where water condenses on the outside. The temperature at which this occurs is called the **dew point,** and signifies that the air has become saturated with water vapor. Any measurement of the dew-point temperature therefore offers a means of determining the relative humidity.

Meteorologists often determine relative

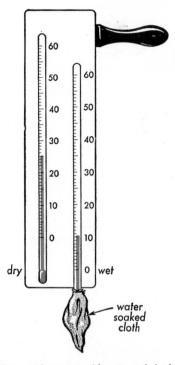

Fig. F. Sling psychrometer with wet- and dry-bulb thermometers for determining the dew point and relative humidity.

humidity from the dew point by means of a **sling psychrometer.** Such a device as shown in Fig. F consists of two identical mercury thermometers mounted on a base with a convenient handle for whirling. One bulb is exposed to the air and is called the **dry bulb,** while the other, with a water-soaked cloth tied to it, is called the **wet bulb.** When the psychrometer is whirled in the air for several minutes, being stopped occasionally to observe the temperature readings, the wet bulb will be observed to drop to some value and remain there during any subsequent whirling.

The lowest obtainable wet-bulb temperature is not the dew point, even though whirling causes evaporation, and evaporation produces cooling. By applying a correction from well-known tables the dew point can be determined from the wet- and dry-bulb readings. Eq. (1) is then applied to the densities read from Table 1.

Summary

Upon fusion, that is, freezing, most substances contract slightly. However, a few substances, like water, expand. By exerting large pressures on cold water its necessary expansion on freezing can be held back until a temperature lower than 0°C is reached.

Pressure on ice will melt it. This is called regelation.

The evaporation of a liquid causes cooling. The more rapid the evaporation the greater is the cooling effect.

The quantity of water vapor present in 1 m³ of air is called the absolute humidity and is given in gm/m³. The ratio of the quantity of water vapor present in any volume of air to the quantity required to saturate the same volume of air at the same temperature is called the relative humidity.

A sling psychrometer, consisting of two identical thermometers, one having a water-soaked wick around its bulb, is used for determining relative humidity.

As air is cooled, a temperature is reached where it becomes saturated (100% relative humidity). Below this temperature, water vapor condenses into fog or rain.

Questions

1. Does water expand or contract on freezing? Does iron expand on freezing?

2. What is regelation? Where does it occur in nature?

3. What is absolute humidity? How is it measured?

4. What is relative humidity? What does it mean to say the air is saturated? If the air is saturated, what is the relative humidity?

5. What is the dew point? How could you find the dew point for the air in the room?

6. What is a sling psychrometer? Could you easily make one? What is the wet bulb?

7. How would you determine the relative humidity if you knew the absolute humidity and room temperature?

8. Why does evaporation produce cooling? How would you go about demonstrating the effect? Why is ether so effective in producing cooling?

Problems

1. If the air contains 16.2 gm of water vapor per cubic meter when the temperature is 77°F, what is (a) the absolute humidity and (b) the relative humidity?

2. One cubic meter of air contains 8.6 gm of water vapor per cubic meter when the temperature is 30°C. What is (a) the absolute humidity and (b) the relative humidity?

3. The air contains 18.4 gm of water vapor per cubic meter when the temperature is 25°C. What is (a) the absolute humidity and (b) the relative humidity?

4. One cubic meter of the air contains 15.0 gm of water vapor per cubic meter when the temperature is 30°C. If the temperature is lowered to 10°C, how many grams of water vapor per cubic meter will be condensed?

5. Dew forms on a drinking glass when the temperature is 68°F. What is the relative humidity if the temperature rises to 86°F?

6. The relative humidity is 42 percent when the room temperature is 86°F. To what value must the temperature be lowered to saturate the air?

7. The air of a room is saturated when the temperature is 59°F. What will be the relative humidity when the temperature rises to 95°F?

8. Plot a graph with the Centigrade temperature horizontally plotted and the water vapor per cubic meter of saturated air vertically plotted. Use the values as listed in Table 1.

9. If, at a temperature of 86°F, the relative humidity is 80%, how much water per cubic meter will be condensed if the temperature goes down to 41°F?

10. If the relative humidity is 78% when the temperature is 95°F, how much water vapor will be condensed if the temperature goes down to 50°F?

Heat | **Lesson 9**

REFRIGERATION AND GEYSERS

Boiling. *The boiling of a liquid is but a state of rapid evaporation.* As the temperature of water is raised, the rate of evaporation increases until at the boiling temperature it reaches a maximum. Beyond this temperature water can exist only in the vapor state.

When water boils at normal atmospheric pressure, evaporation takes place throughout the liquid as well as at the surface. Evidence of this is seen in the bubbles of saturated vapor that form near the bottom of a vessel and increase in size as they rise to the surface. See Fig. A. The bubbles are able to expand because the vapor pressure p, due to the fast moving water molecules striking the walls of the bubbles, is equal to or greater than the external pressure p_0 of the atmosphere. Boiling cannot occur at any point in a liquid unless the vapor pressure is equal to or slightly greater than the pressure within the liquid at that same point.

If in the process of boiling water, while

Fig. A. When water boils, bubbles of steam form at the bottom and grow as they rise to the surface.

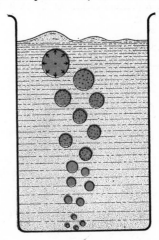

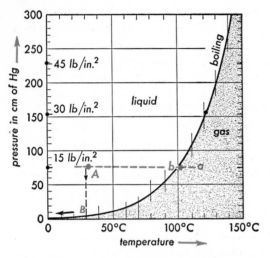

Fig. B. Boiling-point curve for water as it changes with temperature.

Note that at standard atmospheric pressure of 76 cm of mercury Hg, which is about 15 lb/in.², water boils at 100°C. At twice this pressure, however, a temperature of 120°C must be reached, etc.

Consider, for example, the boiling of water in a pressure cooker when the safety gauge is set for 15 lb/in.² See Fig. C. As the water inside gets hotter and hotter, some of it vaporizes and the pressure rises. This pressure continues to rise until it becomes 15 lb/in.² greater than the pressure outside. At this point the safety valve opens slightly and prevents the internal pressure from exceeding this value. Under these conditions the pressure outside the vessel is 15 lb/in.², while the pressure inside is 15 lb/in.² greater, or

bubbles are forming within the liquid, the pressure on the liquid surface is increased, the bubbles will collapse and boiling will cease. Under this increased pressure, however, boiling can be started again by adding heat and raising the temperature to a higher value. In other words, **the higher the pressure on a liquid the higher is the boiling temperature.** Conversely, **the lower the pressure within a liquid the lower is the temperature required to make it boil.**

A graph of the boiling point of water, as it varies with pressure, is shown in Fig. B.

Fig. C. In a pressure cooker set for 15 lb/in.², water boils at 120°C.

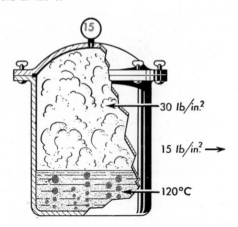

Fig. D. Diagram illustrating the principles of a geyser like "Old Faithful" in Yellowstone National Park.

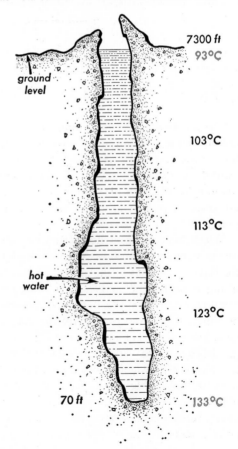

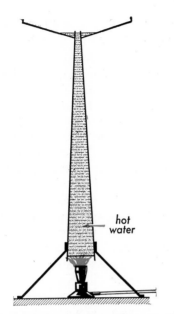

hot
water

Fig. E. Experimental geyser that will erupt periodically.

30 lb/in.^{2} From the graph it will be seen that the confined water must now reach 120°C to boil. At this higher temperature food cooks more quickly. In an open pan the water boils at 100°C, and its temperature will not exceed this value.

Geysers. One of the great wonders of the western world is the spontaneous eruption almost hourly of the mammoth geyser "Old Faithful" in Yellowstone National Park. The following explanation of geyser activity was first given by Bunsen in 1847 and is based upon the above explanation of boiling.

Water from a nearby stream seeps into the vertical shaft or hole where, due to volcanic heat below, it is gradually heated to the boiling point. See Fig. D. Because the water is heated from below, and convection currents are shut off by the narrowness of the shaft, a temperature considerably higher than 100°C must be reached before the water at the bottom can boil. Since atmospheric pressure exists at the surface, the water there will boil at 100°C. Far down the shaft, however, the added pressure of nearly 70 ft of water requires a temperature of 130°C to produce

boiling. Because the water is heated from below, this high temperature is reached near the bottom and boiling begins there before it does at the top. When a sufficiently high temperature is reached, the vapor pressure deep down exceeds the pressure due to the air and water column above, and the rise of numerous bubbles, by pushing up the column of hot water above, starts an eruption. Nearing the surface, the vapor pressure of the superheated water is so high that the remaining water is pushed out with great force.

An excellent demonstration of these principles can be performed by an experimental geyser of the form shown in Fig. E. Such models can be made almost any size from one foot in height to 10 ft or more. The period of their eruption depends upon size as well as the quantity of applied heat.

Boiling at Low Temperatures. Just as water can be made to boil at temperatures higher than 100°C by increasing the pressure, so can it be made to boil at temperatures below 100°C by reducing atmospheric pressure. Because of the practical importance of this basic fact, a detailed explanation should be given. Fig. B is a graph of the saturated vapor pressures of water, and it represents conditions under which water and saturated water vapor can exist together in equilibrium.

Since boiling at the surface of water takes place when the saturated vapor pressure becomes equal to the atmospheric pressure, it follows that by lowering atmospheric pressure a lower vapor pressure can bring about the conditions for boiling. The curved line in the graph is therefore a *boiling point curve*; all pressures and temperatures to the right of the curve represent the gas or vapor state, all points to the left the liquid state.

Consider, for example, water at the normal boiling point of 100°C and 76 cm of Hg. To raise its temperature without raising the pressure, heat must first be added to vaporize the water, and then additional heat will raise the

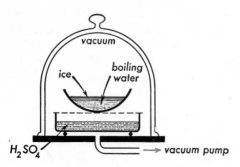

Fig. F. The boiling point of the liquid like water is lowered by lowering the atmospheric pressure. Water in a vacuum will boil and freeze at the same time.

Evidence of this fact is well known to those who like to camp in the higher mountains. There, at reduced atmospheric pressure, it takes longer than usual to cook all kinds of foods. The boiling points given in Table 1 show specific values for different elevations.

Table 1. Atmospheric Pressure and Boiling Point of Water at Various Heights Above Sea Level

Atmospheric Pressure		Boiling Point	Altitude
cm Hg	lb/in.²	°C	ft
271	52.5	140	—
235	45.5	135	—
203	39.3	130	—
174	33.7	125	—
149	28.8	120	—
127	24.6	115	—
107	20.7	110	—
91	17.6	105	—
76	14.7	100	sea level
70.2	13.6	97.8	2,000
65.6	12.7	96.0	4,000
61.0	11.8	94.0	6,000
56.8	11.0	92.1	8,000
52.2	10.1	89.8	10,000
42.4	8.2	84.4	15,000
35.0	6.7	79.6	20,000
22.5	4.4	69.2	30,000
14.1	2.7	58.8	40,000
8.75	1.7	48.9	50,000
0.82	0.16	9.8	100,000

temperature of the resultant steam. To lower its temperature, heat must be given up to liquefy the steam and more heat given up to lower the temperature of all the water.

To go one step further, suppose water at room temperature, 30°C, is placed in a vacuum jar as shown in Fig. F and the pressure is slowly reduced by means of a vacuum pump. Starting at the point **A** on the graph, the pressure decreases until it reaches **B**, about 3.18 cm of Hg, where bubbles form and the water begins to boil. (This is the principle of the refrigerator cooling unit.)

To vaporize water requires heat, and this is taken from the remaining water, thus cooling it to a lower temperature. Continued reduction in pressure causes continued boiling and lowering of temperature until finally the freezing point at approximately 0°C is reached. Continued evaporation cools the surface of the water until ice forms over the surface of the boiling water. Here then is a condition in which water boils and freezes at the same time and at 0°C. (The small dish of sulfuric acid, H_2SO_4, placed in the vacuum chamber absorbs water vapor, thus aiding the pumps in keeping the pressure sufficiently low.)

Although water under normal atmospheric pressure at sea level boils at 100°C, water at higher altitudes boils at lower temperatures.

The boiling point decreases approximately 1°C per 1000 ft elevation above sea level. Flying at high altitudes the water in water-cooled engines boils at lower temperatures. At a height of 6 mi, gasoline boils at the normal temperature of −65°C. At 12-mi elevation, blood boils at the body temperature of 98.6°F (37°C).

Summary

The boiling point of a liquid rises with increased pressure and decreases with decreased pressure. Water at standard atmospheric pressure of 76 cm of mercury boils at 100°C.

The water in a pressure cooker boils at a temperature above 100°C because of a higher pressure than that normally prevailing outside.

Water deep in a geyser like Old Faithful in Yellowstone National Park boils at a temperature well above 100°C. Bubbles of steam rising from the bottom expand as they approach the top, thereby reducing the pressure and starting an eruption.

If the air pressure is lowered sufficiently, water will boil at room temperature. This is the principle of the refrigerator cooling unit.

Water high in the mountains boils at a temperature below 100°C because of reduced air pressure.

Questions

1. Does the boiling point of a liquid depend upon pressure? If so, how?

2. What are the principles of the pressure cooker? Does the water reach a higher temperature?

3. What are the principles of a geyser like Old Faithful in Yellowstone National Park?

4. Can water be made to boil at a temperature of 90°C? Can water be made to boil at room temperature of 25°C? Can water be made to boil at its freezing point?

5. Does the boiling point of water vary with altitude? How much is the boiling point of water lowered for each 1000 ft in elevation?

6. Why does food cook more slowly high in the mountains? Would a pressure cooker speed up cooking in the high mountains?

7. What simple and inexpensive device could you design and make to illustrate one of the principles presented in this lesson?

Problems

1. Plot a graph of the boiling point of water (vertically) against the altitude (horizontally).

2. At what temperature will water boil at the one-mile-high City of Denver, Colorado?

3. At what temperature will water boil at a height of 5 mi?

4. At what temperature will water boil if the pressure is 30 lb/in.²?

5. At what temperature will water boil if the air pressure above it is 200 cm of Hg?

6.* At what temperature would water boil at the bottom of a well where the water is 100 ft deep? Assume normal atmospheric pressure at the water surface.

7.* The opening tube in the lid of a pressure cooker is 0.10 cm². What mass must the pressure weight on top of this opening have if the boiling temperature of the water inside is to be 130°C? (See Fig. C.)

8.* A geyser in Yellowstone National Park is located at an elevation of 8000 ft. What is the boiling temperature (a) at the surface and (b) 34 ft down in the water?

Heat | Lesson 10

NEWTON'S LAW OF COOLING—*Laboratory*

This is an interesting problem experiment described in the accompanying book LABORATORY EXERCISES. You will determine the cooling rate of two cups of hot coffee, one with cream and the other without. Graphs for both cups are plotted and compared.

Heat | Lesson 11

HEAT ENERGY AND GAS LAWS

Thermodynamics. Thermodynamics is that branch of physics dealing with the conversion of mechanical energy into thermal energy, and the reverse process, heat into work. There are numerous ways of carrying out either of these transformations. By rubbing the palms of the hands together, for example, heat is produced; by rubbing two sticks of wood together a fire may be started. If a weight falls freely from some height, heat is developed when the weight strikes the ground. The bearings of a car motor or the wheels of a freight car, if not lubricated, will get hot and either "burn out" or lock together, as in a "hot box." These are all examples of mechanical energy being transformed into heat.

An interesting demonstration is shown in Fig. A. A small hollow brass tube, mounted on the shaft of an electric motor, has a few drops of water in the base and a cork driven into the open end. A wooden clamp, like the one shown at the lower right, is squeezed tightly around the tube as it spins. Because of friction the tube gets hot, boils the water, and steam pressure suddenly blows the cork out as if from a gun.

The First Law of Thermodynamics. The first law of thermodynamics is frequently re-

Fig. A. Cork gun. Friction heat boils water, and steam blows cork out.

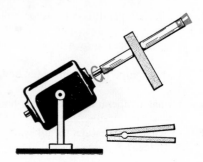

ferred to as the **mechanical equivalent of heat.** It is to the painstaking work of Joule (1843)* that we attribute this fundamental verification of the universal law of conservation of energy. With his apparatus he was able to show that when a moving body is brought to rest, the energy which disappears is directly proportional to the amount of heat produced.

In his most famous experiment he set water into motion in a bucket by means of rotating paddles and then brought the water to rest by stationary paddles. He was able to show that if all of the work used in churning the water goes into producing heat, then the same amount of work will always produce the same amount of heat regardless of the method used to carry out the transformation. In other words, the calorie, which is a unit of heat energy, is equivalent to a definite number of joules of mechanical energy.

The mechanical equivalent of heat is defined as the ratio between any given amount of mechanical energy and the amount of heat energy it can produce.

$$\frac{work}{heat} = \text{mech. equiv. of heat}$$

By experiment

$$1 \text{ cal} = 4.18 \text{ joules} \qquad (1)$$

and

$$1 \text{ BTU} = 778 \text{ ft lb} \qquad (2)$$

As an equation,

$$\frac{W}{H} = J \qquad (3)$$

where

$$J = 4.18 \frac{\text{joules}}{\text{cal}}$$

* James Prescott Joule (1818-89), English physicist, was born on December 24, 1818, near Manchester. Although he owned a large brewery, he devoted his life to scientific research. At the age of 22 he discovered the law giving the relation between electrical energy and heat, and a short time later the law known as the first law of thermodynamics.

or

$$778 \frac{\text{ft lb}}{\text{BTU}}$$

Experiments on Mechanical Equivalent of Heat. There are numerous experimental methods of measuring the mechanical equivalent of heat. If a weight is dropped from any height, heat is developed when it strikes the ground. A 1-lb weight dropped 3.5 ft will, on stopping, produce 1 calorie.

One simple laboratory experiment is to place a measured amount of lead shot (about 200 gm) in a tube 5 cm in diameter and 100 cm long. After finding the temperature of the shot, the tube is turned end for end about 100 times, stopping each time in a vertical position to allow the shot to fall the full 100 cm and strike the bottom. See Fig. B. The temperature of the shot is measured again, and from the mass of the shot, its specific heat, and the temperature rise, the total heat **H** produced can be calculated. The work done lifting the shot to the top of the tube 100 times makes it possible to calculate **W**. By

Fig. B. Experiment for determining the mechanical equivalent of heat.

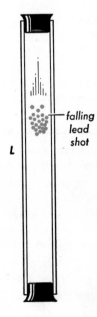

L   falling lead shot

putting these values of **W** and **H** in Eq. (3) the value of **J** can be computed.

Frequent reference has been made to the fact that heat is a form of energy. To add heat to a body is to increase the motion of the molecules. Having mass and velocity, each molecule has kinetic energy, $\frac{1}{2}mv^2$.

The transformation of potential energy into heat usually occurs by first changing it into kinetic energy. In the above experiment, for example, the lead shot acquired a velocity in falling and its kinetic energy $\frac{1}{2}mv^2$ was changed into heat at the bottom. Because of the impact, the molecules of the colliding bodies were given additional kinetic energy.

When two surfaces are rubbed together, the heat generated by friction is a direct and continuous transformation of the work into kinetic energy of individual atoms. With one surface moving past the other, atomic collisions with greater average velocities occur with the net result of a rise in the total kinetic energy.

Kinetic Theory of Gases. According to the kinetic theory of matter the pressure exerted by a gas upon the walls of the containing vessel is due to the continual bombardment of the walls by the rapidly moving gas molecules. If the temperature of the gas is raised, the molecules move faster and the pressure rises; whereas if it is lowered, they move slower and the pressure decreases. The absolute temperature of a gas depends upon the average kinetic energy of translation of the molecules.

The more gas that is pumped into a vessel of constant volume, the more molecules there are to bombard the walls per second and the greater is the resultant pressure. At any given instant of time some molecules are moving in one direction and some in another; some are traveling fast, some slow, and a few are momentarily at rest.

In any reasonably large volume of gas there are many molecules (about 10^{24} molecules/ft^3 at normal atmospheric pressure and

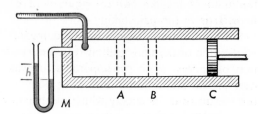

Fig. C. Adiabatic compression and expansion of a gas.

room temperature), and according to the mathematical laws of probability some average speed can be determined which, if possessed by all the molecules, would correspond to the same temperature and give rise to the same wall pressure.

The General Gas Law. Consider a cylinder arranged as shown in Fig. C, with a movable piston, a pressure gage **M**, and a thermometer **T**. Imagine the walls so well insulated as to prohibit any flow of heat in or out of the gas. If the piston is moved in to **B** or **A** to compress the gas into a smaller volume **V**, its temperature **T** will rise and the pressure **p** will increase. If the piston is moved out to expand the gas into a larger volume **V**, the temperature will fall and the pressure will decrease.

The compression and expansion of a gas just described is called an **adiabatic process,** and the curve drawn in Fig. D to represent

Fig. D. Graph of the adiabatic compression and expansion of a gas.

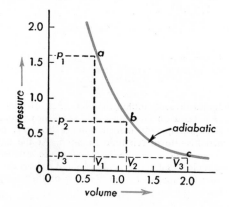

the different pressures and volumes is called an *adiabatic curve*.

Such an adiabatic process as this conforms to a law known as the general gas law. According to this law the pressure of any given quantity of gas is proportional to the absolute temperature and inversely proportional to the volume. As an equation

$$\frac{pV}{T} = \text{constant} \qquad (4)$$

For the three points **a**, **b**, and **c** in the graph, this means

$$\boxed{\frac{p_1V_1}{T_1} = \frac{p_2V_2}{T_2} = \frac{p_3V_3}{T_3}} \qquad (5)$$

The different pressures can be expressed in any of the following units: lb/in.², newton/m², dynes/cm², or cm of mercury. The temperature **T** must be expressed in absolute units of °K, °Abs or °R. See Fig. B, p. 208.

Boyle's Law. Boyle's law* is a special case of the general gas law. The law concerns the changes in pressure and volume of a gas at constant temperature. The ideas and concepts involved are illustrated by an experiment diagramed in Fig. E. A metal cylinder is fitted with a movable piston **C**, a mercury U-tube manometer **M**, and a bent thermometer **T**. For various positions of the piston, **A**, **B**, **C**, etc., the pressure is determined from the manometer height **h** and atmospheric pressure p_0, and the volume by the position of the piston along the cylinder. With each setting, adequate time is allowed

* Robert Boyle (1627-91). English natural philosopher and fourteenth child of Richard Boyle, the great earl of Cork. Fourteen years of age found him in Italy studying the paradoxes of the famous star gazer, Galileo. Besides enunciating the law now known by his name, he discovered how sound is propagated through the air, investigated the refractive powers of crystals, and proposed the corpuscular theory of chemical compounds and mixtures. He had a profound interest in theology and spent much time and money "for proving the Christian religion against all others."

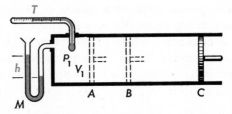

Fig. E. Compression and expansion of a gas obeying Boyle's law.

for the gas to come to the same temperature **T** as noted by the thermometer.

The graph shown in Fig. F gives the conditions for a range of pressures and volumes of the gas and is referred to as an isothermal curve.

It should be noted that as the piston is moved out, the gas cools upon expansion, and heat flows through the walls to bring the temperature back to that of the room. When the piston moves in, the gas heats upon compression, and heat flows out through the walls to again bring the temperature to that of the room.

Since the temperature is constant, we may place $T_1 = T_2 = T_3$ in the general gas law, Eq. (5), and by cancellation obtain

$$p_1V_1 = p_2V_2 = p_3V_3$$

This relation is known as *Boyle's law*.

The Special Gas Laws. Although the general gas law permits all variables—pres-

Fig. F. Isothermal curve for the compression and expansion of gas.

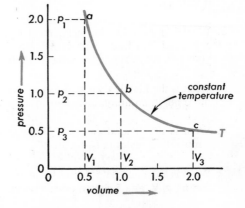

sure, volume, and temperature—to change, there are three special laws in which one is held constant. We have just seen that Boyle's law is a special case in which the temperature remains constant.

Boyle's law: $p_1V_1 = p_2V_2 = p_3V_3$ (6)

If on the other hand the pressure of a gas is held constant, then $p_1 = p_2 = p_3$, and the special case known as **Charles' law I** results.

Charles' law I: $\dfrac{V_1}{T_1} = \dfrac{V_2}{T_2} = \dfrac{V_3}{T_3}$ (7)

Charles' law I may be stated: the pressure of a gas remaining constant, any change in volume is accompanied by a proportional change in temperature.

Similarly, if the volume of a gas remains constant, any change in pressure is accompanied by a corresponding change in absolute temperature.

Charles' law II: $\dfrac{p_1}{T_1} = \dfrac{p_2}{T_2} = \dfrac{p_3}{T_3}$ (8)

Summary

The first law of thermodynamics is concerned with the mechanical equivalent of heat. When mechanical energy is converted into heat energy, the law of conservation of energy holds. The production of 1 calorie of heat requires the expenditure of 4.18 joules of mechanical energy, and the production of 1 BTU requires 778 ft lb.

According to the kinetic theory of gases the pressure exerted on the walls of the containing vessel are due to the continual bombardment of the walls by the rapidly moving gas molecules.

The general gas law relates the pressure, volume, and temperature of a given quantity of a gas as:

$$\frac{p_1V_1}{T_1} = \frac{p_2V_2}{T_2} = \frac{p_3V_3}{T_3}$$

where the temperatures are measured from absolute zero.

By keeping T constant this becomes Boyle's law, and by keeping either the pressure constant, or the valume constant, we have the other two laws sometimes called Charles' laws.

Questions

1. What is the meaning of the word thermodynamics? What is the first law of thermodynamics?

2. What is meant by the mechanical equivalent of heat? When mechanical energy is converted into heat, what is the atomic process? What happens when the palms of your hands are rubbed together? Explain.

3. What is the kinetic theory of gases? To what is gas pressure due? Why does one pump more air in an automobile tire to raise its pressure?

4. What is the general gas law? What three measurable factors does it involve? What temperature scales must be used?

5. What is an adiabatic process? What is an adiabatic curve? Where are each of the three factors p, V, and T shown on such a curve?

6. What is Boyle's law? What is kept constant? What qualities vary? If the volume of a given gas is doubled, how does the pressure change? What is the equation for Boyle's law?

7. What are Charles' laws? What is kept constant in each one? If the absolute temperature of a gas is doubled, how do the other factors vary according to Charles' laws?

8. What simple and inexpensive device could you set up as a project you might set for yourself for demonstrating some one of the principles taken up in this lesson?

Problems

1. A heavy box having a mass of 200 kg is pulled along the floor for 15 meters. If the coefficient of sliding friction is 0.40, how much heat is developed?

2. A horizontal force of 35 newtons is required to pull a heavy trunk along the floor. How much heat is developed for each 100 meters it slides?

3. The water drops 80 m in a large waterfall. Assuming the available energy all goes into heat, find the temperature difference between the water at the bottom and the water at the top.

4.* A 2-ton truck is moving along the highway with a velocity of 60 mi/hr (88 ft/sec) when the brakes are applied, bringing it to rest. If all of this energy goes into heat in the brake drums and shoes, how many BTU of heat are developed?

5. A sports car with a mass of 1200 kg is moving along the highway with a velocity of 72 km/hr when the brakes are applied bringing it to rest. If all of the energy goes into heat in the brake drums and shoes, how many calories are produced?

6. A gas tank contains helium gas at a pressure of 600 lb/in.^{2} when the temperature is 27°C. Calculate the pressure when the temperature goes up to 47°C.

7. A cylinder with a piston like that shown in Fig. C contains 6 m^3 of nitrogen gas at a pressure of 76 cm of mercury and a temperature of 27°C. If the gas is compressed to a volume of 2 m^3 and a pressure of 270 cm of Hg, what is the temperature in °C?

8. An automobile tire has a gauge pressure of 28 lb/in.^{2} when the temperature is 59°F. After running at high speed on a hot pavement, the temperature rises to 140°F. Find the gauge pressure, assuming the volume is unchanged (*Note:* 15 lb/in.^{2} must be added to gauge pressure to obtain the correct gas pressure.)

9. One liter (1000 cm^3) of helium gas at normal atmospheric pressure is compressed to a volume of 250 cm^3. What is the resulting pressure if the compression is isothermal?

10. Five liters (5000 cm^3) of oxygen gas at a temperature of 27°C is heated until it occupies a volume of 10 liters. What will be its temperature? Assume constant pressure.

MECHANICAL EQUIVALENT OF HEAT—*Laboratory*

In performing this experiment as described in the accompanying LABO-RATORY EXERCISES you will verify the fundamental and basic principles involved in the mechanical equivalent of heat. The amount of heat produced by a measured amount of expended mechanical energy is determined.

LIQUID AIR

In this lesson we are going to study the physical properties of matter at very low temperatures. By low temperatures one refers to temperatures of several hundred degrees below the freezing temperature of water.

A schematic diagram of the two absolute temperature scales in common use is given in Fig. A. The zero point of both these scales is called **absolute zero** and represents the temperature at which all molecular motion ceases. While all molecular motion is said to cease at absolute zero, the atoms of which some substances are composed would still have inherent motions that cannot be eliminated.

On the Kelvin scale, water boils at 373°K and freezes at 273°K. Air becomes a liquid at 82°K and a solid at 61°K. Hydrogen gas becomes a liquid at 20°K and freezes at 14°K. Helium liquefies at 4°K and becomes a solid only at 2°K.

Compression and Expansion. The compression of a gas causes heating, and the expansion of a gas causes cooling. To obtain a clear understanding of how this comes about, consider the action of a piston as it moves down, compressing the gas in a cyl-

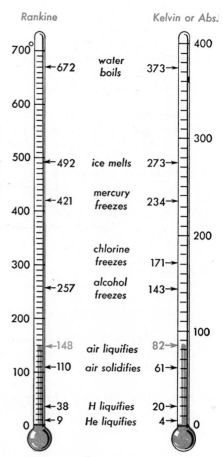

Fig. A. Rankine and Kelvin, or Absolute, temperature scales.

Rankine   Kelvin or Abs.

Rankine		Kelvin or Abs.
700°		400
←672	water boils	373→
600		
		300
500	←492	ice melts	273→
←421	mercury freezes	234→
400		
		200
	chlorine freezes	171→
300		
←257	alcohol freezes	143→
200		
		100
←148	air liquifies	82→
100	←110	air solidifies	61→
←38	H liquifies	20→
0	←9	He liquifies	4→	0

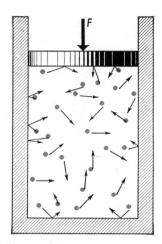

Fig. B. Illustrating the random motions of atoms and molecules in a gas.

inder as shown in Fig. B. Gas molecules striking the side walls and bottom of the cylinder will bounce away with the average velocity of those throughout most of the volume.

Molecules colliding with the downward moving piston, however, will on the average bounce away with a higher velocity. The piston action on the molecules is analogous to a bat as it swings and hits a ball.

As the piston rises in the cylinder, the molecules colliding with it rebound with a lower average velocity, much the same as a ball rebounds with little or no velocity when a batter draws his bat backward in a "bunt."

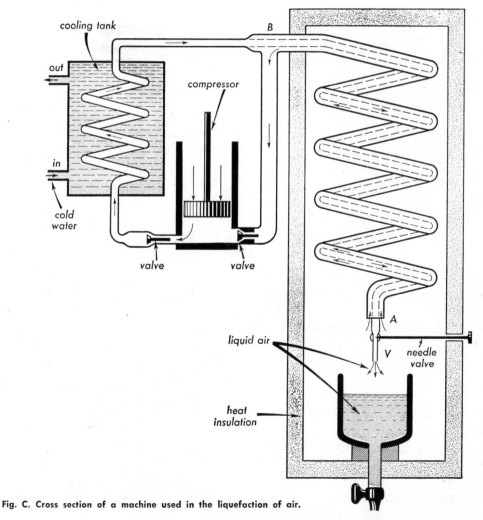

Fig. C. Cross section of a machine used in the liquefaction of air.

Liquefaction of Air. The present method of liquefying air and other gases is based upon the principle of cooling by expansion. It was by this method that Dewar liquefied oxygen for the first time in 1891, and Linde liquefied air in 1895. Oxygen gas becomes a liquid at the extremely low temperature of $-184°C$ and air at $-191°C$. On the Fahrenheit scale these correspond to $-300°F$ and $-312°F$, respectively.

In the liquid air machine (see Fig. C) air is compressed by a pump to a pressure of about 3000 lb/in.^{2} Because of compression this air is heated to a fairly high temperature. It must therefore be cooled by running it through a cooling tank. This cold compressed air passes through the inner tube of a double-walled coil **B** and escapes through the very narrow opening of a needle valve **A**. The escaping air expands so much that its temperature is lowered considerably below room temperature.

The continual pumping of the compressor draws this cold air up through the outer tube of the coil, thus cooling the compressed air on its way down to the needle valve. This air is compressed again and cooled to go around the circuit again. The cycle continues until the temperature in the region of **V** is so low that drops of liquid air form in the jet from the needle valve. These drops fall into the Dewar flask and accumulate to be drawn off later as needed.

Liquid Air Experiments. The physical properties of matter are quite different at

Fig. E. Cooled to the temperature of liquid air, a lead bell will ring.

extremely low temperatures than they are at room temperatures. This may be illustrated by a number of experiments with a small quantity of liquid air.

First of all liquid air has the same general appearance and density as water. When a little is poured out onto the table top or into an open dish, it runs around over the surface in little spherical drops and behaves just like water drops on the flat surface of a hot stove. The drops of liquid air move quickly over the surface, riding on a film of evaporated air, just as the water drops ride around on a steam layer.

Fig. F. At liquid-air temperature a coil of lead solder becomes a spring.

Fig. D. How to make a small mercury hammer.

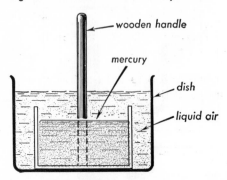

wooden handle

mercury

dish

liquid air

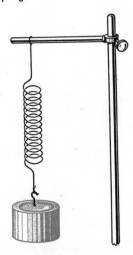

Mercury and gasoline will freeze when cooled in liquid air. An interesting demonstration is to make a small cardboard box about 1 in. × 1 in. × 2 in., fill it with mercury, and clamp a small wooden stick into it as shown in Fig. D. Liquid air poured over the box will soon freeze the mercury. When it is well frozen, the cardboard can be peeled off, and the resulting small mercury hammer used to drive nails in a block of wood.

Take a good rubber ball, hollow and about 2 in. in diameter, and put it into a vessel containing liquid air for several minutes. When the liquid quiets down, indicating the rubber's temperature is closely that of liquid air, remove the ball and drop it to the floor. Instead of bouncing it will break into many small pieces as if it were made of glass. A small bunch of grapes, or a flower, cooled in liquid air will behave the same way and break like fine glass.

An interesting demonstration can be performed by hammering or molding a small bell out of lead metal. Such a bell at room temperature will give only a dull thud, but after being cooled in liquid air, it will ring quite well. See Fig. E.

A piece of wire solder can be wound into a coil spring and suspended from a clamp stand as shown in Fig. F. At room temperature it will neither show elastic properties nor support a mass of several hundred grams. Cooled to liquid-air temperature, however, it will exhibit springlike action.

Summary

Many substances that are gases at normal temperatures may be liquefied by lowering their temperature sufficiently. One of these is air.

The principles of a liquid air machine are to (1) compress air into a pressure tank, thereby raising its temperature; (2) allow the compressed air to cool to room temperature; (3) let the air suddenly expand through a nozzle, thereby cooling it; and (4) using the cold air to lower the temperature of the compressed air not yet expanded.

Many interesting experiments can be performed with liquid air. The physical properties, particularly elasticity, change for most substances when their temperature is lowered to that of liquid air.

Questions

1. What are the two temperature scales that start at absolute zero? What is the temperature at which ice melts?

2. At what temperature does mercury freeze? At what temperature will air become a liquid? Can air be made solid? If so, how?

3. At what temperature on the Centigrade scale does hydrogen liquefy? At what temperature on the Fahrenheit scale does hydrogen liquefy?

4. What is a liquid air machine? What are its principal components called? What is the function of each? Make a diagram and label essential parts.

5. What are the physical properties of liquid air?

6. What happens to a thin rubber ball when it is cooled in liquid air and thrown to the ground to bounce?

7. What changes take place in a lead bell by lowering its temperature to that of liquid air?

8. What change takes place in mercury when cooled to the temperature of liquid air?

9. If a flower were cooled to liquid air temperature, how do you think it would change? Would the petals be highly flexible, rigid, or brittle?

10. Grapes are largely composed of water. What physical properties might they have when cooled to $82°K$?

Heat | Lesson 14

HEAT ENGINES

In general heat engines may be classified under one of the three following headings: (1) *steam engines*, (2) *internal combustion engines*, and (3) *jet propulsion engines*. While the first engines ever made were probably based upon jet propulsion using steam, reciprocating steam engines and turbines were the first to be developed. These were followed by gasoline and diesel engines and in recent years by the jet propulsion engines used principally in airplanes and rockets.

In this lesson we will not be concerned so much with the detailed mechanical parts of all kinds of engines, but rather with the fundamental principles involved in their transformation of heat into mechanical energy and with their general over-all efficiency in the process. To begin with, however, some of the mechanical details of at least one typical heat engine should be given.

The Gasoline Engine. Since the operation of most heat engines is based upon the same thermodynamic principles, an internal combustion engine will be explained as a typical example of all. A cross-sectional diagram of one of the six or more cylinders of the gasoline engine with overhead valves is

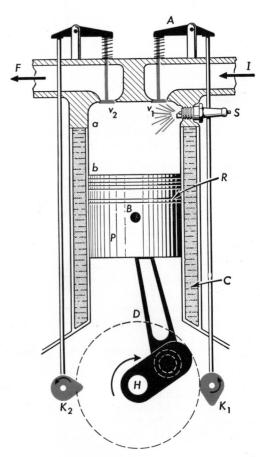

Fig. A. One cylinder of a gasoline engine of the type used in automobiles.

given in Fig. A. As the crankshaft **H** of such a motor turns clockwise as shown, each piston moves up and down in its cylinder while the cam shaft turns the small valve cams **K₁** and **K₂** at half speed.

When the piston shown is at the top of its stroke (a) and it starts down, cam **K₁** opens the intake valve **V₁** and gasoline vapor mixed with air enters from the carburetor. The falling of the piston reduces the pressure and atmospheric pressure outside forces air and gasoline vapor in. Upon reaching (b) the cylinder is full of explosive gasoline mixture and the intake valve closes. The rising piston now compresses the gas, raising its temperature.

This time when the piston reaches the top and starts down, an electric spark at the tip of the spark plug ignites the already hot vapor and the resulting explosion drives the piston down with great force. At the bottom of the stroke the cam **K₂** opens the exhaust valve **V₂** and the rising piston drives the waste fumes out. At the top of this stroke the closing of the exhaust valve is followed immediately by the opening of the intake valve and the above process is repeated.

With this type of engine the piston moves up and down twice for each explosive impulse. The several cylinders of the motor, however, are so connected to the crankshaft that they fire one after the other. In an eight-cylinder engine, for example, two cylinders are at the top when two others are on their way down, two are at the bottom and two more on their way up.

The cylinders then fire one quarter of a turn apart so that in two complete revolutions each cylinder has fired once. With impulses coming at regular intervals one quarter of a cycle apart, the driving action is so nearly continuous that a smooth development of power from the crankshaft to the wheels results.

For the average automobile in high gear five turns of the engine produce one turn of the wheels. At 60 mi/hr, when most cars de-velop their maximum power and the wheels are making about 10 rps, an eight-cylinder motor is turning at 50 rps and firing 200 times/sec.

Carnot's Cycle. The thermodynamic principles of heat engines were first explained by S. Carnot in 1824. He described, as will be done here, a perfect heat engine in which

Fig. B. Diagram showing four stages in the operation of Carnot's ideal heat engine.

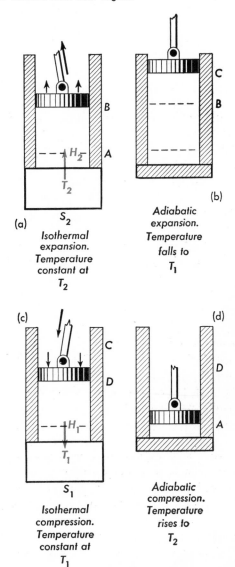

(a)
S_2
Isothermal
expansion.
Temperature
constant at
T_2

(b)
Adiabatic
expansion.
Temperature
falls to
T_1

(c)
S_1
Isothermal
compression.
Temperature
constant at
T_1

(d)
Adiabatic
compression.
Temperature
rises to
T_2

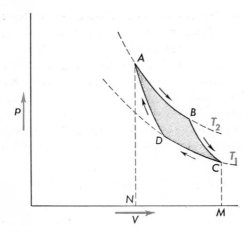

Fig. C. Graphical representation of Carnot's cycle for an ideal heat engine.

four ideal heat processes take place in cyclic procession. He described what is shown schematically in Fig. B, a frictionless one-cylinder engine having perfectly nonconducting walls and a base that is a perfect heat conductor. The box S_2 represents a source of heat capable of delivering any amount of heat at a high temperature T_2, and the box S_1 is a sink which energy can be exhausted at a lower temperature T_1.

The four diagrams (a), (b), (c), and (d) show four separate stages in one complete cycle of Carnot's engine. The four corresponding pressure-volume changes are shown graphically in Fig. C. Starting with diagram (a), an isothermal expansion is carried out in which an amount of heat H_2 at a temperature T_2 flows into the gas, pushing the piston up from position A to position B. This corresponds in Fig. C to a graph-point traversing the curve A to B. At this moment the heat supply is replaced by a perfect heat insulator, diagram (b), and the second half of the expansion stroke takes place. This is an adiabatic change in which no heat flows in or out, work is done by the gas in pushing the piston from B to C, and the gas cools to a temperature T_1.

The cylinder is now shifted to T_1, where in diagram (c) an isothermal compression be-

gins. As the piston in the one diagram, and the graph point in the other, moves from C to D, an amount of heat H_1 flows out of the gas. Shifting finally to the insulated plate, diagram (d), the last part of the stroke is carried out as an adiabatic compression D to A, with a corresponding rise in the gas temperature to T_2.

During the complete cycle an amount of heat H_2 is taken in by the gas at the high temperature T_2 and an amount H_1 is exhausted from it at the lower temperature T_1. External work was done during the complete expansion A to C and some of it was given back upon compression from C to A.

Although proof will not be given here, it can be shown that the external work done during expansion is given by the area ABCMN in Fig. C and that the energy given back to the gas during compression is represented by the area ADCMN. The difference between these two, the area ABCD is therefore the net work performed by the gas. Heat has been supplied and work has been done.

The Efficiency of Heat Engines. While steam and combustion engines do not operate under the ideal circumstances described by Carnot, their maximum efficiency is, in principle, given by the relation

$$\text{efficiency} = \frac{T_2 - T_1}{T_2} \qquad (1)$$

Example. A steam engine takes heat into its cylinders from the steam boilers at a temperature of 200°C and a pressure of 225 lb/in.² and exhausts it at a temperature of 100°C and a pressure of 15 lb/in.² Calculate the maximum efficiency as given by Carnot's formula.

Solution. The specified temperatures correspond to the absolute temperatures of 473°K and 373°K. Substitute these values in Eq. (1).

$$\text{efficiency} = \frac{473 - 373}{473} = 0.21$$

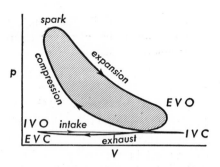

Fig. D. Pressure-volume indicator diagram for a gasoline engine.

Multiplying by 100 gives 21% efficiency. A pressure-volume indicator diagram may be, and frequently is, used to study the operating conditions of various kinds of engines in order to determine what experimental factors may improve their running efficiency. Such indicator diagrams as the one shown in Fig. D are made from actual measurements on machines while running.

The effect produced by premature or delayed opening and closing of valves shows up as reduced curve areas. The larger the area of a curve the greater is its efficiency. The time

of the **Opening** and **Closing** of the **Intake** and **Exhaust** valves is indicated in the diagrams by **IVO**, **IVC**, **EVO**, and **EVC**.

Diesel engines greatly resemble gasoline engines in construction. In operation they employ a lower grade of fuel and no spark plugs. The fuel vapors reach such high temperatures upon compression in the cylinders that they spontaneously ignite at the proper time.

The Gas Turbine and Turbo Jet. This engine, used extensively in high-speed aircraft, is shown schematically in Fig. E. Air needed for combustion enters the nose of the **shroud,** where it is compressed by a fanlike centrifugal **compressor.** This air, along with the fuel to be burned, is injected into a **combustion chamber,** and there the mixture is ignited. The rapidly expanding gases drive a fanlike **turbine** wheel and at the same time create a forward thrust on the walls by exhausting through the rear as shown.

While the principal function of the turbine is to drive the compressor and small auxiliary equipment like fuel pumps, generators, etc.,

Fig. E. Cross-section diagram of a turbojet engine used principally in aircraft (propeller optional). Top speed probably 600 mi/hr.

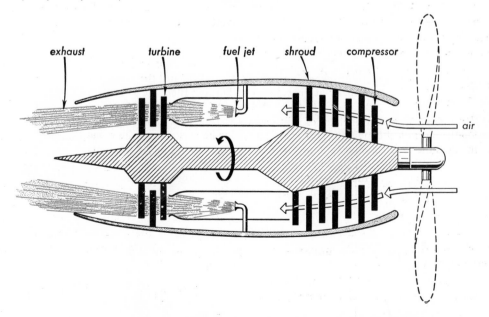

some aircraft installations employ a propeller to assist **take-off.** At high speeds such propellers are stopped and "feathered" by a suitable clutch mechanism, and all forward thrust comes from the exhaust jet.

Fig. F. Rocket ship for interplanetary travel. Top speed almost unlimited.

The Rocket. The rocket of today owes much of its early development to the American experimenter, Goddard. Rockets are classified as engines of very low efficiency but are definitely capable of enormous power and high speeds. While the turbo-jet and the ram-jet engines require large quantities of air for their proper operation and are thereby confined to aircraft operating at relatively low altitudes, the rocket carries its own **oxygen** supply as well as **fuel** and is capable of operating beyond the earth's atmosphere. See Fig. F.

Because **fuel** and **oxidizer** must both be carried along, rocket ships are, as yet, quite limited in range.

Like that of all heat engines, the efficiency of the turbo-jet, ram-jet and rocket depends upon the operating temperatures T_1 and T_2 in Eq. (1). The high temperature T_2 is lim-

ited in large measure by the melting point of the engine parts and a great deal of effort has been expended in the search for materials that will maintain the required mechanical strength at higher temperatures.

The forward thrust of a rocket engine, in air as well as in the vacuum of free space, is due to the momentum it exerts on the burned gases expelled through the exhaust pipes. The law of conservation of momentum, as given by the impulse equation, applies.

$$Ft = mv \qquad (2)$$

where **F** is equal in magnitude to the forward thrust on the rocket, **m** is the mass of the gases exhausted in **t** seconds, and **v** is the exhaust gas velocity measured with respect to the rocket itself.

Summary

The general purpose of a heat engine is to convert heat energy into mechanical energy. It is based upon fundamental laws, taking in heat energy at a high temperature and exhausting it at a lower temperature.

The greater the temperature range between intake and exhaust the greater is the efficiency. The source of heat is usually at the expense of burning fuel.

The thermodynamic principles of heat engines were first explained by Carnot. By assuming the most ideal conditions possible in an engine he was able to show that the efficiency involves the expansion and compression of gases according to the gas laws.

Steam engines have the lowest efficiency and are followed by internal combustion engines, diesel engines, and steam and gas turbines.

Questions

1. What is an internal combustion engine? What are its essential parts? Make a diagram and explain how it works.

2. What is Carnot's cycle? What is an adiabatic process? What is an isothermal process?

3. What determines the efficiency of a heat engine? Why is the efficiency of most engines so very low?

4. Why are steam engines and combustion engines not considered much for space travel?

5. Of what significance is the shaded area on the indicator diagram of a running engine?

6. What is the form of the indicator diagram for an ideal engine of the Carnot type?

7. Why are spark plugs not needed in the diesel engine?

8. What are the four steps taking place in one cycle of a Carnot engine?

Problems

1. A coal-burning locomotive supplies steam to its cylinders at 320°F and exhausts this steam into the surrounding air at 230°F. Find the theoretical efficiency.

2. An oil-burning steam turbine takes in steam at 350°C and exhausts it into the surrounding air at 188°C. Find its theoretical efficiency.

3. While in flight the effective high temperature of the flaming gas in a jet fighter engine reaches 2100°F. If its efficiency is 25%, what is the effective exhaust temperature?

4. Each of the four jet engines in a transport plane operates between a high temperature of 1182°F and an exhaust temperature of 800°F. Find their efficiency.

5. A gasoline engine of modern design, having a compression ratio of 10 to 1, reaches a temperature of 4700°F on ignition and exhausts spent gases at 2950°F. What is its efficiency?

6. A gas turbine operates between the temperatures of 650°C and 350°C. Find its efficiency.

7. A jet fighter plane making 600 mi/hr exhausts gas from the tail pipe at a speed of 8000 ft/sec and at the rate of 10 lb/sec. What is the forward thrust on the plane?

8. A rocket ship far out in space exhausts gas from the tail pipes at the speed of 12,000 ft/sec and at the rate of 0.4 lb/sec. What is the forward thrust on the rocket?

Heat | **Lesson 15**

BOYLE'S LAW—*Laboratory*

In performing this experiment on one of the gas laws as described in the accompanying LABORATORY EXERCISES you will subject a given quantity of gas to a wide range of pressures and measure the corresponding volumes at constant temperature.

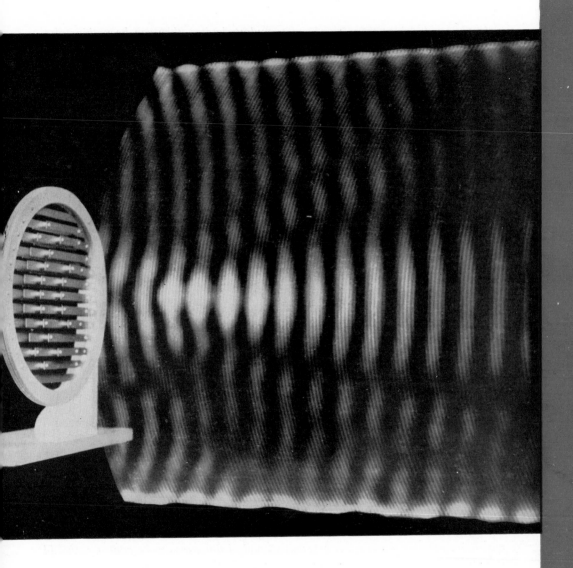

SOUND

As to sounds, since they arise from tremulous bodies, they can be nothing else but pulses of the air propagated through it; and this is confirmed by the tremors which sounds, if they be loud and deep, excite in the bodies near them, as we experience in the sound of drums; for quick and short tremors are less easily excited. But it is well known that any sounds, falling upon strings in unison with the sonorous bodies, excite tremors in those strings.

Sir Isaac Newton's Mathematical Principles, F. Cajori, ed., Andrew Motte, trans., University of California, Berkeley, 1934, p. 382.

In order to find out the truth amidst such a variety of observations [on the velocity of sound], I have made several experiments at different distances, viz. from 1 to 12 miles and upwards: and for measuring the time, employed a very accurate portable movement, with a pendulum vibrating half seconds.

To determine all these inquiries, I caused guns to be fired from towers, and other eminences, at the distance of 1, 2, 3, to 8 miles, but the guns that served this purpose best were those at Blackheath, called sakers, whose flashes I could see from the turret of Upminster church, and hear the report almost in all weathers, and even in the daytime I could with the telescope observe the flash. . . .

Though Kircher be of a different opinion, yet I doubt not, but that the sounds of all bodies, as guns, bells, hammers, etc. have the same degree of velocity; and for this end I compared the strokes of a hammer, and the report of a gun, at the distance of a mile (being the greatest at which I could hear the sound of a hammer) and found that the sound of both reached me in the same time; and that it passed over ¾, ½, and ¼ of the same space, in ¾, ½, and ¼ of the same space, in ¾, ½, and ¼ of the same time.

From what has been said above, I firmly conclude, that sound is propagated with this degree of velocity, viz. That in 9 half seconds and ¼ it moves the space of a mile, or 5280 English feet; or, which is the same thing, 571 feet in a half second of time, or 1142 feet in a whole second. Thus, sound moves through the above space, if the flux of the atmosphere or wind be transverse or across, and is its mean motion; but should the wind increase the rapidity of sound, it is impossible that it may move upwards of 600 feet in a half second of time; or, on the contrary, should it retard sound, it may move not above 560 feet in the same time.

William Derham—*Experiments and Observations on the Motion of Sound*

← Sound can be made visible. Sound waves produced by an audio oscillator are picked up by a microphone controlling the intensity of light coming from a light bulb. As the sound varies in intensity, so does the intensity of light. A camera focused on the light bulb takes time exposures in the dark, the light bulb being attached to a carriage that moves up and down as it moves forward.

Bell Telephone Laboratories

Sound Waves

SOUND IS one of the most interesting of all of the subjects we call physics. This is in large part due to the fact that it is connected with that all-important sensory manifestation we call hearing.

Sound waves and sources of sounds of various kinds were introduced in Lesson 14 on Properties of Matter. Natural vibrations of objects commonly employed to produce sound waves are there described in terms of simple harmonic motion.

Simple harmonic motion is defined as the projection on any diameter of a point moving in a circle with uniform speed.

If the diameter is chosen to be vertical, as shown in Fig. A, the graph point **P** moves around the circle of radius **r** with uniform speed **v**, while the mass point **M** moves up and down between **A** and **B** with a continually changing velocity. It is the motion of **M** that we refer to as simple harmonic, for this is typical of the most natural forms in which objects may be made to vibrate.

If a vibration starts at **A**, it is not completed until the point moves down to **B** and back again to **A**. If it starts at **C** and moves to **A** and back to **C**, only half a vibration has been completed.

The amplitude **r** is defined as the maximum distance any part of a medium moves from its central equilibrium position.

Transverse Waves. Suppose that a rope is somehow supported in a horizontal position as shown in Fig. B, and that one end is moved up and down with simple harmonic motion. As a result of this motion the dis-

Fig. A. Illustration of simple harmonic motion.

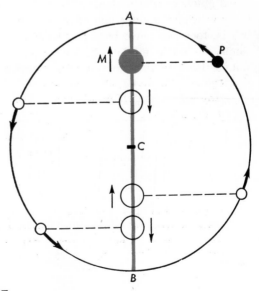

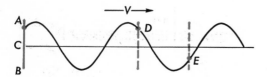

Fig. B. Diagram of a transverse wave along a rope.

turbances travel along the rope in a form of a wave.

If one observes any small section of the rope, like **D** or **E** in the diagram, it will not be found moving along the rope with a velocity **V**, but moving up and down with simple harmonic motion. Since each part of the rope moves up and down, transverse to the direction in which the waves are traveling, such motions are referred to as transverse waves. See Fig. F, p. 200.

Longitudinal Waves. Suppose that a coil spring is suspended by strings in a horizontal position as shown in Fig. C and that one end is moved back and forth with simple harmonious motion. As a result of this motion the disturbance travels along the spring from left to right in the form of bunched sections. Points where the coils are closest together are called *points of condensation,* and where they are farthest apart they are called *points of rarefaction.*

By watching any one coil of the spring it will be found to move back and forth with simple harmonic motion the same as the source. Because such motions are along a

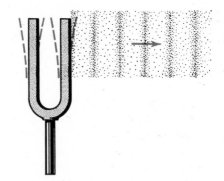

Fig. D. Sound waves are longitudinal waves

line parallel to the direction the waves are traveling, they are called *longitudinal waves.*

Sound waves, whether they travel through solids, liquids, or gases, are longitudinal in character. In Fig. D the prongs of a tuning fork are shown vibrating back and forth with simple harmonic motion. By collisions with air molecules each one sends out longitudinal waves through the atmosphere. The compressional regions in a longitudinal wave are analogous to the troughs in a transverse wave, while the rarefied regions are analogous to the crests in transverse waves.

Sound Transmission. That sound is transmitted by air, or any other gas, may be

Fig. E. A bell ringing in a vacuum cannot be heard.

Fig. C. Demonstration of longitudinal waves.

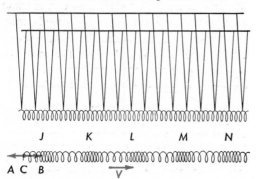

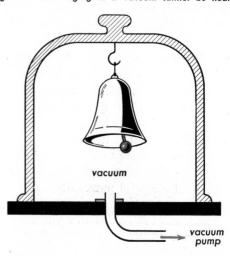

demonstrated by placing a small bell in an evacuated jar. This is illustrated in Fig. E. As the air is slowly removed from the jar, the ringing of the bell grows fainter and fainter until, when a good vacuum is obtained, no sound can be heard. As soon as the air is admitted, however, the ringing becomes clearly audible again. The vibrating bell strikes air molecules, knocking them away from the metal surface. These fast moving molecules strike the adjacent air molecules and they in turn strike others. Upon reaching the side of the jar, the glass walls are periodically bombarded by the molecules and set vibrating. The walls in turn set the outside air vibrating. Arriving at the observer's ear, the disturbance strikes the eardrum, setting it into motion. Without air to transmit the vibrations from the bell to the inside surface of the glass jar, no sound could ever leave the jar.

The transmission of sound by liquids may be illustrated by an experiment shown in Fig. F. A tuning fork with a disk attached to its base is set vibrating and then touched to the surface of a dish of water. The vibrations of the fork and disk travel through the water to the bottom of the dish and to the table top. The table top itself is set into vibration with the same frequency as the fork, thus acting like a **sounding board** to make the sound louder.

The transmission of sound by solids is il-

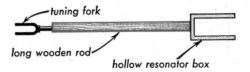

Fig. G. Demonstration of sound waves traveling through wood.

lustrated in Fig. G. A vibrating tuning fork is brought into contact with the end of a long wooden rod. The longitudinal vibrations travel down the length of the rod, setting the hollow wooden box at the other end vibrating. Sound is clearly heard coming from the box.

Speed of Sound. Although light and sound both travel with a finite velocity, the speed of light is so great in comparison that an instantaneous flash may be regarded as taking no time to travel many miles. When we see the light of a distant lightning flash and hear the thunder later, we know that the difference in time is due to the relatively low speed of sound. Knowing that sound requires 5 sec to travel 1 mi, the distance of a passing thunderstorm can be noted by the second hand of a watch. Similarly, when a distant train starts up and we watch for the first puff of smoke as it starts out, the arrival of the accompanying sound is not heard until an appreciable time afterward.

The earliest successful attempts to measure the speed of sound in air were made in 1640 by Marin Mersenne, a French physicist, and in 1656 by Giovanni Borelli and Vincenzo Viviani, Italian physicists. Since that time many experimenters have improved upon these earliest measurements by using various different methods and devices. The most recent and probably the most accurate measurements are those made in 1934 by Miller.*

* Dayton C. Miller (1866-1940), American physicist, noted for his experiments on the quality of musical sounds and on the ether drift. He collected and had in his possession the largest collection of flutes in the world. These instruments he turned over to the Smithsonian Institute in Washington, D. C., where they are now on exhibit. A member of

Fig. F. Demonstration of sound waves traveling through water.

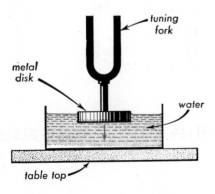

With coast defense guns as a source of sound and a set of receivers located at certain distances apart, very accurate speed determinations were made. The results gave a speed of 331 m/sec at a temperature of 0°C. This is equivalent to 1087 ft/sec at 32°F.

As a general rule, sound travels faster in solids and liquids than it does in gases. This is illustrated by the measured speed for a few common substances given in Table 1.

Table 1. Speed of Sound in Different Substances

Substance	m sec	ft sec
air (at 0°C)..........	331.	1,087.
carbon dioxide......	258	846
water..............	1,435	4,708
alcohol.............	1,213	3,890
iron...............	5,130	16,820
glass..............	5,000	16,410

It is well known that the temperature has a small but measurable effect upon the speed of sound. For each degree centigrade rise in temperature the speed in air increases by 61 cm/sec, or for each degree Fahrenheit rise, 1.1 ft/sec. Written as an equation,

$$V = V_0 + 0.61\ t \tag{1}$$

where V_0 is the speed in meters per second at 0°C, and t is the temperature in °C. If the speed V_0 is in ft/sec at 32°F, and t is the temperature in °F above 32°, the speed V is given by

$$V = V_0 + 1.1\ t \tag{2}$$

A speed of 1087 ft/sec is equivalent to 741 mi/hr. High in the stratosphere where the daytime temperature reaches 200°F, the

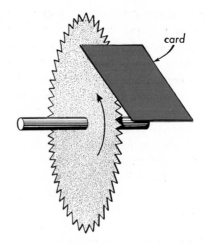

Fig. H. A card held against the teeth of a rotating wheel produces a musical note.

speed of sound increases 185 ft/sec. There a speed of 1272 ft/sec is equivalent to 867 mi/hr.

Pitch. The pitch of a musical note refers to its position on a musical scale and is determined principally by the frequency of the sound impulses sent out by the vibrating source. The dependence of pitch upon frequency can be demonstrated in many ways. Fig. H represents a toothed wheel (called Savart's wheel) rotating at high speed. A small card held against the teeth is set into vibration, giving out a musical note. As the wheel slows down, the vibration frequency of the card decreases and the note lowers in pitch.

Fig. I. Air through rings of holes in a rotating disk can be made to produce a musical scale.

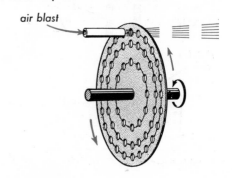

air blast

the National Academy of Sciences, and one-time president of the American Physical Society, he has been awarded the Elliott Cresson Medal and the Cleveland Distinguished Service Medal.

Fig. I represents a siren in which a single blast of air is interrupted by a rotating disk containing several rings of holes. When the air is blown through one ring of holes, the air pulses emerging from the opposite side will produce a note whose frequency depends on the number of **equally spaced holes** in the ring and the speed of the wheel.

Since each ring may contain a different number of holes, a musical scale can be arranged and played by putting the air nozzle in front of the rings in proper succession.

Summary

Most vibrating objects move with what is called simple harmonic motion. Such motions have a frequency and an amplitude.

The two most common forms of wave motion are called transverse waves and longitudinal waves. Such waves are produced by the vibrations of some source.

Sound waves are longitudinal in character and travel through solids, liquids, and gases, and with different speeds. They will not travel through a vacuum.

The speed of sound in air varies with temperature: the higher the temperature, the higher the speed.

The pitch of a sound depends on the frequency of the source. As the frequency increases the pitch rises, and as the frequency decreases the pitch falls.

Questions

1. What is simple harmonic motion? What is amplitude?

2. What are transverse waves? What are longitudinal waves?

3. Will sound waves travel through a vacuum? Will sound travel through gases, liquids, or solids?

4. In what general kinds of matter do sound waves have their highest speeds?

5. What is the speed of sound in air at 0°C and at 32°F? Is the speed of sound affected by a change in temperature?

6. Approximately how long does it take sound to travel one mile in air?

7. What determines the pitch of a sound? How is pitch related to the frequency?

8. What inexpensive device would you like to make for demonstrating one of the principles introduced in this lesson?

Problems

1. Calculate the speed of sound in air if the temperature is 30°C.

2. If the temperature is 72°F, what is the speed of sound in air?

3. Find the speed of sound in air if the temperature is 25°C.

4. What is the speed of sound in air if the temperature is 100°F?

5. Forty-five seconds after a lightning flash is seen, the thunder is heard. How far away did the lightning strike if the air temperature is 75°F?

6. Lightning strikes the arrestor on the top of a building five miles from an observer. How long after the flash of light is the sound heard if the temperature is 60°F?

7. How long does it take sound to travel 1 mi in the metal of an iron pipe?

8. A heavy blow is delivered at one end of an iron pipe 5 mi long. What is the time interval between the arrival of the sound through the iron and through the air? Assume 0°C.

FREQUENCY OF A TUNING FORK—Laboratory

This experiment is described in the accompanying LABORATORY EXERCISES. By means of a pen stylus on the prong of a tuning fork a tracing is made of the vibrations on a moving strip of paper. From recorded time intervals the fork frequency can be determined.

RESONANCE, BEATS, AND DOPPLER EFFECT

Resonance. An experimental demonstration of resonance is easily set up, as shown in Fig. A. Two simple pendulums are suspended from a flexible support. One, **A**, has a heavy bob made of metal, and the other, **B**, a bob made of wood.

The heavy bob **A** is pulled to one side and released to swing freely. The horizontal support responds to the motion and, in swaying back and forth in step with **A**, tries to set the other pendulum swinging. The response of pendulum **B** to this motion depends upon the relative lengths of the two pendulums. If there is considerable difference in their lengths, the response is ever so slight, and the closer they are to the same length the greater is the response.

When **A** and **B** have the same length, their natural periods become equal, and **B** re-

Fig. A. A demonstration of resonance can be performed with two pendulums.

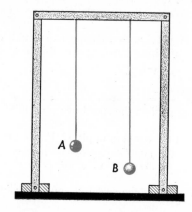

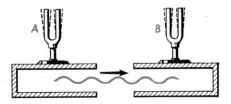

Fig. B. Tuning forks mounted on resonator boxes for demonstrating resonance.

sponds to the swaying support and swings with a large amplitude. It responds in sympathy, or resonance, to the driving pendulum **A**.

If two violin strings are tuned to the same frequency and one is set vibrating, the other stationed some distance away will soon pick up the vibrations and give out the same note. This too is a case of resonance, a phenomenon which occurs only if two objects have the same natural frequency of vibration.

Another experimental demonstration of resonance is illustrated in Fig. B. Two tuning forks with exactly the same pitch are mounted on separate hollow boxes as shown. Fork **A** is first set vibrating for a moment and then stopped by touching the prongs with the fingers. Fork **B** will then be found vibrating. Taking into account the hollow boxes, whose purpose it is to act as sounding boards and intensify the sound, the explanation is quite simple. Each sound pulse emerging from the box with each vibration of fork **A** passes into the other box, pushing out the sides at just the right time to make the prongs of fork **B** move in the same direction.

Beat Notes. When two notes of slightly different pitch are sounded together, beats are heard. This phenomenon is used in organ pipes to produce the familiar vibrato effect. Two pipes tuned to slightly different frequencies are used for every note.

The phenomenon of beats may be demonstrated by two tuning forks mounted as shown in Fig. B. One fork is made slightly out of tune with the other by looping rubber bands *tightly* around the prongs. If the two forks are sounded simultaneously, the intensity of loudness of the sound rises and falls periodically. This is illustrated by means of vibration graphs as shown in Fig. C. The upper curve represents the sound vibrations arriving at the ear from one fork, and the second curve the vibrations from the other. Both waves arriving at the ear are first in phase, i.e., in step with each other, then out of phase, then in phase, then out of phase, etc.

The resultant action of these two waves on the eardrum is represented by the third curve. When the waves are in phase the resultant has a large amplitude equal to the sum of the amplitudes of the two. When they are out of phase the amplitude becomes zero. The number of beats per second **N** is determined by the difference between n_2 and n_1, the respective frequencies of the two sources producing the sound.

$$\text{beat frequency } N = n_2 - n_1 \qquad (1)$$

When the beat frequency lies between about 1 and 6 vibrations per second, the ear

Fig. C. Wave graphs illustrating how beat notes are produced by two different frequencies.

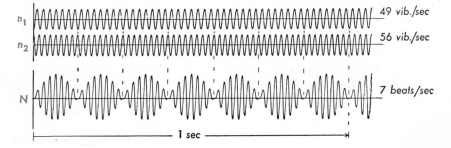

perceives an intertone halfway between the two, but periodically waxing and waning in intensity. As the beat frequency increases, the smooth rise and fall gives way to a succession of pulses, then to a sensation of roughness, and finally to two clearly perceived tones.

The Doppler Effect.   Nearly everyone has at some time, perhaps without realizing it, observed the *Doppler effect.* The sounding horn of a car passing at high speed on the highway exhibits this phenomenon. The pitch of the horn, as the car goes by, drops as much as two whole notes on the musical scale. A similar observation can be made by listening to the roar of the motor of a racing car as it approaches and recedes from an observer at the race track. The motor seems to slow down as it passes by. Again, the pitch of the whistle on a fast moving train sounds higher as the train approaches the observer than it does after the train has passed by.

This change in pitch is due to the relative motions of the source of sound and the observer. To see how this produces the effect, consider the following example. In blowing its whistle a train at rest sends out waves traveling with the same velocity in all directions. To all stationary observers, no matter in which direction they are located, the true pitch of the whistle is heard, since just as many waves arrive at the ear per

Fig. D. The Doppler effect. The pitch of a whistle on a fast-moving train sounds higher to an observer in front of the train, lower to an observer in back, and normal to observers off at the sides.

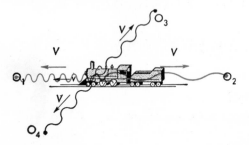

second as there are waves leaving the whistle. If, on the other hand, the train is moving as shown in Fig. D, the whistle is moving away from the waves traveling to the rear and toward the waves traveling forward. The result is that the waves behind are considerably drawn out while those in front are crowded together. With each new wave sent out by the source, the train is farther from the preceding wave sent out to the rear and nearer to the one sent out ahead. Since the velocity of sound is the same in all directions, an observer at O_1 therefore hears more waves per second and an observer at O_2 hears fewer.

To an observer O_3 or O_4, at right angles and at some little distance from the moving source, the pitch remains unchanged. For these side positions the source is neither approaching nor receding from the observer, so that approximately the same number of waves are received per second as there are waves leaving the source.

The general relations for the Doppler effect are given by the following single equation:

$$\frac{n_o}{V - v_o} = \frac{n_s}{V - v_s} \qquad (2)$$

where n_s is the frequency of the source, n_o is the frequency heard by the observer, V is the velocity of sound, v_s the velocity of the source, and v_o the velocity of the observer. *The velocity of sound V at the observer is positive, and its direction is taken as the positive direction for all velocities. V_o or v_s* is either positive if it is directed along the positive direction or negative if it is oppositely directed.

Case 1.   If source and observer are approaching each other, v_s is +, and v_o is −.

Case 2.   If source and observer are moving in the same direction, v_s and v_o are both +.

Case 3.   The observer is at rest and the

source is approaching at a velocity $v_s = 2$ **V**. Here $v_o = 0$ and v_s is $+$. This is an interesting case, since n_o is the negative of n_s. The observer hears the sound backward, as if played backward on a tape recorder, and it is heard after the source has passed him.

Summary

If two mechanical systems have the same natural frequency of vibration, the sounding of one in the close proximity of the other will set it vibrating also. This phenomenon can be demonstrated with tuning forks, violin strings, etc., and is known as sympathetic vibrations or resonance.

When two sources of sound have slightly different frequencies, they get in and out of step with each other and produce a sound of periodically increasing and decreasing intensity. These are called beats.

When a source of sound is moving with respect to an observer, the frequency heard by the observer is generally higher or lower than that of the source.

If the distance between source and observer is decreasing, the frequency received is higher than that of the source. If the distance is increasing, the frequency is lowered.

Questions

1. What is resonance? How can it be demonstrated? Can resonance be achieved with two vibrators of different frequency? Two different musical instruments having the same natural frequency?

2. How can resonance be demonstrated with tuning forks?

3. What are beat notes? How can they be demonstrated with tuning forks?

4. What is meant by the beat frequency? How can one determine the beat frequency of two known frequencies?

5. What is the Doppler effect? If a source of sound is moving away from an observer, what change in the sound is observed?

6. If an observer is receding from a source of sound, what happens to the apparent pitch?

7. If a source of sound and an observer are both moving in the same direction with the same velocity, does the observer hear the same pitched note he would hear if both are at rest?

8. If a source of sound moving with twice the speed of sound passes a stationary observer, what kind of sound is heard?

9. What device would you propose as a project you might undertake to demonstrate one or more of the principles presented in this lesson?

Problems

1. Two tuning forks have frequencies of 135 and 220 vib/sec, respectively. Find the beat frequency.

2. The A and E strings of a violin have frequencies of 440 and 660 vib/sec, respectively. Find their beat frequency.

3. Three notes are sounded simultaneously: 264, 352, and 440 vib/sec. (a) Taken in pairs what three beat frequencies are produced? (b) List the notes and beat frequencies in the order of increasing frequency.

4. A train approaching a station at 45 mi/hr (66 ft/sec) blows its whistle of 300 vib/sec. What frequency is heard (a) in the station and (b) by a stationary observer behind the train? Assume the speed of sound to be 1100 ft/sec.

5. The horn of a car is blown as the car approaches an intersection at 60 mi/hr. If the horn has a frequency of 200 vib/sec and the velocity of sound is 1100 ft/sec, what frequency is heard by an observer standing at the intersection? (*Note:* 60 mi/hr = 88 ft/sec.)

6. The siren of a ranger station along the highway is sounded with a frequency of 500 vib/sec. What frequency is heard by motorists traveling 60 mi/hr along the highway if they are (a) approaching and (b) receding from the station? Assume the speed of sound to be 1120 ft/sec.

7.* An airplane flying close to the ground at 300 mi/hr produces an engine roar of 500 vib/sec. What frequency is heard by a ground observer when the plane is (a) approaching and (b) receding? Assume sound to travel 1150 ft/sec.

8.* Two cars approach each other from the opposite directions on the highway, when one sounds his horn with a frequency of 200 vib/sec. If they are both traveling at 60 mi/hr (88 ft/sec), what frequency is heard in the other car when they are (a) approaching and (b) receding? Assume sound to travel 1130 ft/sec.

Sound | **Lesson 4**

VIBRATING STRINGS AND AIR COLUMNS

In this lesson we will begin the study of musical sounds as they are produced by musical instruments of all kinds. Musical instruments in general can be classified under one of three headings: **strings, winds,** and **percussions.**

In taking up the subject of stringed instru-

ments we may begin by considering the waves produced on a string or rope as one end is moved up and down with simple harmonic motion. As shown in Fig. A, three measurable quantities are to be associated with such waves. As defined in Properties of Matter, Lesson 14, these are **velocity V, frequency n,** and **wave length** λ.

These three factors are related to each other by the so-called wave equation

$$V = n\lambda \tag{1}$$

The length of one wave λ multiplied by

Fig. A. Transverse waves along a string or rope.

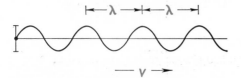

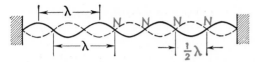

Fig. B. Standing transverse waves on a vibrating string or rope.

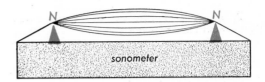

Fig. C. Single string vibrating with its fundamental frequency.

the number of waves passing by per second *n* is equal to the distance a wave travels in one second, *V.*

Standing Waves. Standing waves in a string may be produced by two trains of waves of the same frequency and wave length traveling in opposite directions. One of the ways of accomplishing these conditions is shown in Fig. B. One end of a string or rope is fastened to a post and the other end is moved up and down with simple harmonic motion.

As the waves reach the far end, they are reflected back to meet the succeeding waves just coming up. If the waves have just the right frequency, the rope will sustain both wave trains, and the general appearance will be that of dividing the rope into stationary sections of equal length as shown. The points labeled **N**, where the rope has no up-and-

down motion, are called **nodes,** and the points halfway between, where the motion has the greatest amplitude, are called **antinodes.** The heavy line represents the rope at one instant only, while the other lines represent it at other instants. An entire wave section between two consecutive nodes is called a **loop.**

Note carefully that each loop has a length of $\frac{1}{2}\lambda$.

Stringed Instruments. There are two principal reasons why stringed instruments of different kinds do not sound alike as regards **tone quality**—first, the design of the instrument, and second, the method by which the strings are set into vibration. The violin and cello are bowed with long strands of tightly stretched horsehair, the harp and guitar are plucked with the fingers or picks, and the

Fig. D. Vibration modes for strings of musical instruments.

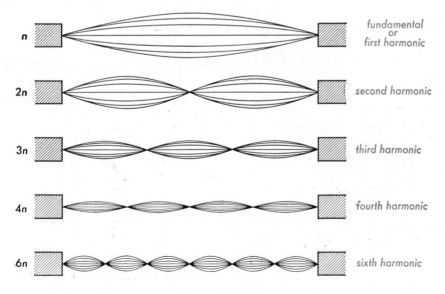

Fig. E. String vibrating with its fundamental and first overtone simultaneously.

piano is hammered with light felt mallets.

Under very special conditions a string may be made to vibrate with nodes at either end as shown in Fig. C. In this state of motion the string gives rise to its lowest possible note, and it is said to be vibrating with its **fundamental frequency.**

Every musician knows that a thick heavy string has a lower natural pitch than a thin one, that a short string has a higher pitch than a long one, and that the tighter a string is stretched the higher is its pitch. The **G** string of a violin, for example, is thicker and heavier than the high-pitched **E** string, and the **bass** strings of the piano are longer and heavier than the strings of the **treble.**

Harmonics and Overtones. When a professional violinist plays **in harmonics,** he touches the strings lightly at any one of various points and sets each one vibrating in two or more segments as shown in Fig. D. If a string is touched at the center, a node is formed at that point and the vibration frequency becomes double that of the fundamental. If the string is touched lightly at a point one third the distance from the end, it will vibrate in three sections and have a frequency three times that of the fundamental.

It is clear from these diagrams that the vibrating string of any musical instrument is an example of **standing waves** of the **transverse** character.

It is not difficult to set a string vibrating with its fundamental and several of its higher harmonics at the same time. This is accomplished by plucking or bowing the string vigorously. As an illustration a diagram of an ideal string vibrating with two normal har-

Fig. F. Experiment for observing the detailed vibrations of stretched string.

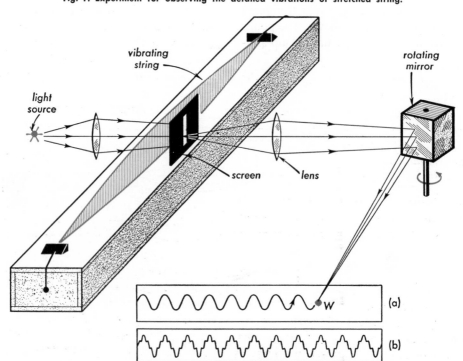

monics, or modes, at the same time is shown in Fig. E. As the string vibrates in two loops with a frequency **2 n**, it also moves up and down as a single loop with the fundamental frequency **n**.

The sound wave sent out by such a vibrating string is composed of two frequencies, the fundamental or first harmonic of frequency **n** and the second harmonic or first partial with the frequency **2 n**.

An interesting experiment with a vibrating string is diagramed in Fig. F. Light from an arc lamp is focused on the central section of a stretched steel string, which, except for a small vertical slot, is masked by a screen. An image of the slot and the string section seen through it is focused by a second lens, after reflection from a rotating mirror, on a screen. As the string vibrates up and down, only a blurred image of the short section of string is seen; but when the mirror is rotated, the wire section draws out a clearly visible curve **W**.

If the string is plucked gently near the center, a smooth wave form (a) is drawn out on the screen; but if it is plucked hard near the end to produce a harsh sounding note, the wave form is more complex as shown in (b). In the first case the string is vibrating only with its fundamental mode, while in the second case various overtones, or partials, are also present.

As a string vibrates with *transverse waves*, it strikes air molecules all around it, sending periodic impulses through the air as *longitudinal waves*.

The Theory of Vibrating Strings.

The velocity in m/sec of transverse waves along a rope or string under tension is given by

$$V = \sqrt{F/m} \qquad (2)$$

where **F** is the tension in newtons and **m** is the mass per unit length of string in kg/m. When standing waves are produced, the distance **L** between any two consecutive nodes is just equal to half a wavelength, $\frac{1}{2}\lambda$. Accordingly,

$$\lambda = 2L \qquad (3)$$

To obtain an equation for the fundamental frequency of a vibrating string, the general wave equation $V = n\lambda$ is used. If we transpose this equation and obtain

$$n = \frac{V}{\lambda}$$

and then substitute the above values for **V** and λ, we obtain

$$n = \frac{\sqrt{F/m}}{2L} \qquad (4)$$

Accurate measurements with vibrating strings and musical instruments confirm this equation.

Wind Instruments.

Musical instruments often classified as **wind instruments** are usually divided into two subclasses: **wood winds** and **brasses**. Under the heading of wood winds we find such instruments as the flute, piccolo, clarinet, bass clarinet, saxophone, bassoon, and contra bassoon, and under the brasses such instruments as the French horn, cornet, trumpet, tenor trombone, bass trombone, and tuba (or bombardon).

The fundamental principles involved in the production of musical sounds by wind instruments concern standing waves in the columns of air inside the instrument. Longitudinal air waves—usually produced near one end of the instrument by some vibrating system such as a reed, the lips, or the edge tones from the sharp edge of an opening—travel down the length of a confined air column. Upon reflection from the other end, the conditions of two wave trains traveling in opposite directions exist and we have standing waves.

The existence of standing waves in a resonating air column may be demonstrated by a long hollow tube filled with illuminating gas

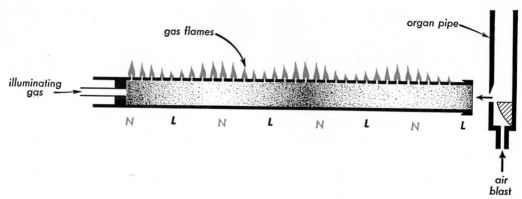

Fig. G. Standing waves in a long tube containing illuminating gas.

as shown in Fig. G. Entering through an adjustable plunger at the left, the gas escapes through tiny holes spaced at regular intervals in a row along the top. Sound waves from an organ pipe enter the gas column by setting into vibration a thin paper sheet stretched over the right-hand end. When resonance is attained by sliding the plunger to the correct position, the small gas flames will appear as shown. Where the nodes occur in the vibrating gas column, the gas molecules are not moving; at these points the pressure is high and the flames are tallest. Halfway between are the anti-nodes—region where the molecules vibrate back and forth with large amplitudes, and the flames are low. Bernoulli's principle is chiefly responsible for the pressure differences, for where the velocity of the molecules is high the pressure is low, and where the velocity is low the pressure is high.

Summary

Musical instruments are divided into three general classes: the strings, winds, and percussions. The fundamental relation for the frequencies they produce is $V = n\lambda$.

Vibrating strings are standing transverse waves with a node at either end. Strings may vibrate with any one of a series of frequencies called harmonics. Harmonics have frequencies that are whole-number multiples of the first harmonic, or fundamental.

As a string vibrates with standing transverse waves, the sound waves they produce are longitudinal in character. Strings are set vibrating by means of a bow, by plucking, or by impact.

The source of the musical sound in a wind instrument arises from standing longitudinal waves in the confined air column. Such air columns may be set into motion by edge tones from a sharp edge at one opening, the lips in vibration, or reeds.

Questions

1. Into what three classes are all musical instruments assigned? What are the subclasses of wind instruments?

2. What is the basic equation for the frequency of all musical sounds?

3. What kinds of waves are involved with stringed instruments? What different ways are strings made to vibrate?

4. How many natural vibration frequencies are possible for any one string? What are they called? How are the frequencies related?

5. How are different notes on a musical scale produced by one string? What is a string's lowest frequency?

6. Upon what three factors does the frequency of a string depend? Write down the equation.

7. What are the differences between the treble and bass strings of a piano? Why do bass strings look like coiled springs?

8. What kinds of waves are involved in wind instruments? What different ways are they set into motion?

9. How many natural vibration frequencies are possible with a single air column? What are these frequencies called? How are these frequencies related?

10. What project could you undertake in the making of an inexpensive device for demonstrating one or more of the principles presented in this lesson?

Problems

1. The end of a string is moved up and down with a frequency of 124 vib/sec. If the waves produced have a velocity of 42 m/sec, what is their wavelength?

2. What frequency applied to a string will produce waves 25 cm long if the wave velocity is 160 m/sec?

3. The A and E strings of a violin have fundamental frequencies of 440 vib/sec and 660 vib/sec, respectively. Find the frequencies of their first five harmonics.

4. The lowest pitched note produced by a B♭ cornet has a frequency of 116.7 vib/sec. What would you expect for the frequencies of the first eight harmonics?

5. The lowest pitched note from a bugle has a frequency of 66 vib/sec. What are the frequencies of the lowest six notes it can produce?

6.* Waves travel along a stretched steel wire at 50 m/sec. What is the tension in the wire if its mass is 0.08 gm/cm length?

7.* If a long wire of mass 0.05 gm/cm is put under a tension of 500 newtons, with what velocity will transverse waves be propagated?

8.* A piano string 20 cm long has a frequency of 1056 vib/sec and a mass of 0.008 kg/m length. Find its tension in newtons.

9.* Find the mass per unit length of a violin string 35 cm long if under a tension of 500 newtons it has a vibration frequency of 440 vib/sec.

10.* A violin string 35 cm long has a mass of 0.066 gm/cm length. Find the tension in newtons if the frequency is 440 vib/sec.

VIBRATING STRINGS—*Laboratory*

This experiment on transverse wave vibrations on a string under tension is described in the accompanying LABORATORY EXERCISES. A vibrating tuning fork is used to drive the string, and the distances between nodes are determined for different applied tensions. A velocity vs wave-length graph is plotted from the results.

WIND AND PERCUSSION INSTRUMENTS

When a source of sound waves is located at one end of a hollow pipe, as shown in Fig. A, a continuous train of longitudinal waves travels down the pipe, reflects from the other end, and travels back toward the source. If the frequency of the source can be continually increased over a considerable range, the pipe will remain quiet most of the time. At certain definite frequencies, however, it will sing out in resonance to the overlapping waves.

Under such resonant conditions as these, standing longitudinal waves exist within the pipe. At certain equidistant points **N** along the pipe the air molecules remain essentially undisturbed, while at points halfway between they move back and forth with the frequency of the source. These points, just as with vibrating strings, are called **nodes** and **antinodes,** respectively, and whatever the total number of each may be, a node al-

ways forms at the closed end of a pipe and an antinode at the open end.

Since standing longitudinal waves are difficult to represent in diagrams, it is convenient in drawings to indicate nodes and antinodes as if they were standing transverse waves. See the lower diagram Fig. A.

Vibrating Air Columns. The various modes in which air columns may vibrate in open or closed pipes are shown in Fig. B. Starting at the top, a pipe open at both ends may vibrate with (1) a single node at the middle and an antinode at both ends, (2) two nodes and three antinodes, or (3) with three nodes and four antinodes, etc. On the other hand, a pipe closed at one end and open at the other may vibrate with (1) one node and one antinode, (2) two nodes and two antinodes, or (3) three nodes and three antinodes, etc.

In all vibrating air columns an antinode always forms at an open end and a node at a closed end.

The various possible frequencies to which a pipe may resonate are definite and fixed in value and depend only upon the length of the pipe and the velocity of sound in air. If, for example, the pipes in Fig. B are all 2 ft long

Fig. A. Standing-wave diagrams for a resonating air column.

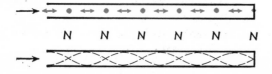

N   N   N   N   N   N

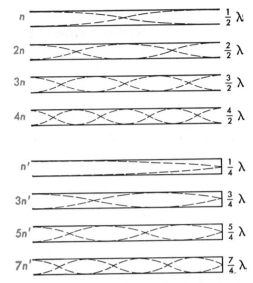

Fig. B. Resonating air columns, showing nodes and loops.

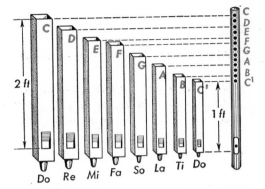

Fig. C. Organ pipes arranged in a musical scale. The longer the pipe, the lower is its fundamental frequency and pitch. The vibrating air column of the flute is terminated at various points by openings along the tube.

and the velocity of sound in air is 1120 ft/sec, the wave equation $V = n\lambda$ shows that they will vibrate with the following respective frequencies:

n	$2n$	$3n$	$4n$
280	560	840	1120
n'	$3n'$	$5n'$	$7n'$
140	420	700	980

With an open pipe the lowest possible vibration frequency is called the **fundamental,** and the others, **2 n, 3 n, 4 n**, etc., which are whole-numbered multiples of the fundamental frequency, are called **harmonics.** With closed pipes the lowest frequency is again the fundamental and the others with odd integral multiples, **3 n', 5 n', 7 n'**, etc., are harmonics. All these vibration modes are referred to as natural modes and their corresponding frequencies as **natural frequencies. The fundamental is also called the first harmonic.**

Theory of Vibrating Air Columns. The various notes produced by most wind instruments are brought about by varying the length of the vibrating air column. This is illustrated by the organ pipes in Fig. C. The longer the pipe the lower the fundamental frequency or pitch of the note. In a regular concert organ, the pipes vary in length from about 6 in. for the highest note to almost 16 ft for the lowest. For the middle octave of the musical scale the open-ended pipes vary from 2 ft for middle C to 1 ft for C^1 one octave higher. In the wood winds, like the flute, the length of the column is varied by openings in the side of the instrument; and in many of the brasses, like the trumpet, by means of valves. A valve is a piston which on being pressed down throws in an additional length of tube.

The basic equation for sound waves through a gas was first derived by Newton and later modified by Laplace.

$$V = \sqrt{K \frac{p}{\rho}} \qquad (1)$$

where V is the wave velocity in cm/sec, p is the gas pressure in dynes/cm², ρ the density in gm/cm³, and K is a proportionality constant. For diatomic gases like air $K = 1.40$, for monatomic gases $K = 1.67$, and for triatomic gases $K = 1.33$.

For standing waves the distance L between any two consecutive nodes, i.e., the length of one loop, is just equal to half a wave length, $\lambda/2$. Accordingly

$$\lambda = 2L$$

Having the speed of the waves **V** and the wave length λ one can use the wave equation

$$V = n\lambda$$

for all wind instruments.

Edge Tones. Although the pitch of the note sounded by any wind instrument is determined by the vibration of an air column according to principles of resonance, the method by which the air is set into vibration varies widely among instruments. In instruments like the saxophone, clarinet, oboe, and bassoon, air is blown against a thin strip of wood called a reed, setting it into vibration. In most of the brasses the musician's lips are made to vibrate with certain required frequencies, while in certain wood winds, like

Fig. D. A steady stream of air blown across the lip of an organ pipe sets up whirlwinds along both sides of the partition.

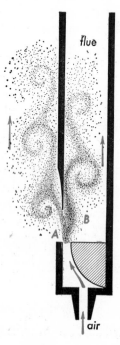

the flute and piccolo, and in organs and whistles, air is blown across the sharp edge of an opening near one end of the instrument, setting the air into vibration. A brief discussion of these source vibrations is therefore important here.

When wind or a blast of air encounters a small obstacle, little whirlwinds are formed in the air stream behind the obstacle. This is illustrated by the cross section of a flue organ pipe in Fig. D. Whether the obstacle is long, or a small round object, the whirlwinds are formed alternately on the two sides as shown. The air stream at **B** waves back and forth, sending a pulse of air first up one side and then the other. Although the wind blows through the opening **A** as a continuous stream, the separate whirlwinds going up each side of the obstacle become periodic shocks to the surrounding air. Coming at perfectly regular intervals, these pulses give rise to a musical note often described as **edge tones.**

The number of whirlwinds formed per second, and therefore the pitch of the edge tone, increases with the wind velocity. When the wind howls through the trees, the pitch of the note rises and falls, its frequency at any time denoting the speed of the wind. For a given wind speed, smaller objects give rise to higher pitched notes than large objects. A finely stretched wire or rubber band, when placed in an open window or in the wind, will be set into vibration and give out a musical note. Each whirlwind shock to the air reacts on the obstacle (the wire or rubber band), pushing it first to one side and then the other. These are the pushes that cause the rope of a flagpole to flap periodically in the breeze, while the waving of the flag at the top of a pole shows the whirlwinds that follow each other along each side.

Percussion Instruments. Vibrating Rods. If a number of small sticks are dropped upon the floor, the sound that is heard is described as a noise. If one stick alone is dropped, one

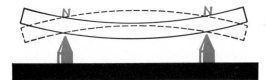

Fig. E. Transverse vibrations of a uniform rod or bar.

would also describe the sound as a noise, unless, of course, a set of sticks of varying length are arranged in order of length and each one dropped in its order. If this is done, one notices that each stick gives rise to a rather definite musical note and that the set of sticks could be cut to the proper lengths to form a musical scale. The use of vibrating rods in a musical instrument is found in the *xylophone*, the *marimba*, and the *triangle*. Standing waves in a rod, like those in a stretched string, may be any one of three different kinds: *transverse, longitudinal*, and *torsional*. Only the first two of these modes of vibration will be treated here.

Transverse waves in a rod are usually set up by supporting the rod at points near each end and striking it a blow at or near the center. As illustrated in Fig. E, the center and ends of the rod move up and down, forming nodes at the two supports. Like a stretched string of a musical instrument, the shorter the rod the higher is its pitch, and the longer and heavier the rod the lower is its frequency of vibration and pitch.

The xylophone is a musical instrument based upon the *transverse vibrations* of wooden rods of different lengths. Mounted

Fig. F. Diagram of the bars and pipes of a marimba.

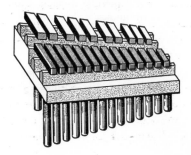

as shown in Fig. F, the longer rods produce the low notes and the shorter ones the higher notes. The marimba is essentially a xylophone with a long straight hollow tube suspended vertically under each rod. Each tube is cut to such a length that the enclosed air column will resonate to the sound waves sent out by the rod directly above. Each resonator tube, being open at both ends, forms a node at its center.

Vibrating Plates. Although the drum or the cymbals should hardly be called musical instruments, they are classified as such and made use of in nearly all large orchestras and bands. The noise given out by a vibrating drumhead or cymbal plate is in general due to the high intensity of certain characteristic overtones. These overtones in turn are due to the very complicated modes of vibration of the source.

Cymbals consist of two thin metal disks with handles at the centers. Upon being struck together, their edges are set into vibration with a clang. A drumhead, on the other hand, is a stretched membrane of leather held tight at the periphery, and is set into vibration by being struck a blow at or near the center.

To illustrate the complexity of the vibrations of a circular plate, two typical sand patterns are shown in Fig. G. The sand pattern method of studying the motions of plates was invented in the eighteenth century by Chladni, a German physicist. A thin circular metal plate is clamped at the center C and sand is sprinkled over the top surface. Then, while touching the rim of the plate at two points N_1 and N_2, a cello bow is drawn down over the edge at a point L. Nodes are formed at the stationary points N_1 and N_2 and antinodes in the regions of L_1 and L_2. The grains of sand bounce away from the loops and into the nodes, the regions of no motion. At one instant the regions marked with a $(+)$ sign all move up, while the regions marked with a $(-)$ sign all move down. Half a vibra-

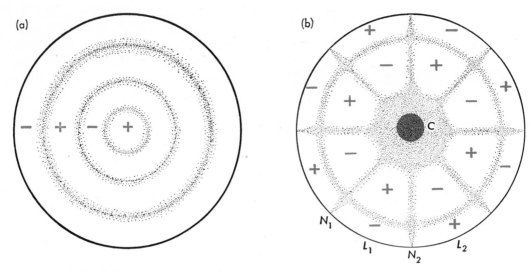

Fig. G. Chladni's sand figures showing the nodes and loops of (a) a vibrating drumhead (clamped at the edge) and (b) a vibrating cymbal plate (clamped at the center).

tion later the + regions are moving down and the − regions up. Such diagrams are called **Chladni's sand figures.**

With cymbal plates held tightly at the center by means of handles a node is always formed there, and antinodes are always formed at the periphery. With a drumhead, on the other hand, the periphery is always a node and the center is sometimes but not always an antinode.

Summary

The sources of sound waves in wind instruments are the standing longitudinal waves in the confined air columns. Nodes are always formed at the closed end of a pipe and antinodes at the open ends. The lip of a flute, or organ pipe, behaves as an open end.

The natural vibration frequencies of pipes open at both ends correspond to all the harmonics of the fundamental, while those for pipes closed at one end correspond to the odd-numbered harmonics only.

In passing by small objects an air stream produces alternate whirlwinds on either side of the object. These air pulses are periodic and give rise to a definite sound frequency and are called edge tones.

Percussion instruments consist of metal rods, plates, and stretched diaphragms. Their vibration modes are very complicated and are produced by hammerlike impacts. Nodes and antinodes are produced, but the sounds are not very harmonious.

Questions

1. What kinds of waves are produced in wind instruments? Where are the nodes and antinodes formed?

2. Do wind instruments have harmonic frequencies?

3. How do the pipe ends affect the possible harmonic frequencies?

4. How are the notes of a musical scale produced in most wind instruments?

5. Upon what factors does the velocity of sound waves in a gas depend? Which of these factors are the same in all wind instruments? Which ones, if any, are different?

6. How is wave length related to loop length in a vibrating air column? How can one calculate the fundamental frequency of an air column of known length?

7. What are edge tones? What natural sounds are produced by edge tones?

8. Can you name five percussion instruments commonly used in symphony orchestras? How are such instruments made to vibrate?

9. Are standing waves involved in the vibration modes of percussion instruments? Are nodes and antinodes formed?

10. What inexpensive device could you make as a project for demonstrating any of the principles presented in this lesson?

Problems

1. Find the frequency of (a) the fundamental and (b) the third harmonic of a 16-ft organ pipe, closed at one end and open at the other. Assume the speed of sound to be 1100 ft/sec.

2. An air column 24 in. long is open at one end. What is its lowest natural frequency if the speed of sound is 1120 ft/sec?

3. The lowest frequency of an air column open at both ends is 264 vib/sec. What is its length if the speed of sound is 1120 ft/sec?

4. The third harmonic of a resonating air column 3.24 ft long and open at both ends is 528 vib/sec. Find the speed of sound.

5. What is the shortest length of pipe, open at both ends, that will resonate to a frequency of 440 vib/sec? Assume the speed of sound to be 1100 ft/sec.

6.* Calculate the speed of sound in nitrogen at normal atmospheric pressure. The density of nitrogen is 1.25×10^{-3} gm/cm³.

7.* Calculate the speed of sound in helium at normal atmospheric pressure. The density of helium is 1.78×10^{-4} gm/cm³.

8.* Find the speed of sound in carbon dioxide at 0°C and 76 cm of mercury pressure. The density is 1.98×10^{-3} gm/cm³.

9. An air column 1.6 m long and open at both ends is filled with helium. What would be its natural fundamental frequency? Assume the speed of sound to be 980 m/sec.

RESONATING AIR COLUMN—*Laboratory*

This experiment, concerned with the production and measurements of standing longitudinal waves in air and in metal, is described in the accompanying LABORATORY EXERCISES. From wave length and velocity measurements you will determine the speed of sound in a metal.

SOUND ENERGY AND HEARING

Intensity of Sound. There are three fundamental characteristics of all sounds: (1) **intensity,** (2) **pitch,** and (3) **tone quality.** The intensity of sound is characterized by its loudness and is measured scientifically by the amount of energy in a given volume of the space through which the sound is traveling. In other words, sound waves constitute a flow of energy through matter. This may be demonstrated by an experiment, arranged as shown in Fig. A. A vibrating tuning fork is placed near one opening of a Helmholtz* resonator and a very lightly constructed pin wheel is placed near the other. Air pulses from the vibrating prongs of the fork traveling through the resonator come out reinforced at the other opening and strike the vanes of the pin wheel, setting it in motion. When the fork is removed, the pin wheel stops rotating.

Loudness is a subjective measurement of sound power and is therefore a sensory

magnitude. Intensity, on the other hand, is an objective measurement of the sound power.

One method of specifying the intensity of a sound is to state the amount of energy flowing through unit area per second. Since the rate of flow of energy in most common sounds is extremely small, the ordinary unit of power, the **watt,** is too large to be practical. Consequently a unit one million times smaller, the **microwatt,** is used. One microwatt equals 10^{-6} watt.

Sound intensity is defined as the power flowing through a unit area taken normal to the direction of the waves. See Fig. B.

Fig. A. A pin wheel may be set rotating by sound waves from tuning fork, demonstrating that sound waves have energy.

* Hermann Helmholtz (1821-1894), noted German physicist, who during his lifetime made outstanding contributions to the subjects of light, sound, and electricity. Probably his greatest contribution was his explanation of tone quality in musical notes. He demonstrated that quality depends upon the number and intensity of the overtones or harmonics present in the musical tone.

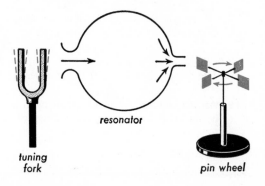

resonator

tuning fork

pin wheel

One microwatt is equivalent to 10^{-6} joules/sec, or 10 ergs/sec.

A common method, of specifying intensity is to compare the power in a given sound with the power in another. **When the power in one sound is ten times that in another, the ratio of intensity is said to be 1 bel.** The **bel** is so named in honor of Alexander Graham Bell, the inventor of the electric telephone. According to this definition, an intensity scale in bels is

E/E_o = 1	10	100	1000	10,000
Bels 0	1	2	3	4

where **E** is the intensity, or power, of one sound and **E_o** that of another.

According to these figures a sound with 1000 times the power of another is 3 bels louder.

Because the **bel** represents large differences in intensity, a smaller unit, the **decibel** (*abbr.* db), has been introduced and used by telephone and radio engineers, as well as by physicians (ear specialists). According to this smaller unit, the bel is divided into ten equal ratios in the following way:

relative power E/E_o	relative intensity, in decibels db
1.00	0
1.26	1
1.58	2
2.00	3
2.51	4
3.16	5
3.98	6
5.01	7
6.31	8
7.94	9
10.0	10

Each power ratio in the first column is 26% greater than the preceding value. Because such a change is just detectable by the

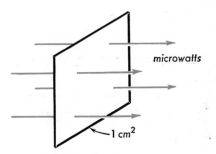

Fig. B. Sound intensity is measured in microwatts of power flowing through 1 cm² of area.

human ear, the decibel is considered a practical unit. The sounds from several common sources are compared in different units, as follows:

Table 1. Relative Intensities of Sounds

	Sound level in decibels	Intensity in microwatts/cm²
threshold of hearing..	0	10^{-10}
rustling leaves.......	20	10^{-8}
talking (at 3 ft)......	40	10^{-6}
noisy office or store...	60	10^{-4}
subway car.........	100	1
threshold of feeling...	120	100

An audiogram for the normal human ear is given in Fig. C. The lower curve gives the faintest sounds that can be heard and the upper curve the loudest that can be heard without pain. It will be noted that the ear is most sensitive to frequencies between 2000 and 4000 cycles and that the sensitivity diminishes rapidly at higher and lower frequencies.

As a practical matter, sound experts have adopted as a zero level of sound intensity, $E_o = 10^{-10}$ microwatts/cm² at a frequency of 1000 cycles. This is the limit of audibility of the average human being for a thousand cycle note.

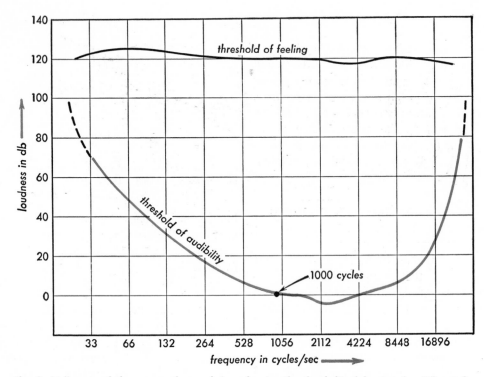

Fig. C. Audiogram of the average human being, showing the threshold of hearing for different frequencies of sound.

Inverse Square Law. Theory indicates, and experiments prove, that the intensity of sound is inversely proportional to the square of the distance from the source. As an equation,

$$E = \frac{E_o}{d^2} \qquad (1)$$

where E_o is the intensity at unit distance (1 cm, 1 m, or 1 ft) and E is the intensity at any distance d in the same units. This is called the **inverse square law**.

If **S** in Fig. D represents a source of sound, the waves travel outward in straight lines. Whatever sound energy flows through area **A** at 1 m, the same energy will flow through area **B** at 2 m, and area **C** at 3 m. Since these areas have the ratios 1:4:9, the energy flow per second, through unit area at each distance, will be E_o, $E_o/4$, and $E_o/9$, respectively.

The Human Ear. The ear is by far the most important and most universal receiver of sound. It has an enormous range of frequency and sensitivity, and can distinguish between musical tones whose frequencies differ by less than 1%. In addition to this it can analyze some sounds into their component notes and concentrate on these notes one at a time.

Fig. D. Illustrating the inverse square law.

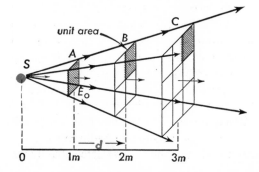

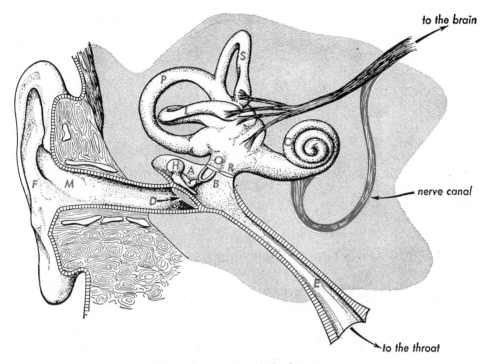

to the brain

nerve canal

to the throat

Fig. E. Cross section of the human ear.

The outer ear, see Fig. E, consists of the pinna **F**, used to collect the sound waves from the outside, and the ear canal **M** to carry the waves to the eardrum **D**.

The middle ear contains three small bones **H**, **A**, and **B** called the **hammer** (malleus), **anvil** (incus), and **stirrup** (stapes) respectively, and is connected to the nasopharynx and thus to the outside air by means of a small canal, the **Eustachian tube E**. The function of the three bones is to transmit the vibrations of the eardrum to the **oval window** of the inner ear.

The inner ear itself consists of two essential parts: the **cochlea C** and the **semicircular canals P**, **L**, and **S**. In the cochlea are found the nerve endings which are stimulated by sound vibrations and give rise to the sense of hearing, and in the semicircular canals are the nerve endings which give rise to a sense of balance.

The entire inner ear is contained within the cavity of a solid bony structure, some-

times referred to as the **bony labyrinth**. This labyrinth is entirely filled with a watery liquid through which the sound vibrations from the outside are transmitted to the sensitive membranes of the cochlea. The cochlea consists of two and one-half turns of a spiral cavity shaped like a snail shell and divided lengthwise into three parts by what are called the **spiral lamina** and **Reissner's membrane**. Cross sections of the cochlea are shown in Fig. F. Diagram (a) represents a section directly across one turn of the spiral, and diagram (b) a lengthwise cross section as it would appear if the cochlea could be straightened out.

Throughout the total length of the basilar membrane, which is just a little over 3 cm in length, there are about 30,000 nerve endings. This amounts to 1000 nerves per millimeter length which must pass through the bony spiral lamina and into the cochlear nerve canal leading to the brain. The work of many experimentalists shows that the nerve end-

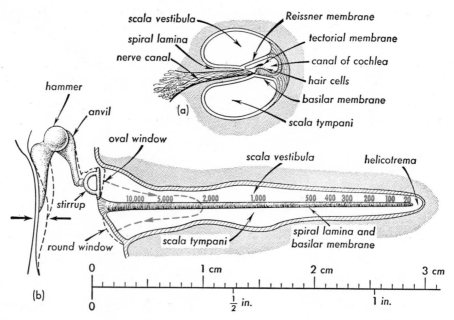

Fig. F. Detail of the cochlea of the human ear: (a) typical cross section and (b) straightened cochlea illustrating the various regions of the spiral lamina sensitive to sounds of various frequencies.

ings nearest the oval window, where the sound vibrations enter the **scala vestibula,** respond to the notes of highest pitch, whereas those at the farther end respond to those of lowest pitch. The various regions sympathetic to the entire frequency scale is shown in the diagram.

The eardrum and the bones of the middle ear act as a lever mechanism to decrease the amplitude of the vibrations from the air, a very light medium, to the liquid, a much more dense medium. This reduction in the motion gives rise to a pressure on the stirrup which is from 30 to 50 times that exerted on the eardrum. As the stirrup tips in and out with a low frequency, the entire liquid column from the oval window down the **scala vesti-bula** to the **helicotrema,** and back along the **scala tympani** to the **round window,** is set

into vibration. Since liquids are practically noncompressible, the round window moves out when the oval window and stirrup move in, and vice versa.

When a higher frequency like 2000 vib/sec is sounded, the vibrations in the liquid, set up by the motion of the stirrup at the oval window, travel the path shown by the dotted line in Fig. F, diagram (b). As the waves travel through the thin Reissner membrane and across the edge of the spiral lamina, there is a relative motion set up between the **basilar membrane** and the **tectorial membrane,** which causes the local hair cells to stimulate the nerve endings at their base. Somewhere in this stimulation and motion, part of the energy is transformed into electrical impulses which travel along the cochlear nerve canal to the brain.

Summary

The three fundamental characteristics of sound are (1) intensity, (2) pitch, and (3) tone quality. The intensity of sound is measured in bels and decibels. These are units of the rate of flow of energy in the form of sound waves, and are therefore power.

The bottom of the sound intensity scale is taken as that sound for which the power $E_o = 1 \times 10^{-10}$ microwatt/cm². To increase any sound by one decibel (1 db) the power must be increased by 26%.

The intensity of sound varies inversely as the square of the distance from the source. Double the distance from a source and the intensity drops to one-quarter.

The human ear is a complicated and marvelous detector of sound energy. Its frequency range varies between individuals but extends on the average from 20 to 16,000 vib/sec.

Questions

1. What is the difference between the intensity of a sound and its loudness?

2. How is intensity measured? What is a watt? What is a microwatt?

3. What is a bel? What is a decibel? What is the sound intensity of ordinary conversation?

4. How does the intensity of a sound vary with the distance from the source?

5. What are the three main parts of a human ear? What is the function of each part?

6. What is the purpose of the round window? How does the changing pressure on the outer eardrum compare with that in the cochlea?

7. How long is the inner ear cavity (stretched out)? How many nerve endings are there per cm? Where with respect to the stirrup are the nerve endings for detecting the highest frequencies?

8. What is the nature of the impulses that travel through the nerve canal from the cochlea to the brain?

9. Think of some inexpensive device you might make as a project for demonstrating one of the ideas or principles introduced in this lesson.

Problems

1. If one sound is 8 db louder than another, what are their relative powers?

2. If one sound is 15 db more intense than another, what are their relative powers?

3. If one sound is 50 db more intense than the other, what are their relative powers?

4. What minimum absolute intensity of sound in decibels is required for the average human being at a frequency of 132 cycles/sec? See Fig. C.

5. If the intensity of sound 1 ft from a source is 5 microwatts/cm², what is the intensity at a distance of 40 ft?

6. If the intensity of a sound 2.5 m from a source is 1 microwatt/cm², what is the intensity at a distance of 1000 meters?

7. The noise from a racing car motor is 60 db at a distance of 1 meter. How loud is it at a distance of 10 meters?

8. At a distance of 1 m from a jet plane the noise level is 80 db. What is the noise level at the ground when the plane flies overhead at 1000 meters?

9. Plot a graph of relative power, E/E_o (vertically) against relative intensity in decibels (horizontally). Plot from 0 to 10 db only.

10. Plot a graph as outlined in Problem 9, but for the vertical scale use the divisions of the A scale on the slip stick of a slide rule. Use centimeter divisions for the horizontal scale.

Sound | Lesson 9

THE SCIENCE OF THE MUSICAL SCALE

From the scientific point of view the musical scale is based upon the relative frequencies of different sound waves. The frequencies of the various notes are so chosen that they produce the greatest amount of **harmony.** Two or more notes are said to be **harmonious** or **concordant** if they are pleasing to the ear. If they are not pleasant to hear, they are **discordant.**

The general form of the musical scale is illustrated by the **notes, letters, intervals,** and **scale ratios** given in Fig. A. The numbers indicate frequency ratios. Whatever frequency is selected for the keynote C, the frequency of the octave C^1 will be twice as great, the frequency of the fifth, G, will be three halves as great, the fourth, F, will be four thirds as great, etc. These fractions are important because they have the same values in all octaves of the musical scale.

The musical pitch of an orchestral scale is usually determined by specifying the frequency of the A string of the first violin, although sometimes it is given by the middle C on the piano. In the history of modern music the standard of pitch has varied so widely and changed so frequently that no set pitch can universally be called standard.* For many scientific purposes the A string of the violin is tuned to a frequency of 440 vib/sec, whereas in a few cases the slightly different scale of 256 vib/sec, sometimes called middle C, is used for the keynote.

The Diatonic Scale. The diatonic musical scale, first introduced by Zarlino in 1558, is based entirely on harmonious tone intervals. The middle octave of the scale is given in Table 1 assuming as a standard of pitch

* For a brief historical discussion of normal standards of pitch the student is referred to the book, "The Science of Musical Sounds," by D. C. Miller. For other treatments of the science of music see "Sound," by Capstick, "Science and Music," by James Jeans, "Sound and Music," by J. A. Zahn, and "Hearing," by Stevens and Davis.

Table 1. Diatonic Scale

C	D	E	F	G	A	B	C¹
Do	Re	Mi	Fa	So	La	Ti	Do
24	27	30	32	36	40	45	48
264	297	330	352	396	440	495	528

8:9   9:10 15:16   8:9   9:10   8:9   15:16   8:9

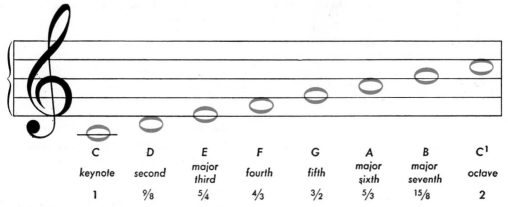

C	D	E	F	G	A	B	C¹
keynote	second	major third	fourth	fifth	major sixth	major seventh	octave
1	⅛	5/4	4/3	3/2	5/3	15/8	2

Fig. A. Diagram giving the names, and fractional ratios of the frequencies, of the different tone intervals on the diatonic musical scale.

A = 440 vib/sec. The **frequencies** of all the notes are given in the fourth row. These numbers represent the actual frequencies of the vibrating source producing the note as well as the frequencies of the waves that travel through the air and reach the ear.

Of equal importance are the **ratio numbers** in the third row. These are the smallest whole numbers that are proportional to the actual **frequencies**. They are readily used to calculate the frequencies for all octaves of the scale. If the ratio numbers in row three are multiplied by 11, they give the actual frequencies in the fourth row. If these same ratio numbers are multiplied by 22, they will give the frequencies of the first octave above; if multiplied by 5.5, they will give the first octave below the middle.

The various octaves above the middle are labeled with numerical superscripts, while the octaves below the middle are designated by subscripts.

Each of the **tone ratios** given at the bottom of Table 1 represents the ratio between the frequencies of two consecutive notes. The fraction representing the frequency ratio designates what is called an **interval**. Throughout the scale it will be noted that between successive notes there are but three different intervals: **major tones** with a frequency ratio 8/9, **minor tones** with a ratio 9/10, and **diatonic semitones** with a ratio 15/16. The

C_2	D_2	E_2	F_2	G_2	A_2	B_2
66	74.2	82.5	88	99	110	123.8
C_1	D_1	E_1	F_1	G_1	A_1	B_1
132	148.5	165	176	198	220	247.5
C	D	E	F	G	A	B
264	297	330	352	396	440	495
C^1	D^1	E^1	F^1	G^1	A^1	B^1
528	594	660	704	792	880	990
C^2	D^2	E^2	F^2	G^2	A^2	B^2
1056	1188	1320	1408	1584	1760	1980
C^3	D^3	E^3	F^3	G^3	A^3	B^3
2112	2376	2640	2816	3168	3520	3960

semitone, it will be noted, is a little larger than half of either a major or minor tone.

A better understanding and appreciation of the diatonic scale is to be had by a study of other intervals and their frequency ratios. Of interest to every composer of music are the following intervals:

perfect consonances	octave	1:2	C C¹
	fifth	2:3	C G
	fourth	3:4	C F
imperfect consonances	major third	4:5	C E
	minor third	5:6	E G
	major sixth	3:5	C A
	minor sixth	5:8	E C¹
dissonant intervals	second	8:9	C D
	major seventh	8:15	C B
	minor seventh	9:16	D C¹

A study of these tone intervals clearly indicates that harmony* is associated with the simplicity of the ratios between frequencies. The smaller the whole numbers expressing the ratio of any two notes, the more **harmonious** or **consonant** is the musical effect. The larger the whole numbers, the more **discordant**, or **dissonant**, is the effect.

Chords. The simultaneous sounding of two or more notes, each of which forms a **concordant** interval with the others, constitutes a chord. An added restriction is that the highest and lowest notes be not more than one octave apart. Two notes sounded together constitute a **dyad**, three notes a **triad**, and four notes a **tetrad**. The **octave**, **fifth**, and **fourth**, considered in detail in the previous section, are examples of **harmonious dyads**.

Musicians generally agree that there are six harmonious triads, and these are listed as follows:

Harmonic Triads or Chords

major third followed by minor third
fourth   followed by major third
minor third followed by major third
minor third followed by fourth
major third followed by fourth
fourth   followed by minor third

Frequency Ratio Examples

4 : 5 : 6	C E G
3 : 4 : 5	C F A
5 : 6, 4 : 5	E G B
5 : 6, 3 : 4	E G C¹
4 : 5, 3 : 4	C E A
3 : 4, 5 : 6	E A C¹

* The essential difference between *melody* and *harmony* is quite generally recognized by everyone. Melody consists of a succession of notes and conveys the idea of motion that should go on and on, while harmony consists of the simultaneous and often sustained sounding of several notes like a chord, followed by other similar combinations of notes. The latter seem to stand still, each chord of notes being more or less complete in itself.

The first chord in the tabulation above is generally called a perfect major chord, and the second a perfect minor chord. It is quite common practice to add the octave to each of these triads to form the tetrads CEGC¹ and CFAC¹.

The Chromatic Scale. Contrary to the belief of many, the sharp of one note and the flat of the next higher major or minor tone are not of the same pitch. The reason for this false impression is that on the piano the black keys represent a compromise. The piano is not tuned to the diatonic scale but to an **equal-tempered scale**. Experiments with eminent musicians, and particularly violinists, have shown that they play in what is called **pure intonation**, i.e., to a **chromatic scale** and not according to **equal temperament**, as will be described in the next section.

On the chromatic scale of the musician the ratio between the frequency of one note and the frequency of its sharp or flat is 25:24. This interval, the smallest usually used in music, is just the difference between a diatonic semitone and a minor tone, i.e., $15/16 \div 9/10 = 25/24$. The actual frequencies of the various sharps and flats for the middle octave of the chromatic scale, based upon $A = 440$, are shown in Fig. B. C♯, for example, has a frequency of 275, whereas D♭ is 285. This is a difference of 10 vib/sec, an interval easily recognized at this pitch by almost everyone.

The Equal Tempered Scale. The white keys of the piano are not tuned to the exact frequency ratios of the diatonic scale; they are tuned to an **equal tempered scale**. Each octave is divided into twelve equal ratio intervals as illustrated in Fig. B. The **whole-tone** and **half-tone** intervals shown represent the white keys of the piano, and the sharps and flats represent the black keys. Including the black keys, all twelve tone intervals in every octave are exactly the same.

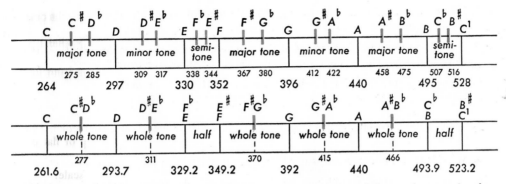

Fig. B. Scale diagrams showing the diatonic and chromatic scale above and the equal tempered scale below.

The reason for tuning the piano to an equal tempered scale is to enable the pianist to play in any key and yet stay within a given pitch range. In so doing, any given composition can be played within the range of a given person's voice. In other words, any single note can be taken as the keynote, or tonic, of the musical scale.

The frequency of any note in the equal tempered scale turns out to be 6% higher than the one preceding it. More accurately, the frequency of any one note multiplied by 1.05946 gives the frequency of the note one-half tone higher. For example, A = 440 multiplied by 1.05946 gives A♯ or B♭ as 466.1 vib/sec.

Summary

The diatonic musical scale is based upon harmony. Harmony is based upon the frequency ratios between two or more notes. This is true whether the notes are sounded simultaneously as in chords or one after the other as in melody.

All octaves of the musical scale can be obtained from a set of ratio numbers, 24, 27, 30, 32, 36, 40, 45, and 48. To raise the pitch of any note one octave, the frequency is doubled. The diatonic scale contains three kinds of intervals: major tones, 8:9; minor tones, 9:10; and semitones, 15:16.

The perfect consonances, which are the most harmonious intervals, or dyads, are (a) the octave, 1:2; (b) the fifth, 2:3; and (c) the fourth, 3:4.

Chords are comprised of 2, 3, or 4 notes sounded simultaneously. The smaller the whole numbers that specify the ratios of actual frequencies the more harmonious or pleasing is the chord.

The chromatic musical scale is based on the diatonic scale and introduces sharps and flats. The piano, or equal-tempered scale, is a compromise and is not so harmonious as the chromatic scale. Its advantages are that it permits any note to be used as a keynote, and thus greatly reduces the required number of keys.

Questions

1. What is harmony? What is discord?

2. How many notes are there in one octave of (a) the diatonic musical scale, (b) the piano scale, and (c) the chromatic scale?

3. What note is the standard used in symphony orchestras? What is its generally accepted frequency?

4. What are the ratio numbers for the diatonic musical scale? List them. Of what use are these numbers?

5. How do you find the frequencies of the middle octave of the diatonic scale from the ratio numbers? How would you obtain those for an octave above?

6. What is a dyad? What is a triad? What is a tetrad? What is a chord?

7. What can you say about the frequencies of a triad if it is harmonious?

8. What is the chromatic scale? How does one find the frequency of a sharp or flat of any note?

9. What is the equal-tempered scale? How does it differ from the chromatic scale?

10. What do you think would be a good project for making some inexpensive demonstration of one or more principles introduced in this lesson?

Problems

1. Make a diagram of the middle octave of the diatonic musical scale. Show the scale notes starting with C, the ratio numbers, and the frequencies.

2. Calculate the frequencies of the notes four octaves above the middle octave of the diatonic scale based on 440 vib/sec.

3. What three notes on the diatonic scale form a harmonic triad with G as the lower frequency if the two intervals consist of a major third followed by a minor third?

4. If the three notes of a triad are C, E, and G, what are the smallest whole numbers that give the frequency ratios?

5. The three notes of a chord are C, F, and A. (a) Taking these in pairs, what beat frequencies are produced? (b) Since the ear can hear both the notes and their beat notes, make a list of all frequencies heard when this triad is sounded. (c) What are the smallest whole numbers that give the ratios of all these frequencies?

6. Calculate the frequencies for G$\sharp$ and G for the first octave above the middle octave of the chromatic scale.

7. Calculate the frequency of E$\sharp$ for the first octave above the middle octave on (a) the chromatic scale and (b) the equal-tempered scale.

8. (a) Find the frequencies and the beat frequencies for the tetrad C E G C^1. (b) What are the smallest ratio numbers for all these frequencies?

Sound | **Lesson 10**

SPEED OF SOUND—*Laboratory*

This experiment on measuring the speed of sound in several gases is described in the accompanying LABORATORY EXERCISES. The method used is that of measuring loop lengths in standing longitudinal waves, produced in gases by means of a tuning fork.

THE QUALITY OF MUSICAL SOUNDS

Quality of Musical Notes. Although two musical notes have the same pitch and intensity, they may differ widely in tone quality. Tone quality is determined by the number and intensity of the harmonics present. This is illustrated by a detailed examination of either the vibrating source or of the sound waves emerging from the source. There are numerous experimental methods by which this is accomplished.

A relatively convenient and simple demonstration is given in Sound, Lesson 4, Fig. F, where the vibrating source of sound is a stretched piano string. If the string is made to vibrate with its fundamental alone, its own motion or that of the emitted sound waves has the form shown in diagram (a) of Fig. A. If it vibrates in two segments or six segments (see Sound, Lesson 4, Fig. D), the wave forms will be like those in diagrams (b) and (d), respectively. Should the string be set vibrating with its fundamental and second harmonic simultaneously, Sound, Lesson 4, Fig. E, the wave form will appear something like diagram (c). If, in addition to the fundamental, a string vibrates with the second and sixth harmonics, the wave will look like diagram (e). This is like diagram (c) with the sixth harmonic added to it.

It is difficult to make a string vibrate with its fundamental alone. As a rule there are many harmonics present. Some of these harmonics harmonize with the fundamental and some do not. Those which harmonize are

Fig. B. Wave forms of sounds from different musical instruments singing the same note.

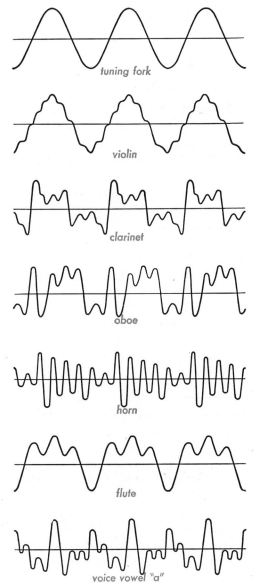

tuning fork

violin

clarinet

oboe

horn

flute

voice vowel "a"

Fig. A. Sound wave vibrations from a string.

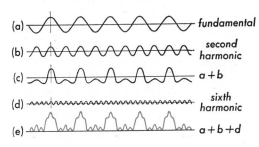

(a) fundamental

(b) second harmonic

(c) a + b

(d) sixth harmonic

(e) a + b + d

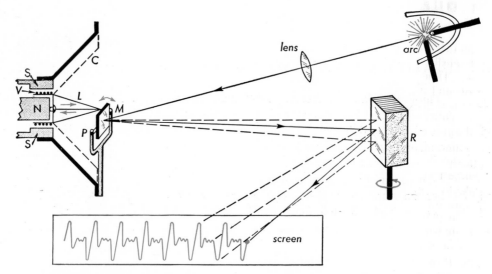

Fig. C. Radio loud-speaker attachment and apparatus for observing the wave forms of musical sounds.

called **concordant overtones,** and those which do not are called **discordant overtones.** If middle C = 264 is sounded with its next seven harmonics, they will have 2, 3, 4, 5, 6, 7, and 8 times 264 vib/sec. These on the diatonic scale will correspond to notes C^1, G^1, C^2, E^2, G^2, X, and C^3. All of these except X, the seventh harmonic, belong to some harmonic triad. This very overtone is discordant and should be suppressed. In a piano this is accomplished by striking the string one-seventh of its length from one end, thus preventing a node at that point.

The seven different wave forms in Fig. B represent the sound vibrations coming from different musical instruments all singing the note A = 440 vib/sec. Observe that each wave form is repeated four times in the same time interval but that the overtones, the small "wiggles" in the curves, are different in every case.

When complicated sound vibrations enter the ear, they are analyzed into their component frequencies. One set of nerve endings responds to the fundamental frequency, while other sets respond to the various overtones. The fundamental frequency generally has most of the energy and therefore the greatest

amplitude, whereas the overtones with their higher frequencies have relatively small amplitudes.

An excellent experiment for demonstrating the wave forms of musical sounds is diagramed in Fig. C. A small mirror **M** is connected to the voice coil **V** of a radio loudspeaker by three small aluminum wires **L.** As the voice coil vibrates, moving the paper cone **C** back and forth to produce sound, the tiny mirror **M** tips back and forth around the pivot **P.** As the voice coil and cone move out to the right, the mirror tips forward; and when the voice coil and cone move to the left, the mirror tips back.

Light from an arc lamp and lens is reflected as a narrow beam from the vibrating mirror **M** to a rotating mirror **R** and then to a screen as shown. The beam from **M** to **R** moves up and down with the exact motion of mirror **M,** and the rotation of **R** sweeps the beam across the screen, thus tracing out the vibrations as shown. Each of the four mirrors on **R** sweeps out a wave across the screen. If the sound is a sustained note the successive wave forms are alike and may be made to overlap, whereas if the notes are continually changing, each wave form is different. Per-

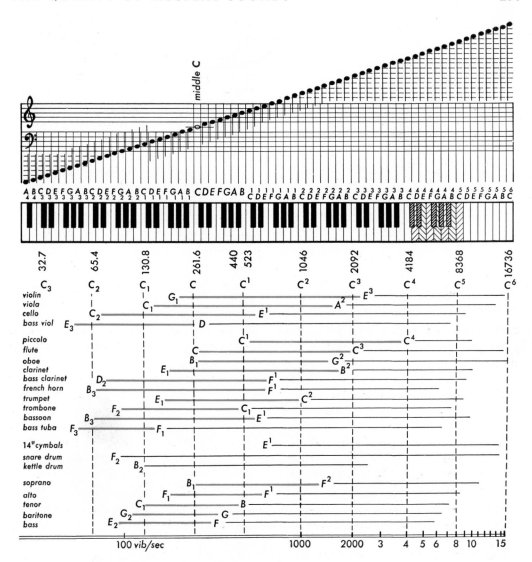

Fig. D. Chart showing the frequency range of various musical instruments.

sistence of vision enables the observer to see a long wave instead of a moving point. (With distances of several feet between mirrors and screen, wave amplitudes of at least 1 ft are readily obtained on a large screen or on the walls of a room.)

The Ranges of Musical Instruments. A chart showing the ranges of various musical instruments and singing voices is given in Fig. D. The male speaking voice has an average

fundamental frequency of about 150 vib/sec with a singing range of about six notes up and six down, whereas the average female voice has a frequency of about 230 vib/sec with approximately the same singing range. The **quality,** or **timbre,** depends almost entirely on two sets of overtones. Good quality singing voices emphasize two sets of overtones or partials, one around 500 cycles and the other around 2400 to 3200 cycles. The lower frequency seems to be the natural frequency

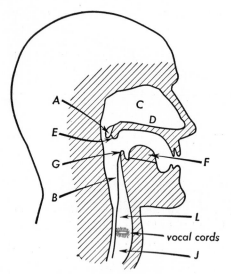

Fig. E. Cross-section diagram showing the mouth, throat, and nasal cavities of the human head.

very interesting experiment with the human voice. Voice sounds originate in the vibrations of the vocal cords in the larynx (see Fig. E). This source of vibration, which determines the fundamental pitch of the speaking or singing voice, is controlled by muscular tension on the vocal cords. The quality of the voice is determined by the size and shape of the throat, mouth, and nasal cavities.

If a gas lighter than air is breathed into the lungs, Eq. (1) in Sound, Lesson 6 shows that the voice quality should change. The demonstration can be performed by exhaling completely and then filling the lungs with helium gas (hydrogen is unsafe). Upon speaking, the experimenter will be observed to have a very peculiar, high-pitched voice, which must be heard to be appreciated. The peculiarities arise from the fact that the fundamental pitch, due to the vocal-cord frequency, remains practically normal, while the harmonics from the resonating mouth, throat, and nasal cavities are raised by about two and one-half octaves.

of the **pharynx** (see **B** in Fig. E) and the higher frequencies to other throat, mouth, and nasal cavities.

The effect of the density of a gas on the pitch of a note may be demonstrated by a

Summary

The quality of a musical note is determined by the relative intensities of the harmonics that are produced along with the fundamental note. It is these harmonics that enable one to distinguish one instrument from another, as well as one human voice from another.

Not all of the harmonics of a note harmonize with the fundamental frequency. The seventh harmonic of any note is one such discordant frequency.

There are various devices one can use to study the wave form of sound waves from any source.

The frequency range capabilities of musical instruments vary widely. The range for most of them is confined to two or three octaves, as is also the human voice. The piano, however, has a range of over seven octaves.

Questions

1. What determines the quality of a musical sound? What determines its pitch?

2. Which of the first eight harmonics of a given note do not harmonize with the fundamental?

3. When the same note, for instance middle C, is sounded by two different musical instruments, what is there about the two wave forms that is (a) the same and (b) different?

4. Are the frequencies of the notes from musical instruments in any way associated with the size of the instrument? In what way are they related?

5. What is the range of your own voice? What is the range of the voice of the average soprano? Of an average baritone?

6. What instrument in the violin family produces the lowest pitched note? Which produces the highest?

7. What inexpensive device would you propose to construct as a project for demonstrating the wave forms of sound waves?

Problems

1. Make a frequency list of the first 10 harmonics of the fundamental frequency of the musical note C_1. To what notes of the diatonic musical scale do these belong?

2. Make a list of the first 10 harmonics of the fundamental frequency of the musical note F_2. To what notes of the diatonic musical scale do these belong?

3. Make a list of the first 15 harmonics of the musical note C_2. To what notes of the diatonic musical scale do these belong?

4. To what notes on the chromatic scale do the first ten harmonics of $E = 330$ vib/sec correspond?

5. To what notes on the chromatic scale do the first ten harmonics of $G_1 = 198$ vib/sec correspond?

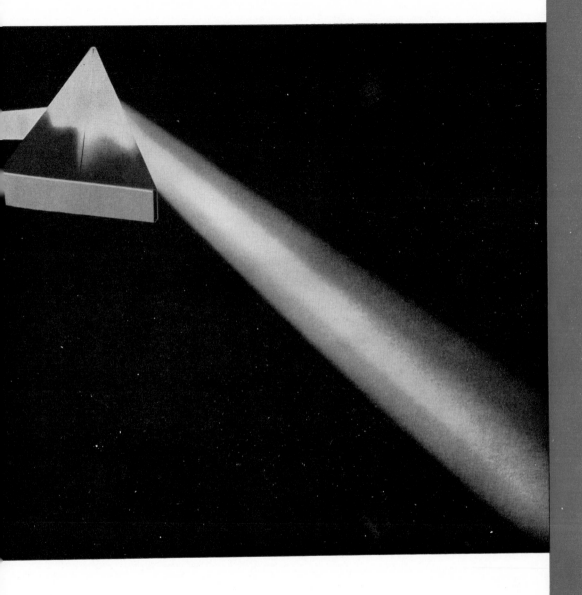

LIGHT

It is inconceivable to doubt that light consists in the motion of some sort of matter. For whether one considers its production, one sees that here upon the earth it is chiefly engendered by fire and flame which contain without doubt bodies that are in rapid motion, since they dissolve and melt many other bodies, even the most solid; or whether one considers its effects, one sees that when light is collected, as by concave mirrors, it has the property of burning as a fire does, that is to say, it disunites the particles of bodies. This is assuredly the mark of motion, at least in the true philosophy, in which one conceives the causes of all natural effects in terms of mechanical motions. This, in my opinion, we must necessarily do, or else renounce all hopes of ever comprehending anything in physics.

And as, according to this philosophy, one holds as certain that the sensation of sight is excited only by the impression of some movement of a kind of matter which acts on the nerves at the back of our eyes, there is here yet one reason more for believing that light consists in a movement of the matter which exists between us and the luminous body.

Christian Huygens, *Treatise on Light,* trans. by Sylvanus P. Thompson, Macmillan, London, 1912, pp. 3-4.

The propagation of light in the ether is produced in a manner similar to that of sound in the air; and just as the vibrations occasioned in the particles of air constitute sound, in like manner the vibration of the particles of ether constitutes light or luminous rays; so that light is nothing else but an agitation or concussion of the particles of ether, *which is everywhere to be found on account of its extreme subtilty, in virtue of which it penetrates all bodies.*

Leonhard Euler, *Of the Propagation of Light*

← Mirrors, lenses, and prisms change the paths of light. Here is shown a prism refracting a beam of light.

Bausch & Lomb Optical Company

The Nature of Light

A<small>LL OF</small> the various known properties of light are conveniently described in terms of the experiments by which they were discovered and the many and varied experiments by which they are now commonly demonstrated. Numerous as they are, these experiments may be grouped together and classified under one of the three following heads: *geometrical optics, physical optics,* and *quantum optics.*

Sources of Light. Outside of the sun itself the most common source of light today is the *tungsten filament lamp* used in house lighting. The light is produced by sending an electric current through a very fine tungsten wire placed at the center of a glass bulb as shown in Fig. A. The purpose of the current is to heat the wire to a very high temperature. The light comes from the hot solid tungsten wire and not from the electric current.

The tungsten filament of most light bulbs, if examined with a magnifying glass, will be found to be made of very fine wire wound in a spiral-like coil or spring. Being closely wound with about two hundred turns to the inch, this spiral appears to the naked eye as a larger but straight solid wire.

Tungsten filament lamps ranging from about 0.03 candle power (0.17 watts) up to 120,000 candle power (50,000 watts) have been made. Their efficiencies range from about 0.2 up to 2 candle power per watt.

Perhaps next in importance to the tungsten filament lamp as a source of light is the **car-**

Fig. A. Cross section of a common tungsten filament lamp used in house lighting.

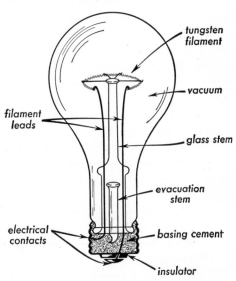

tungsten filament

vacuum

filament leads

glass stem

evacuation stem

electrical contacts

basing cement

insulator

297

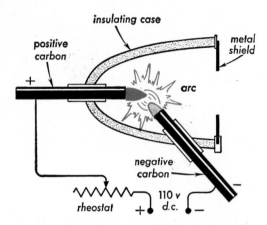

Fig. B. Cross section of a carbon arc showing connections to a rheostat and a direct-current line source of 110 volts.

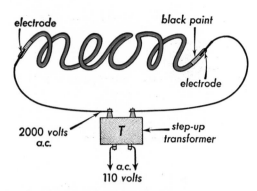

Fig. C. Diagram of a neon sign showing the electrodes in each end of the glass discharge tube and the transformer connections.

bon arc. These very bright sources were at one time used for street lighting. Today they are used in moving picture projectors, in searchlights, lighthouses, and wherever a very bright and concentrated source is required.

An ordinary laboratory arc consists of two carbon rods connected to the positive and negative sides of a battery or generator supplying anywhere from 50 to 250 volts. As shown in Fig. B a resistance is connected *in series* to keep the current down to about 10 amperes for normal operation. The arc is started by bringing the ends of the rods together and pulling them apart. This striking of the arc produces a flame of burning carbon. It is through this flame that the electric current passes from one carbon tip to the other.

The tip of the positive carbon reaches a temperature of about 4000°K, whereas the negative carbon reaches about 3500°K. Most of the visible light comes from the positive carbon and relatively little from the vapor in the arc flame.

The carbon arcs used in search lights require a current of about 150 amperes, and the positive carbon tip reaches a temperature of 4500 to 5000°K.

The neon signs so commonly used for ad-

vertising purposes consist of long narrow tubes partially filled with neon, argon, or krypton gases. The tubes, after being bent into the required shape, are thoroughly evacuated and a small amount of gas is admitted to bring up the gas pressure inside to about one-fortieth of an atmosphere. By means of a high-voltage transformer and small wires sealed into both ends of each tube, an electric current is sent through the rarefied gas. The electrical connections are shown in Fig. C. The passage of the electric current through **neon gas** produces the characteristic red light with which everyone is familiar. Argon and krypton produce a white light. The action of the electric current in producing the light is called an electric discharge.

In recent years fluorescent materials have been used for general illumination purposes. Long glass tubes, containing argon and nitrogen gas and a small drop of mercury, are painted on the inside with luminescent paint.

A section diagram of all essential parts and electrical connections of a standard fluorescent lamp is shown in Fig. D. When the switch is closed, applying 110 volts from the house lighting circuit, the voltage at the **automatic starter** terminals **F** and **G** is sufficient to produce a glow discharge between the U-shaped **bimetal strip** and the straight contact. The heat generated by the glowing argon gas inside causes the bimetallic strip to bend over,

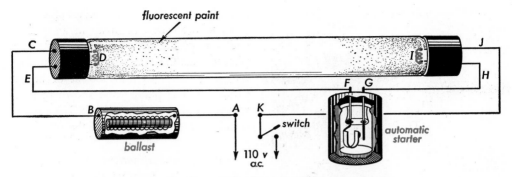

Fig. D. Section diagram of a fluorescent light and accessories.

bringing the contacts together. Contact stops the glow and at the same time completes the entire lamp circuit to allow full current to flow through the lamp heater filaments **D** and **I** and **ballast coil.**

The function of the heaters is to vaporize the mercury in the fluorescent tube. Because the starter glow is shorted out, the contacts soon open the circuit and the sudden collapsing magnetic field of the ballast gives a high voltage "kick" that starts the glow in the fluorescent tube. The voltage at the starter is insufficient thereafter to cause the switch to operate, so the starter consumes no energy during lamp operation.

Fluorescent lamps have a relatively high efficiency of 3 to 5 candle power per watt.

This is due largely to the conversion of invisible ultraviolet light emitted by the mercury gas atoms into visible light by the fluorescent coating.

The Rectilinear Propagation of Light. The rectilinear propagation of light is another way of saying that **light travels in straight lines.** The fact that objects may be made to cast fairly sharp shadows is an experimental demonstration of this principle.

Another illustration is the image formation of an object produced by light passing through a small opening, as diagrammed in Fig. E. In this figure the object is an ordinary incandescent light bulb. In order to see how an image is formed, consider the rays of light

Fig. E. Illustrating the principle that light travels in straight lines.

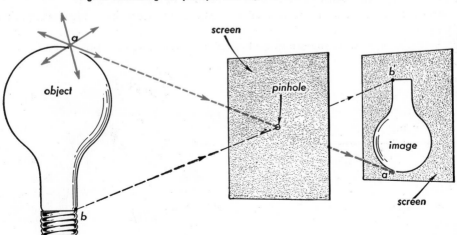

Fig. F. Photograph taken with a pinhole camera.

emanating from a single point *a* near the top of the bulb. Of the many rays of light radiating in all directions, the ray which travels in the direction of the hole passes through to the point *a'* near the bottom of the image screen. Similarly, a ray leaving *b* near the bottom of the bulb and passing through the hole will arrive at *b'* near the top of the image screen. Thus it may be seen that an inverted image is formed.

If the image screen is moved closer to the pinhole screen, the image will be proportionately smaller; whereas if it is moved farther away, the image will be proportionately larger. The same thing happens when either the object or the pinhole is moved. Excellent photographs can be made with this arrangement by making a pinhole in one end of a

small box and placing a photographic film or plate at the other. Such an arrangement is called a pinhole camera. For good sharp photographs the hole must be very small, as its size determines the amount of blurring produced. The photograph shown in Fig. F was taken with such a camera. Note the undistorted perspective lines of the building.

Galileo's Experiment on the Velocity of Light. History tells us that Galileo once tried to measure the velocity of light but without success. Galileo stationed himself on one hilltop with one lamp and an assistant on another hilltop with a similar lamp. Galileo would first uncover his lamp for an instant, sending a short flash of light to the assistant. As soon as the assistant saw this light he uncovered his own lamp, sending a flash back to Galileo, who noted the total time elapsed.

After numerous repetitions of this experiment at greater and greater distances between observers Galileo came to the conclusion that they could not uncover their lamps fast enough and that light probably travels with an infinite speed. Knowing as we do now that light travels with the amazing speed of 186,000 mi/sec, it is easy to see why Galileo's experiment failed.

Fizeau's Experiment. The first terrestrial method of measuring the velocity of light was devised by Fizeau in 1849. His experimental

Fig. G. Experimental arrangement used by Fizeau in determining the velocity of light.

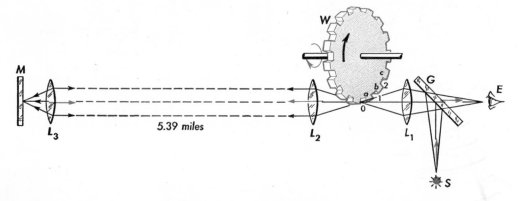

arrangement is shown in Fig. G. Light from an intense source **S** was reflected from a semi-transparent mirror **G** and then brought to a focus at the point **O** by means of a lens L_1. After being made into a parallel beam by a second lens L_2, the light traveled a distance of 5.39 mi to a hilltop, where a mirror **M** and lens L_3 reflected the light back again. Returning by the same path, some of the light passed through the mirror **G** and entered the eye of the observer at **E**.

The purpose of the rotating toothed wheel was to chop the light beam into short flashes and to measure the time it takes each of these signals to travel over to the far mirror and back. With the wheel at rest and in such a position that the light passes through an opening between 2 teeth at **O**, the observer at **E** will see an image of the light source **S**.

If the wheel is now set rotating with slowly increasing speed, a condition will soon be reached in which the light passing through **O** will return just in time to be stopped by **a**, that passing through opening **1** will return just in time to be stopped by **b**, etc. Under these conditions the image will be completely eclipsed from the observer.

By further increasing the speed, the light will reappear, increasing in intensity until a maximum is reached. This will occur when the flashes set out through the openings **0**, **1**, **2**, **3**, etc., return just in time to get through the openings **1**, **2**, **3**, **4**, etc., respectively. With a wheel containing 720 teeth, Fizeau observed this maximum at a speed of 25 rps. The time required for the light to travel over and back can therefore be calculated as 1/25 times 1/720, or 1/18,000th of a second. This, from the measured distance over and back of 10.78 mi, gives a velocity of 194,000 mi/sec, or 313,000 km/sec.

Michelson's Measurements of the Velocity of Light. In the years that followed these earliest experiments, several investigators improved upon Fizeau's apparatus and methods of observation and obtained more accurate values for the velocity of light. Of these, Michelson's* contributions and improvements stand out above the rest. Replacing the toothed wheel by a small eight-sided mirror and increasing the light path to some 44 mi, Michelson in 1926 obtained a value of 299,796 km/sec.

An extensive and critical study of the values of the velocity of light measured by all observers has been made by Birge. He concludes that the most probable value at the present time is as follows:

$$c = 299{,}793 \text{ km/sec}$$

or

$$c = 186{,}282 \text{ mi/sec}$$

Because the velocity of light in the metric system is within one-tenth of one percent of being 300,000 km/sec, it is common practice to use this value in calculations

$$c \cong 300{,}000 \text{ km/sec}$$

In other metric units this is equivalent to

or

$$c = 3 \times 10^8 \text{ m/sec}$$

$$c = 3 \times 10^{10} \text{ cm/sec}$$

* Albert A. Michelson (1852-1931). Distinguished American physicist, celebrated for the invention and development of the interferometer, an optical instrument now named in his honor, and its use in establishing the length of the standard meter in terms of the wave length of light, in the ether drift experiments, in determining the rigidity of the earth, in the measurement of distances and diameters of giant stars, and for the measurement of the velocity of light. He was the first American scientist to have been awarded the Nobel Prize (1907).

Summary

All optical phenomena are classified under one of the three headings: geometrical optics, physical optics, or quantum optics.

The sun is our most important source of light. Of the other sources, the tungsten filament lamp, the fluorescent tube, neon sign, and the carbon arc are the most widely used. The fluorescent lamp is the most efficient.

Light travels in straight lines. This is well illustrated by the principle of the pinhole camera.

The velocity of light was first measured in the laboratory by Fizeau in 1849. Using a fast rotating wheel to chop up a beam of light into pulses, the reflected light from a mirror on a distant hilltop could be timed with accuracy. The velocity of light, to within one-tenth of one percent, is

$$c = 3 \times 10^8 \text{ m / sec}$$

Questions

1. What are the three branches of optics? What does the term geometrical optics suggest?

2. What is our most important light source? What are the most important manufactured sources?

3. What is the source of light in the tungsten filament lamp? What is the efficiency in candle power per watt?

4. What is a carbon arc? Where in the arc does most of the light originate? What are they principally used for? Why? What disadvantages do you think they might have?

5. What is the source of light in a neon sign?

6. What are the principles of the fluorescent lamp? To what is their high efficiency attributed?

7. What is meant by the rectilinear propagation of light? What is a pinhole camera? How does it work?

8. Who made the first terrestrial determination of the speed of light? How was it done? What is the most probable value of the velocity of light in (a) the metric system and (b) the English system?

9. What inexpensive device would you like to make as a project for utilizing or demonstrating principles introduced in this lesson?

Problems

1. How long will it take light to travel from the moon to the earth if its distance is 239,000 mi?

2. How long will it take light to reach the earth from the sun at a distance of 93 million miles?

3. How long would it take light to travel a distance equal to the circumference of the world?

4.* How fast would the toothed wheel of 720 teeth in Fizeau's experiment have to rotate if the distant mirror were 50 km away? Assume the returning light produces a maximum intensity?

5.* How fast would a wheel with 1000 teeth have to rotate in Fizeau's type of experiment to produce the first light maximum from the light pulses returning from a mirror 30 km away?

LIGHT AND ILLUMINATION

The Velocity of Light in Stationary Matter. In 1850 Foucault completed and published the results of an experiment in which he had measured the velocity of light in water. This was a crucial experiment for it settled a long existing controversy concerning the nature of light. According to Newton and his followers, light was believed to be made up of small particles or corpuscles emanating from a source. Huygens, on the other hand, regarded light as being composed of waves, similar in nature perhaps to water waves or sound waves. Now, Newton's corpuscular theory required light to travel faster in a dense medium like water than it did in a less dense medium like air, whereas Huygens' wave theory required it to travel slower. By sending light back and forth through a long tube of water, Foucault found its velocity to be less than that in air. This was a strong confirmation of Huygens' wave theory.

Years later Michelson also measured the velocity of light in water and found a value of 225,000 km/sec. This is just three-quarters the velocity in a vacuum. In common glass the velocity is still lower, being about two-thirds the velocity in vacua, or 200,000 km/sec. In air the velocity is very little less than the velocity in a vacuum, differing only by about 70 km/sec at sea level and less at higher altitudes where the air is less dense. For most practical cases this difference can be neglected, and the velocity in air said to be the same as in a vacuum.

The Refractive Index. The ratio between the velocity of light in a vacuum and the velocity in a medium is called the **refractive index,** or the **index of refraction** of the medium.

$$\frac{\text{vel. of light in vac.}}{\text{vel. of light in med.}} = \text{refractive index}$$

Symbolically,

$$\frac{c}{v} = \mu \qquad (1)$$

The Greek letter μ (mu) is frequently used to represent this ratio. Substituting the velocities given in the preceding section, the following refractive indices may be calculated:

$$\text{for water, } \mu = 1.33 \qquad (2)$$
$$\text{for glass, } \mu = 1.5 \qquad (3)$$
$$\text{for air, } \quad \mu = 1.00 \qquad (4)$$

The Inverse Square Law. One direct consequence of the rectilinear propagation of light is the inverse square law. This law applies to the illumination of a surface due to the luminous intensity of a point source of light. While no source of light is actually confined to a point, many are so small in comparison with the distances to illuminated areas that they may be regarded as point sources.

The illumination of a surface is called **illuminance** and is defined as the amount of light falling on a unit area. If a screen is placed one foot from a point source of one

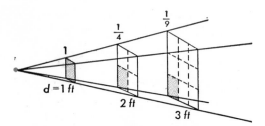

Fig. A. Illustration of the inverse square law.

candle power, the illuminance will be one foot-candle. One foot from a 50 candle-power source the illuminance will be 50 ft-candles, etc.

When the top surface of a table is illuminated by a single light directly above it and then the light raised to twice the height, the illuminance on the surface will only be one-fourth as great. If it is raised to three times the first height, the illuminance will only be one-ninth as great, etc. In other words, *illuminance is proportional to the luminous intensity of the light source and is inversely proportional to the square of the distance.* This, the inverse square law, is illustrated in Fig. A by the three shaded patches of equal area. If the letter I represents the luminous intensity of a light source in candles and d the distance to the illuminated surface in feet, the illuminance E in foot-candles will be given by

$$E = \frac{I}{d^2} \qquad (5)$$

To illustrate this equation, consider the following example.

Example. The illuminance on the road directly under a street light suspended 25 ft above the ground is 1.2 ft-candles. Calculate the candle power of the lamp.

Solution. Transposing Eq. (5) and substituting the known values, $E = 1.2$ ft-candles, and $d = 25$ ft, gives

$I = Ed^2 = 1.2 \times (25)^2 = 750$ candle power

Candle Power. Candle power refers to the *luminous intensity* of any light source and is a term commonly employed to specify the total light output of a lamp. The *standard candle*, or *international candle* as it is frequently called, is the luminous intensity of the flame of a certain make of candle, the constituents of which were at one time specified by international agreement. Many years ago this form of standard was found to be unsatisfactory and it has since been replaced by the light emitted by an incandescent platinum metal surface. Platinum metal, at its very high melting temperature of 2033°K., has a luminance of 60 candle/cm² of projected area.

Ordinary tungsten filament light bulbs used in general house lighting give a little more than one candle power per watt of electrical power used. A 60-watt lamp, for example, has a luminous intensity I of about 66 candle power, and a 100-watt lamp a luminous intensity of about 127 candle power. Luminescent tubes, on the other hand, have considerably higher efficiency and yield about 4 candle power per watt.

Photometry. The word photometry is applied to the experimental process by which the intensities of two light sources are compared and measured.

One of the earliest methods for accomplishing this is due to Count Rumford and is known as the *shadow photometer*. His experimental arrangement consists simply of casting two shadows of the same rod as shown in Fig. B. The distances between screen and lamps are varied until the illumination of the two shadows appears equal.

Fig. B. Illustrating the principle of the shadow photometer.

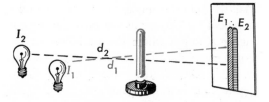

A plan diagram of such an arrangement will show that the shadow cast by lamp I_1 is illuminated only by lamp I_2, while the shadow cast by I_2 is illuminated only by lamp I_1. By the inverse square law, Eq. (5),

$$E_1 = \frac{I_1}{d_1^2} \qquad E_2 = \frac{I_2}{d_2^2}$$

When the illuminated shadow areas are equally bright, E_1 is equal to E_2, and the two equations above become equal to each other. Equating the right sides,

$$\frac{I_1}{d_1^2} = \frac{I_2}{d_2^2}$$

or

$$\boxed{\frac{I_1}{I_2} = \frac{d_1^2}{d_2^2}} \qquad (6)$$

In words, the relative intensities of the two lamps are directly proportional to the square of their relative distances from the screen.

If the candle power of one of the lamps is known, its value, along with the measured distances d_1 and d_2, may be substituted in either of these equations and the candle power of the unknown lamp calculated.

The Lumen. Light sources in general do not radiate the same in all directions. When, for example, a tungsten filament lamp is photometered, the calculated candle power will vary considerably with the direction. The radial graph for a 60-watt lamp given in Fig. C shows how in the direction of the lamp base the radiation falls practically to zero.

Because of such variations it has become common practice among illuminating engineers to describe light sources and the visible light they emit in terms of power. Traveling as it does in straight lines, light constitutes a flow of energy radially outward from the source. The flow of light energy is called the light *flux* and is measured in *lumens.*

The lumen is defined as the amount of visible light flux which falling normally on one square foot of area will produce an

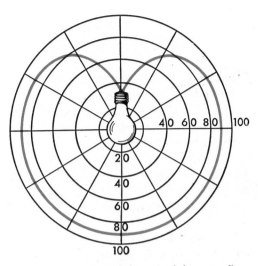

Fig. C. Polar graph of light emitted by an ordinary 60-watt tungsten filament bulb.

illuminance of one foot-candle. On this basis it can readily be shown that a one candlepower source radiating equally in all directions would give out 4π lumens of light (see Fig. D). Imagine a hollow sphere of one foot radius surrounding a point source of one candle power. Being one foot away at all points, $d = 1$ ft, the surface illuminance is 1 ft-candle, while the total area of the surface is $4\pi r^2$, or 4π ft^2.

Fig. D. Unit light flux is called the lumen.

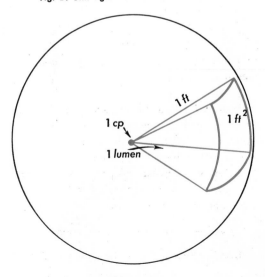

$$1 \text{ cp} = 4 \pi \text{ lumens}$$
$$1 \text{ cp} = 12.57 \text{ lumens} \qquad (6)$$

Luminance (or Brightness). Whether a body is self-luminous or just a reflector of the light that falls upon it, luminance refers to the light the surface gives off in the direction of an observer. Suppose as an experiment that a number of different kinds of surfaces like rough and polished metal, cotton fabric, black, grey and white paint, wood, etc., are equally illuminated from above as shown in Fig. E.

Because of different amounts of reflection and absorption some of these surfaces will appear to be brighter than others. Furthermore, as the angle of observation is altered, the brightness of some will change markedly while others will remain practically constant.

Brightness is a subjective measurement of the visible light coming from a surface and is therefore a sensory magnitude.

Luminance is an objective measurement of the luminous power coming from a surface.

An increase in the luminance results in an increase in brightness.

Luminance is measured in candles per square centimeter of area, c/cm^2. Examples of luminance, as measured in the metric system, are given in the following table for a number of common surfaces and fields of view.

clear blue sky.............	1 c/cm^2
desert sand...............	1.5 c/cm^2
fluorescent lamp...........	2 c/cm^2
frosted mazda lamp........	5 c/cm^2
full moon.................	3 c/cm^2
snow in sunlight...........	3 c/cm^2
sun.....................	50,000 c/cm^2
tungsten filament..........	2,500 c/cm^2

Recommended Illumination. One important factor concerned with the maintenance of good health involves good seeing conditions brought about by proper illumination. Experiments on the speed with which people see things show that it gains rapidly at first, with increasing illuminance, and then begins leveling off with an illuminance of about 25 ft-candles. This is borne out by numerous checks on the output of factory pieceworkers of all kinds.

Carefully conducted research in schools, hospitals, office buildings, etc., have also been made to determine proper lighting needed for the most efficient execution of various duties. The results of statistical studies by illuminating engineers, physicians, dentists, etc., under controlled conditions have led to the following values.

	foot-candles
hospital operating rooms......	1000
dental clinic................	250
fine needle work............	50-100
bookkeeping, auditing, drafting	20-50
offices, class rooms, laboratories	10-30
library reading rooms.........	10-25
factories...................	10-50

These are minimum values only and higher levels of illumination are often desirable and recommended.

Luminance and Illuminance. These two terms, commonly used by illumination engi-

Fig. E. Although equally illuminated, the brightness of different surfaces may be widely different.

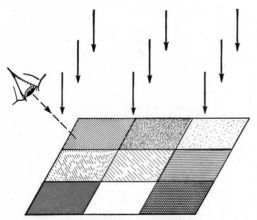

neers, sound so nearly alike they are often confusing. **Luminance** refers to the light given off by a source or surface, while **illuminance** refers to light falling on a body or surface. Each are commonly measured in the following units:

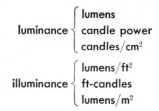

$$\text{luminance} \begin{cases} \text{lumens} \\ \text{candle power} \\ \text{candles/cm}^2 \end{cases}$$

$$\text{illuminance} \begin{cases} \text{lumens/ft}^2 \\ \text{ft-candles} \\ \text{lumens/m}^2 \end{cases}$$

Summary

The French physicist Foucault made the first determination of the speed of light in stationary matter in 1850. The speed of light in water was found to be about three-fourths the speed in air.

The refractive index, or index of refraction, for any optical medium like water, glass, plastic, air, etc., is a constant whose value is the ratio of the speed of light in a vacuum to the speed of light in the medium.

The illumination of a surface is proportional to the intensity of a light source and inversely proportional to the square of the distance from the source.

Light source intensity is called luminance and is measured in lumens, candle power, or candles per cm². The amount of light falling on a surface is called illuminance and is measured in ft-candles, lumens per ft², or lumens per m².

Brightness is a subjective estimate of the light coming from any source or surface.

Photometry is a laboratory process by which the light output of lamps is determined.

Questions

1. Who was first to measure the speed of light in stationary matter? Of what significance were the results of this experiment?

2. What is meant by the refractive index? What is meant by the index of refraction? What is the refractive index for (a) water, (b) glass, and (c) air?

3. What is the inverse square law? To what does it apply?

4. How is the light output of a lamp measured? What is a standard candle? What is the standard light source used today?

5. What is photometry? What law is made use of in the method?

6. What is the lumen? What is luminance? How is it measured? What is brightness? What is illuminance? How is it measured?

7. What illumination is recommended for classroom or office work? Why should surgery require high levels of illumination?

8. What inexpensive device could you make as a project for demonstrating or utilizing principles introduced in this lesson?

Problems

1. A 120 candle-power lamp is located 3 ft above a table top. What is the illuminance in ft-candles?

2. A 1000 candle-power lamp is located 20 ft above the street. What is the illuminance in ft-candles?

3. A 100 watt lamp, located 3 ft above a table top, has an efficiency of 1.27 candles per watt. Find the luminance (a) in candle power and (b) in lumens, and the illuminance (c) in ft-candles.

4. A 60 watt lamp, located 2 ft above a table top, has an efficiency of 1.1 candles per watt. Find the luminance (a) in candle power and (b) in lumens, and the illuminance (c) in ft-candles.

5. A fluorescent lamp tube is 3 cm in diameter and 100 cm long. Calculate its candle power if it has a luminance of 2 c/cm^2.

6. Find the speed of light in plastic if the refractive index is 1.425. Assume the speed of light in a vacuum to be 186,282 mi/sec.

7. Find the speed of light in carbon bisulfide if the refractive index is 1.670. Assume $c = 186,282$ mi/sec.

8. A 40 candle-power lamp is located 120 cm from an unknown lamp. If a photometer screen placed between the lamps is equally illuminated when it is 40 cm from the unknown lamp, what is its luminance?

9. A 75 candle-power lamp is located 8 ft from a lamp of unknown candle power. If a photometer screen placed between the lamps is equally illuminated when 3 ft from the unknown lamp, what is its candle power?

10.* Two lamps $I_1 = 60$-cp and $I_2 = 240$ cp, respectively, are located 3 m apart. At what position along a straight line through the lamps will equal illumination be produced? (*Note:* If you find two answers, both may be correct.)

Light | Lesson 3

PHOTOMETRY—*Laboratory*

This experiment, in which the candle powers of a set of tungsten filament lamps are determined, is described in the accompanying LABORATORY EXERCISES. The principles of photometry are employed, and a graph is drawn from the results.

REFLECTION FROM PLANE SURFACES

The Law of Reflection. Experiment shows that whenever a ray of light is reflected from a plane surface, the nature of the reflected light can be described in terms of a number of simple and well-defined laws. The simplest of these is the one known as **the law of reflection**. According to this law, *the angle at which a ray of light strikes the reflecting surface is exactly equal to the angle the reflected ray makes with the same surface.* Instead of measuring the **angle of incidence** and the **angle of reflection** from the mirror surface, however, it is customary to measure both from a line perpendicular to the plane of the mirror. This line as shown in Fig. A is called the **normal**. As the angle *i* increases, the angle *i'* increases by exactly the same amount, so that, for all angles of incidence,

$$\text{angle } i = \text{angle } i' \tag{1}$$

A second part of this law stipulates that the reflected ray lies in the plane of incidence, the plane of incidence being defined as the plane containing the incident ray and the normal. In other words, **the incident ray, the normal and the reflected ray all lie in the same plane.**

In speaking of a mirror surface one does not necessarily mean a silvered plate of glass; a mirror is any surface smooth enough to produce regular reflection as it has just been described.

Image in a Plane Mirror. The image of one's self seen in a mirror is formed by rays of light traveling in straight lines which are reflected according to the law of reflection. All objects seen in a plane mirror are images formed by reflection. This can be demonstrated by the experiment shown in Fig. B. A lighted candle **O** is placed on the table near a plate of glass **MN**. With the candle itself hidden in the box **H**, the observer at **E** sees only the reflected image at **I**. If a glass of water is placed at **B**, this image appears as a real candle burning under water.

As shown in the top view, all rays of light leaving the source **O** are reflected according to the law of reflection. To an observer anywhere between **L** and **R** on the right side of the mirror, all light appears to come from the same point **I**. This image point is just as far behind the mirror as the object **O** is in front of it, the two lie on the same perpendicular to the mirror.

The image one sees in a plane mirror is not a real image but a virtual image. A virtual image is one from which rays seem to radiate but actually do not. In the figure the rays do not come from **I** ; they come from **O** and by reflection reach the observer.

This experiment illustrates a trick used by many "Mediums" to make ghostlike figures appear to move about a room or stage. Light from real persons or objects, located below or above the stage, is reflected from a large

Fig. A. Illustrating the law of reflection from a plane surface.

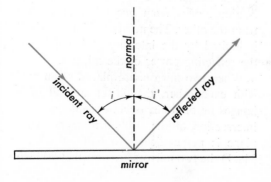

mirror

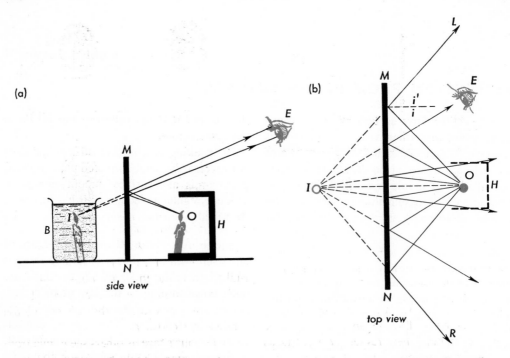

(a)

side view

(b)

top view

Fig. B. An experiment illustrating reflection from a mirror or plate of glass. Light from the candle flame at O appears to come from *I*.

sheet of plate glass at the front of the stage. With proper drapes and a darkened room, the illusion is very effective.

The image of any object seen in a plane mirror is the same size as the object and appears to be just as far behind the mirror as the object is in front of it.

Multiple Reflections. When light is reflected from two plane mirrors a number of

Fig. C. Multiple images as seen in two parallel mirrors all lie in a straight line.

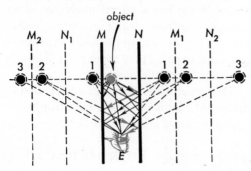

virtual images may be seen. If the two mirrors are parallel to each other, as illustrated by **MN** in Fig. C, the images all lie on a straight line, a line which passes through the object perpendicular to both mirrors. The images M_1, M_2, N_1, N_2, etc., of both mirrors are all equally spaced and the images 1, 2, 3, of the object are symmetrically located on each side of them.

The solid lines representing real rays show that images numbered 2 appear after two reflections, once from each mirror, and that images numbered 3 appear after three reflections, once from one mirror and twice from the other. The number of images visible is limited by the intensity of the light and the reflecting power of the mirrors.

When two mirrors are placed at an angle with each other, the object and all of its images lie on a circle whose center is at the intersection of the two mirrors and whose plane is perpendicular to both mirrors. In Fig. D the two mirrors are shown at 90° with

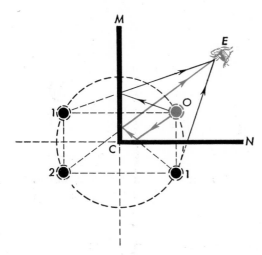

Fig. D. Multiple images as seen in two mirrors at an angle all lie in a circle.

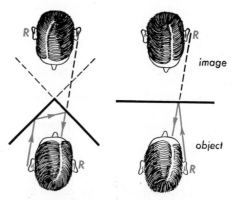

Fig. E. One's own image seen in 90° mirrors is normal; that seen in a plane mirror is perverted.

each other. The two images numbered *1* appear after one reflection and are the same distances behind their respective mirrors as the object is in front. Image *2* appears after two reflections. If the mirrors are placed at an angle of 60°, five virtual images may be seen, in addition to the object, making six in all. If the angle is 45°, seven virtual images may be seen, in addition to the object, making eight in all. Drawings of these are left as exercises for the student.

If one looks at his own face in a plane mirror, the image observed is technically described as *perverted.* The image is the same

as though the face were reproduced as a rubber mask and the mask turned inside out and viewed from the new front. The right ear of the subject becomes the left ear of the image and vice versa.

To see one's face as others see it, two front silvered mirrors should be placed 90° apart and touching each other along one edge as shown in Fig. E. The observer's right ear will then be seen, because of two reflections, as the right ear of his image, etc. This experiment must be performed to be appreciated since many people's faces are, unknowingly, slightly unsymmetrical. Seen in 90° mirrors all such irregularities are reversed and therefore appear double in magnitude and are very noticeable.

Summary

When a ray of light is reflected from a smooth, flat surface, the angle of incidence equals the angle of reflection. In optics, the angles are always specified as measured from a surface normal.

The image of any object seen in a plane mirror is the same size as the object and appears to be just as far behind the mirror as the object is in front. Corresponding object points and image points lie on the same normal to the surface.

When two plane parallel mirrors face each other some distance apart, an object located between them is observed as a long row of images extending in both directions.

If two mirrors make an angle with each other, the images of any object between them appear to lie in a circle with a center at the intersection of the mirrors.

Questions

1. What is the law of reflection? From what line are the angles measured?

2. How does the image distance from the mirror compare with the object distance?

3. How does the image size compare with the object size?

4. Is the image seen in a plane mirror a real image? What is it?

5. What is a virtual image? What is a perverted image?

6. When you look at your face in a plane mirror and put your hand to your right ear, which ear of the image does it appear to be?

7. How can a person see his or her own face as others see it?

8. What would you like to plan as a project for the making of some inexpensive device utilizing the principles introduced in this lesson?

Problems

1. Make a diagram showing two mirrors with their edges together and forming an angle of 45° with each other. Place an object between them and locate all images.

2. A room with six equal walls, each 4 ft long, has the shape of a hexagon. A lamp is located in one corner 1 ft from each of two walls. Make a diagram and show the positions of all images formed by one reflection only.

3. A box 2 feet wide and 3 feet long has mirrors on the inside walls. A lamp is located in one corner 6 in. from each of the two walls. Make a diagram and show the positions of all images formed by single and double reflections only.

4. Find the distance from the object to the farthest image due to only one reflection for the box in problem 3.

5. What must be the minimum length of a mirror in order for a man to see a full view of himself in it?

6. Two mirrors make an angle of 60° with each other. Make a drawing showing an object point closer to one mirror than the other and (a) locate all the images. (b) Show the path of light reaching the eye from the farthest image. (Locate the eye closer to the other mirror.)

7. Two mirrors make an angle of 90° with each other. Make a drawing showing an object in the form of an arrow close to but making an angle of about 30° with one mirror. Locate the images.

8. Make a drawing showing two plane parallel mirrors some distance apart. Show an object in the form of an arrow close to but making an angle of about 30° with one mirror. Locate the first three images as seen in each direction.

REFLECTION FROM PLANE
SURFACES—*Laboratory*

This experiment, involving the geometrical location of images seen in a plane mirror, is described in the accompanying LABORATORY EXERCISES. The results confirm the law of reflection and the positions of mirror images.

REFLECTION FROM CURVED SURFACES

Concave Mirrors. The concave mirror is an optical device which may by pure reflection form images on a screen. Such mirrors are often used in optical instruments in place of lenses.

A spherical mirror has the form of a circular section of a hollow sphere as shown in Fig. A. The center point **A** of the section is called the **vertex,** and a line from the center through the vertex is called the **principal axis.** The radius of the sphere **r** is called the **radius of the mirror.**

Because spherical mirrors are symmetrical about their axes, cross-section diagrams are usually drawn to show their optical properties. If the mirror is silvered on the inner

Fig. A. A spherical mirror is a circular section of a sphere.

surface, it is called a **concave mirror,** while if silvered on the outer surface, it is a **convex mirror.**

A cross-sectional diagram showing how a beam of parallel light is reflected by a concave mirror is shown in Fig. B. Each ray striking the mirror obeys the law of reflection, namely, that the angle of incidence **i** equals the angle of reflection **i'**.

The point **F** where the rays cross the principal axis is called the **principal focus,** and the distance **A** to **F** is called the **focal length f.**

If the mirror is silvered on the outer surface as in Fig. C, it becomes a convex mirror and parallel incident light rays are reflected as if they came from a point **F** on the axis. The different rays, each obeying the law of

Fig. B. Illustrating the focal point F and focal length f of a concave mirror.

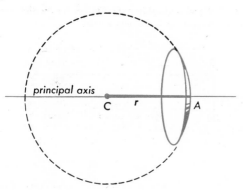

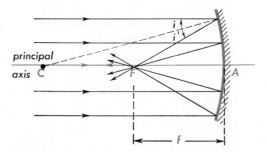

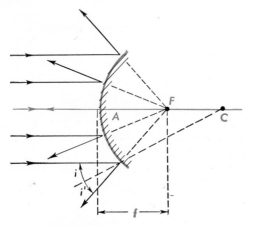

Fig. C. Illustrating the focal point F and focal length f of a convex mirror.

reflection, diverge after reflection and never come to a focus.

Nevertheless, the distance **A** to **F** is called the *focal length* of the convex mirror and it is assigned a minus sign in all optical formulas.

The geometry of the incident and reflected rays as shown in Figs. B and C can be used to show mathematically that the focal point **F** is halfway between **C** and **A**. In other words

$$AF = \tfrac{1}{2} \, AC$$

or

$$f = \tfrac{1}{2} \, r \qquad (1)$$

Image Formation. If an illuminated object **O** is located in front of a concave mirror as shown in Fig. D, a real image **I** can be formed nearby. All rays emitted by the object point **Q** and reflected by the mirror come to a focus at **Q′**. All rays emitted by the

object point **M** (not shown) would upon reflection come to a focus at **M′**. For every object point in **QM** emitting rays, there will be a corresponding image point in **Q′M′** where focus is produced.

If the eye is located at **E**, the illuminated object will appear at **Q′M′**, but inverted. If a screen is located at **Q′M′**, a sharply defined image will be observed there. Because the image can be formed on a screen, it is called a *real image*.

Object Image Formula. Let d_o represent the distance from the object point **M** to the mirror vertex **A**, and d_i the distance from the image point **M′** to **A**; then one finds that

$$\frac{1}{d_o} + \frac{1}{d_i} = \frac{1}{f} \qquad (2)$$

where d_o is called the **object distance,** d_i the **image distance,** and **f** the **focal length.**

As an illustration, consider the case shown in Fig. E, of an object **O** located 30 cm from a concave mirror of 20 cm radius. By eq. (1) the focal length $f = \tfrac{1}{2} \, r$, or $f = +10$ cm. A light ray from **O** parallel to the principal axis is reflected, by definition of the focal point, through **F**. By the reversibility of light rays, another ray from **O** passing through **F** is reflected parallel to the principal axis. Where these two rays cross at **I**, the image is formed. A third ray from **O** through the center of curvature **C** strikes the mirror normally and is reflected back on itself where it passes

Fig. E. Showing graphical construction for locating the image formed by a concave mirror.

Fig. D. A concave mirror forms a real image.

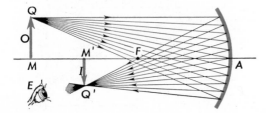

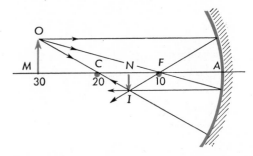

through **I**. Any two of these three rays are sufficient to locate the image. The third ray is then a check upon the other two. This graphical construction for image formation is called the **parallel ray method**.

To solve this mirror arrangement as a problem, Eq. (2) can be applied directly. Given are the quantities, $d_o = 30$ cm, $f = +10$ cm. By substitution in Eq. (2) we obtain

$$\frac{1}{30} + \frac{1}{d_i} = \frac{1}{10}$$

$$\frac{1}{d_i} = \frac{1}{10} - \frac{1}{30}$$

Using the common denominator of 30,

$$\frac{1}{d_i} = \frac{3}{30} - \frac{1}{30}$$

$$\frac{1}{d_i} = \frac{2}{30}$$

or

$$d_i = +15 \text{ cm}$$

An interesting experiment can be performed with a large concave mirror under the conditions illustrated in Fig. F. A flower hanging upside down in a box and placed just below the center of curvature will form a real and erect image at **I** directly above. An observer to the left cannot see the flower directly but can see the real image. So real is this image that it cannot be distinguished from a real object; the rays of light as shown in the diagram diverge from **I** the same as they would if the object were located there.

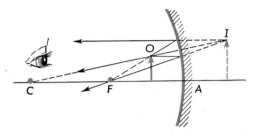

Fig. G. Diagram showing the formation of a virtual image.

In Fig. G an object is placed inside the focal point of a concave mirror and the rays after reflection diverge as if they had come from the point **I**. To the eye of an observer at **E** a virtual image is seen magnified and right side up at **I**. As a problem let the object distance $d_o = 10$ cm, the focal length $f = +20$ cm. Substitution of these in Eq. (2) gives

$$\frac{1}{10} + \frac{1}{d_i} = \frac{1}{20}$$

$$\frac{1}{d_i} = \frac{1}{20} - \frac{1}{10}$$

$$\frac{1}{d_i} = \frac{1}{20} - \frac{2}{20}$$

$$\frac{1}{d_i} = -\frac{1}{20}$$

$$d_i = -20 \text{ cm}$$

The image is located 20 cm from the mirror, the minus sign indicating that it is virtual

Fig. H. Diagrams showing the caustic curve obtained with a spherical mirror and the point focus with a paraboloidal mirror.

Fig. F. Diagram for the phantom bouquet.

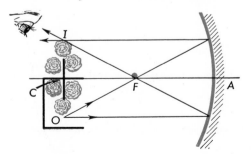

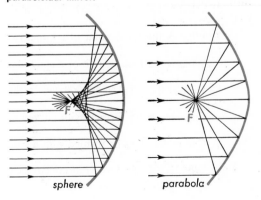

sphere   parabola

and on the opposite side of the mirror from the object.

No matter where a real object is located in front of a convex mirror, the image is **virtual** and cannot be formed on a screen. When in using Eq. (2) the focal length of a convex mirror is known, its value is substituted with a minus sign.

In Fig. H the focusing property of a large diameter mirror is compared with that of a parabolic mirror. A spherical mirror deviates the outer rays to a shorter focus than those near the center. This focusing defect is called **spherical aberration.** The parabola, on the other hand, brings all rays to focus at one point. A small source of light located at the focal point of a parabolic reflector becomes a parallel beam after reflection, a principle used in astronomical telescopes, spotlights, searchlights, and automobile headlights.

Spherical aberration for a spherical mirror is reduced by reducing the diameter or, what is the same thing, by keeping the focal length large compared with the reflector diameter.

Summary

A spherical mirror is a section of the surface of a sphere. Rays of light reflected from a concave or convex mirror obey the law of reflection at all points. All such mirrors have image-forming properties, a principal axis, radius of curvature, focal point, and focal length.

The focal length of a spherical mirror is one-half the radius of curvature. Concave mirrors are capable of forming real images. A real image is one that can be formed on a screen.

Convex mirrors are not capable of forming a real image. Images seen in a convex mirror are virtual.

The object image formula, which holds for both concave and convex mirrors, is

$$\frac{1}{d_o} + \frac{1}{d_i} = \frac{1}{f}$$

Slight defects are observed in the image formed by spherical mirrors and may be ascribed to what is called spherical aberration. Parabolic mirrors are free of this effect.

Questions

1. What is a concave mirror? What is a convex mirror?

2. What is the principal axis of a spherical mirror?

3. What is the focal point of a concave mirror? A convex mirror?

4. What is the focal length of a spherical mirror?

5. How is the focal length related to the radius of curvature?

6. Can images be formed with curved mirrors? Are such images ever real?

7. Can real images be formed with a convex mirror?

8. What is spherical aberration? How can it be eliminated? Does a convex mirror have spherical aberration?

9. What are parabolic mirrors used for?

10. What project would you like to see carried out making use of the principles developed in this lesson?

Problems

1. An object 2 cm high is located 15 cm in front of a concave mirror of 12 cm radius. Find the image distance (a) graphically and (b) by formula. (c) What is the image height?

2. An object 1 cm high is located 10 cm in front of a concave mirror of 12 cm radius. Find the image position (a) graphically and (b) by formula. (c) What is the image height?

3. An object 1.5 cm high is located 4 cm in front of a concave mirror having a 20 cm radius. Find the image position (a) graphically and (b) by formula. (c) Find the image height.

4. An object 2 cm high is located 5 cm in front of a concave mirror having a 30 cm radius. Find the image position (a) graphically and (b) by formula. (c) Find the image height.

5. An object 2 in. high is located 12 in. in front of a convex mirror of 16-in. radius. Find (a) the image position and (b) the image size. (c) Find the image graphically.

6. An object 3 cm high is located 5 cm in front of a convex mirror of 10 cm focal length. (a) Where is the image formed? (b) Is the image real or virtual? (c) Find the image graphically.

7. An object 1.5 cm high is located 6 cm in front of a convex mirror of 24 cm radius. (a) Find the image distance. Graphically find (b) the image distance and (c) the image height.

8. An object 2 cm high is located 6 cm in front of a convex mirror of 6 cm focal length. (a) Find the image distance. (b) Graphically find the image distance.

9.* A concave mirror has a focal length of 10 in. Where should an object be placed if the image distance is to be three times the object distance?

10.* A concave mirror has a focal length of 12 cm. Where should an object be placed to form a virtual image twice as far from the mirror?

Light | **Lesson 7**

REFRACTION OF LIGHT

Refraction. When light falls upon the smooth surface of a transparent substance like water or glass, part of it is reflected according to the law of reflection and the remainder is refracted into the medium (see Fig. A). This bending is due to the change in the velocity of the light upon entering the second medium. The direction of

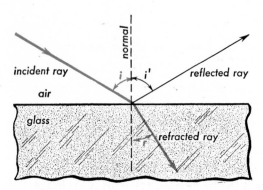

Fig. A. Reflection and refraction of light at the boundary of a glass surface.

the refracted ray, like the incident and reflected rays, is always measured by the angle it makes with the normal.

The angle of refraction **r** is found by experiment to depend upon two factors: (1) **the angle of incidence i**, and (2) **the index of refraction** μ.

The index of refraction is the ratio of the speed of light in vacuo to the speed of light in the medium. To determine the angle of refraction from these two factors we perform the following graphical construction (see Fig. B).

Assume the refracting surface is that of glass, with air above, and the refractive index

Fig. B. Illustrating the graphical method of determining the angle of refraction.

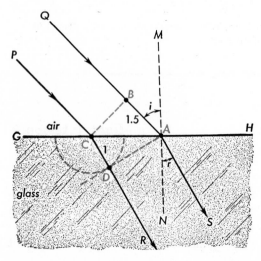

$\mu = 1.5$. First a ray of light **QA** is selected, incident on the surface at an angle **i**. Using a ruler, a line segment is measured back from **A** to a point **B** such that **AB** = the refractive index. The unit of length to be chosen here is arbitrary and may be 1 cm, or 1 in., or any other. From **B** a line is next drawn perpendicular to **QA**, intersecting the surface **GH** at **C**. Line **CP** is now drawn parallel to **QA** to represent the other boundary of the incident beam of width **CB**.

Now with a compass of radius 1.0 unit, and center at **C**, a circular arc is drawn as shown. Through the point **A** a tangent is drawn, and from the point of contact **D** the refracted ray **CDR** is drawn. The other ray **AS** is finally drawn parallel to **CR** to represent the other edge of the refracted beam of width **DA**.

The law of refraction may now be stated in terms of the line segments **BA** and **CD** as follows:

$$\frac{BA}{CD} = \mu \qquad (1)$$

It was the Dutch astronomer and mathematician, Willebrord Snell,* who first discovered, from experiments, that the ratio of these two lines for a given substance is the same for all angles of incidence. In other words, μ is a constant. The relation as given by Eq. (1) is therefore called Snell's law. The reason for the constancy of this ratio is that while the light travels from **B** to **A** in air, it travels the corresponding lesser distance **CD** in glass.

Snell's Law of Refraction. It is customary, in treating the refraction of light, to express Snell's law in trigonometric terms. Re-

* Willebrord Snell (1591-1626), Dutch astronomer and mathematician, was born at Leyden in 1591. At the age of twenty-two he succeeded his father as professor of mathematics at the University of Leyden. In 1617 he determined the size of the earth from measurements of its curvature between Alkmaar and Bergen-op-Zoom. In 1621 he discovered the law of refraction which now carries his name.

ferring to Fig. B, triangles **ABC** and **ACD** are right triangles. Since line **PC** is $\perp$ to **CB**, and line **MA** is $\perp$ to **AC**, angle $i =$ angle **BCA**. By similar relations angle $r =$ angle **CAD**. From triangles **ABC**, and **ACD**,

$$BA = AC \sin i$$

$$CD = AC \sin R$$

Substituting these values on the right for **BA** and **CD** in Eq. (1) gives

$$\frac{BA}{CD} = \frac{AC \sin i}{AC \sin r} = \frac{\sin i}{\sin r} = \mu$$

or

$$\mu = \frac{\sin i}{\sin r} \qquad (2)$$

This latter is the most useful form of Snell's law. For the boundary separating any given transparent substances, the ratio of the sine of the angle incidence to the sine of the angle of refraction is the same for all angles of incidence and is equal to the refraction index, μ. Since μ is the ratio of the velocities of light in the two media (see Light, Lesson 2), Snell's law may also be written

$$\frac{\sin i}{\sin r} = \frac{V_1}{V_2} = \mu \qquad (3)$$

where V_1 represents the velocity in the first medium and V_2 the velocity in the second medium.

Example. Light, in air, is incident at an angle of 45° on the surface of a glass plate for which the refractive index is 1.52. Through what angle is the light deviated upon refraction at the top surface?

Solution. First find the angle of refraction r by use of Eq. (2). By transposing and substituting the given quantities, we obtain

$$\sin r = \frac{\sin i}{\mu} = \frac{\sin 45°}{1.52} = \frac{0.707}{1.52} = 0.465$$

If we look up 0.465 in a table of natural sines, we find that angle $r = 27.7°$. Since the deviation of the light is the difference between angle i and angle r (45° − 27.7°),

$$\text{deviation} = 17.3°$$

Displacement in a Parallel Plate. One very useful principle concerning the behavior of light is *the reversibility of light rays*. If, in any of the experiments or illustrations already described, the light rays could be reversed in direction, they would be found to retrace their paths exactly.

If a beam of light, on being refracted into a denser medium like glass, is bent toward the normal, light passing through and out of this denser medium into the air should be bent away from the normal. This can be demonstrated by sending light through a plane-parallel plate of glass as illustrated in Fig. C. In (c) the light is incident on the first surface at an angle i and is refracted at an angle r. This internal ray is now incident on the second surface at the same angle r and is refracted into the air at the same angle i. The light thus emerges in a direction parallel to the original beam but displaced from it laterally.

Fig. C. Illustrating the lateral displacement of a beam of light passing through a parallel plate of glass.

(a)   (b)   (c)   (d)

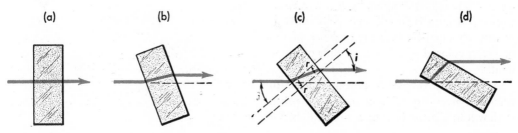

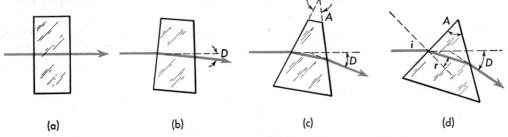

Fig. D. Illustrating the bending of a beam of light by prisms made of the same glass.

This lateral displacement is zero for normal incidence as in (a) and increases with the angle *i* as shown in figures (b), (c), and (d), respectively. If the parallel plate is very thin, as in the case of an ordinary windowpane, the displacement is quite small and for most practical purposes can be neglected.

Refraction by a Prism. When light passes through a prism, it is refracted at two surfaces, once on the way in and once on the way out. If the two sides involved are parallel, as they are in Fig. D, diagram (a), the emergent ray is always parallel to the incident ray. If the sides are not parallel, as in diagrams (b), (c), and (d), the emergent ray has a different direction. The larger the angle **A** between the two refracting surfaces, the larger is the angle of deviation **D**. Upon entering the prism at the first surface, see diagram (d), the light is bent toward the normal. Emerging into the air from the second surface, the light is bent away from the normal. Note in Fig. D that neither the apex nor the base of the prism has any effect on the deviation of the light.

In verifying these results by experiment, light of only one color should be used, because white light will spread out into a spectrum of colors. Light of one color only is readily obtained by inserting a piece of red or green colored glass into a beam of white light.

A relatively simple graphical method of tracing a given ray of light through a prism is shown in Fig. E. Given: a ray of light **VP**

incident at an angle *i* on the first face of a prism of angle **A** and refractive index μ. In this diagram **A** = 60°, μ = 1.5, and *i* = 60°.

Starting at one side a line **EF** is first drawn parallel to the incident ray **VP**. With a center at any point **O**, and with radii, in this particular case, of 1.0 unit and 1.5 units, arcs **CS** and **BR** are drawn of indefinite length. From the intersection **C** a line is now drawn parallel to the normal **M**, intersecting the second arc at **R**. The line **OR** is drawn next, and from the point **P** of the prism a parallel line is drawn intersecting

Fig. E. Graphical construction for refraction by a prism.

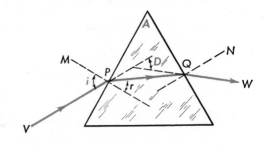

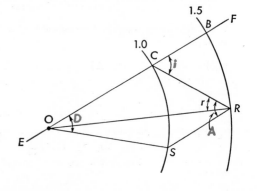

the second face at **Q**. Starting at **R** a line is next drawn parallel to the normal **N**, intersecting the first arc at **S**. Finally the line **OS** is drawn in, and from the point **Q** on the second prism face a parallel line **QW** is drawn as the emergent ray.

Since the above construction obeys Snell's law, the accuracy of the results depends upon the sharpness of the pencil used and the care with which the diagram is made. Furthermore the left-hand diagram as well as the prism diagram includes all of the angles involved in the prism, including the angle of deviation **D.**

Summary

Light crossing the boundary separating two different optical media bends. This bending at the boundary is called refraction. Measurements of angles show that refraction obeys Snell's law.

$$\mu = \frac{\sin i}{\sin r}$$

The angle of incidence i and the angle of refraction r are both measured from the normal to the surface. The ratio of the sines of these two angles is constant for any given pair of materials. This constant is called the refractive index, or index of refraction.

If at any point along a ray the direction is reversed, the light will retrace its path.

Rays of light entering a parallel plate emerge from the second surface parallel to the direction in which they entered. Such rays, however, may be laterally shifted.

When light enters and leaves a prism with sides that are not parallel, the light emerges in a different direction from that in which it entered.

Questions

1. What is refraction? Where exactly does it take place?

2. What is Snell's law? What is the refractive index? Does Snell's law hold for all angles?

3. What is meant by the sine of an angle?

4. What is the principle of reversibility of light? Does it hold for both reflection and refraction?

5. How does the principle of reversibility apply to refraction by a parallel plate of glass? When is light not shifted laterally by a thick glass plate?

6. Upon what factors does the deviation of light by a prism depend? Does the angle of deviation depend on the refractive index?

7. What is the graphical method of tracing a ray through a prism? Make a diagram and explain.

8. What project would you propose for the making of some device that would utilize or demonstrate some of the principles developed in this lesson?

Problems

1. Light is incident at 50° on the surface of a clear crystal whose refractive index is 1.25. Construct a refraction diagram similar to Fig. B and determine the angle of refraction. Check your result by calculation, using Snell's law.

2. Light is incident at 60° on the surface of glass whose refractive index is 1.65. Calculate the angle of (a) refraction and (b) deviation.

3. Light is incident at an angle of 70° on the surface of a diamond whose refractive index is 2.42. Calculate the angle of (a) refraction and (b) deviation.

4.* Light is incident at an angle of 55° on one face of a 60° prism. Graphically find the total deviation of the light if the refractive index is 1.50.

5. A rectangular aquarium with glass sides and filled with water is 1 ft thick. Find the lateral displacement of a beam of light incident on one of the sides at 30°. Neglect the glass thickness. (Refractive index for water $\mu = 1.33$.)

6.* Light is incident at an angle of 60° on one face of a 5-cm glass cube whose refractive index is 1.50. Calculate lateral displacement of the light that emerges from the opposite side.

7.* A ray of light incident on a glass surface at an angle of 45° is deviated through an angle of 18°. Find the refractive index.

8.* Light is incident at an angle of 45° on one face of a 60° glass prism. Calculate the total deviation of the light if the refractive index is 1.65.

9. Calculate the deviation of a beam of light incident on a glass surface of index 1.50 at the following angles: (a) 0°, (b) 15°, (c) 30°, (d) 45°, (e) 60°, (f) 75°, and (g) 90°.

10. Plot the results of problem 9 as a graph, the angle of incidence horizontally and the deviation angle vertically.

Light | Lesson 8

INDEX OF REFRACTION—*Laboratory*

This experiment on the refraction of light by the polished surface of a block of glass is described in the accompanying LABORATORY EXERCISES. By measuring angles of incidence and refraction you will determine the refractive index.

Light | Lesson 9

LENSES

Lenses. The primary function of a lens is to form images of real objects. Although most lenses are made of common glass, a few special lenses are made of other transparent materials like **quartz** and **fluorite.** To understand the principles upon which

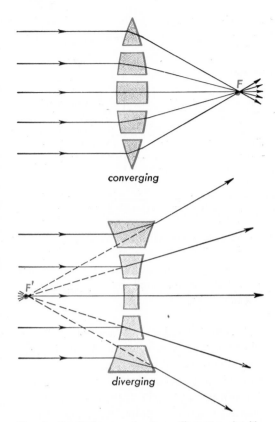

converging

diverging

Fig. A. Matched sets of prisms illustrating lenslike action.

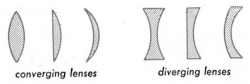

converging lenses   *diverging lenses*

Fig. B. Cross sections of standard forms of common lenses.

shown in Fig. B. The first three lenses, which are thicker in the center, are called **converging** or **positive lenses**, while the last three, which are thinner in the center, are called **diverging** or **negative lenses**. Special names attached to each of the six lens types shown are (1) **double convex**, (2) **plano-convex**, (3) **convex miniscus**, (4) **double concave**, (5) **plano-concave**, and (6) **concave miniscus**.

Diagrams showing the refraction of light by converging and diverging lenses are given in Fig. C. The principal axis in each case is a straight line passing through the center of a lens, perpendicular to the two faces at the points of intersection. The principal focus **F** lies on the principal axis and is defined for a

a lens functions, imagine a set of several matched prisms and blocks of glass arranged in the order shown in Fig. A.

In the first arrangement the prisms are made so as to refract the incoming parallel light rays and to converge them to a focus at **F**. In the second arrangement the parallel rays are made to diverge as if they had come from a common point **F'**. In each system the greatest deviation occurs at the outermost prisms, for they have the greatest angle between the two refracting surfaces. No deviation occurs for the central rays, for at that point the glass faces are parallel to each other.

A real lens is not made of prisms, as indicated in Fig. A, but of a solid piece of glass with surfaces ground to the form of a sphere. Cross sections of several standard forms are

Fig. C. Converging and diverging lenses.

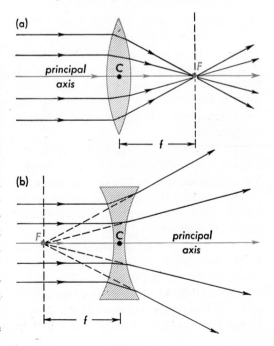

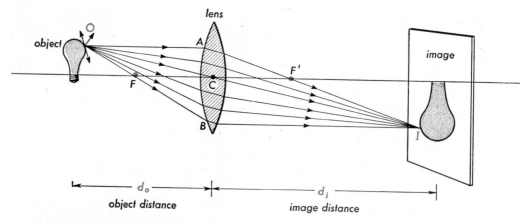

lens

object

A

F'

image

F

C

B

I

d_o

object distance

d_i

image distance

Fig. D. Ray diagram illustrating the formation of a real image by means of a single converging lens.

converging lens as the point where parallel light rays are brought together, and for a negative lens as a point from which parallel light rays appear to originate.

By symmetry every lens has two principal foci, one on each side of the lens and at the same distance from the center of the lens. The distance from the focal point to the lens is called the **focal length.**

$$CF = focal\ length = f$$

A plane perpendicular to the principal axis which passes through either principal focus is called the **focal plane.** Parallel light rays entering the lens from any other direction than shown in the diagrams will come to a focus at some point on the focal plane. This point is readily located by remembering that a ray through the lens center does not change in direction.

The greater the curvature of the two surfaces of a lens, the shorter is its focal length. The reason for this, as can be seen from the diagrams, is that the greater the curvature the greater is the deviation of the light rays passing through near the edges of the lens.

One important principle concerning lenses is the reversibility of light rays. If a point source of light is placed at **F'** in Fig. C(a), the rays of light which strike the lens will be refracted into a parallel beam of light moving to the left. Similarly, in Fig. C(b) if light

rays are converging toward the focal point **F'** they will be refracted by the lens into a parallel beam.

Image Formation. When an object is placed on one side of a converging lens beyond the principal focus, a real image will be formed on the opposite side of the lens. This is illustrated in Fig. D. If the object is moved closer to the focal point, the image will be formed farther away from the lens and will be bigger, that is, magnified. As the object is moved farther away from the lens, the image is formed closer to the focal point and is smaller in size.

In general there are two ways of accurately determining the position of an image: one is by graphical construction and the other is by use of the lens formula.

$$\frac{1}{d_o} + \frac{1}{d_i} = \frac{1}{f} \tag{1}$$

where **d_o is the object distance, d_i the image distance,** and **f the focal length.**

The graphical method is illustrated in Fig. E. Consider the light emitted by some one particular point like **O** in the object. Of the rays going out from this point in all directions the ray **OA** traveling parallel to the principal axis will be refracted to pass through the focal point **F'** (see Fig. C(a)). The ray **OC**

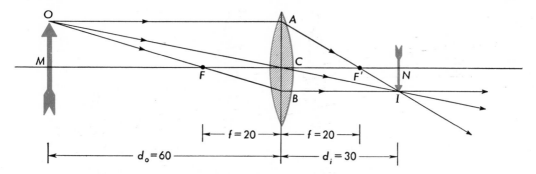

Fig. E. Graphical determination of image position and size.

arriving at the center of the lens where the faces are parallel will pass straight through, meeting the other ray at some point *I*. These two rays locate the tip of the image at *I*. All other rays from the point **O** which strike the lens will be brought to a focus at this same point. To check this note that the ray **OF**, which passes from **O** through the focal point **F**, by the principle of the reversibility of light rays, will be refracted parallel to the principal axis, crossing the other ray at **I**, as shown.

The use of the lens formula can be illustrated by the following example. Let an object be placed 60 cm in front of a lens of focal length 20 cm. If we solve Eq. (1) for d_i, we obtain the expression:

$$d_i = \frac{d_o \times f}{d_o - f} \qquad (2)$$

Then substituting the known quantities, we obtain

$$d_i = \frac{60 \times 20}{60 - 20} = 30 \text{ cm}$$

The image is formed 30 cm from the lens or 10 cm from **F**.

If a centimeter rule is used to construct this problem graphically, the resultant diagram will be similar to Fig. E. Each line is drawn in its proper position and size, and when the image is located by rays (1), (2), and (3), its position and size are measured by the same scale. Drawn carefully, the graphical results will agree in every detail with those calculated by the above formula.

Virtual Images. The images formed by the lenses in Figs. D and E are **real**. **Real images** are defined as those which can be formed on a screen and are characterized by the fact that rays of light are actually brought together to a focus there. **Virtual images** are not real, they cannot be formed on a screen, and the rays from different points on the object do not pass through corresponding points in the image. Virtual images may be observed with a converging lens by placing an object close to the lens and inside the focal point, or by a diverging lens with the object

Fig. F. Illustration of the formation of virtual images.

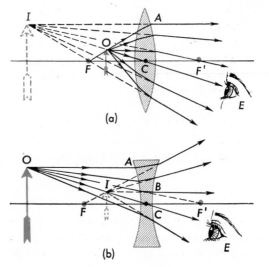

(a)

(b)

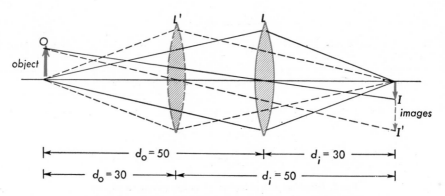

Fig. G. Illustrating conjugate foci for a single converging lens.

at any point. These two examples are illustrated in Fig. F.

In the first case the lens is used as a magnifier, or reading glass. Rays of light radiating from the point of the object at **O** are refracted in the proper direction but are not sufficiently deviated to come to a focus. To the observer's eye at **E** these rays appear to be coming from a point **I** back of the lens. This is a *virtual image, right side up and magnified.* To find this image graphically we observe that the ray **FOA** must be refracted parallel to the principal axis. The ray **OC** through the center of the lens goes on undeviated. These two refracted rays extended backward intersect at **I**. If the lens formula Eq. (2) is used

to find the image in such a case, the image distance d_i will come out as a negative quantity, showing it is a virtual image on the same side of the lens as the object.

Conjugate Foci. In demonstrating conjugate distances with a lens and screen the object and image can be interchanged in position, or, the lens can be moved. If, for example, an object distance $d_o = 30$ cm and an image distance $d_i = 50$ cm, the lens may be moved to a new position $d_o = 50$ cm and the image will be formed at $d_i = 30$ cm. In other words, for a fixed distance between object and image screen there are two lens positions of good image formation (see Fig. G).

Summary

Most lenses are ground and polished with spherical surfaces. Lenses that are thickest in the center act to converge light and are capable of forming real images. Lenses that are thinnest in the center act to diverge light, and the images are never real.

Lenses have two focal points, one on either side of the principal axis and equidistant from the lens.

The lens formula most commonly employed is

$$\frac{1}{d_o} + \frac{1}{d_i} = \frac{1}{f}$$

where d_o, d_i, and f are the object distance, image distance, and focal length, respectively. Because of the reversibility of light rays every object point and its corresponding image point are interchangeable. Such pairs of points are said to be conjugate foci.

Questions

1. What is a converging lens? What is a diverging lens? How can you tell a converging from a diverging lens by feel?

2. How does one find the focal points of a lens? What is the focal length?

3. If you know the focal length of a lens, how can you produce a parallel beam of light? Can a diverging lens be used? Why?

4. If the object distance and the focal length are known, how can you find the image formed by a single lens? Write down the formula.

5. Where does the object have to be placed to form a virtual image with a converging lens? Where should it be to insure that a real image will be formed?

6. Can an object be located at any point near a concave lens such that (a) a real image is formed or (b) a virtual image cannot be formed?

7. What are conjugate foci? If object and image are interchanged, will the image be the same in both cases? (Try this with a lens.)

8. What demonstration experiment could you undertake as a project on image formation by lenses?

Problems

1. An object 5 cm high is located 12 cm in front of a converging lens of focal length + 8 cm. Find (a) the position and (b) the size of the image by the lens formula and by the graphical method.

2. An object 3 in. high is located 20 in. in front of a converging lens of focal length + 12 in. Find (a) the position and (b) the size of the image by the lens formula and by the graphical method.

3. A converging lens has a focal length of +6 cm. Find the position and size of the image if an object 4 cm high is located 15 cm in front of the lens.

4. An object 3 cm high is located 8 cm in front of a converging lens of focal length 12 cm. Find the position of the image.

5. An object 3 cm high is located 10 cm in front of a converging lens of 5 cm focal length. Find (a) the image distance by calculation and (b) the image size by graphical construction.

6. An object 2 cm high is located 5 cm in front of a converging lens of 10 cm focal length. Find (a) the image distance by calculation and (b) the image size by graphical construction.

7. An object is located 15 cm in front of a diverging lens with a 5 cm focal length. Find (a) the image distance by calculation and (b) the image size by graphical construction.

8. An object is located in the focal plane of a diverging lens. (a) Where is the image formed? (b) How large is the image? (c) Is it real or virtual? (d) Is it inverted or erect?

9. An object 1 cm high is located 4 cm in front of a converging lens of 5 cm focal length. (a) Where is the image formed? (b) Make a diagram and find the height of the image. (c) How much larger is the image than the object.

10. A real image is to be formed three times as far from a converging lens as the object. Find (a) the object distance and (b) the image distance.

LENSES—*Laboratory*

This experiment on the image formation by means of converging lenses is described in the accompanying LABORATORY EXERCISES. From object and image measurements you will determine the magnification as well as focal length of a lens.

DISPERSION

The Critical Angle. When light passes from a medium, such as air, into a more dense medium, like glass or water, the angle of refraction is always less than the angle of incidence. As a result of this decrease in

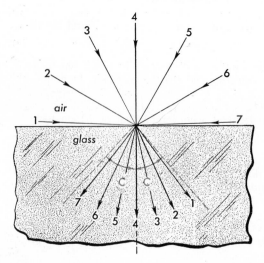

Fig. A. Illustrating the critical angle.

angle there exists a range of angles for which no refracted light is possible. To see what this range of angles is, consider the diagram in Fig. A, where for several angles of incidence the corresponding angles of refraction are shown. It is to be noted that in the limiting case where the incident rays approach the angle of 90°, i.e., where they graze along the surface, the refracted rays approach a certain angle **c**, beyond which no refracted light is possible. In any medium this limiting angle, called **the critical angle,** depends for its value upon the index of refraction.

To calculate the critical angle of refraction, it is noted that the angle of incidence $i = 90°$ and angle $r =$ angle **c**. Since $\sin 90° = 1$, Snell's law becomes

$$\mu = \frac{1}{\sin c}$$

or

$$\boxed{\sin c = \frac{1}{\mu}} \qquad (1)$$

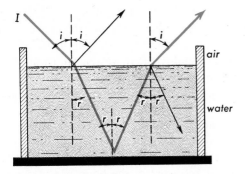

Fig. B. Illustration of reflection and refraction.

incident light is reflected as indicated by the fine-lined arrows.

When a beam of light within a medium like water or glass approaches the surface at an angle greater than the critical angle, all of the light is reflected back into the medium. In other words, a water-to-air or glass-to-air surface acts under these conditions like a perfect reflector. This phenomenon is called **total reflection.** Since no light can be refracted into the water at such an angle (see Fig. A), none inside the water and at large angles of incidence can be refracted out. The experiment is illustrated with a tank of water as shown in Fig. C. If light is sent into the water through a glass plate in one end, the light approaches the upper surface at an angle greater than **c**, there to be totally reflected back into the water as shown.

The critical angle is the minimum angle of incidence at which light is totally reflected at a boundary.

For the most common of crown glass $\mu = 1.515$, so that substitution in this formula gives $c = 41.3°$. For water of index $\mu = 1.33$ and substitution gives $c = 49°$. It should be noted in particular that the critical angle is measured from the normal and not from the refracting surface.

Total Reflection. Another experiment illustrating the reversibility of light rays is shown in Fig. B. A beam of light is refracted at an angle **r** into a tank of water. From there it is reflected from a silvered mirror at the bottom of the tank, illustrating the law of reflection in a medium other than air. The reflected ray arriving at the upper surface at the same angle **r** is refracted into the air at the incident angle **i**. At each refraction at the air-water boundary a small amount of the

An interesting demonstration can be performed with a clear glass or plastic rod bent into almost any form as shown in Fig. D. Light, on entering one end, reflects from wall to wall by total reflection, causing it to follow the rod to the end and emerge as a divergent beam. Various instruments used by physicians and surgeons employ this principle for internal body observations.

Total reflection is also employed in optical instruments such as telescopes, microscopes, prism binoculars, spectroscopes, etc. The optical parts employing this principle are known as **total reflection prisms.** Such prisms are usually made of common glass with one angle a right angle and the other

Fig. C. Illustration of total reflection and the critical angle c.

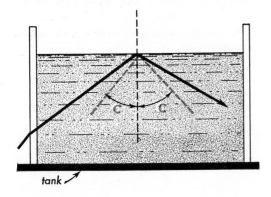

Fig. D. Light follows a bent rod by total reflection.

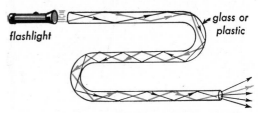

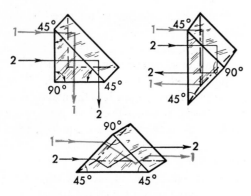

Fig. E. Total reflection prisms.

two 45° angles. As illustrated in Fig. E there are three ways in which these prisms may be used. Incident normally upon the first surface, as in (a), the light enters the prism without deviation. Arriving at the second surface at an angle of 45°, just 3° greater than the critical angle, the light is totally reflected according to the law of reflection. Having thus been deviated through 90°, the light passes normally through the third surface without further deviation. The prism has therefore acted like a plane mirror.

Dispersion. It was known to the ancients that sunlight, on passing through transparent crystals and jewels of various kinds, would

Fig. F. Refraction of white sunlight into its spectrum colors.

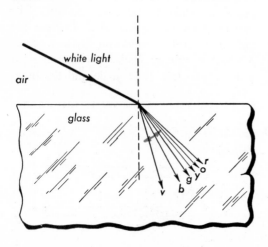

produce brilliant colors of light. The early philosophers, attempting to explain the phenomenon, attributed the origin of the colors to the crystal itself. It was Newton who first demonstrated with prisms that the colors were already present in the white sunlight and that the function of the prism was to separate the colors by refracting them in different directions.

We have already seen how light of one color is refracted at the boundary of a medium like glass or water and how it is deviated by a prism. It may be seen in Fig. F how, **with white light, each color is refracted by a different amount** to produce its own angle of deviation. **Red light is refracted least and violet light is refracted most.**

The angular spread of all the colors produced by sending white light through a prism is called the **dispersion** and the band of color so produced is called **a spectrum.** See Fig. G.

If white light is sent through a group of similar prisms made of different substances each prism will be found to have a different dispersion. This can be demonstrated for solids by **flint** and **crown glass prisms,** and for liquids by **kerosene, carbon dioxide,** and **water.** It will be noted that the two glass prisms in Fig. H, one of flint glass and the other of crown glass, produce quite different dispersions. The liquid prisms, produced by filling thin-walled glass troughs with liquid, also disperse light by different amounts.

Since different colors are refracted by different amounts, the index of refraction is different for each color. In a vacuum all

Fig. G. Refraction at both surfaces of a prism produces higher dispersion.

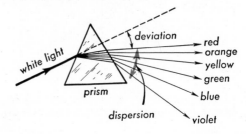

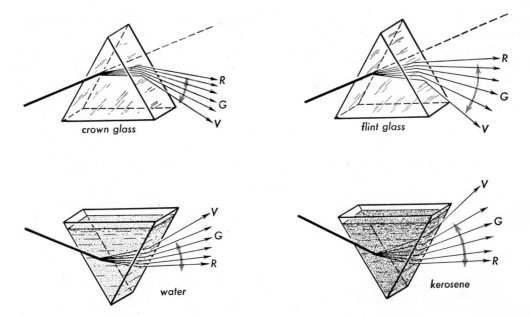

Fig. H. Illustrating the relative dispersions of solid as well as liquid prisms.

colors travel with the same speed, 186,300 mi/sec, but in a transparent medium, like glass or water, they travel considerably slower and at different speeds. Among the spectrum colors, red travels the fastest and violet the slowest, with the speeds of all other colors somewhere in between. In air there is very little dispersion and in a vacuum there is absolutely none. This latter statement is proved by the fact that when the dark star of an eclipsing binary passes in front of its brighter companion, all colors disappear and reappear simultaneously. If one color were to travel slightly faster than another, the dip in stellar intensity for that color would have plenty of time in its many years of travel to the earth to get ahead.

The refractive indices for a number of transparent solids are given in Table 1. It will be noted that although the values for any one substance do not vary greatly between colors, the values for blue and violet are the largest and those for orange and red are the smallest. Note the relatively high values for diamond and the relatively low values for ice.

Table 1. Refractive Index for Several Transparent Solids

Substance Color wave length λ × 10^{-8} cm	Violet 4100	Blue 4700	Green 5300	Yellow 5900	Orange 6100	Red 6700
crown glass............	1.5380	1.5310	1.5260	1.5225	1.5216	1.5200
light flint...............	1.6040	1.5960	1.5910	1.5875	1.5867	1.5850
dense flint.............	1.6980	1.6836	1.6738	1.6670	1.6650	1.6620
quartz.................	1.5570	1.5510	1.5468	1.5438	1.5432	1.5420
diamond...............	2.4580	2.4439	2.4260	2.4172	2.4150	2.4100
ice....................	1.3170	1.3136	1.3110	1.3087	1.3080	1.3060

In the physics laboratory the index of refraction is determined with a prism, and usually one having an angle of 60°. The prism is placed on a spectrometer where the spectrum of white light is observed in a small telescope and the angle of minimum deviation is measured for each color separately. As the prism is slowly turned, the spectrum widens or narrows continuously and each color goes through its own angle of minimum deviation just as the rays of that same color make equal angles with the two prism faces.

Summary

When light crosses the boundary from one medium into one of lower index, the refracted beam is deviated away from the surface normal.

When the ray of light in the more dense optical medium is incident at an angle greater than the critical angle, there is no allowed refraction and all of the light is reflected.

The phenomenon of total reflection is utilized in various optical devices and instruments, principally through the use of prisms.

When white light is refracted, it is broken up into a spectrum of colors: red, orange, yellow, green, blue, and violet. Red light is deviated the least, and violet light the most.

The refractive index of any given optical medium has a different index for the different parts of the spectrum. The index is greatest for violet light and decreases continuously for the spectrum colors to become least for red light.

Questions

1. What is the critical angle? How is it determined from the refractive index?

2. What is total reflection? How can it be demonstrated?

3. What is a total reflecting prism? How is it used?

4. What is dispersion? What kind of light is composed of all colors? Where do the colors come from? Name the colors in their proper order, starting with red.

5. What spectrum color is deviated the most? What color is deviated the least?

6. If 45° prisms were made of the six materials shown in Table 1, which one do you think would produce the largest dispersion?

7. For which color is the refractive index the greatest for a given optical material? For which color is it the least?

8. What would you propose as a project for the making of some device based upon principles developed in this lesson?

Problems

1. Calculate the critical angle for yellow light and crown glass.

2. Calculate the critical angle for violet light and diamond.

3. Calculate the critical angle for green light and ice.

4. If the critical angle of a piece of glass is 40°, what is its refractive index?

5. If the critical angle of a transparent material is 54°, what is its refractive index?

6.* Light is incident at an angle of 60° on a crown glass surface. Find (a) the angles of refraction for red and violet light and (b) the dispersion angle between the two colors.

7.* Light is incident on dense flint glass at an angle of 60°. Find (a) the angles of refraction for red and violet light and (b) the dispersion angle between the two colors?

8.* A ray of white light is incident on one facet of a diamond at an angle of 60°. Find the dispersion angle between red and violet.

9.* A 60° prism is made of dense flint glass. A ray of white light is incident on the first surface at an angle of 45°. Find (a) the total deviation for the red and violet light, and (b) the dispersion angle of the spectrum produced.

Light | **Lesson 12**

COLOR

Color vision is perhaps the most valued gift of nature. While color is for the most part a physiological phenomenon, its origin is considered by some to belong to the realm of physics. The science of color mixing has been made possible through the discovery that all colors can be completely analyzed by spreading them out into a prismatic spectrum.

When sunlight falls on a red rose, red yarn, red paint, or red glass, all of the colors except red are absorbed and do not get through or out again. The red, as it passes through, is reflected and refracted by the fine grains of pigment and comes out in all directions as shown in Fig. A.

Not all of the other colors are completely absorbed, for a small amount of each color is reflected from the first surface the white light strikes.

Fig. A. Illustration of color.

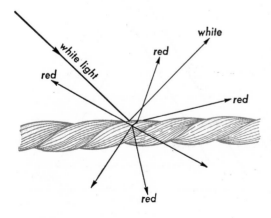

Mixing Spectrum Colors. Over a period of many years different color charts and color theories have been proposed, some of them good and some of them bad. Although the most successful theories have, of necessity, been detailed and complicated, only some simplification of their concepts and an explanation of their common principles can be given here.

As a starting point, consider the experiment shown in Fig. B in which a narrow beam of white light from a carbon arc and

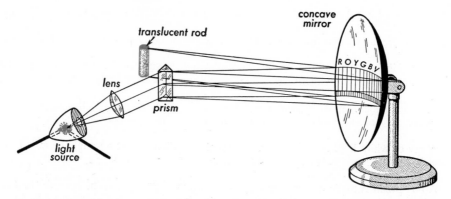

Fig. B. Experimental arrangement for mixing pure spectrum colors to form all primary colors.

lens falls on a glass prism and is spread out into a complete spectrum. With the prism located near the center of curvature of a large concave mirror, all colors after reflection are brought to a focus on a translucent glass rod where, combined again, they produce white. A large white card is next held in front of the mirror to act as a screen to control the colors that are permitted to mix at the rod. By screening off violet, blue, and green, for example, the remaining colors—red, orange, and yellow—come together and the rod appears orange.

We proceed to divide the spectrum into three equal parts as shown at the lower left in Fig. C and to call these parts the **additive primaries.** When red and orange are allowed to mix, the rod appears a bright red; when yellow and green are mixed, the rod appears bright green; and when blue and violet are mixed, it appears blue-violet. As colors these additive primaries—red, green, and blue—appear like the three large circular areas at the upper left in Fig. C.

The next step is to mix two **primary colors** at a time and to observe their resultant color mixture. When primary red and primary green mix at the glass rod, they produce yellow; red and blue produce magenta; and green and blue produce cyan, a light blue-green. These colors, the so-called **subtractive primaries,** are shown by the three large circles at the upper right in Fig. C and by the

overlapping areas at the upper left. The pure spectrum colors that go to make up each subtractive primary are shown at the lower right.

The Color Triangle. The color triangle, as illustrated in Fig. D, is a triangular arrangement of the additive and subtractive primaries with white at the center. Red, green, and blue are located at the corners, while magenta, yellow, and cyan are located at the sides. The order of the colors is such that the sum of any two additive primaries at the corners gives the subtractive primary between them on the sides, and the sum of all three gives white at the center.

Fig. D. Diagram of the color triangle, with the additive primaries at the corners and the subtractive primaries at the sides.

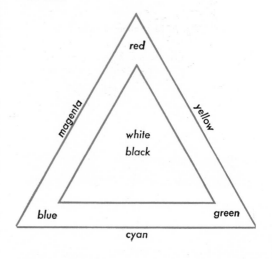

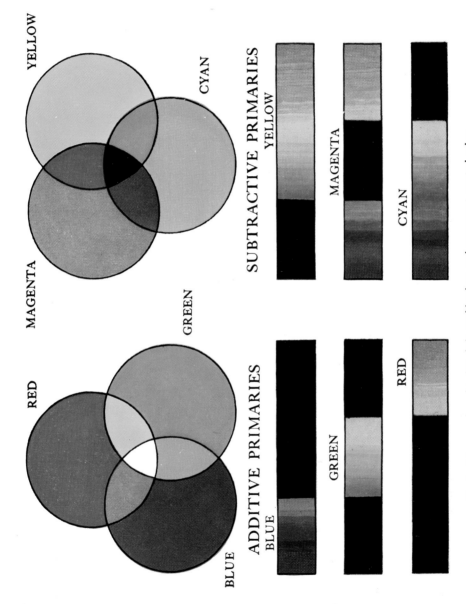

Fig C. Primary colors showing their combinations and component spectral colors.

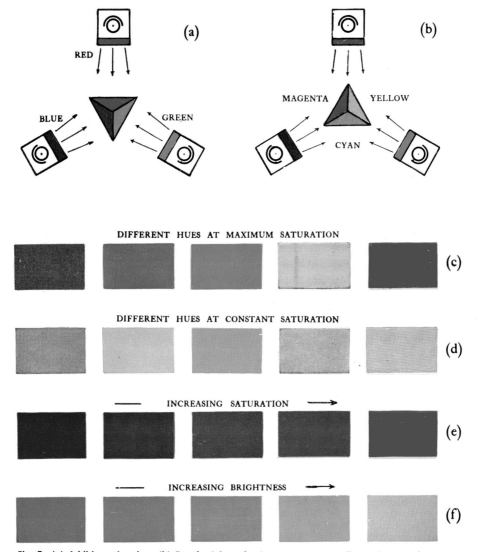

Fig. E. (a) Additive primaries. (b) Equal mixing of primary pairs. (c) Different hues at their maximum saturation values. (d) Different hues at constant saturation and equal brightness. (e) The same hue at constant brightness but increasing saturation. (f) The same hue at constant saturation but increasing brightness.

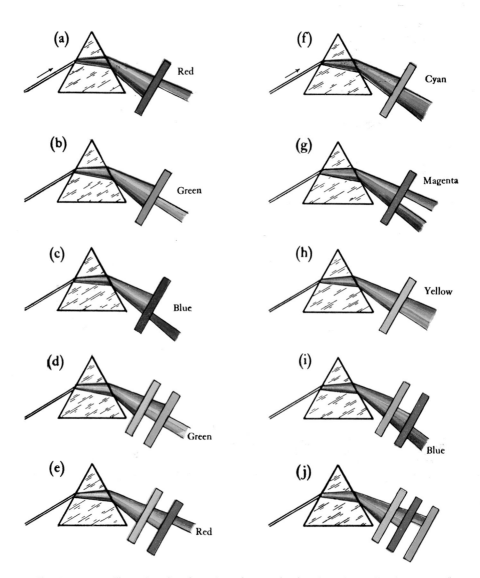

Fig. F. Diagram illustrating the absorption of spectral colors by colored filters and the subtractive method of color mixing.

Colors opposite each other on the color triangle are **complementary**. *Two colors are said to be complementary if when added together they produce white.* Magenta and green are complementary, for when added together, as can be seen from their spectral distributions in Fig. C, they contain all of the spectrum colors of white light. Similarly red and cyan, as well as yellow and blue, are complementary.

Additive Method of Color Mixing. The mixing of colored lights described in the two preceding sections is called the additive method of color mixing and differs greatly from the subtractive method to be described in the following section. An interesting experiment for demonstrating the additive method is shown in Fig. E. Three boxes containing white lights are arranged to illuminate separately the three sides of a white pyramid. A matched set of glass filters, one for each of the additive primary hues—red, green, and blue, respectively—are placed in front of each box opening, thereby illuminating the pyramid faces as shown in the left-hand diagram.

Upon rotating the pyramid slowly a point is reached, as shown in the right-hand diagram, where pairs of lights mix in equal amounts on each of the three faces. These mixtures are the subtractive primaries, magenta, yellow, and cyan. As the pyramid turns from position (a) to position (b), all variations of two colors are seen on the pyramid faces. Television in full color is produced by the additive method of color mixing.

Subtractive Method of Color Mixing. This is the method most familiar to everyone, the method used in the mixing of pigments to produce various colored paints. For this purpose the subtractive primaries, **magenta, yellow,** and **cyan,** often referred to by artists as **red, yellow,** and **blue,** are the most useful. The mixing in equal amounts of any two subtractive primaries will produce the addi-

tive primary lying between them on the color triangle. When cyan and yellow paints are mixed, the result is green.

At first it seems strange that yellow and cyan, neither one of which has the appearance of an additive primary, should produce green when mixed together. A spectrum analysis of these two colors, as shown at the lower right in Fig. C, shows that green and yellow are spectrum colors common to both.

Mixing by the subtractive method is demonstrated with prisms and filters in Fig. F. To see what happens to each spectral hue in each filter, the white light is first spread out into its complete spectrum. To illustrate, the yellow filter alone in diagram (h) absorbs blue and violet, and the cyan filter alone in (f) absorbs red and orange. When both are inserted as in diagram (d), only green and yellow are transmitted. To the eye this mixture appears bright green. The other two pairs of filters in diagrams (e) and (i) give the other two primaries red and blue.

To carry these experimental demonstrations to the mixing of paint, each little grain of pigment is like a piece of colored glass (see Fig. G). Assuming the oil in which the yellow pigment is imbedded to be transparent, white light entering the paint is reflected and refracted as shown. Wherever blue or

Fig. G. Illustration of the absorption of blue and violet light by yellow paint and the emission of red, orange, yellow, and green.

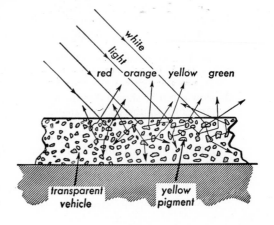

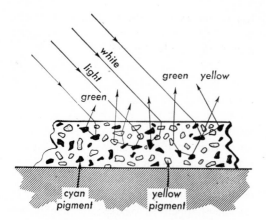

Fig. H. When blue and yellow paints are mixed together, green and yellow are the only pure spectral colors transmitted by both pigments.

violet rays pass through the yellow pigment grains, they are absorbed. After many reflections and refractions, the red, orange, yellow, and green can still escape. Together

these four colors (see Fig. C) appear as yellow.

When yellow and cyan pigments are mixed together as illustrated by the detailed diagram in Fig. H, only green and yellow light is transmitted by both pigments.

The essential difference between the additive method and subtractive method of color mixing is just that suggested by the name: in the additive method the resultant color is just the **sum** of the two constituents used to produce it, and in the subtractive method it is just the **difference** between the two. Addition always produces a brighter color and subtraction produces a darker color. Just as the additive mixing of red, green, and blue produces white, so the subtractive mixing of magenta, yellow, and cyan produces black. Similarly, two complementary colors, when mixed additively, produce white, and when mixed subtractively, produce black.

Summary

The subject of color mixing is technically based upon the spectrum of white light. The visible spectrum is divided roughly into three bands of color.

A simplified system combines the six colors into three pairs: red plus orange, yellow plus green, and blue plus violet. Together these are called the additive primaries: red, green, and blue; they occupy the corner positions of the color triangle.

There are two methods of color mixing: the additive method and the subtractive method. The subtractive primaries are magenta, yellow, and cyan. These are produced by pairs of the additive primaries, and they occupy the side positions on the color triangle.

Questions

1. How are the six spectrum colors divided to give the additive primaries? What spectrum colors produce the subtractive primaries?

2. What is the color triangle? What colors are located at the corners? What colors are located at the sides? What mixtures go in the center?

3. How can it be shown that the actual colors of the spectrum combine to form the colors shown on the color triangle? Describe the experiment.

4. What are complementary colors? When two complementary colors are added together, what spectrum colors would be present? If they are mixed subtractively, what spectrum colors would be present?

5. Which of the two methods of color mixing produces brighter colors as the result of mixing?

6. Which of the following colors is the brightest: red, yellow, or blue?

7. The following pairs of colors are mixed as pigments: (a) magenta and cyan, (b) yellow and cyan, (c) magenta and yellow, (d) red and cyan, and (e) magenta and green? What is the resultant color in each case?

8. Make a diagram of the color triangle from memory.

9. What color added to red will give (a) white, (b) magenta, and (c) yellow?

10. What color mixed subtractively with yellow will produce (a) green, (b) red, and (c) black?

11. Make a diagram and briefly explain how yellow and cyan pigments when (a) mixed as paints can produce green. (b) Do the pigment particles themselves become green?

12. What project would you like to undertake in the construction of a device for demonstrating some of the principles of color mixing?

Light | Lesson 13

MAGNIFYING POWER—*Laboratory*

This experiment on the magnifying power of a single converging lens of short focal length is described in the accompanying LABORATORY EXERCISES. You will determine magnification from direct measurements of object and image sizes.

Light | Lesson 14

THE EYE AND OPTICAL INSTRUMENTS

The Camera. Since the photographic camera employs but a single lens unit, it may be considered as one of the simplest of all optical instruments. As illustrated by the roll-film camera in Fig. A, a converging lens forms a **real** and **inverted image** on the film. If the object is far away, the light rays approaching the lens are nearly parallel and the image is formed at the focal plane. If the object is close up, the image will be formed beyond the focal plane as shown in the diagram.

To permit distant landscapes or "close ups" to be taken with the same camera, a bellows

Fig. A. Diagram of the image formation by a camera.

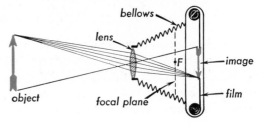

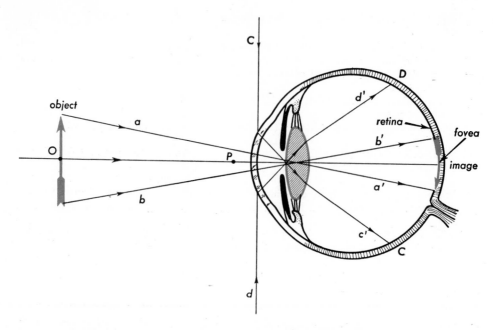

Fig. B. The human eye is similar to a camera. All retinal images are inverted.

is used, allowing the lens distance to be varied at will. Motion of the lens to the proper image distance is called **focusing.**

Only a simple converging lens is used in the cheapest of cameras, which means that all of the common defects of images are present to give rise to a slightly blurred or diffuse image. In more expensive cameras, however, the most objectionable defects are fairly well corrected by a compound lens made of several individual lenses.

The Eye. When light from a distant object passes through the lens system of the eye, it is refracted and brought to a focus on the retina. There a real but inverted image of the object is formed. It is a most amazing fact that while all retinal images are inverted, as shown in Fig. B, they are interpreted by the brain as being erect.

Accommodation is the ability to focus the eyes on near and far objects. In a camera the focusing of a picture on the photographic film or plate is accomplished by moving the lens toward or away from the film. In the human eye, however, **focusing is brought about by changing the shape of the crystalline lens.** This is accomplished by a rather complicated system of ligaments and muscles. Because of a tension which exists in the lens capsule the crystalline lens, if completely free, would tend to become spherical in shape. The edge of the lens is surrounded by the **ciliary muscle,** which, by contracting, causes the lens to bulge out. This reduces the focal length of the lens, bringing nearby objects to focus on the retina. When the ciliary muscle relaxes, the suspensory ligaments, being under tension, pull at the edges of the lens, thus tending to flatten it. Under these conditions the focal length increases, bringing distant objects to focus on the retina. This is the accommodation process.

The normal eye is most relaxed when it is focused for parallel light, i.e., for objects far away. To study the detail of an object, however, the object should be brought close to the eye. The reason for this is that the closer the object is to the eye, the larger is the image formed on the retina. A distance of about

(a)   (b)

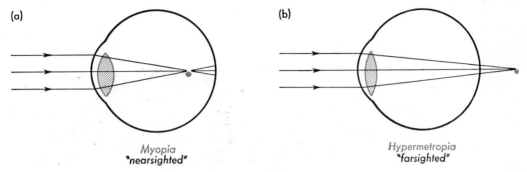

Myopia
"nearsighted"

Hypermetropia
"farsighted"

Fig. C. Typical eye conditions of certain humans.

10 in. is found to be the distance of most distinct vision. Prolonged observation at distances of 10 in. or less will result in a considerable amount of fatigue and eyestrain.

Eye Correction with Spectacle Lenses. As the average person grows older, the crystalline lens of the eye tends to harden and the muscles that control it to grow weaker, thus making accommodation more and more difficult. The existence of these conditions is referred to as *presbyopia.* The speed of the hardening varies between individuals. If the length of the eyeball is such that parallel incident rays converge to a point in front of the retina (see Fig. C(a)), the person is nearsighted and is said by the eye specialist to have *myopia.* If parallel incident rays converge to a point back of the retina, as in diagram (b), the person is farsighted and is said to have *hypermetropia.*

To correct these defects a diverging spectacle lens of the proper focal length is placed in front of the myopic eye and a converging lens of the proper focal length in front of the hypermetropic eye. The function of such lenses is shown in Fig. D. For the nearsighted eye, rays from a nearby object at some point **P** will, in the absence of spectacles, come to focus on the fovea **F.** Insertion of the proper diverging lens will now diverge parallel rays as if they came from **P** and thus bring a distant object to focus at **F.** For the farsighted eye a converging lens adds some convergence to the incoming rays before they meet the eye lens and thus enable distant objects to be seen in good focus. To see close at hand this same eye requires the use of a converging lens of still greater power. In other words this person should wear bifocals, lenses whose upper and lower halves have different focal lengths.

The Telescope. History informs us that the first telescope was probably constructed in Holland in 1608 by an obscure spectacle

Fig. D. Nearsighted and farsighted eyes can be corrected by the proper selection of spectacle lenses.

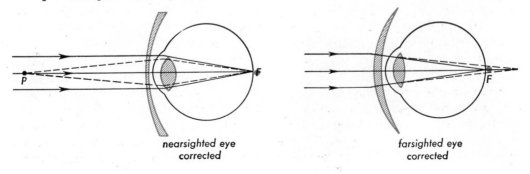

nearsighted eye
corrected

farsighted eye
corrected

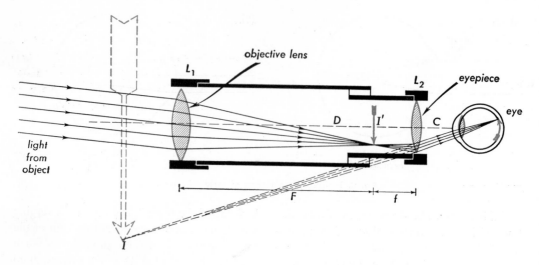

Fig. E. Illustrating the paths of light rays in a simple astronomical telescope.

lens grinder, Hans Lippershey. A few months later Galileo, upon hearing that objects at a distance may be made to appear close at hand by means of two lenses, designed and made with his own hands the first authentic telescope. The elements of this telescope are still in existence and may be seen on exhibit in Florence, Italy.

Astronomical telescopes today are practically the same in principle as they were in the earliest days of their development. A diagram of a small telescope is shown in Fig. E. Light rays from a single point of a far

Fig. F. Cutaway of a prism binocular showing the lenses and reflecting prisms. (Courtesy of Bausch & Lomb Optical Company)

distant object are shown entering the **objective lens** as a parallel beam. These rays are brought to a focus and form a point image at I'. In a similar manner, parallel sets of rays from other points of the same object (not shown) will form point images in the focal plane of the objective. Assuming that the distant object is an arrow pointing upward, the image, as shown in the diagram by a red arrow, is **real** and **inverted**.

The function of the second lens in a telescope is to magnify the image formed by the objective. For this purpose a converging lens of short focus, called the **eyepiece,** is usually used.

The magnifying power of a telescope is defined as the ratio between the angle subtended at the eye by the final image I and the angle subtended at the eye by the object itself. In other words, it is the number of times larger an object appears to be when viewed with the telescope. When plane geometry is applied to a simple light-ray diagram of a telescope, it is found that the magnifying power is equal to the ratio of the focal lengths of the two lenses.

$$\text{magnifying power} = \frac{F}{f} \qquad (1)$$

where **F** is the focal length of the objective, and **f** is the focal length of the eyepiece.

Prism Binoculars. Prism binoculars are in reality a pair of twin telescopes mounted side by side, one for each of the two eyes. The objective lenses in front and the eyepieces at the rear are converging lenses as in the astronomical telescope, but each pair of total reflecting prisms (see Fig. F) inverts the rays to give erect images. The doubling back of the light rays has the advantage of enabling long focus objective lenses to be used in short tubes, thus giving higher magnification. In addition to good achromatic lenses and accurately ground prisms, there are three features that go to make up good binoculars: these are (1) *magnification*, (2) *field of view*, and (3) *light gathering power*.

For hand-held use, binoculars with a 6-, 7-, or 8-power magnification are most generally useful. Glasses with powers above 8 are desirable but require a tripod mount to hold them steady. For powers less than 4, lens aberrations usually offset the magnification and the average person can usually see better with the unaided eyes.

Summary

The simplest optical instruments in principle are those involving one lens. The photographic camera and the human eye may be considered in this category. The images formed by both of these devices are real and inverted.

Nearsighted and farsighted people have myopia and hypermetropia, respectively. Myopia can be corrected by wearing diverging spectacle lenses, hypermetropia by wearing converging lenses.

The astronomical telescope consists of two lenses. The largest lens, called the objective, has a long focal length and forms a real and inverted image of the object received. The eyepiece is a short focus lens and is used as a magnifier to observe the real image. The final image is formed on the retina of the eye.

Prism binoculars are similar to a pair of telescopes, side by side. Prisms are used to erect the inverted image as seen in the astronomical telescope.

Questions

1. What are the principal elements of a camera? What kind of an image does it form? How is focus accomplished?

2. What are the principal elements of the human eye? What kind of image is formed on the retina? How is focus accomplished? What is this process called?

3. What is myopia? What causes it? How can it be corrected optically?

4. What is hypermetropia? What causes it? How can it be corrected or improved?

5. How many lenses are required to make a telescope? What are they called?

6. What is the function of the objective lens? Why should it have a long focal length?

7. What is the function of the eyepiece? Why should it have a short focal length?

8. What determines the magnifying power of a telescope? Where is the final image formed?

9. In what ways do prism binoculars differ from an astronomical telescope? What do the prisms accomplish? How many prisms are required?

10. What would you consider as a good project for making some inexpensive device that utilizes or demonstrates the basic optical principles presented in this lesson?

Problems

1. A farsighted person sees distant objects clearly but cannot accommodate for objects close by. What focal length should his spectacles have if he is to read a book held 16 in. away?

2. A nearsighted person sees objects clearly at a distance of 12 in. (a) What kind of spectacle lenses should he use to see distant objects? (b) What should be the focal length?

3.* A person with myopia sees clearly objects 6 in. from his eyes. What focal length lenses should this person use to see things clearly (a) far away and (b) at 18 in.?

4. The objective lens of an astronomical telescope has a focal length of +8 ft, while the eyepiece has a focal length of +2 in. What is its magnifying power?

5. The eyepiece of a 12-power astronomical telescope has a focal length of +0.75 in. What is the focal length of the objective?

6. An astronomical telescope objective has a focal length of +60 cm. What focal length eyepiece will give it a magnification of 15?

7.* To an observer on the earth the moon subtends an angle of approximately 0.5 degrees. If a telescope objective lens with a focal length of +20 ft is used to photograph the moon, what will be the diameter of the image formed at the focal plane of the lens?

8. The objective lenses of a pair of binoculars have a focal length of 25 cm. What is the focal length of the eyepieces if the magnifying power is 7?

9.* A pair of prism binoculars (marked 8 × 50) have a magnification of 8. The objective lenses have a diameter of 50 millimeters and a focal length of 27 cm. Find (a) the focal length of the eyepieces and (b) the diameter of the image of the objective lenses formed by the eyepieces. (These images are the exit pupils of the binoculars.)

Light | Lesson 15

PRINCIPLES OF THE MICROSCOPE—*Laboratory*

This experiment involves the over-all magnification or magnifying power of two short focus lenses in tandem and is described in the accompanying LABORATORY EXERCISES. Measurements of object and image distances as well as object and image sizes are directly involved.

DIFFRACTION AND INTERFERENCE

Shadows. When light passes close to the edge of any object, it is bent in its path and travels on in a new direction. This bending of light around corners is called *diffraction*. In the preceding chapters light has been assumed to travel in straight lines and to obey the laws of reflection and refraction. Furthermore, according to the rectilinear propagation of light, it is customary to assume that an object will cast a sharp and well-defined shadow. A close examination of every shadow, however, shows that the edges are not sharp, but blurred and diffused.

If one is careful to choose a small source of light, such as the light emanating from a pinhole in a screen, the shadow of an object cast on a distant screen is bounded at the edges by narrow bands or fringes of light. To observe these effects the following simple experiment may be performed in a darkened room. A box containing a light bulb and a pinhole is placed on one side of the room and a ground glass observing screen or photographic film is placed on the other. The objects whose shadows are to be observed are

Fig. A. Photographs of the shadows cast by small objects. The narrow bands are due to the diffraction of light.

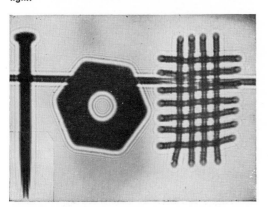

then placed about halfway between the source and the screen. This is the arrangement used in obtaining the original photographs reproduced in Fig. A. This is a photograph of light diffracted by a pin, a small hexagonal nut, and a piece of wire screen.

Huygens' Wave Theory of Light. The wave theory of light was first proposed by the English physicist, Robert Hooke, in 1665, and improved twenty years later by the Dutch scientist and mathematician, Christian Huygens.*

Everyone has at some time or other dropped a stone in a still pond of water and watched the waves spread slowly outward in ever-widening concentric circles. In the analogous case of a point source of light, the spreading waves form concentric spheres moving outward with the extremely high velocity of 186,300 mi/sec. This is represented diagrammatically in Fig. B. Each circle represents the crest of a wave so that the distance between consecutive circles is one wave length.

According to Huygens' principle every point on any wave front may be regarded as a new point source of waves. Regarding each

---

* Christian Huygens (1629-1695), famous Dutch physicist and contemporary of Isaac Newton. Born at The Hague in 1629, young Christian got his first ideas about waves and their propagation by watching the ripples on the canals about his home. Although his chief title-deed to immortality is his development of the wave theory of light, he made many and valuable contributions to mathematics and astronomy. He improved upon the method of grinding telescope lenses and discovered the Orion nebula, part of which is now known by his name. He was elected to the Royal Society of London in 1663, and delivered before that august body the first clear statement of the laws governing the collision of elastic bodies. He died a confirmed bachelor at The Hague in 1695.

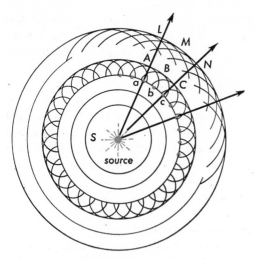

Fig. B. Diagram of waves spreading out from a point source. The secondary wavelets and new wave fronts illustrate Huygens' principle.

of any number of points like **a**, **b**, **c**, etc., as point sources like **S**, secondary wavelets spread out simultaneously as shown. The envelope of these an instant later is the new wave front **A**, **B**, **C**, etc., and still later the wave front **L**, **M**, **N**, etc. Although Huygens' principle at first hand might seem to be a useless play with circles, it has quite general application to many optical phenomena.

Diffraction at a Single Small Opening.

A direct experimental demonstration of

Fig. C. Diagram of the diffraction of waves at a small opening. Huygens' principle.

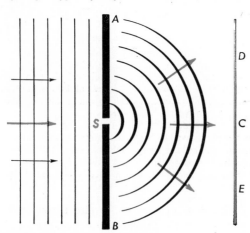

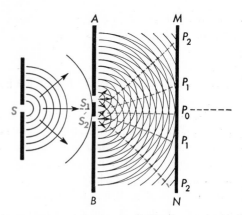

Fig. D. Diagram of Young's double-slit experiment illustrating the interference of light waves.

Huygens' principle is illustrated in Fig. C. Plane waves approaching a barrier **AB** from the left are reflected or absorbed at every point except at **S** where they are allowed to pass on through. When the experiment is carried out with water waves, one can see the waves spreading out in all directions as if **S** were a point source. The lines represent crests of waves, one wave length apart.

Young's Double-Slit Experiment.

The crucial test between Newton's corpuscular theory of light and Huygens' wave theory came in 1801 when Thomas Young performed his now famous interference experiment. This is represented schematically in Fig. D. Sunlight from a pinhole **S** was allowed to fall on a distant screen containing two pinholes, S_1 and S_2. The two sets of spherical waves emerging from the two holes interfered with each other in such a way as to form a symmetrical pattern of bands on another

Fig. E. Interference fringes produced by a double-slit as in Young's experiment.

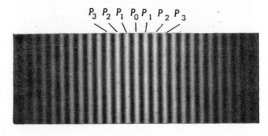

screen **MN**. This experiment is now regarded as the first definite proof that light is a wave motion.

For convenience it is now customary to repeat Young's experiment with narrow slits in place of pinholes. If **S**, **S₁**, and **S₂** in Fig. D represent the cross sections of three narrow slits, the light falling on the farther screen **MN** has the appearance of equidistant bands or fringes as shown by the photograph in Fig. E. The bright fringes correspond to the points **P₀**, **P₁**, **P₂**, etc., and the dark fringes to the points halfway between.

As the waves travel outward from each slit **S₁** and **S₂**, they cross each other only at points which lie along the dotted lines shown in the diagram. These represent the points where the crests of two waves come together and produce a maximum brightness. About halfway between these dotted lines lie other points where the crest of one wave and the trough of another cancel each other and produce darkness. This is called **interference.** Where the bright fringes are formed there is **constructive interference,** and where the dark fringes appear there is **destructive interference.**

Measuring the Wave Length of Light. A formula for the wave length of light can be derived from the geometry of Young's double-slit experiment as shown in Fig. F. Let **P** be the position of any bright fringe on the screen and **x** its distance from the central fringe at **P₀**. **P₀** is located on the perpendicular bisector of the double slit **S₁** and **S₂**. A

Fig. F. Geometrical relations for the double-slit experiment.

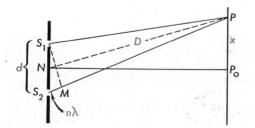

straight line from each slit to the point **P** is drawn, and with a compass of radius **S₁P** the arc of a circle **S₁M** is scribed. By this construction line **MP** is made equal to **S₁P** and the short line **S₂M** becomes the extra distance light must travel from the lower slit. To produce a bright fringe at **P** the interval **S₂M** must be equal to one whole wave length, two whole wave lengths, three whole wave lengths, etc., for only then will the waves from **S₁** and **S₂** arrive at **P** in phase. Therefore, **S₂M** must be equal to $n\lambda$, where **n** is a whole number, $n = 0, 1, 2, 3, 4$, etc., and λ is the wave length of the light.

Since the distance **d** between slit centers is extremely small compared with the distance **D** to the screen, line **S₁M** may be considered straight and at right angles to all three lines **S₁P**, **NP**, and **S₂P**. With corresponding sides mutually perpendicular to each other, triangles **S₁S₂M** and **NPP₀** are similar to each other. From the well-known theorem that corresponding sides of similar triangles are proportional,

$$\frac{n\lambda}{d} = \frac{x}{D}$$

or

$$\lambda = \frac{xd}{nD} \qquad (1)$$

If we let x_1 be the distance from the central fringe to the first one on either side, then $n = 1$, and the equation becomes

$$\lambda = x_1 \frac{d}{D} \qquad (2)$$

Because the fringes are evenly spaced, x_1 represents the spacing all along the pattern. By measuring the three distances **d**, **x**, and **D**, the wave length of light can be calculated. Repeated experiments, carefully performed, give the following results.

red,	$\lambda = 0.000066$ cm
orange,	$\lambda = 0.000061$ cm
yellow,	$\lambda = 0.000058$ cm
green,	$\lambda = 0.000054$ cm

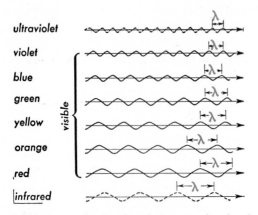

Fig. G. Diagram showing the relative wave lengths of light.

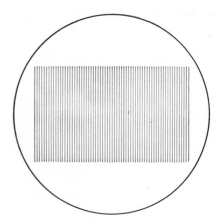

Fig. H. Schematic diagram of the grooves or rulings on a diffraction grafting.

| blue, | λ = 0.000046 cm |
| violet, | λ = 0.000042 cm |

As illustrated by waves in Fig. G, red light has the longest waves.

The Diffraction Grating. The diffraction grating is an optical device widely used in place of a prism for studying the spectrum and measuring the wave lengths of light. Gratings are made by ruling fine grooves with a diamond point either on a glass plate to produce a transmission grating or on a polished metal mirror to produce a reflecting grating. As illustrated in Fig. H, the rulings are all parallel and equally spaced. The best gratings are several inches in width and contain from 5000 to 30,000 lines/in.

If white light is sent through such a grating and then onto a distant screen, all of the different colors are spread out into a highly colored array consisting of a number of spectrum bands, each complete in itself from red to violet. Such a grating and the spectrum it is capable of producing are the subject of a laboratory experiment in another lesson.

Summary

White light travels in straight lines in a homogeneous medium and bends when it crosses the boundary separating two media, light also bends around the edges of solid matter. This bending around corners is called diffraction and, along with interference between the waves, gives rise to narrow bands of light along the edges of shadows.

Young's double-slit experiment is considered to be a proof of the wave nature of light. Light waves from two narrow and closely spaced slits interfere with each other and produce interference bands. Measurements of band widths, as well as the double-slit separation and distance from a screen, make it possible to determine the wave lengths of light.

The diffraction grating, made by thousands of parallel and equally spaced slits, or rulings, spreads light into its various spectrum colors or wave lengths. Grating measurements, similar to those for a double slit, permit accurate wave-length measurements of light waves.

Questions

1. What is diffraction? How does it modify the edges of otherwise sharp shadows?

2. What is Huygens' principle? How does it apply to light passing through a single, but narrow, opening?

3. What was Young's original double-slit experiment? Was diffraction involved? Where?

4. Is interference involved in Young's double-slit experiment? Where?

5. What is observed on the screen in Young's experiment? What quantities are measured for calculating the wave length of light?

6. What are the wave-length limits for visible light? What color of light has the longest wave length? The shortest wave length?

7. What is a diffraction grating used for? How is it made?

8. What device would you propose as a project you might undertake for demonstrating or for using the principles of interference and diffraction?

Problems

1. Red light of wave length 6×10^{-5} cm is used in observing the interference fringes produced by a double slit. If the centers of the two slit openings are 0.5 mm apart and the distance to the observing screen is 2 m, what is the fringe spacing?

2. Green light of wave length 5×10^{-5} cm falls on a double slit, and 2 m away on a white screen interference fringes are formed 5 mm apart. Calculate the double-slit separation.

3. Monochromatic light falls upon a double slit. The distance between the slit centers is 1.1 mm and the distance between consecutive fringes on a screen 5 m away is 0.3 cm. What is the wave length and the color of the light?

4. Light falling on a double slit with a spacing of 1 mm forms fringes with a 2.1-mm spacing on a screen 5 m away. (a) Calculate the wave length of the light. (b) What is its color?

5. Light of wave length 0.000054 cm falls on a double slit with a spacing of 0.5 mm. How far away should a screen be located from the double slit if the fringes are to be 2 mm apart?

6. Light of wave length 0.000061 cm falls on a double slit and produces 8 fringes per centimeter on a screen located 2.5 meters away. What is the double-slit spacing?

Light | **Lesson 17**

POLARIZATION OF LIGHT

The experiments described in the preceding lesson illustrating the **diffraction** and **interference** of light are generally regarded as proof that **light is a wave motion.** Although such experiments enable the physi- cist to measure accurately the wave lengths of light, they give no information of the kinds of waves involved. The reason for this is that all types of waves, under the proper conditions, will exhibit diffraction and interference.

The desired information in the case of light waves is found in another group of phenomena known as **polarized light**. Some of the phenomena, which will be described in this lesson, are considered to be a proof that **light is a transverse wave motion** in contrast with the longitudinal wave motion in sound.

Plane-Polarized Light. A better understanding of the experiments to be described can best be attained by first presenting the graphical methods of representing transverse waves. We assume at the outset that each light wave is a transverse wave whose vibrations are along straight lines at right angles to the direction of propagation. (See Sound, Lesson 6, Fig. A.) Furthermore, we assume that a beam of ordinary light consists of millions of such waves, each with its own plane of vibration, and that there are waves vibrating in all planes with equal probability. Looking at such a beam end-on as in Fig. A, there should be just as many waves vibrating in one plane as there are vibrating in any other. This then can be referred to as perfect symmetry.

If, by some means or other, all the waves in a beam of light are made to vibrate in planes parallel to each other, the light is said to be plane-polarized. Diagrams illustrating

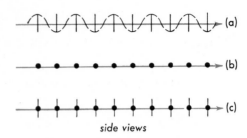

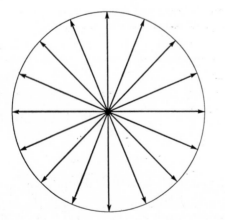

Fig. A. End-on view of a beam of unpolarized light illustrating schematically the equal probability of all planes of vibration.

side views

Fig. B. Diagrams illustrating plane-polarized rays of light.

such light are shown in Fig. B. The top diagram (a) represents plane-polarized light waves traveling to the right and vibrating in a vertical plane, while the second diagram (b) represents a ray of plane-polarized light vibrating in a horizontal plane. The dotted line indicating waves in diagram (a) is usually omitted.

It can be shown that a beam of ordinary unpolarized light, vibrating in all planes, may be regarded as being made up of two kinds of vibrations only, half of the waves vibrating in a vertical plane as in diagram (a) and the other half vibrating perpendicular to it as in diagram (b). Diagram (c), therefore, represents ordinary unpolarized light.

Polarization by Reflection. When ordinary unpolarized light is incident at an angle of about 57° on the polished surface of a plate of glass, the reflected light is plane-polarized. This fact was first discovered by Etienne Malus, a French physicist, in 1808. The experiment usually performed to demonstrate his discovery is illustrated in Fig. C.

A beam of unpolarized light **AB** is incident at an angle of 57° on the first glass surface at **B**. This light is again reflected at the same angle by a second glass plate **C** placed parallel to the first, as in diagram (a). If now the lower plate is rotated about the line **BC** by slowly turning the pedestal on which it is mounted, the intensity of the reflected beam **CD** is found to decrease slowly and vanish completely at an angle of 90°. With further rotation the reflected beam **CD** appears again,

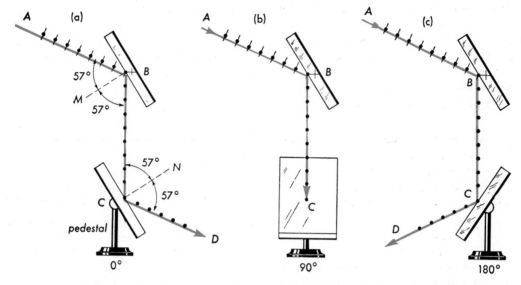

Fig. C. Common experiment performed to demonstrate the polarization of light by reflection from a smooth glass surface.

reaching a maximum at an angle of 180° as shown in diagram (c). Continued rotation causes the intensity to decrease to zero again at 270° and to reappear and reach a maximum at 360°, the starting point as in diagram (a). During this one complete rotation the angle of incidence on the lower plate, as well as the upper, has remained at 57°.

The explanation of the above experiment is made clearer by a detailed study of what happens to ordinary light reflected at the

Fig. D. Light reflected from glass at an angle of 57° is plane polarized, while the refracted light is only partially plane polarized.

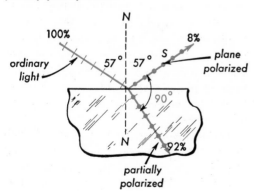

polarizing angle of 57° from glass. As illustrated in Fig. D, 8% of the light is reflected as plane-polarized light vibrating in the plane at right angles to the plane of incidence, and the other 92% is refracted as partially plane-polarized light, 42% vibrating perpendicular to the plane of incidence and 50% vibrating parallel to the plane of incidence. The plane of incidence is defined as the plane passing through the incident ray and the ray normal **NN**. In nearly all diagrams the plane of the page is the plane of incidence.

If in Fig. D the angle of incidence is changed to some other value than 57°, the reflected beam will not be plane-polarized but will contain a certain amount of light vibrating parallel to the plane of incidence. In general, the light reflected from a transparent medium like glass or water is only partially plane-polarized, and only at a certain angle, called the **polarizing angle,** is it plane-polarized. It was Sir David Brewster, a Scottish physicist, who first discovered that **at the polarizing angle the reflected and refracted rays are 90° apart.** This is now known as **Brewster's law.**

(a)   (b)

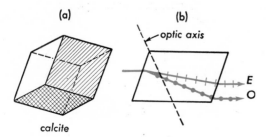

calcite

Fig. E. Diagrams of calcite and its behavior with light.

The polarizing angle ϕ for any optical substance of refractive index μ is given by

$$\tan \phi = \mu \qquad (1)$$

Double Refraction. The double refraction of light by Iceland spar (calcite) was first observed by a Swedish physician, Erasmus Bartholinus, in 1669, and later studied in detail by Huygens and Newton. Nearly all crystalline substances are now known to exhibit the phenomenon. The following are but a few samples of crystals which show the effect: **calcite, quartz, mica, sugar, topaz, selenite, aragonite,** and **ice.** Calcite and quartz are of particular importance because they are used extensively in the manufacture of special optical instruments.

Calcite as found in nature always has the characteristic shape shown in Fig. E(a)

Not only is light doubly refracted by calcite but both rays are found to be plane-polarized. One ray, called the **ordinary ray,** is polarized with its vibrations in one plane, and the other ray, called the **extraordinary ray,** is polarized with its vibrations in a plane

Fig. F. Only one ray obeys Snell's law in double refraction.

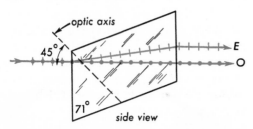

side view

at right angles to the first. This polarization is illustrated by **dots** and **lines,** and can be proved by a glass plate rotated as plate **C** in Fig. C, or with some other analyzing device like a **polarizing film.** These latter devices will be described in the next two sections.

Since the two opposite faces of a calcite crystal are always parallel to each other, the two refracted rays always emerge parallel to the incident light and are therefore parallel to each other. If the incident light falls perpendicularly upon the surface of the crystal, as in Fig. F, the extraordinary ray will be refracted away from the normal and come out parallel to, but displaced from, the incident beam, and the ordinary ray will pass straight through without deviation.

In general, the **O** ray obeys the ordinary laws of refraction, that is, it obeys Snell's law. In this way the crystal acts like glass or water. The **E** ray obeys no such simple law, behaves quite abnormally, and does not obey Snell's law.

In other words, the **O** ray travels with the same velocity regardless of its direction through the crystal, whereas the velocity of the **E** ray is different in different directions. This is the origin of the designations ordinary and extraordinary. Along the optic axis all vibrations travel with the same speed and there is no double refraction.

Polarization by Selective Absorption. When ordinary light enters a crystal of tourmaline, double refraction takes place in much the same way that it does in calcite, but with this difference: one ray, the so-called **O** ray, is entirely absorbed by the crystal, while the other ray, the **E** ray, passes on through. This phenomenon is called **selective absorption** because the crystal absorbs light waves vibrating in one plane and not those vibrating in the other.

Tourmaline crystals take in ordinary light, dispose of the **O** vibrations, and transmit plane-polarized light is illustrated in Fig. G (a). When two such crystals are lined up

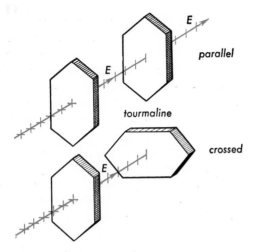

Fig. G. Tourmaline crystals polarize light.

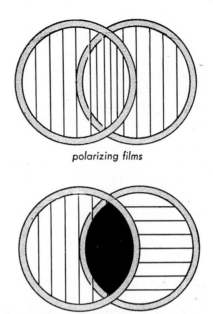

Fig. H. Polarizing films in the parallel and crossed positions.

parallel, with one behind the other, the plane-polarized light from the first crystal passes through the second with little loss in intensity. If either crystal is turned at 90° to the other, i.e., in the **cross position,** the light is completely absorbed and none passes through.

The behavior of tourmaline and similar optical substances is due to the molecular structure of the crystal. To draw an analogy, the regularly spaced molecules of a single crystal are like the regularly spaced trees in an orchard or grove. If one tries to run between the rows of trees carrying a very long pole held at right angles to the direction of motion, the pole must be held in a vertical position. If it is held in the horizontal plane, the runner will be stopped.

A more satisfactory substance for this purpose which does transmit white light is a manufactured material known as "Polaroid." This material is made in the form of very thin films which have the general appearance of a plastic and is made from small needle-shaped crystals of an organic compound **iodo-** **sulphate of quinine.** Lined up parallel to each other and embedded in a **nitrocellulose mastic,** these crystals act like tourmaline by absorbing one component of polarization and transmitting the other.

Two such films mounted separately in rings between thin glass plates are shown schematically in Fig. H. In the crossed position no light can pass through both films, whereas in the parallel position white light vibrating in the plane indicated by the parallel lines is transmitted. Polarizing films of this kind are finding many practical applications, particularly wherever glaring light is not desired. The glaring light reflected at an angle from a table top, a book, a window pane, the water, or the road ahead when driving a car, is polarized and can be partly eliminated by polarizing films.

Summary

A beam of light is ordinarily unpolarized and consists of transverse waves with as many waves vibrating in one plane as in any other.

Plane-polarized light is composed of waves all vibrating in the same plane. Plane-polarized light can be produced by (a) reflection, (b) double refraction, and (c) selective absorption.

When light is incident at the proper angle on a clear, transparent substance like glass, water, plastics, etc., the reflected light is plane polarized. The proper angle is called the polarizing angle ϕ and is given by Brewster's law,

$$\tan \phi = \mu$$

When a ray of unpolarized light falls on the face of certain crystals, the refracted light is composed of two different rays. Both these rays are plane polarized, and their planes of vibration are at right angles to each other. This is called double refraction.

Some crystals show a strong absorption for one of the refracted rays but transmit the other. This is called selective absorption.

Questions

1. What are transverse waves? What is meant by unpolarized light?

2. What is plane-polarized light? How is unpolarized light broken down into two plane-polarized components?

3. What are the three methods of polarizing light? Can sound waves be polarized?

4. What is Brewster's law? What is meant by the polarizing angle? Is refracted light ever plane-polarized?

5. What is double refraction? What is the nature of the light in the refracted rays?

6. Do the O and E rays obey Snell's law? Is it possible to obtain only one refracted ray in a crystal like calcite?

7. What is selective absorption? What is Polaroid? Where is Polaroid used? What is tourmaline?

8. What simple device would you propose to make as a project for demonstrating or utilizing some of the principles introduced in this lesson?

Problems

1. What is the polarizing angle for a dense flint glass having a refractive index of 1.720?

2. What is the polarizing angle for water, with its refractive index of 1.33?

3. Find the polarizing angle for diamond, with its refractive index of 2.41.

4. If the polarizing angle of a transparent plastic is found to be 55°, what is the refractive index?

5. What is the refractive index of flint glass if the polarizing angle is 59°?

6.* If the refractive index for a plastic is 1.45, what is the angle of refraction for a ray of light incident at the polarizing angle?

7.* Light is incident at the polarizing angle on the surface of a block of glass of index 1.65. Find the angle of deviation for the refracted ray.

8. The refractive index for the ordinary ray in calcite is 1.658. Find the angle of deviation if the angle of incidence is 30°.

Light | **Lesson 18**

RAINBOWS, BLUE SKIES, AND RED SUNSETS

The Rainbow. The rainbow is nature's most spectacular display of the spectrum of white light. The required conditions for the appearance of the phenomenon are that the sun be shining in one part of the sky and the rain be falling in the opposite part of the sky. Turning one's back to the sun, the bright primary bow and sometimes the fainter secondary bow, with colors reversed, are seen as the arcs of circles. From a high vantage point or an airplane, these bows may form complete circles whose common center lies in the direction of the observer's shadow.

The general characteristics of the **primary** and **secondary bows** are satisfactorily accounted for by considering only the reflection and refraction of light by spherical raindrops. To understand how the phenomenon arises, we first confine our attention to an individual raindrop as shown in Fig. A. A ray of sunlight is shown entering a single raindrop at a point **A** near the top. At this point some of the light is reflected (not shown), and the remainder is refracted into the liquid sphere. At this first refraction the light is dispersed into its spectrum colors, violet being deviated the most and red the least.

Arriving at the opposite side of the drop, each color is partly refracted out into the air (not shown) and partly reflected back into the liquid. Reaching the surface at the lower boundary, each color is again reflected (not shown) and refracted. This second refraction is quite similar to that of a prism (see Light, Lesson 11, Fig. G), where refraction at the second surface increases the dispersion already produced at the first. This is the path

Fig. A. Dispersion of sunlight by a single raindrop. (Primary rainbow)

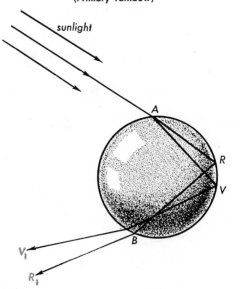

Fig. B. Dispersion of sunlight by a single raindrop. (Secondary rainbow)

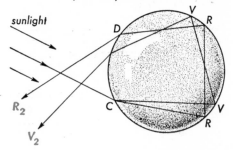

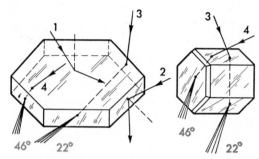

Fig. D. Typical forms of ice crystals showing reflected and refracted rays of sunlight giving rise to halos and "mock suns."

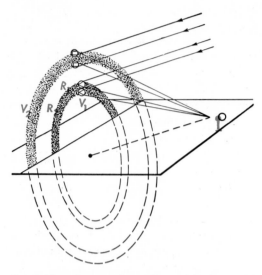

Fig. C. The primary and secondary rainbows as seen by an observer at O.

of the light in thousands of drops giving rise to the bright primary rainbow.

In Fig. B a ray of sunlight, coming from the same direction as in Fig. A, is shown entering a single raindrop at a point **C** near the bottom. After one refraction and two internal reflections, the light is again refracted and dispersed, this time in a direction not greatly different from that in Fig. A. This is the path of the light in thousands of drops giving rise to the fainter secondary rainbow.

As shown in Fig. C, the primary bow appears inside the secondary bow and arises from sunlight entering the tops of drops prop-

erly located. Those in a region **R₁** refract red light toward the observer's eye at **O**, and the violet and other colors over his head. Drops in the region of **V₁** refract violet light to the observer's eye at **O**, and the red and other colors toward his feet. In other words, the light seen from any one drop is but one color, all drops giving this color lying on the arc of a circle.

Halos. Halos are commonly observed as faint rainbowlike rings around the sun or moon and are due to tiny ice crystals floating in the upper atmosphere. Such crystals are hexagonal in shape and, acting like prisms, refract and disperse white light into a spectrum. Two halos are frequently observed, the brighter one making an angle of 22° with the luminary and the fainter one an angle of 46°.

Fig. E. Experiment demonstrating colors produced at minimum deviation by a single rotating prism.

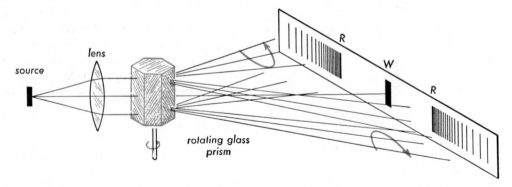

Both exhibit confused spectrum colors with a decided red tint on the inside.

Crystals, like prisms, have an angle of minimum deviation for each color of light (see Fig. D) and, because they are oriented at random in space, millions of them appear to each observer to concentrate the light in a circle with the luminary at the center.

A demonstration of such color effects can be produced as shown in Fig. E by means of a hexagonal or octagonal glass prism rotated rapidly about its axis in a strong beam of white light. Dispersed light refracted by alternate faces sweeps in from either side of the screen, slows down, and stops at minimum deviation, and then retreats again. The blurred patches of light on the screen are brightest at the minimum deviation angles **R**.

Scattering and the Blue Sky.   The blue of the sky and the red of the sunset are due to a phenomenon called scattering. When sunlight passes through the earth's atmosphere, much of the light is "picked" up by the air molecules and given out again in some other direction. The effect is quite similar to the action of water waves on floating objects. If, for example, the ripples from a stone dropped in a still pond of water encounter a small cork floating on the surface, the cork

Fig. F. Light waves are scattered by air molecules.

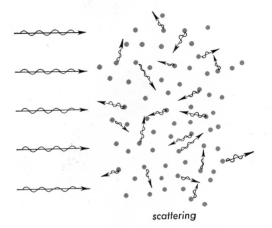

scattering

is set bobbing up and down with the frequency of the passing waves.

Light is pictured as acting in the same way on air molecules and fine dust particles. Once set into vibration by a light wave, a molecule or particle can send out the absorbed light again, sometimes in the same direction but generally in almost any other direction. This is illustrated schematically in Fig. F, where waves of light are shown being scattered at random in all directions.

Experiments show, in agreement with the theory of scattering, that the shortest waves are scattered more readily than longer waves. To be more specific, the **scattering is inversely proportional to the fourth power of the wave length.**

$$\text{scattering} \propto \frac{1}{\lambda^4} \qquad (1)$$

According to this law the short waves of violet light are scattered ten times as readily as the longer waves of red light. The other colors are scattered by intermediate amounts. Thus when sunlight enters the earth's atmosphere, **violet** and **blue light** are scattered the most, followed by **green, yellow, orange,** and **red,** in the order named. For every ten violet waves scattered from a beam, there is only one red wave.

red	orange	yellow	green	blue	violet
1	2	3	5	7	10

At noon on a clear day when the sun is directly overhead, the whole sky appears as **light blue.** This is the composite color of the mixture of colors scattered most effectively by the air molecules. As illustrated by the spectral colors in the lower right spectrum in Light, Lesson 12, Fig. C, light blue, like cyan of the color triangle, is obtained by the added mixture of **violet, blue, green,** and **yellow.**

The Red Sunset.   The occasional observation of an orange-red sunset is attributed to

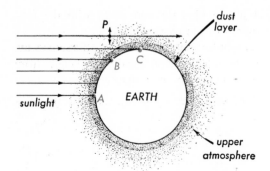

Fig. G. The scattering of light by a layer of dust near the earth's surface causes the sun to turn yellow, then orange, and finally red at sunset.

the **scattering of light** by fine dust and smoke particles near the earth's surface. This is illustrated in Fig. G. To an observer at **A**, it is noonday and the direct sunlight from overhead, seen only by looking directly at the sun itself, travels through a relatively short dust path. As a result, very little violet and blue are scattered away and the sun appears white.

As sunset approaches, however, the direct sunlight has to travel through an everincreasing dust path. The result is that an hour or so before sundown, when the observer is at **B**, practically all of the blue and violet have been scattered out, and owing to the remaining colors—red, orange, yellow, and a little green—the sun appears yellow. At sunset, when the observer is at **C**, the direct rays must travel through so many miles of dust particles that all but red are completely scattered out and the sun appears red. At this same time the sky overhead is still light blue. If the dust blanket is too dense, even the red will be scattered appreciably from the direct sunlight and the deepening red sun will become lost from view before it reaches the horizon.

An excellent demonstration of scattering

Fig. H. The sunset experiment. Demonstration of the scattering and polarization of light by small particles.

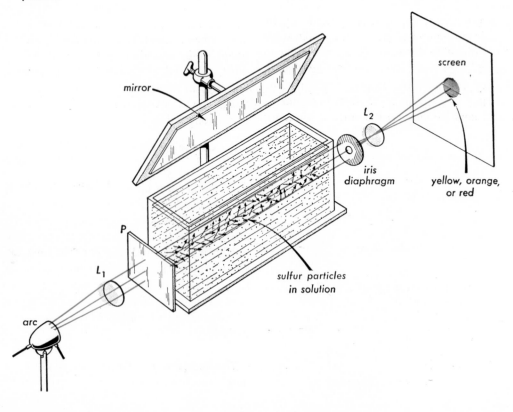

by fine particles is illustrated in Fig. H. A parallel beam of white light from a carbon arc and lens L_1 is sent through a water trough with glass sides. After passing through an iris diaphragm at the other end, a second lens L_2 forms an image of the circular opening on the screen.*

Tiny sulfur particles develop slowly over

* [To produce the fine particles for scattering, about 40 gm of photographic fixing powder (hyposulfite of soda) are first dissolved in about 2 gallons of water. Next, about 1 to 2 cm³ of concentrated sulfuric acid are added and the two thoroughly mixed in the trough. The correct amount of acid to produce the best results is determined by trial. The first visible precipitate should appear after 2 or 3 min.]

a period of from 5 to 10 min. During this time the beam through the tank turns a sky blue, while the circular disk of light on the screen, representing the sun, turns from white to yellow to orange to red.

Polarization by Scattering. If the blue of the sky is observed through a piece of Polaroid in a direction at right angles to the sun's rays, the light is found to be partially plane-polarized. This polarization can also be seen in the scattering experiment described above. Observed through a Polaroid film, the beam in the tank appears bright at one orientation of the Polaroid and disappears with a 90° rotation.

Summary

The rainbow is caused by the refraction and dispersion of sunlight by spherical raindrops. The primary bow is produced by one internal reflection of rays entering the upper side of drops and the secondary bow by two internal reflections of rays entering the lower side.

The observer's shadow lies at the center of curvature of the rainbow arc.

Tiny ice crystals in the atmosphere also give rise to colored rings around the sun or moon. These ice crystals have a hexagonal structure and disperse light into its spectrum colors. Such crystals behave as prisms, with two prism angles of 60° and 90°, respectively, and give rise to two spectrum bands at deviation angles of 22° and 46°, respectively.

Sunlight in passing through the atmosphere is scattered by the air molecules as well as by fine dust and smoke particles. Since blue and violet light are scattered more than other colors, the sky is blue and the sunset may be highly colored.

Questions

1. Under what conditions is a rainbow observed? What is the order of the colors in the primary rainbow? In the secondary rainbow?

2. Could the complete rainbow circle be observed? What are the conditions?

3. What is a halo? What are the conditions for observing halos? How is the color produced?

4. What is scattering? How does it vary with the wave length of light? How does scattering vary with color?

5. Why is the sky blue? If violet light is scattered more than blue, why is the sky light blue in color rather than violet?

6. Under what conditions will the setting sun turn from white to yellow, to orange, and to red? Explain.

7. How can one demonstrate all these phenomena in the laboratory? If you do this experiment, look at the beam of light in the water through a Polaroid and see if it is polarized.

8. Make a diagram showing the refraction and dispersion of white light by a single raindrop. Do the same for an ice crystal.

9. What would you like to propose as a project for demonstrating one or more of the principles introduced in this lesson?

Problems

1. What is the ratio of the scattering of light waves between red light of wave length 7×10^{-5} cm and violet light of wave length 4×10^{-5} cm.

2. For every 200 waves of red light scattered by the air, how many waves of orange light will be scattered? Assume the wave lengths to be 7×10^{-5} cm and 6×10^{-5} cm, respectively.

3. Calculate the ratio of the numbers of light rays scattered by the air for violet light ($\lambda = 4 \times 10^{-5}$ cm) and green light ($\lambda = 5 \times 10^{-5}$ cm).

4. Find the ratio of light waves scattered by fine particles between blue light ($\lambda = 4.3 \times 10^{-5}$) and red light ($\lambda = 7.0 \times 10^{-5}$ cm).

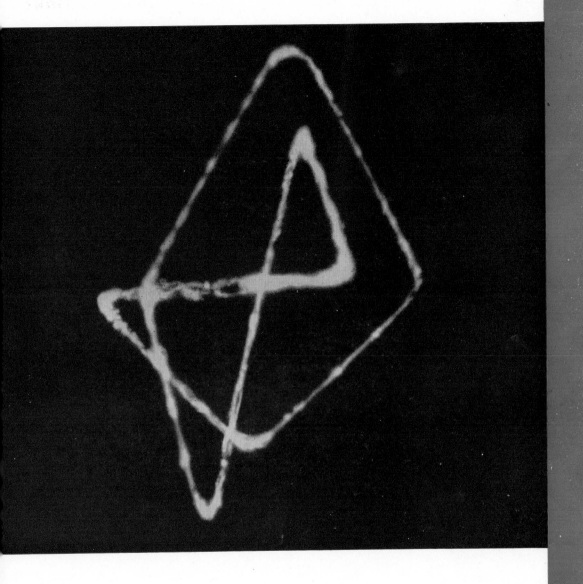

ELECTRICITY
AND MAGNETISM

In experimental philosophy we can, by the phaenomena presented, recognize various kinds of lines of force; thus there are the lines of gravitating force, those of electro-static induction, those of magnetic action, and others partaking of a dynamic character might be perhaps included. The lines of electric and magnetic action are by many considered as exerted through space like the lines of gravitating force. For my own part, I incline to believe that when there are intervening particles of matter (being themselves only centres of force), they take part in carrying on the force through the line, but that when there are none, the line proceeds through space. Whatever the view adopted respecting them may be, we can, at all events, affect these lines of force in a manner which may be conceived as partaking of the nature of a shake or lateral vibration.

Michael Faraday, *Philosophical Magazine*, vol. 28, London, 1846, pp. 347-348.

← **This picture shows the electrodynamic orbit of a 20-micron diameter charged aluminum particle held in suspension in a vacuum chamber by oscillating and static electric fields. By the application of properly chosen alternating and static fields, electrically charged particles can be maintained in dynamic equilibrium in a vacuum against interparticle and gravitational forces.**

Ramo-Wooldridge

Electricity at Rest

IT IS IMPOSSIBLE to say when electricity was first discovered. Records show that as early as 600 B.C. the attractive properties of amber were known. Thales of Miletus (640-546 B.C.), one of the "seven wise men" of ancient Greece, is credited with having observed the attraction of amber, when previously rubbed, for small fibrous materials and bits of straw. Amber was used by these people even as it is now, for ornamental purposes. Just as the precious metals had their names of gold and silver, so amber had its name **electron.**

It is now a well-established fact that all bodies when rubbed together become electrified and that amber is just one of a number of substances which show electrification most strongly.

Electrostatic Attraction. The word **electrostatic** means electricity at rest, and the word **attraction** refers to the force exerted by one body upon another at a distance. To demonstrate electrostatic attraction one often uses a rubber or amber rod and rubs it with a piece of flannel or fur. This electrifies the rod so that when it is held close over some small bits of paper they jump up to the rod and hold fast.

The attraction of an electrified rubber rod for wood is illustrated in Fig. A. A small arrow cut from a piece of dry wood is mounted so that it is free to turn as shown. When the electrified rubber rod is brought near the pointed end of the arrow, it attracts the wood, turning the arrow until it points toward the rod. Brought near the opposite end, the wood is again attracted, turning the arrow to point away from the rubber rod.

An ordinary hard rubber comb when drawn through the hair becomes charged with electricity and will attract light objects in the same way. So great are the electrical charges sometimes produced on a comb that tiny sparks can be seen to jump between the comb and hair. This is particularly noticeable in a darkened room. These sparks are the cause for the crackling noise so often heard when hair is being combed.

Fig. A. An electrified rod attracts a wooden arrow.

wooden arrow

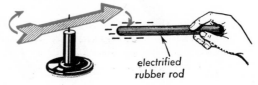

electrified rubber rod

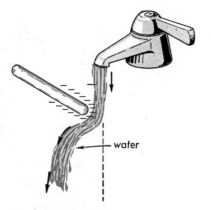

Fig. B. A stream of water is easily deflected by a charged rod.

A spectacular effect is produced by bringing a charged rubber rod close to one side of a smoothly running stream of water from a faucet. As shown above in Fig. B, the stream is diverted to one side and even into the horizontal before it falls again.

An ordinary sheet of writing paper placed on the panel of a door or other similar flat surface and rubbed will hold fast and remain there for some little time without falling down.

Electricity + and −. When two different substances are rubbed together and then sep-

arated, both are found to be electrified, one with one kind of electricity and the other with another. To illustrate this, one end of a rubber rod is charged by rubbing with fur and then suspended in a small wire stirrup as shown in Fig. C. When the electrified end of a similarly charged rod is brought close by, as shown in diagram (a), the suspended rod turns away, showing repulsion. If the fur is brought close by in place of the rubber, the suspended rod is attracted and turns toward the fur. When a glass rod, previously rubbed with silk, is brought close by, as in diagram (b), there is attraction, and when the silk is brought up, there is repulsion.

Since the fur, as well as the glass, attracts the electrified rubber rod, they each have the same kind of electrification: they are said to be **positively charged.** By similar notation the rubber and silk by their actions are said to be **negatively charged.** Positive charges are designated by a (+) sign and negative charges by a (−) sign.

Not only do the above experiments indicate the existence of two kinds of electrification but also they demonstrate a rule concerning the action of one kind or another. Diagram (a), illustrating a negatively charged rubber rod repelling a similar rod,

Fig. C. Like charges of electricity repel each other and unlike charges attract.

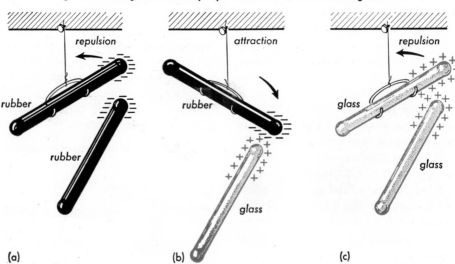

(a)   (b)   (c)

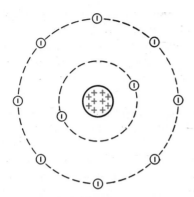

Fig. D. Schematic diagram of a neon atom showing its nucleus at the center with ten positive charges (called protons) surrounded on the outside by ten negative charges (called electrons).

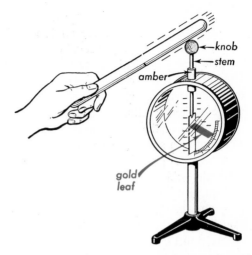

Fig. E. A gold-leaf electroscope is charged by a rod.

shows that two negative charges repel each other. Diagram (b) shows that positive and negative charges attract each other, and diagram (c) that two positive charges repel each other. The general law can therefore be stated that *like charges repel and unlike charges attract.*

Theory of Electrification. The modern theory of electrification by friction is based upon the principle that all substances are made of atoms and molecules. Each atom contains a nucleus having a known amount of positive charge (see Fig. D). This positive charge is due to the presence in the nucleus of a certain number of **protons.** All protons are alike and have the same mass and positive charge. Around every atomic nucleus there are a number of negatively charged particles called **electrons.**

Normally each atom of a substance is electrically neutral; in other words, it has equal amounts of negative and positive charge. Since each electron has the same amount of charge as every other electron and the same amount as every proton but of opposite sign, there are just as many protons in every nucleus as there are electrons around the outside. While protons are much smaller than electrons in size, they contain the bulk of the mass of every atom. One proton, for example, weighs nearly two thousand times as much as an electron. The electrons therefore are light particles or objects around a small but relatively heavy nucleus.

The Electroscope. An electroscope is an instrument for measuring the electrical potential of a charged body. A thin strip of gold leaf is fastened to the side of a long narrow rod of metal and mounted in a metal and glass box (see Fig. E). The gold-leaf support, which will here be called the "stem," is insulated with amber from the box. When the metal knob **N** is touched by a charged

Fig. F. The negatively charged gold leaf rises when a negatively charged body is brought close to the knob.

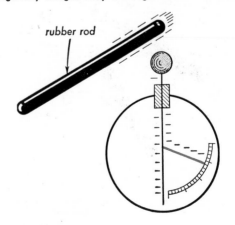

rubber rod, some of the charge flows onto and distributes itself over the gold leaf and support. Since like charges repel each other, the gold leaf is pushed out as shown in the diagram. When the source of charge is taken away, the electroscope retains its acquired charge, which, distributing itself more or less uniformly over the stem, causes the leaf to stand out at a somewhat smaller angle. The more charge given the electroscope, the higher the gold leaf is repelled.

If an electroscope is first charged negatively and then a negatively charged body is brought close to but not touching the knob, as shown in Fig. F, the gold leaf will rise as indicated. The reason is that the electrons are repelled away from the knob to the far end of the stem, causing the gold leaf to rise still higher. As long as the two bodies do not touch each other and allow more negatives to go to the electroscope, the gold leaf will fall back to its original angle when the negatively charged rod is taken away.

If a positively charged body is brought up as shown in Fig. G, negatives from the stem and gold leaf are attracted to the knob, causing the gold leaf to fall. **Thus with a negatively charged electroscope, a positive charge brought nearby causes the gold leaf**

to drop, and a negatively charged body causes it to rise. If the electroscope is positively charged, the reverse action will take place, a positive charge causes it to rise and a negative causes it to fall.

Conductors and Insulators. Not all substances are good conductors of electricity. As a general rule, metals are good conductors whereas nonmetals are poor conductors. The poorest of conductors are commonly called **insulators,** or **nonconductors.** Several examples of conductors and nonconductors are the following

Conductors	Nonconductors
nickel	glass
platinum	amber
iron	rubber
mercury	mica
silver	sulfur
aluminum	porcelain
copper	paper
gold	silk

The property of electrical conduction is illustrated by an experiment in Fig. H. One end of a long thin copper wire is connected to an electroscope and the other end to a small brass knob mounted on a glass pedestal. When a charged rubber rod is touched to the knob as shown, the gold leaf of the distant electroscope rises immediately. Electrons have been conducted along the wire. If a positively charged rod contacts the knob,

Fig. G. The negatively charged gold leaf falls when a positively charged body is brought close to the knob.

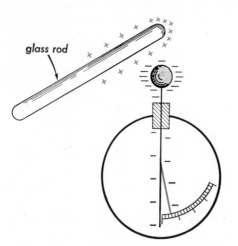

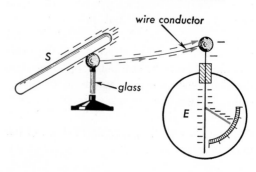

Fig. H. Illustration of an electron current.

electrons flow away from the electroscope, leaving the gold leaf with a positive charge.

If the copper wire in the above experiment is replaced by a nonconductor, like a silk thread, the electroscope cannot be charged by the rod contacting the distant knob. Poor conductors, such as glass and amber, are used to support metal parts of electrical apparatus for the purpose of insulating them from unnecessary losses of electricity. An electroscope, for example, will retain its electric charge well if the gold leaf and stem are insulated from the electroscope case with amber as shown in Fig. E.

The difference between a conductor and an insulator, or dielectric, is that in a conductor there are free electrons, whereas in an insulator all the electrons are tightly bound to their respective atoms.

In an uncharged body there are an equal number of positive and negative charges. In metals a few of the electrons are free to move from atom to atom, so that when a negatively charged rod is brought to the end of a conductor, it repels nearby free electrons in the conductor, causing them to move. They in turn repel free electrons in front of them, thus giving rise to a flow of electrons all along the conductor. Hence in Fig. H it is not necessarily the electrons from the charged rubber rod that actually reach the electroscope leaf, but rather the electrons from the end of the wire where it touches the electroscope knob.

Summary

When two different substances are brought into contact and then separated, one is found to contain a positive charge and the other a negative charge. Some substances, like hard rubber and cat fur, produce larger charges than others.

Electrified bodies attract uncharged bodies. Like charges repel each other and unlike charges attract each other.

Atoms are composed of positively charged nuclei, surrounded by negatively charged particles called electrons. When static charges are produced, only the electrons are free to move.

A negatively charged body contains an excess of electrons, whereas a positively charged body has a deficiency of electrons.

An electroscope containing a gold leaf may be used to detect and measure electrical charge.

Some substances, like most of the common metals, are good conductors of electrons, while others, like glass, paper, and rubber, are nonconductors of electrons.

Questions

1. How many kinds of electrical charges are there? What are they called? What is meant by electrostatic?

2. What is the rule regarding repulsion and attraction? How can the rule be demonstrated?

3. What is an electroscope? How is it made?

4. What is the structure of the atom? How much negative charge does a neutral atom have?

5. What is the present-day explanation of electrification? Why are things rubbed together to charge them? What kinds of charges do not move in electrification?

6. What is meant by a nonconductor? What kinds of charges move through solid conductors?

7. When a positively charged rod is brought up and touched to the knob of an electroscope, the gold leaf rises. When the rod is taken away, the leaf drops part way back only. Why?

8. When a negatively charged rod is brought up close to the knob of a negatively charged electroscope, what happens?

9. When a negatively charged rod is brought up close to the knob of a positively charged electroscope, what happens?

10. Do you think that the flow of a liquid through a pipe might produce electrical charges? Do you know of any examples of where this occurs?

11. While combing your hair, crackling noises are sometimes heard. Why? How can you show that your comb becomes electrically charged?

12. Plastic seat covers in automobiles sometimes cause the driver to be electrically shocked. Why?

13. Why are some substances good conductors of electrons and others not? Do all substances contain electrons?

Electricity and Magnetism | **Lesson 2**

COULOMB'S LAW—ELECTROSTATICS

The Law of Electrostatic Force. It has already been demonstrated that like charges repel and unlike charges attract. Nothing which has thus far been said, however, has indicated just how strong the repulsion or attraction might be, nor how it depends on the magnitude of the charges and the distance between them.

The first quantitative measurements of the force between two charged bodies was made in 1780 by Coulomb, a French scientist and engineer. He proved experimentally that *the force acting between two charges is directly proportional to the product of the two charges and inversely proportional to the* square of the distance between them. Symbolically this law is usually written as an algebraic equation,

$$F = k \frac{QQ'}{d^2} \qquad (1)$$

where **F** is the force, **Q** and **Q'** are the charges, and **d** is the distance between them (see Fig. A). The constant of proportionality **k** has a value which depends upon the units of charge chosen.

In the mks system, force is given in **newtons,** distance in **meters,** charge in **coulombs,** and $k = 9 \times 10^9$. It is customary to define

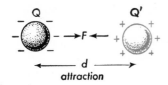

Fig. A. Two like charges repel each other and two unlike charges attract each other.

the coulomb in terms of electric currents. (See Electricity and Magnetism, Lesson 3.)

One coulomb is that quantity of electric charge which flowing past any point in a wire in one second produces a current of one ampere.

Experiments described in later chapters show that electrons are all alike and that each carries a charge

$$e = 1.6019 \times 10^{-19} \text{ coulomb} \qquad (2)$$

This means that when a body has a unit negative charge of one coulomb, it has an excess of 6.24×10^{18} electrons and that a body charged positively with one coulomb has a deficiency of 6.24×10^{18} electrons.

$$1 \text{ coulomb} = 6.24 \times 10^{18} \text{ electrons} \qquad (3)$$

Since the unit of charge in the mks system is measured in terms of electric currents, the numerical value of k in Eq. (1) must be determined experimentally. The best value to date is $k = 8.9878 \times 10^9$. For most practical problems the approximation $k = 9 \times 10^9$ will be used.

$$k = 9 \times 10^9 \frac{\text{newton-meter}^2}{\text{coulomb}^2} \qquad (4)$$

To simplify some of the equations that are derived from Coulomb's law it is convenient to introduce a new constant ϵ_o,

$$k = \frac{1}{4\pi\epsilon_o} \qquad (5)$$

and write Coulomb's law

$$F = \frac{1}{4\pi\epsilon_o} \cdot \frac{QQ'}{d^2} \qquad (6)$$

Using the numerical value of k from Eq. (4) it follows from Eq. (5) that

$$\epsilon_o = \frac{1}{4\pi k} = \frac{1}{4\pi \times 9 \times 10^9}$$

$$= 8.85 \times 10^{-12} \frac{\text{coulomb}^2}{\text{newton-meter}^2} \qquad (7)$$

This is the so-called rationalized mks system.*

Problem. A charge of $+25 \times 10^{-9}$ coulombs is located 6 cm from a charge of -72×10^{-9} coulombs. Calculate the force between them.

Solution. The given quantities are $Q = 25 \times 10^{-9}$ coulombs and $Q' = -72 \times 10^{-9}$ coulombs, $d = 0.06$ m. Substitution in Eq. (1) gives

$$F = 9 \times 10^9 \frac{\text{newton-m}^2}{\text{coulomb}^2}$$

$$\times \frac{(25 \times 10^{-9})(-72 \times 10^{-9}) \text{ coulomb}^2}{(0.06)^2 \text{ m}^2}$$

$$F = -4.50 \times 10^{-3} \text{ newton}$$

The minus sign indicates attraction.

Attraction of Neutral Bodies. An interesting demonstration of electrostatic attraction is shown in Fig. B. A tiny ball cut from the pithy core of a corn cob is coated with tin foil or metallic paint and suspended by a silk thread. When a charged rod is brought near by as in (a), the pith ball is attracted to the rod and upon contact bounces away. As the rod is now moved toward the ball, it

* Some books define ϵ_o by the equation $\epsilon_o = 1/k$ instead of $1/4\pi k$. Coulomb's law then becomes $F = QQ'/\epsilon_o d^2$, where $\epsilon_o = 1.11 \times 10^{-10}$. This is the so-called nonrationalized mks system. One must be careful in reading other texts to determine which system is being used.

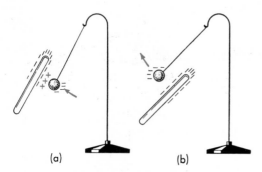

(a)   (b)

Fig. B. (a) A metallic-coated pith ball is attracted by a charged rod. (b) After contact the pith ball is repelled.

avoids the rod and keeps as far away as possible.

To explain this result, assume the rod negatively charged in the position shown in (a). Free electrons on the sphere are repelled to the opposite side, leaving an equal number of positives on the near side unneutralized. Attraction now takes place because the positive charges are closest and the attractive force acting on them is greater than the repelling force on the negatives. When contact is made, negatives on the rod neutralize all the positives and the ball moves away with its negative charges by mutual repulsion.

Charging by Induction. To charge a body by induction is to give it a charge without touching it. One method of inducing a charge is illustrated in Fig. C. Two metal spheres **A** and **B**, insulated by glass standards, are touching each other when a charged rubber rod is brought close to one of them. If

Fig. C. Expermient showing how bodies may be charged by induction.

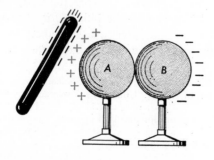

sphere **B** is now moved away and then the rod removed from the vicinity, both spheres are found to be charged, sphere **A** positively and sphere **B** negatively.

The explanation is similar to that of the pith ball in the preceding section: the close proximity of the charged rod repels free electrons from sphere **A** to the far side of sphere **B**, leaving unneutralized positives behind. Separated under these conditions, both spheres are left with their respective charges. This is called *charging by induction.*

Faraday Ice-Pail Experiment. The distribution of charge over a metallic conductor, can in part be demonstrated by an experiment first performed by Michael Faraday in 1810. This demonstration, known as *Faraday's ice-pail experiment,* involves a small metal ball, a hollow metal container like a tin pail, and an electroscope, as shown in Fig. D.

If the ball is charged from another source and then lowered into the pail, the leaf of the electroscope rises. Upon moving the ball around inside the pail and even touching the inside surface with it, no change in the potential is shown by the electroscope leaf. After the ball has been removed, the inner surface of the pail and the ball are found to be completely free of charge.

Fig. D. Diagram illustrating Faraday's ice-pail experiment.

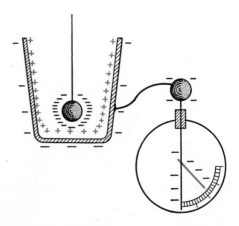

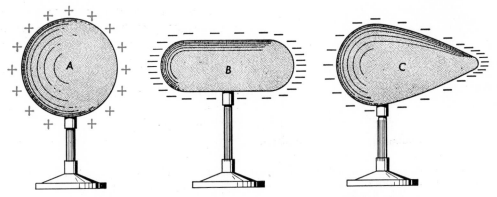

Fig. E. Charge density on conductors is greatest in regions of greatest curvature.

To explain what happens, let the ball be charged negatively and lowered to the position shown. Free electrons in the metal pail are repelled to the outer surface and to the connecting electroscope, leaving positives on the inside unneutralized. When the ball touches the pail, all negatives leave the ball and neutralize an equal number of positives. The fact that the electroscope leaf remains fixed when the ball is removed shows (1) that there is no redistribution of the negative charges on the outer pail surface and (2) that the number of induced positives is equal to the number of negatives on the ball.

When static charges are acquired by a nonconductor like hard rubber, glass or am-

ber, they remain where they were first located. When a conductor like copper, silver, or gold acquires a charge, however, the charge quickly spreads over the entire surface. With a metallic sphere, whether solid or hollow, the charge spreads uniformly over the surface as shown in Fig. E. On other shaped conductors the charge distributes itself according to surface curvature, concentrating more at points and less where the walls are more nearly straight.

Where a charged conductor has a sharp point, the charges crowd very close together, and mutual repulsion forces crowd electrons off of a negatively charged point and attract electrons to a positively charged point.

Summary

The law of force between electrically charged bodies is given by Coulomb's law,

$$F = k \frac{QQ'}{d^2}$$

Charges **Q** are measured in coulombs, the distance **d** between them in meters, and the force **F** in newtons.

Charged bodies attract uncharged bodies. This is due to a shift or movement of the electrons within the uncharged bodies.

An object can be charged positively or negatively by induction. A charged body brought up close to an uncharged conductor will attract or repel the electrons within the conductor, and by separation of the parts the bodies are charged.

The surplus charges on a metal conductor are distributed over the surface. Where the surfaces are flat, the charges are far apart; where the surface is curved, they are close together. At points the charges become so close that mutual repulsion crowds electrons off or onto the body. This is the cause for electrical discharges at points.

Questions

1. What is Coulomb's law? What is the unit of charge used? What are the units of force and distance?

2. How many electrons are there in 1 coulomb?

3. Why will a charged body attract an uncharged body? Make a diagram and explain.

4. Will a charged body attract an uncharged conductor?

5. How can a body be charged positively by induction?

6. Can a negatively charged body be used to charge an electroscope positively? How could you do this?

7. If an egg-shaped conductor is charged negatively, where are the charges most concentrated? Where are they least concentrated?

8. What would you propose as a project for making some inexpensive device for demonstrating some of the principles presented in this lesson?

Problems

1. A positive charge of 5×10^{-8} coulomb is located 5 cm from a negative charge of 10×10^{-8} coulomb. Calculate the force in newtons exerted by either charge upon the other.

2. A charge of -5×10^{-7} coulomb is located 20 cm from another charge of -5×10^{-7} coulomb. Calculate the force in newtons exerted by one charge upon the other.

3. Two charges of -9×10^{-7} coulomb each are located 6 cm apart. What is the repelling force on each in newtons?

4. Two unlike charges of 20×10^{-8} coulomb each are located 30 cm apart. What is the attracting force on each in dynes?

5. Two equal charges are located 12 cm apart and repel each other with a force of 0.36 newtons. Find the magnitude of each charge in coulombs.

6. Two small metal spheres 24 cm apart, and having equal negative charges, repel each other with a force of 1×10^{-3} newton. Find the total charge on the two bodies in coulombs.

7. What charge Q placed 4 cm from a charge of 8×10^{-8} coulomb will produce a force of 0.015 newtons?

8.* Four equal charges of $+5 \times 10^{-8}$ coulomb each are located at the corners of a square, 5 cm on each side. Calculate the resultant force on each charge and show its direction on a diagram drawn to scale.

9.* Two positive charges, $+5 \times 10^{-7}$ coulomb each, are located diagonally opposite each other on a square 5 cm on a side. Two negative charges, -5×10^{-7} coulomb each, are located at the other corners, respectively. Calculate the resultant force on each charge and show this resultant on a diagram drawn to scale.

ELECTRICITY IN MOTION

To make an electron current flow continuously along a wire, a continuous supply of electrons must be available at one end and a continuous supply of positive charges at the other (see Fig. A). This is like the flow of water through a pipe: to obtain a continuous flow, a continuous supply of water must be provided at one end and an opening for its escape into some receptacle at the other. The continuous supply of positive charge at the one end of a wire offers a means of escape for the electrons. If this is not provided, electrons will accumulate at the end of the wire and their repulsion back along the wire will stop the current flow.

There are two general methods by which a continuous supply of electrical charge is obtained: one is by means of **a battery** and the other is by means of **an electric generator.** The battery is a device by which chemical energy is transformed into electrical energy and the generator is a device by which mechanical energy is transformed into electrical energy.

Electric current is measured in units called **amperes. The ampere,** named in honor of the French physicist Ampère,* **is defined as the flow of one coulomb per second.** In other words, one coulomb flowing past any given point in a wire in one second constitutes a current of one ampere (amp).

$$1 \text{ ampere} = \frac{1 \text{ coulomb}}{1 \text{ second}}$$

If twice this quantity passes by in one

* André M. Ampère (1775-1836), French physicist and mathematician. Ampère began his career as professor of physics and chemistry at Bourg at the early age of 26 and later established the relation between electricity and magnetism, and helped to develop the subject he called electrodynamics. His only son, Jean J. Ampère, also became famous as a philologist, lecturer, and historian.

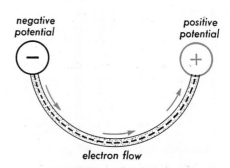

negative potential

positive potential

electron flow

Fig. A. Two terminals at different potentials and connected by a conductor give rise to an electric current.

second, the current is 2 amp. Thus electric current is analogous to the rate of flow of water through a pipe.

$$\text{current} = \frac{\text{quantity of charge}}{\text{time}}$$

$$I = \frac{Q}{t} \qquad (1)$$

Remembering that one coulomb = 6.24×10^{18} electrons (see Electricity and Magnetism, Lesson 2), a current of one ampere means a flow of 6.24×10^{18} electrons per second past any given point.

This enormous number does not mean that the electrons are moving with high speed through a conductor. Actually the number of moving charges is so large that their average velocity is but a small fraction of a millimeter per second. When we picture a solid conductor as a crystal lattice, similar to that shown in Fig. E, p. 157, the electrons are thought of as moving through the intervening spaces. This movement is not completely free, however, but is influenced by the repulsion and attraction of like and unlike charges.

Many years ago, before it was known which of the electric charges, (+) or (−), moved through a wire, there seemed to be

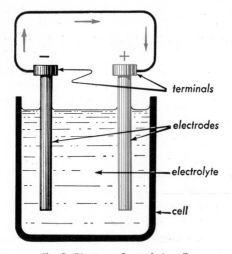

Fig. B. Diagram of a voltaic cell.

more than one hundred years ago. Today battery cells are manufactured in two common forms: (1) dry cells, as used in flashlights, portable radios, etc., and (2) wet cells, as used in automobiles, airplanes, boats, etc.

The Voltaic Cell. The voltaic cell, as shown in Fig. B, is composed of three parts, a pair of dissimilar metal plates called **electrodes,** a dilute acid solution called the **electrolyte,** and a nonconducting liquid container called the **cell.** While many different combinations of materials have been tried and used in such cells, zinc and carbon as electrodes, dilute sulfuric acid as the electrolyte, and a glass or hard rubber container as the cell, are the most common.

Electrolytic Dissociation. Individual molecules of sulfuric acid (written H_2SO_4) are composed of seven atoms each: two hydrogens, one sulfur, and four oxygens. When concentrated acid is poured into water to form a dilute solution, a small percent of the molecules split up, that is, they dissociate. The two hydrogens split off from the molecule, each leaving an electron behind with the remaining SO_4 molecule. Similarly some of the water molecules, each composed of two hydrogens and one oxygen, dissociate by having one of the hydrogen atoms split off without an electron. See Fig. C.

some evidence that it was the positive charge and not the negative. This notion became so thoroughly entrenched in the minds of those interested in electrical phenomena that in later years, when it was discovered that the negatives move in solid conductors and not the positives, it became difficult to change.

The convention that electric current flows from plus to minus is still to be found in many books and is used by some electrical engineers in designing electrical machines and appliances. The rapid growth and the importance of radio engineering and electronics, however, has brought about a change in this practice, and we shall hereafter in this text speak of current as one of electron flow from $(-)$ to $(+)$ and call it electron current.

Batteries. Batteries as continuous sources of electrical energy are the result of a long series of experiments which started with the discoveries of Alessandro Volta*

* Alessandro Volta (1745-1827), Italian scientist, and for more than twenty years professor of physics at Pavia. Traveling considerably throughout Europe, he became acquainted with many celebrities. In 1801 he was awarded the Copley medal of the Royal Society of London, and then was called to Paris and awarded a medal by Napoleon. In 1815 the emperor of Austria made him director of the philosophical faculty of the University of Padua. A statue now stands in his memory at Como, his birthplace.

Fig. C. Some of the sulfuric acid molecules and water molecules in a dilute solution dissociate.

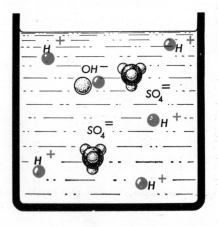

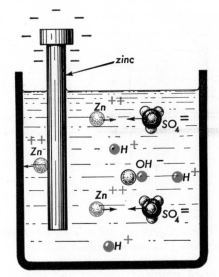

Fig. D. A zinc metal electrode in dilute sulfuric acid.

Since each hydrogen atom leaves an electron behind, it has a net positive charge and is called a **positive ion**. Each remaining SO_4 fragment from the acid and OH fragment from the water has a surplus of negative charge and is called a **negative ion**.

Electrode Action. If we now insert a zinc rod into this electrolyte, chemical action

is initiated, whereby individual zinc atoms break off from the surface leaving two electrons behind. See Fig. D. Going into solution as doubly charged positive ions, they strongly attract SO_4^{--} ions. With each encounter of two such ions, combination takes place, resulting in the formation of neutral $ZnSO_4$ molecules.

$$Zn^{++} + SO_4^{--} = ZnSO_4$$

As more and more zinc ions go into solution, the negative charge on the zinc electrode increases and soon reaches a maximum.

If instead of a zinc rod we insert a carbon rod into the electrolyte as shown in Fig. E, hydrogen ions are attracted to the electrode. There each H^+ ion acquires an electron from the carbon, and two such particles form a neutral hydrogen molecule, H_2.

Since hydrogen is a gas at normal temperatures, the accumulation of H_2 molecules results in the formation of bubbles of gas rising to the surface. In giving up electrons the carbon electrode acquires a positive

Fig. F. The emf of a voltaic cell is measured with a voltmeter.

Fig. E. A carbon rod in dilute sulfuric acid.

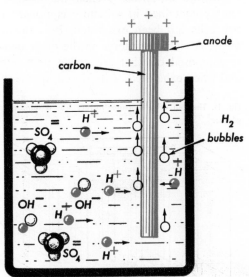

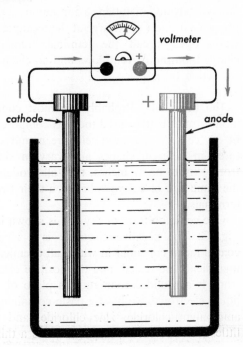

charge and a certain definite positive potential.

$$2(H^+) + 2(e^-) = H_2 \uparrow$$

The Cell Electromotive Force. If we now insert both the zinc and carbon electrodes into the electrolyte as shown in Fig. F, each one acquires its appropriate charge. The positive electrode, called the **anode,** acquires a positive potential; and the negative electrode, called the **cathode,** acquires a negative potential.

When a voltmeter is connected to the two terminals of the cell, the pointer indicates the **difference of potential** in volts, and this we call the **electromotive force** (*abbr.* emf).

Since the voltmeter completes the electric circuit between cathode and anode, a small electron current will flow from cathode to anode through the connecting wires and the voltmeter. Electrons leaving the zinc metal surface change the cathode potential, and electrons arriving at the carbon neutralize positives, thereby changing the anode potential. With the tendency of the potential difference to fall, chemical action takes place immediately and maintains a continuous supply of (+) and (−) charge at the terminals. Upon open circuit the terminals remain charged, but no current flows and no chemical action takes place.

The Dry Cell. Probably the most common form of battery used today is composed of dry cells. While these cells are manufactured in different shapes and vary in size from $\frac{1}{8}$ in. to many inches, they all produce the same emf of 1.5 volts between their two terminals.

One common form of dry cell is shown in Fig. G. The negative electrode is a zinc-coated metal container in which all chemical ingredients are sealed, and the positive electrode is a round carbon rod. In place of a liquid electrolyte we have a paste containing ammonium chloride, zinc chloride, and a little water. Surrounding the anode is a thin

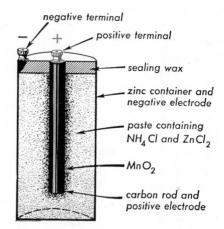

Fig. G. Cross-section diagram of a dry cell or "flashlight" battery, showing the essential elements.

layer of powdered carbon and manganese dioxide.

When current is being supplied by the dry cell, zinc ions form at the cathode, while ammonium ions gain electrons at the carbon rod, forming hydrogen and ammonia gas. The hydrogen reacts chemically with the manganese dioxide, and the ammonia gas with the zinc chloride. While the emf of all dry cells is 1.5 volts, the larger the cell the greater is the current and the total electrical energy that can be supplied.

Storage Batteries. When the electrical energy contained in a battery composed of dry cells has been exhausted, it is thrown away. A storage battery, on the other hand, is composed of what are called **wet cells,** and when exhausted of its stored up energy,

Fig. H. The cell of a storage battery has a number of plates.

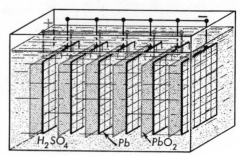

such a battery can be rejuvenated or *re-charged.*

The negative electrode of a storage cell, as shown in Fig. H, is composed of a set of parallel lead grills filled with **spongy lead** (Pb), while the positive electrode is another set of lead grills filled with porous **lead dioxide** (PbO_2).

When a current is supplied by the cell, PbO_2 in one set of grills and Pb in the other, combine with the dissociated H+ and SO_4^{--} ions of the dielectric and form lead sulfate ($PbSO_4$) and water (H_2O). When the surfaces of all plates become coated with lead sulfate, they behave chemically alike, and no more current can be drawn from the cell.

To recharge a storage cell the two terminals are connected to a direct current generator. The current flowing through the electrolyte reverses the chemical process, changing them back to their original form. Chemically, one writes

$$PbO_2 + Pb + 2H_2SO_4$$

$$\text{charge} \uparrow \quad \downarrow \text{discharge} \qquad (4)$$

$$2PbSO_4 + 2H_2O$$

Upon charging a cell too rapidly, some of the dissociated water molecules of the electrolyte are converted into hydrogen gas at the cathode and oxygen gas at the anode. These rise to the surface as bubbles and necessitate the occasional addition of water to the cell.

Regardless of the size, each such cell develops an emf of 2.2 volts. While many other kinds of storage cells have been developed, the lead battery is the most widely used in the United States.

Summary

Electric currents are measured in amperes. Current is defined as the rate of flow of electric charge,

$$I = \frac{Q}{t}$$

The charge **Q** is measured in coulombs and **t** in seconds.

Batteries are composed of one or more cells. Each cell of a battery contains two electrodes, an electrolyte, and a container.

Dilute acid molecules dissociate into parts called ions. Those with a net positive charge are called positive ions, while those with a negative charge are called negative ions.

The difference of potential between the two terminals of a cell is measured in volts and is sometimes called the electromotive force.

Dry cells in common use contain a pastelike dielectric.

Storage battery cells can be recharged.

All cells depend on chemical action between the electrode metals and the ions of the electrolyte.

Questions

1. How is current defined? What is the ampere? How many electrons pass by any point in a wire when a current of 1 ampere flows?

2. What is a voltaic cell? What is a battery? What are the three principal constituents of a battery cell?

3. What are ions? Where are they produced?

4. What is electromotive force? In what units is it measured?

5. What is the source of electrical energy in a cell? What is the emf of a dry cell? Of a storage cell?

6. Of what is the storage cell electrolyte composed? Of what elements are the electrodes composed?

7. What is meant by dissociation? What is a terminal? What is a cathode? What is an anode?

Problems

1. Make a diagram of a voltaic cell composed of zinc and carbon electrodes and dilute sulfuric acid in water as an electrolyte. Briefly explain what happens on a closed circuit.

2. Make a diagram of a dry cell showing the electrode and chemical materials used.

3. Make a diagram of a lead storage cell, label the essential elements, and write down the chemical reactions taking place on (a) charge and (b) discharge.

Electricity and Magnetism | **Lesson 4**

ELECTROMOTIVE FORCE OF A BATTERY CELL—*Laboratory*

In performing this experiment you will measure the electromotive force of a number of voltaic cells composed of different electrolytes and various pairs of metal electrodes. Details are given in the accompanying LABORATORY EXERCISES.

Electricity and Magnetism | **Lesson 5**

OHM'S LAW

The Battery. If two or more cells are connected together as shown in Fig. A, they form what is called a battery. In this diagram the battery is composed of four dry cells connected **in series.** By series connec- tions is meant that the (+) terminal of one cell is connected to the (−) terminal of the next.

The purpose in connecting two or more cells in series is to obtain a higher emf than

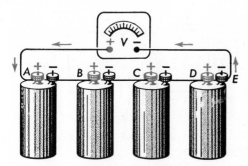

Fig. A. Four dry cells connected in series form a 6-volt battery.

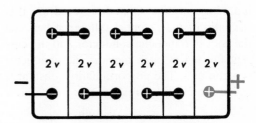

Fig. C. Series connections for a 12-volt storage battery.

that available with one cell alone. The potential difference between the extreme end terminals **A** and **E** of any battery is just the sum of those for the individual cells.

Each dry cell produces an emf of 1.5 volts, so that if the voltmeter is connected to two points, it will indicate 1.5 volts between **A** and **B**, 3.0 volts between **A** and **C**, 4.5 volts between **A** and **D**, and 6 volts between **A** and **E**.

The common flashlight contains several dry cells connected in series as shown in Fig. B. When new cells are inserted, they are all turned in the same direction so that the (+) terminal at the center of each cell makes good contact with the (−) case of the next cell. The closing of the switch shown in the figure applies the end terminal voltage of 4.5 volts to the light bulb.

The storage battery commonly used in automobiles contains six wet cells of 2 volts each, connected in series as shown in Fig. C. Note how the heavy crossbars connect the (−) terminal of any one cell with the (+) terminal of the next. With six cells in series the end terminals produce a resultant of 12 volts, hence its name of *twelve-volt battery.*

Fig. B. Cross section of a 3-cell flashlight.

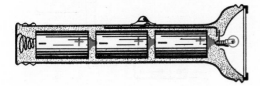

It is customary in circuit diagrams to represent battery cells as shown in Fig. D. The (+) and (−) terminals of each cell are indicated by long and short lines, respectively. The first four diagrams shown represent one, two, three, and four cells, respectively, connected in series. If many cells are to be represented, four or five can be drawn and the over-all terminal voltage written beneath it as shown by **V** = 45 volts.

Ohm's Law.* This is the well-known and fundamental law in electricity which makes it possible to determine the current flowing through a circuit when the resistance of the circuit and the potential difference applied to

* George Simon Ohm (1787-1854), German physicist, was born at Erlavgen and educated at the university there. After teaching mathematics in Cologne for sixteen years, and in Nuremburg for sixteen more, he became professor of experimental physics in the high school at Munich. His writings were numerous and but for one exception were not of the first order. This single exception consists of a pamphlet on electric currents, the most important part of which is summarized in what is now called "Ohm's law." For this work he was awarded the Copley Medal of the Royal Society of London in 1841 and made a foreign member of the society one year later.

Fig. D. Circuit diagrams indicating the cells of a battery.

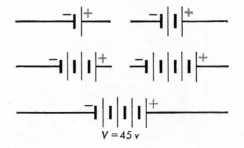

$V = 45\ v$

it are known. What Ohm discovered was that the ratio of the potential difference between the ends of a metallic conductor and the current flowing through the metallic conductor is a constant. The proportionality constant is called the electrical **resistance**.

$$\text{resistance} = \frac{\text{potential difference}}{\text{current}}$$

Symbolically, Ohm's law is often written

$$R = \frac{V}{I} \qquad (1)$$

In electrical units,

$$1 \text{ ohm} = \frac{1 \text{ volt}}{1 \text{ amp}}$$

The law is of great importance because of its very general application to so many electrical phenomena. One of its simplest applications is illustrated in Fig. E. A dry cell is directly connected by wires to a small light bulb. The battery maintains a potential difference of 1.5 volts across the lamp. If the electron current flowing through the circuit is 0.5 amp, the resistance of the circuit is

$$R = \frac{1.5 \text{ volts}}{0.5 \text{ amp}} = 3 \text{ ohms}$$

Fig. E. A dry cell connected to a small light bulb.

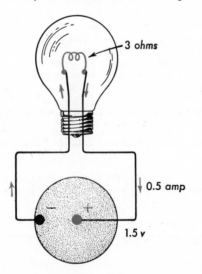

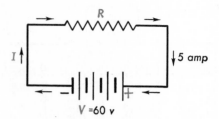

Fig. F. Circuit diagram of resistor R connected to 60-volt battery.

Although the resistance as found here is assumed to be the resistance of the light bulb, it really includes the resistance of the connecting wires as well as the resistance of the battery. In practice one usually uses wires of such low resistance that they can be neglected in most calculations. If they are not small, they cannot be neglected and must be added in as part of the **R** in Ohm's law.

Consider the illustration shown in Fig. F, where a battery of many cells maintains a potential difference of 60 volts across a circuit and a current of 5 amps through it. By Ohm's law the resistance of the circuit is given by Eq. (1) as

$$R = \frac{V}{I} = \frac{60 \text{ volts}}{5 \text{ amps}} = 12 \text{ ohms}$$

Resistance in circuit diagrams is represented by a saw-toothed line as shown, and the word **ohm** is represented by the capital

Fig. G. Connector board for determining electrical resistance.

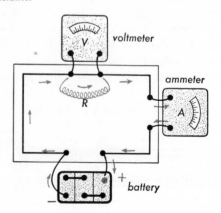

Greek letter omega, Ω. In Fig. F the resistance

$$R = 12 \, \Omega$$

Resistance may be defined as the opposition offered to a flow of current through a circuit.

The Experimental Method. To determine the resistance of any electrical circuit it is common practice to use a voltmeter and an ammeter. The voltmeter is applied across the circuit to measure the potential difference, and the ammeter is connected in series to measure the current.

Fig. G represents a connector board arranged for measurements of this kind. An appliance, or unknown resistor **R**, is connected between two terminals at the top, so the current supplied by the battery below must pass through it as well as the ammeter. The voltmeter is connected across **R** to measure the potential difference between its ends.

Suppose that three heating elements, commonly used as replacement elements for electrical kitchen utensils, are connected in turn to the two terminals at the top of the board and a 6-volt storage battery is applied to the terminals below. The voltage **V** and the current **I** from a sample set of measurements give the following results.

Table 1. Recorded Data

Element	Volts	Amps
toaster...........	6.3	2.3
waffle iron........	6.2	1.6
iron..............	6.1	1.8

By Ohm's law, Eq. (1), the resistance of each element can be calculated. This will be left as an exercise for you, the reader.

Resistors in Series. When several electrical devices are connected together in series,

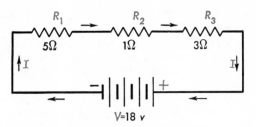

Fig. H. The same current flows through all resistors when connected in series.

the resistance **R** of the combination is equal to the sum of the resistances of the individuals. Symbolically,

$$R = R_1 + R_2 + R_3 + R_4 + \text{etc.} \qquad (2)$$

This, the law of series resistances, is illustrated by an application of Ohm's law to the complete electric circuit in Fig. H. Three resistors $R_1 = 5$ ohms, $R_2 = 1$ ohm, and $R_3 = 3$ ohms are connected in series with a battery of nine storage cells. The sum of the resistances given by Eq. (2) is

$$R = 5 + 1 + 3 = 9 \, \Omega$$

and the potential difference supplied by the battery is

$$V = 9 \times 2 = 18 \text{ volts}$$

Applying Ohm's law, Eq. (1), the electron current flowing through the circuit is

$$I = \frac{18 \text{ volts}}{9 \, \Omega} = 2 \text{ amps}$$

This means that the same electron current of 2 amps flows through the high resistance of 5 ohms as well as through the 1-ohm and 3-ohm resistors. Like water flowing through pipes of different sizes connected one after the other, just as much water passes through one pipe per second of time as through any other, and none can accumulate at any point. The battery acts like a pump and keeps a constant and steady current flowing in the circuit.

Summary

When cells are connected in series with each other, they form a battery whose over-all emf, or potential difference, is the sum of those for the separate cells. Each dry cell in a battery produces an emf of 1.5 volts, and each storage cell 2.2 volts.

Ohm's law is the basic equation for electrical circuits of all kinds and relates the three quantities current, voltage, and resistance,

$$R = \frac{V}{I}$$

where R is in ohms, V is in volts, and I is in amperes.

Common electrical measurements are made with instruments called voltmeters and ammeters. By measuring the current through a circuit with an ammeter and the battery voltage applied to the circuit with a voltmeter, Ohm's law can be applied to find the circuit resistance.

When two or more resistors are connected in series, their various resistances are added together to find their resultant.

Questions

1. How are cells usually connected to form a battery? What determines the emf of a battery?

2. What is the voltage of a single dry cell? Of a single storage cell?

3. What is Ohm's law? In what units is each quantity measured?

4. What common electrical instruments are used to determine the factors in Ohm's law?

5. What is the equivalent resistance of two or more resistors connected in series?

6. What is the abbreviated notation for battery cells in series? How is a resistor shown in a circuit diagram?

7. Does the same current flow through each resistor in series connections?

8. If the resistance of a circuit, and the applied voltage were known, how could you determine the current?

9. What inexpensive device would you propose to make as a project illustrating or making use of Ohm's law?

Problems

1. A battery of 5 dry cells is used in series in a flashlight having a bulb with a resistance of 22 ohms. What electron current flows when the light is turned on?

2. A 12-volt storage battery supplies a current of 48 amperes when the starter in a car is turned on. What is the resistance of the starter motor?

3. Three resistors $R_1 = 7\ \Omega$, $R_2 = 4\ \Omega$, and $R_3 = 10\ \Omega$ are connected in series to a battery of 10 dry cells. Calculate the current.

4. Three resistors of 10, 15, and 20 Ω, respectively, are connected in series to a battery composed of 45 dry cells. Calculate the current through the circuit.

5. Six resistors of 5, 10, 18, 24, 38, and 12 Ω, respectively, are connected in series to a storage battery of 12 cells. Find the current through the circuit.

6. Three resistors of 4, 5, and 6 Ω are to be taken two at a time and connected in series to a 120-volt battery. Find the current for each of the three cases.

7. A string of seven Christmas tree lights, each with a resistance of 60 Ω, are connected in series to a house lighting circuit of 110 volts. Find the current.

8. Two coils of an electric stove element are so connected that by proper switches either one or the other can be connected alone to the house lighting voltage of 120 volts, or they may be connected in series. Find all three possible currents if their resistances are 4 and 8 Ω, respectively.

9. Four resistors of 4, 5, 6, and 9 Ω, respectively, may be connected three at a time only, in series with a 90-volt battery. Find all possible currents from the allowed combinations.

Electricity and Magnetism | Lesson 6

SERIES CIRCUITS—*Laboratory*

In performing this experiment you will determine the resistance of several resistors alone, as well as in series, by means of a voltmeter, an ammeter, and Ohm's law. Details are given in the accompanying LABORATORY EXERCISES.

Electricity and Magnetism | Lesson 7

PARALLEL CIRCUITS

Although the terms **electromotive force** and **potential difference,** as applied to electrical circuits in general, are both measured in **volts,** there is a real distinction between them. This difference may be illustrated by a demonstration experiment shown by a circuit diagram in Fig. A.

A battery of four dry cells is connected to a resistor **R** of about 3 Ω. When the switch **S** is open, no current will flow around the circuit. The voltmeter, however, with its very high resistance of several thousand ohms will draw a negligibly small current from the battery, yet one that will indicate the electromotive force ε. For the four dry cells it would read 6.0 volts.

When the switch **S** is closed to complete the electric circuit, a current **I** of about 2 amps will flow around and through **R**, and the voltmeter will show a potential difference **V**

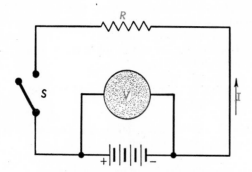

Fig. A. The measured voltage V changes when the switch is closed.

between the battery terminals of about 5.4 volts.

The drop in battery voltage from 6.0 volts on open circuit to 5.4 volts on closed circuit is due to the **internal resistance** of battery cells. This internal resistance behaves as though it were in series with the battery and may be illustrated circuitwise as shown in Fig. B. The total resistance of this circuit is composed of the external resistance R_e in series with the battery's internal resistance R_i. When the switch is closed, the current I flowing through the circuit is given by Ohm's law as,

$$I = \frac{\mathcal{E}}{R} \tag{1}$$

where, by the law of series resistances,

$$R = R_e + R_i \tag{2}$$

and $\mathcal{E}$ is the internal electromotive force of the battery ($\mathcal{E} = 6.0$ volts).

If the internal resistance $R_i = 0.3 \; \Omega$, and

Fig. B. Batteries have an internal resistance R_i.

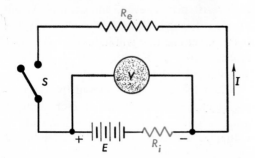

$R_e = 2.7 \; \Omega$, the total resistance $R = 3.0 \; \Omega$, and a current of 2 amperes will flow through the circuit. The IR drop across R_i will be $2 \times 0.3 = 0.6$ volts, and the voltmeter will indicate $V = 5.4$ volts instead of the 6.0 volts it indicates on open circuit.

The emf $\mathcal{E}$ may be thought of as the driving force of the battery acting on the electrons in the circuit conductors. A voltmeter always measures the potential difference between the two points to which it is connected. This is true whether they are battery terminals or two points anywhere in the circuit. We see therefore that the effective V across a battery will depend upon the battery emf, the current being drawn from that battery and the internal resistance.

Instead of applying Eq. (1) to a circuit it is customary to measure or specify V on closed circuit and then apply Ohm's law in the form

$$I = \frac{V}{R} \tag{3}$$

where R is the external resistance only.

Parallel Circuits. A circuit diagram showing three resistors R_1, R_2, and R_3 connected in parallel is shown in Fig. C. The electron current I, leaving the battery at the lower left, divides at the first junction, part I_1 going through R_1, and the remainder goes on to the next junction. Part of this current I_2 goes through R_2, and the remainder goes on and through R_3. These three currents recombine at the top junctions and form, finally, the same total current I returning to the battery.

Fig. C. Parallel circuit for three resistors R_1, R_2, and R_3.

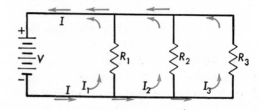

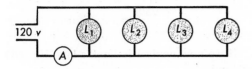

Fig. D. Parallel circuit of four light bulbs.

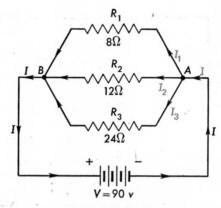

Fig. E. Three resistors in parallel, illustrating Kirchhoff's law.

It is clear from this explanation that for any number of resistors in parallel

$$I = I_1 + I_2 + I_3 + \text{etc.} \qquad (4)$$

where I is the total current and I_1, I_2, I_3, etc., are the separate currents through the resistors. Eq. (4) is the second of Kirchhoff's laws. Kirchhoff's first law, as developed in Electricity and Magnetism, Lesson 6, is concerned with the voltages, or IR drops, around any complete circuit and is written

$$V = V_1 + V_2 + V_3 + \text{etc.} \qquad (5)$$

An excellent demonstration of Eq. (4) is shown in Fig. D, where four ordinary tungsten filament light bulbs are connected in parallel to a house lighting circuit of 120 volts. The lamps may be the same or all different.

Suppose the lamps are rated as 25, 50, 75, and 100 watts, respectively, and we begin with all lamps sufficiently loose in their screw bases to be disconnected. Each lamp in turn should now be tightened in its socket, the ammeter current read and recorded, and then that lamp loosened again. Suppose these recorded currents are those shown at the left in Table 1.

As the second step, tighten each lamp in turn without loosening any, and as each new lamp comes on, record the current. These current totals could well appear like those shown at the right in Table 1.

Table 1. Recorded Data

$I_1 = .24$ amp	$I_1 = .24$ amp
$I_2 = .44$ amp	$I_1 + I_2 = .68$ amp
$I_3 = .65$ amp	$I_1 + I_2 + I_3 = 1.33$ amps
$I_4 = .85$ amp	$I_1 + I_2 + I_3 + I_4 = 2.18$ amps

Such current sums represent an experimental confirmation of Kirchhoff's law, as given by Eq. (4).

The Law of Parallel Resistances. Another type of diagram frequently drawn for parallel circuits is shown in Fig. E. Three resistors R_1, R_2, and R_3 are connected in parallel to a 90-volt battery. To find the total current through such a circuit we proceed to find a single resistance R which when substituted for the parallel combination of R_1, R_2, and R_3, will result in the same current. This equivalent resistance is given by **the law of parallel resistances**, as

$$\frac{1}{R} = \frac{1}{R_1} + \frac{1}{R_2} + \frac{1}{R_3} + \text{etc.} \qquad (6)$$

To illustrate its use, let $R_1 = 8$ Ω, $R_2 = 12$ Ω, and $R_3 = 24$ Ω, as shown in Fig. E. By direct substitution in Eq. (5)

$$\frac{1}{R} = \frac{1}{8} + \frac{1}{12} + \frac{1}{24}$$

Since the common denominator is 24,

$$\frac{1}{R} = \frac{3}{24} + \frac{2}{24} + \frac{1}{24} = \frac{6}{24}$$

from which

$$R = \frac{24}{6} = 4 \ \Omega$$

If we now imagine the parallel combination of three resistors replaced by a single resistor $R = 4\ \Omega$, the circuit will have the general form as Fig. A, and the current I will be given by Ohm's law as follows:

$$I = \frac{V}{R} = \frac{90 \text{ volts}}{4\ \Omega} = 22.5 \text{ amps}$$

This is the total current I supplied by the battery to the parallel circuit of Fig. E.

To find how this current divides at **A** into three parts I_1, I_2, and I_3, we note that the full 90 volts are directly applied to the opposite ends of each resistor. Therefore Ohm's law can be applied to each resistor separately as follows:

$$I_1 = \frac{90 \text{ volts}}{8\ \Omega} = 11.25 \text{ amps}$$

$$I_2 = \frac{90 \text{ volts}}{12\ \Omega} = 7.50 \text{ amps}$$

$$I_3 = \frac{90 \text{ volts}}{24\ \Omega} = 3.75 \text{ amps}$$

If we now apply Kirchhoff's law, Eq. (4) we find

$$I = 11.25 + 7.50 + 3.75 = 22.5 \text{ amps}$$

and this is a check upon the previous total current. Note that the largest of the three currents, $I_1 = 11.25$ amps, flows through the smallest resistance, and the smallest current I_3 flows through the highest resistance.

Kirchhoff's Law of Currents is frequently stated as follows:

The sum of all the currents flowing into any junction point is equal to the sum of all the currents flowing out.

An inspection of junction **A** or junction **B** in Fig. E, will show how this definition gives us Eq. (4).

Summary

All batteries have an internal resistance **R**. The electromotive force $\mathcal{E}$ of a battery is its open circuit voltage. When a battery is supplying a current I to any circuit, there is an $I R$ drop within the battery.

The potential difference **V** across the battery, as read by a voltmeter, is equal to $\mathcal{E} - I R$. It is customary to apply Ohm's law to the external circuit only and, therefore, to use **V** in place of $\mathcal{E}$.

When resistors are connected in parallel, each resistor carries part of the current only. The total current supplied by the battery is the sum of the individual currents. This is expressed by Kirchhoff's law for currents.

$$I = I_1 + I_2 + I_3 + \text{ etc.}$$

The resistance **R** of any parallel circuit is given by the reciprocal formula

$$\frac{1}{R} = \frac{1}{R_1} + \frac{1}{R_2} + \frac{1}{R_3} + \text{ etc.}$$

Questions

1. What is meant by the emf of a battery? How is it measured?

2. What is meant by the potential difference? How is it measured? Is the potential difference across battery terminals always the same?

3. How is Ohm's law applied to a circuit if the emf and internal resistance are given?

4. How is Ohm's law applied when the potential difference of the battery on closed circuit is specified?

5. How can you find the equivalent resistance of a parallel circuit. How does this differ from the series circuit formula?

6. How does the current divide in a parallel circuit? Which resistor carries the largest current? Which carries the smallest current?

7. If several resistors are in parallel and connected to a battery, how is the current through each resistor calculated? What is the same for all resistors?

8. What do you think would make a good project for the making of some inexpensive device for demonstrating the principles of parallel circuits?

Problems

1. A battery has an emf of 26 volts and an internal resistance of 0.4 Ω. (a) Find the current supplied when the battery is connected to a 10 Ω appliance. (b) What is the IR drop within the battery? (c) What is the potential difference across the battery?

2. A battery has an emf of 45 volts and an internal resistance of 1.0 Ω. (a) What current is supplied when it is connected to a 24 Ω resistor? (b) What is the potential difference across the battery? (c) What is the IR drop across the resistor?

3. A battery has an emf of 22 volts and an internal resistance of 0.5 Ω. What is the potential difference between the battery terminals when connected to an external resistance of 5 Ω?

4. Two resistors of 6 Ω and 12 Ω, respectively, are connected in parallel to a battery supplying a potential difference of 20 volts. Find (a) the equivalent resistance of the parallel circuit, (b) the total current, and (c) the current through each resistor.

5. Two resistors of 10 Ω and 30 Ω, respectively, are connected to a 45-volt battery. Find (a) the equivalent resistance of the parallel circuit, (b) the total battery current, and (c) the current through each resistor.

6. Three appliances of 6 Ω, 18 Ω, and 36 Ω, respectively, are connected in parallel to a 90-volt battery. Find (a) the equivalent resistance of the parallel circuit, (b) the total current supplied by the battery, and (c) the electron current through each appliance.

7. Three hot plates of 4 Ω, 5 Ω, and 20 Ω, respectively, are connected in parallel to a 48-volt battery. Find (a) the circuit resistance, (b) the total current, and (c) the current through each hot plate.

8. Four appliances of 5 Ω, 6 Ω, 10 Ω, and 30 Ω, respectively, are connected in parallel to a house lighting circuit capable of maintaining $V = 120$ volts. Find (a) the equivalent resistance of the parallel circuit, (b) the total current supplied by the battery, and (c) the electron current through each appliance.

9.* Two resistors of 5 Ω and 20 Ω are connected in parallel. This parallel circuit is in series with an 8 Ω resistor, and the entire circuit is connected to a 60-volt battery. Find the equivalent resistance of (a) the parallel combination and (b) the entire circuit. (c) Find the electron current through each resistor.

10.* Three light bulbs of 50 Ω, 75 Ω, and 150 Ω, respectively, are connected in parallel. This combination is connected in series with a 15 Ω appliance and the entire circuit is connected to a 120-volt line. Find the equivalent resistance of (a) the parallel combination and (b) the entire circuit. (c) What current flows through each device?

THE ELECTRIC FIELD AND POTENTIAL

Electrical Potential. When a body has an excess of electrons (and is not close to other charged bodies), it has a *negative potential*. When it has a deficiency of electrons, it is said to have a *positive potential*. There are numerous exceptions to this, however, and it is customary to define positive potential and negative potential in a more general way. This is usually done as follows. If the connection of a body to the ground by an electrical conductor would cause electrons to flow onto the body from the ground, the body is at a *positive potential* (see diagram (a) in Fig. A). Conversely, if the connection of a body to the ground would cause electrons to flow off the body into the ground, the body is at a negative potential (see diagram (b)).

In these definitions of positive and negative potential *it is assumed that the earth is at zero potential*. The bodies therefore had positive and negative potentials respectively before they were grounded, but after they were grounded, the flow of electrons *to* or *from* the ground brought them to *zero potential*. Electrical potential is analogous to the potential energy of a body in mechanics.

In mechanics if a body is raised to a certain height *h* above sea level, its potential energy is positive, i.e., it can in returning to the ground perform an amount of work equal to *mgh*. See Fig. B. Conversely, a body at a distance *h* below sea level has a negative potential energy *mgh* for in lowering it to that point energy is given up. To raise it again requires the expenditure of energy. Just as sea level is sometimes taken as the zero level of potential energy in mechanics, so the earth's potential is taken as the zero point of potential in electricity.

A quantitative definition of electrical potential is usually given in terms of work or energy.

The electric potential V of a body is equal to the amount of work per unit positive charge done in carrying any charge Q from the ground up to the charged body.

$$V = \frac{W}{Q} \qquad (1)$$

where **W** represents the work done and in the mks system is measured in *joules*. If the work done is large, the potential of the body is highly positive. If the work done is negative, i.e., if work is given up, the potential is nega-

Fig. A. Showing the direction of the flow of electrons when a positively or negatively charged body is connected to the ground by a wire conductor.

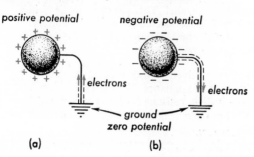

positive potential   *negative potential*

electrons

electrons

ground
zero potential

(a)   (b)

Fig. B. Electrical potential in electricity is analogous to potential energy in mechanics.

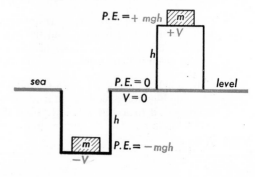

P.E. = + *mgh*   +V

h

sea   P.E. = 0   level
                           V = 0

h

m   P.E. = − *mgh*

−V

tive. As a rule this energy is expressed in **volts,** and we speak of a potential of a body as being $+110$ volts, -2500 volts, etc.

It is also proper to speak of the potential of a point located anywhere in the free space around one or more charged bodies.

The electric potential at any point in an electric field is equal to the work per unit positive charge done in carrying any charge from the ground up to that point.

To give specific units to this definition, if the unit of charge is one coulomb and the work done is one joule, the potential is one volt.

$$1 \text{ volt} = 1 \frac{\text{joule}}{\text{coulomb}}$$

One one-thousandth of a volt is called a **millivolt** (**mv**), one-millionth of a volt a **microvolt** (μv), one thousand volts a **kilovolt** (**kv**), and one million volts a **megavolt** (**Mv**).

The work per unit positive charge done in carrying a charge from the ground up to a point near a small body of charge **Q** is given by

$$\boxed{V = k \frac{Q}{d}} \qquad (2)$$

where **d**, as shown in Fig. C, is the straight line distance from the center of the charged body to the unit test charge, and **k** is given by $\frac{1}{4}\pi\epsilon_0$. See Eq. (4), Lesson 2.

If the charge is located on a small spherical

Fig. C. Potential near a charged spherical conductor.

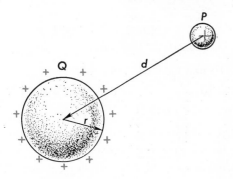

conductor of radius **r**, the potential at all points outside the sphere is the same as though the charge were concentrated at the center. At all points inside the sphere the potential is the same as it is at the surface, namely

$$V = k \frac{Q}{r} \qquad (3)$$

It will be noted from Eq. (2) that as **d** is made larger and approaches infinity, **V** becomes smaller and approaches zero. Mathematically speaking then the ground, referred to in the above definitions and statements, with its arbitrary assigned potential of zero, corresponds in Eq. (2) to **d** $= \infty$.

Example 1. A spherical conductor of radius 1 cm has a charge of $+ 25 \times 10^{-10}$ coulombs. Calculate the potential at a point 10 cm from the center.
Solution. Apply Eq. (2), and use mks units.

$$V = 9 \times 10^9 \frac{25 \times 10^{-10}}{0.10} = 225 \text{ volts}$$

Potential Difference. The potential of a body is defined as the work per unit positive charge done in carrying any charge from infinity to that body.

The difference of potential V between two bodies is defined as the work per unit positive charge done in carrying any charge from one of the bodies to the other.

For example, the potential difference between the two terminals of a car storage battery is 12 volts. This means that the work per unit positive charge done in carrying a charge from one terminal to the other is 12 joules per coulomb.

The Electric Field. In the space around a charged body is an invisible something called an **electric field.** This field is just another way of describing the action at a distance of one charge upon another.

The intensity of the electric field at any

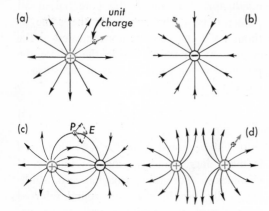

Fig. D. Diagrams of the electric field around charged bodies.

point in the neighborhood of a charged body is equal to the force per unit charge exerted on any charge placed at that point.

Since force is a vector quantity, an electric field has magnitude and direction. The field about a positive charge is therefore radially outward as shown in Fig D(a). It is radially outward since a positive charge placed at any point is repelled along a line through the two charges. By a similar reasoning the field about a negative charge is radially inward as shown in diagram (b).

The electric field around two charged bodies is shown in diagrams (c) and (d). Each of these fields may be experimentally mapped by placing a positive charge at any one point and moving it always in the direction of the force **F** exerted on it. The lines traced out by such a charge are called **electric lines of force**. It is to be noted that as many lines as desired can be drawn and that no two lines ever cross. Furthermore, the lines themselves are imaginary and do not actually exist. They were first introduced by Michael Faraday about 1820 as an aid to the understanding of various electrical phenomena.

The direction of the lines of force is given by the arrowheads and the relative magnitude of the field at any region is given by the relative number of the lines passing through that region. In agreement with Coulomb's law

the intensity of the field at any point near a single charged body is inversely proportional to the square of the distance away.

Since **E**, the electric field intensity, is defined as the force per unit charge placed there, **F/Q**, Coulomb's law may be used to obtain a formula for the field intensity at any point near a small body of charge **Q**. Transposing **Q'** to the other side in Eq. (1), Electricity and Magnetism, Lesson 2, gives

$$\frac{F}{Q'} = k \frac{Q}{d^2}$$

or

$$E = k \frac{Q}{d^2} \qquad (4)$$

The charge **Q** is in **coulombs**, the distance **d** to the field point is in **meters**, the field **E** at that point is in **newtons per coulomb**, and $k = 9 \times 10^9$ newton meters^2/coulomb^2. See Eq. (4) Electricity and Magnetism, Lesson 2. Since **E** represents the force per unit charge, the force on any charge **Q'** placed at that point will be

$$F = Q' \times E$$

$$\left(1 \text{ newton} = 1 \text{ coulomb} \times 1 \frac{\text{newton}}{\text{coulomb}}\right) \quad (5)$$

Example 2. A proton is an atomic particle having a mass of 1.672×10^{-27} kg and a positive charge of 1.602×10^{-19} coulombs. Calculate the force on a proton in an electric field of 5000 newtons per coulomb and compare this with its weight.

Solution. To find the electrical force apply Eq. (5).

$$F = Q'E = 1.602 \times 10^{-19} \times 5 \times 10^3$$
$$= 8.010 \times 10^{-16} \text{ newton}$$

To find the weight of a proton,

$$W = mg = 1.672 \times 10^{-27} \times 9.80$$
$$= 1.638 \times 10^{-26} \text{ newton}$$

A comparison of these two forces clearly indicates how negligibly small the gravitational force on atomic particles is when compared with the force due to electric fields commonly employed in the laboratory.

Uniform Electric Field.   In many experimental studies of atomic structure a great deal of knowledge can be obtained by observing the behavior of charged atomic particles traversing a uniform electric field. To obtain such a field, that is, a field constant in magnitude and direction over a specified volume of space, two flat metal plates are set up parallel to each other as shown in Fig. E.

When the terminals of a battery with a voltage **V** are connected to these plates, as indicated in the diagram, a uniform electric field **E** is produced between the plates. Outside the plates and near the ends the field is not uniform.

In mechanics **work done** is defined as **force times distance, W = F × d**. The electrical equivalent of this equation follows, therefore, by direct substitution of the equiva-

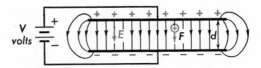

Fig. E. The electric field between two parallel charged plates is uniform.

lent electrical quantities for **W** and **F**. Since work done per unit charge is potential difference **V**, and the force per unit charge is the electrical field intensity **E**, see Eqs. (1) and (5), the work equation **W = F × d** becomes

$$V = E \times d$$

or

$$E = \frac{V}{d} \qquad (6)$$

If **V** is in volts and **d** is in meters, **E** is in **volts/meter.**

$$1 \; \frac{\text{volt}}{\text{meter}} = 1 \; \frac{\text{newton}}{\text{coulomb}}$$

Summary

The potential of all charged bodies is specified with respect to the earth. The earth is assumed to have a zero potential.

The potential of a body is a measure of the work done in carrying a charge from the ground to that body:

$$V = \frac{W}{Q}$$

Work done **W** is in joules, **Q** is in coulombs, and **V** is in volts.

The potential of any point in space near a charged body is given by the work done in carrying a charge from the ground to that point:

$$V = \frac{kQ}{d}$$

The distance **d** from the body of charge **Q** to the point in question is measured in meters, and the constant $k = 9 \times 10^9$.

The potential difference between two points is a measure of the work done in carrying a charge from one point to the other and is measured in volts.

Around every charge body or system of bodies there is an electric field. The field intensity **E** at any point is a measure of the force per unit charge exerted on any charged body placed there,

$$E = \frac{F}{Q'}$$

Questions

1. What is potential? How is it defined? How is it measured? What are the units of potential?

2. What is the potential of a point in space? How is it defined?

3. What is potential difference? What are the units of potential difference?

4. What is meant by an electric field? How could one find the electric field intensity at a point in space? What are the units of the electric field intensity E?

5. What is a uniform electric field? How is such a field produced? How is its magnitude determined by calculation? How is the direction of a field determined?

6. Define (a) electrical potential of a body, (b) electrical potential of a point in space, (c) difference of potential, and (d) electric field intensity.

Problems

1. If 2.4×10^{-5} joule of work is done in carrying a charge of 5×10^{-8} coulomb up to a charged body, what is its potential?

2. A charge of 8×10^{-7} coulomb is carried from a distant point up to a charged body. What is the potential of that body if the work done is 2×10^{-4} joule?

3. A spherical conductor 2 cm in diameter has a charge of 5×10^{-9} coulomb. Calculate the potential of (a) a point 8 cm from the center and (b) the sphere.

4. A spherical conductor 3 cm in diameter has a charge of 2×10^{-9} coulomb. Calculate the potential of (a) the sphere and (b) a point 5 cm from the center.

5. A metal sphere is suspended by a silk thread and charged negatively. In carrying a negative charge of 4×10^{-8} coulomb from a great distance to the metal sphere, an amount of work equal to 8×10^{-5} joule is done. What is the potential of the sphere?

6.* Two flat metal plates 2 cm apart are connected to a 1000-volt battery. A proton with its positive charge of 1.6×10^{-19} coulomb is located between these plates. Find (a) the electric field intensity between the plates and (b) the force on the proton in newtons.

7.* Two flat metal plates 2 cm apart are connected to a 2000-volt source. A small charge Q of 5×10^{-9} coulomb is located in the field. Find (a) the electric field intensity and (b) the force on the charge Q.

8.* A battery of 8000 volts is applied to two parallel plates 5 mm apart. What is the force of an electron of charge 1.60×10^{-19} coulomb when it passes through the uniform electric field between the plates?

PARALLEL RESISTANCES—*Laboratory*

This experiment is described in the accompanying LABORATORY EXERCISES. The currents flowing through, and the voltages applied to, resistors in parallel, are measured with an ammeter and a voltmeter. Ohm's law and Kirchhoff's laws are applied to the recorded data.

CAPACITANCE

The Capacitor. A capacitor is an electrical device for storing quantities of electricity in much the same way that a reservoir is a container for storing water or a steel tank is a container for storing gas. The general form of a capacitor is that of two parallel conducting plates as shown in Fig. A.

Such plates are of relatively large area, close together, and contain between them a nonconducting medium called the **dielectric.** Common dielectrics are **air, glass, mica, oil,** and **waxed paper.**

Quantitatively, the capacitance of a capacitor is a measure of its ability to store up electricity. To increase the capacitance of a capacitor one or more of the following things can be done: first, the area of the plates may be increased; second, the plates may be put closer together; and third, a more suitable dielectric may be inserted between the plates. If the plates of a capacitor are small in area and at the same time relatively far apart, the capacitance is small. If the area is large and the plates close together, the capacitance is large.

The principles of the capacitor are illustrated in Fig. A. One plate of this capacitor is grounded and the other is insulated but connected to an electroscope or electrometer. If the right-hand plate is now given a nega-

tive charge as shown, electrons in the other plate are repelled into the ground, leaving that plate positively charged. If the insulated plate is given a positive charge (not shown), electrons from the ground are attracted to the other plate and it acquires a negative charge.

In either case the grounded plate is, by definition, at **ground potential,** or **zero potential.** The right-hand plate is at negative potential, since if connected to the ground, its electrons would escape into the ground. As shown in the diagram, however, the capacitor is charged.

If, while in the charged condition, the two plates of a capacitor are suddenly connected by a conductor, the negatives can flow through the conductor to the positives, thus neutralizing the charges. The capacitor has thus been discharged.

Fig. A. Demonstration of the principles of a capacitor.

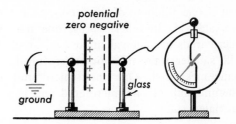

During the time a capacitor is being charged the plates acquire a greater and greater difference of potential. If in Fig. A more electrons are added to the insulated plate, the potential difference is increased. The amount of charge stored up in this way is limited only by the breakdown of the dielectric between the two plates. When the charge becomes too great, a spark will jump between the plates, thus discharging the capacitor.

Capacitance is not determined by the amount of charge a capacitor will hold before sparking occurs; it is defined as the amount of charge **Q** on one plate necessary to raise the potential **V** of that plate one volt above the other. Symbolically,

$$C = \frac{Q}{V} \qquad (1)$$

The unit of capacitance, the **farad**, named in honor of Michael Faraday is defined as the capacitance of a capacitor of such dimensions that **a charge of one coulomb will give the plates a difference of potential of one volt.**

$$1 \text{ farad} = \frac{1 \text{ coulomb}}{1 \text{ volt}} \qquad (2)$$

Whether one plate of a 1-farad capacitor is grounded or not, the potential difference between the plates will be one volt when one plate has a positive charge of one coulomb and the other plate has a negative charge of one coulomb. The grounded plate will have one coulomb of charge, but its potential will be zero.

A capacitance of one farad is very large and for practical purposes is not used. The **microfarad** is more convenient. The smaller unit is one-millionth of the farad and is abbreviated μf. In other words, one million microfarads are equivalent to one farad. A still smaller unit, the **micromicrofarad,** is sometimes used. One micromicrofarad is one-millionth of one microfarad and is abbreviated $\mu\mu$f.

$$1 \ \mu f = 10^{-6} \ f \qquad (3)$$
$$1 \ \mu\mu f = 10^{-12} \ f \qquad (4)$$

The charging of a capacitor until the difference of potential is one volt is analogous to raising the level of water in a tank to one foot, whereas the charging of the same capacitor to the point where it sparks over is like filling the tank until water runs over the top. A large capacitance is like a tank of large cross-sectional area, and a small capacitance is like a tank of small area. It takes more charge to raise the potential of a large capacitance one volt, and it takes more water to raise the level in a large tank one foot.

Capacitors in common use today are of various kinds, sizes, and shapes. Perhaps the most common is the so-called "paper capacitor" used commonly in radios and the ignition system of automobiles. Two long strips of tin foil are glued to the two faces of a strip of thin paper. This paper is then soaked in paraffin or oil and rolled up with another paraffin-soaked strip of paper into a small compact unit. Each sheet of tin foil becomes one plate of the capacitor and the paper becomes the dielectric separating them.

Another type of capacitor is the variable capacitor commonly used in tuning radios (see Fig. B). The capacitance of such a device can be varied in amount at will by the turning of a knob. The turning of a knob moves one set of plates between the other set, thus increasing or decreasing the effec-

Fig. B. Variable capacitor commonly used in radio sets. (Courtesy of Hammarlund Manufacturing Co.)

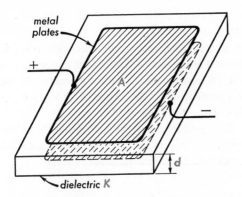

Fig. C. Diagram of the principal elements of a capacitor.

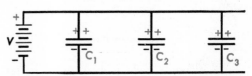

parallel capacitors

Fig. D. Circuit diagram of parallel capacitors.

tive plate area, and hence, the capacitance. The capacitance of such variable air capacitors is from zero to some 4000 $\mu\mu$f.

Calculation of Capacitance. A general formula for calculating the capacitance of a parallel plate capacitor is the following:

$$C = \epsilon \frac{A}{d} \qquad (5)$$

where, as shown in Fig. C, A is the area of either of the parallel plates in meters², d is the distance between them in meters, ϵ a constant of the separating medium, and C is the capacitance in farads.

The constant ϵ, called the **permittivity,** is the product of the constant $\epsilon_o = 8.85 \times 10^{-12}$ and K the **dielectric constant,** or **dielectric coefficient.**

$$\epsilon = \epsilon_o K \qquad (6)$$

Values of the dielectric constant of a few substances are given in Table 1.

In the mks system permittivity has the units of farads/meter or, what is the equivalent, coulombs²/newton meter².

Example. Two rectangular sheets of tinfoil 20 cm × 25 cm are stuck to opposite sides of a thin sheet of mica 0.1 mm thick. Calculate the capacitance if the dielectric constant is 5.

Solution. The given quantities are $K = 5$, $d = 1 \times 10^{-4}$ m, and $A = 0.20 \times 0.25 = 0.05$ m². By substituting in Eqs. (5) and (6), we obtain

$$C = 5 \times 8.85 \times 10^{-12} \frac{0.05}{1 \times 10^{-4}}$$

$$= 221 \times 10^{-10} \text{ farad} = 0.0221 \ \mu f$$

When capacitors are connected in parallel, as shown in Fig. D, their combined capacitance is just the arithmetic sum of the individual capacities.

parallel capacitors

$$C = C_1 + C_2 + C_3 + \text{etc.} \qquad (7)$$

When capacitors are connected in series, as shown in Fig. E, the combined capacitance

Table 1. Dielectric Constants

Dielectric	K
vacuum............	1.0000
air................	1.0006
glass..............	5-10
rubber.............	3-35
mica...............	3-6
glycerine..........	56
petroleum..........	2
water..............	81

Fig. E. Circuit diagram of series capacitors.

series capacitors

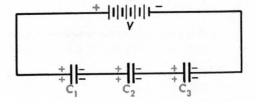

is given by the reciprocal of the sum of the reciprocals.

series capacitors

$$\frac{1}{C} = \frac{1}{C_1} + \frac{1}{C_2} + \frac{1}{C_3} + \text{etc.} \qquad (8)$$

The first formula is derived from the principle that capacitors in a parallel combination each have the same potential difference V given by $V = Q/C$, while $Q = Q_1 + Q_2 + Q_3 +$ etc. The second of these formulas is derived from the principle that capacitors in a series combination acquire the same charge Q given by $Q = CV$, while $V = V_1 + V_2 + V_3 +$ etc.

It should be noted with care that these two formulas are just the reverse of those for series and parallel resistors.

Summary

The capacitor is composed of parallel conducting plates separated by a nonconducting layer called the dielectric. Capacitance is a measure of the electrical charge that can be stored in a capacitor. It is given by

$$C = Q/V$$

The unit of capacitance is the farad. Because this unit is so large, a smaller unit, the micro-farad, is commonly used $(1 \ \mu f = 10^{-6} \ f)$.

Capacitance depends upon three factors: (1) the plate area A (in square meters), (2) the plate separation d (in meters), and (3) the permittivity ϵ of the separating medium.

$$C = \epsilon A/d$$

When capacitors are connected in parallel, their equivalent capacitance is given by their arithmetic sum. When they are in series, the familiar reciprocal formula applies.

Questions

1. What is a capacitor? What three elements go to make up a capacitor?

2. What is capacitance? What are the units of capacitance? What is the formula? Is Q the sum of the charges on both plates?

3. How does capacitance change when the plate area is doubled? What happens when the plate separation is increased?

4. How does capacitance change when air between the plates is replaced by glass?

5. What is the formula for capacitance in terms of its dimensions? What is permittivity?

6. What is the dielectric constant? What is the dielectric constant for a vacuum? What is the permittivity for a vacuum?

7. What is the equation for capacitors in parallel? What is the formula for series connection?

8. If the negatively charged plate of a capacitor is connected to the ground, do the electrons leave the plate? Is the plate at zero potential?

9. Could a capacitor plate have a net positive charge and a negative potential? If so, how could you produce it?

Problems

1. A 1000-volt battery is connected to a 10-μf capacitor. What is the charge on each plate?

2. A 250-volt battery is applied to a 6-μf capacitor. Find the charge on each plate.

3. Two sheets of tinfoil 20 cm × 50 cm are glued to opposite faces of a glass plate 0.8 cm thick. Find its capacitance if the dielectric constant for glass is 5.

4. Two flat metal plates 40 cm × 100 cm are mounted parallel to each other and 1 cm apart. Find the capacitance when they are immersed in oil of dielectric constant 2.

5. A parallel plate capacitor with air as a dielectric has a capacitance of 5 μf. What will be its capacitance if submerged in glycerine?

6. A parallel plate capacitor with glass as a dielectric has a capacitance of 0.05 μf. What will be its capacitance if the glass (dielectric constant 8) is replaced by mica (dielectric constant 3)?

7. A capacitor is made up of 16 sheets of tinfoil each 4 cm × 15 cm, separated by mica sheets 0.25 mm thick. Find the capacitance in microfarads if alternate sheets of tinfoil are connected together. Dielectric constant of mica = 4.8.

8. Three capacitors 8, 12, and 24 μf, respectively, are connected in series. Find the capacitance of the system.

9.* Three capacitors 4, 5, and 20 μf are connected in series to a 300-volt battery. Find (a) the capacitance and (b) the charge on each capacitor plate, and (c) the voltage across each capacitor.

10.* Two capacitors of 5 μf and 20 μf, respectively, are connected in parallel, and the combination in series with a third capacitor of 10 μf. Find (a) the capacitance of the parallel circuit, (b) the total capacitance, and (c) the voltage across each capacitor, if the ends are connected to a 1000-volt battery.

Electricity and Magnetism | Lesson 11
THE POTENTIAL DIVIDER—Laboratory

In performing this experiment as described in the accompanying *LABO-RATORY EXERCISES* you will measure the wide range of voltages that can be obtained from a slide wire resistor. Such devices are used in many electrical appliances and devices.

MAGNETISM

Magnetism was known to the early Greek philosophers. One story goes that Magnes, a shepherd, when on Mt. Ida of the island Crete, was so strongly attracted to the ground by the tip of his staff and the nails in his shoes that he had difficulty in getting away. Upon digging into the ground to find the cause, he discovered a stone with the most amazing properties of attracting iron. This stone is now called lodestone or magnetite.

The idea that a lodestone can be used as a compass is a very old one. There is some evidence that the Chinese had a knowledge of this as far back as A.D. 121. At any rate, a Chinese author writing as early as the beginning of the twelfth century explains that a needle, rubbed with lodestone and suspended free to turn, will point toward the south. This appears to be the first evidence that a piece of iron could be magnetized by a lodestone and used as a compass. The action of a lodestone or a bar magnet when suspended free to turn about a vertical axis is illustrated in Fig. A, diagrams (a) and (b).

A compass as it is often made for demonstration purposes consists usually of a straight steel needle which has been magnetized and

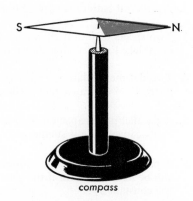

compass

Fig. B. A compass needle points toward the north.

mounted free to turn on a sharp pointed rod as shown in Fig. B.

Magnets. Until recent years magnets have been made of hardened steel and molded or rolled into many shapes. Perhaps

Fig. C. The attraction of a magnet for iron acts through all substances.

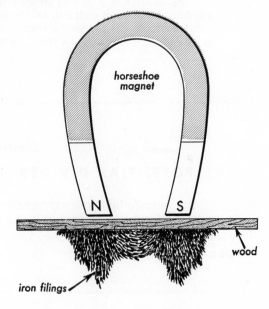

horseshoe magnet

N   S

wood

iron filings

Fig. A. A lodestone and a bar magnet point north and south.

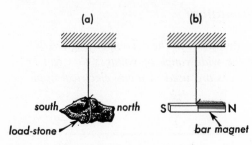

(a)   (b)

south north   S   N

load-stone   bar magnet

the most common of these is the horseshoe magnet shown in Fig. C, or the straight bar magnet shown in Fig. A(b). The strongest magnets are now made of an alloy containing aluminum, cobalt, nickel, and iron. Small magnets of this alloy are strong enough to lift hundreds of times their own weight.

Pure iron, sometimes called soft iron, when magnetized will not retain its magnetism and is therefore useless in making what are called permanent magnets. Soft iron is used, however, in the construction of electromagnets. These devices will be discussed and demonstrated in another chapter. Of the many practical applications of permanent magnets, the compass, the telephone receiver, and the radio loudspeaker are perhaps the most common.

The Power of Attraction. Nearly everyone has at sometime or other played with a small horseshoe magnet and discovered for himself that it attracted only things containing iron. Upon drawing the same magnet through the dry sand or dirt you probably discovered that it will pick up small grains of iron ore.

If more extensive experiments are carried out, a magnet can be shown to attract magnetic substances at a distance even though matter lies in the intervening space. In other words, magnetic attraction acts right through matter of all kinds. This can be demonstrated as shown in Fig. C by picking up iron filings on one side of a thin wooden board by holding a magnet close to the other side. If a sheet of copper, or brass, or, as a matter of fact, any substance, is placed over the magnet the power of attraction is not destroyed. A small region of space can be partially shielded from magnetic fields if it is entirely surrounded by layers of soft iron.

While a few metals are known to be feebly attracted by a magnet, most substances like aluminum, copper, silver, gold, wood, glass, paper, etc., do not exhibit any noticeable effect.

Fig. D. The attraction of iron filings by a straight bar magnet shows greater attraction near the ends. These regions of greatest attraction are called *magnetic poles.*

Magnetic Poles. When an ordinary straight bar magnet is dipped into a box of iron filings, the tiny bits of iron are observed to cling to the ends as shown in Fig. D. These preferred regions of attraction are called **magnetic poles.** If this same magnet is suspended by a thread as shown in Fig. A(b), it will come to rest in a position close to the north-south direction. The end toward the north is therefore called the **N** or *north-seeking pole,* and the other end the **S** or *south-seeking pole.*

That the **N** and **S** poles of a magnet are different may be shown by bringing the magnet close to a compass needle. Such an experiment is illustrated in Fig. E. When the **S**

Fig. E. Unlike magnetic poles attract each other, while like magnetic poles repel each other.

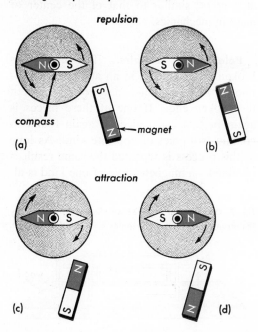

pole of the magnet is brought close to the **S** pole of the compass needle as in diagram (a) there is a force of repulsion acting and the compass needle turns away as shown. A similar repulsion occurs between the two **N** poles as shown in diagram (b). If the **N** and **S** poles are brought near to each other, however, a very strong attraction arises and the compass needle turns toward the other as shown in diagrams (c) and (d). These experiments show, therefore, that *two kinds of magnetic poles exist* and that *like poles repel and unlike poles attract.*

Permanent magnets can now be made so strong that one magnet can be lifted by the repulsion of another. This is illustrated in Fig. F. Unless guide rods of glass or some other substance are used, however, the floating bar will move to one side and then fall. In other words, the forces of repulsion are such that the upper bar is not in stable equilibrium.

It should be pointed out that each magnetic pole in a magnetized body is not confined to a single point but extends over a finite region. From a distance, however, each polar region acts as though it were concentrated at a point, similar to that of the center of mass in mechanics.

Poles Exist in Pairs. If a magnet is broken in the middle in an attempt to separate the poles, one finds new poles formed at the broken ends. If one of these pieces is again broken, each piece is again found to contain two poles of opposite kind. As long as this process is repeated the same result is obtained—a magnetic pole of one kind is al-

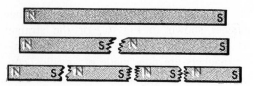

Fig. G. The poles of a magnet cannot exist alone. When a bar magnet is broken, poles appear on either side of the break, such that each piece has two opposite poles.

ways accompanied by a pole of opposite polarity.

This is conveniently illustrated by magnetizing a hack-saw blade and breaking it successively into smaller and smaller pieces as shown in Fig. G. Each time a piece is broken, each fragment, upon being tested with a compass, is found to have an **N** pole on one side and an **S** pole on the other. A hack-saw blade is readily magnetized by stroking it from one end to the other with one of the poles of a magnet.

It is possible to magnetize a bar of steel so that it has three or more polar regions. This is illustrated in Fig. H where a hacksaw blade has been magnetized with an **N** pole at each end and an **S** polar region in the center. The combined strength of the **N** poles is seen by the quantity of iron filings to be equal to the **S** pole strength in the center. We might say, therefore, that the magnet has four poles: an **N** pole at either end and two **S** poles at the center.

Magnetization. When a strong magnet is brought close to a piece of soft iron, the iron takes on all the properties of a new but somewhat weaker magnet. This phenomenon, called *magnetization,* is illustrated in Fig. I(a). As long as the permanent magnet is held close to the soft iron bar, the iron filings

Fig. F. One magnet may be suspended in mid-air by the strong repulsion of like poles from another magnet.

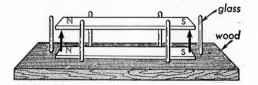

Fig. H. Diagram of a bar magnet with iron filings showing three polar regions.

permanent magnets

soft iron

iron nails

(a)   (b)

Fig. I. Soft iron may be magnetized by induction at a
distance or by contact.

cling to the end as shown. When the permanent magnet is removed, however, the soft
iron immediately loses its magnetism and the
iron filings drop off.

When a piece of iron is magnetized, a pole
of opposite sign is created at the points of
closest approach as shown in the diagrams.
If a common iron nail is brought up to the
N pole of a permanent magnet, it will become
magnetizied with a **S** pole at the point of contact and an **N** pole at the other end as shown
in diagram (b). Having two poles, the nail is
thus magnetized and will attract another nail
and magnetize it in the same way. With a
good strong magnet this process can be repeated by adding one nail after the other.

It is now clear how iron filings line up
with the lines of force of a magnet. Each filing becomes magnetized and, like a small
compass, turns parallel to the field in which
it is located.

Magnetic tape used in TV and sound recording consists of a continuous strip of such
magnetic material. In passing close to an
electromagnetic recording head, myriads of
tiny poles of different strengths and spacings
are induced along the tape.

Molecular Theory of Ferromagnetism.
The modern theory of magnetism which is
now quite firmly established as being correct
is that a piece of iron consists of myriads of
tiny elementary magnets. These tiny ultramicroscopic magnets consist of individual
atoms and molecules themselves or of groups
of atoms aligned to form small elementary
iron crystals. How single atoms act as magnets will be explained later. Before a piece of
iron or steel has been magnetized these elementary magnets may be thought of as being
oriented more or less at random throughout
the metal as shown in Fig. J(a).

During the time a piece of iron is being
magnetized the elementary magnets are

Fig. J. Schematic diagrams of the elementary magnets within a piece of iron, (a) unmagnetized and
(b) magnetized.

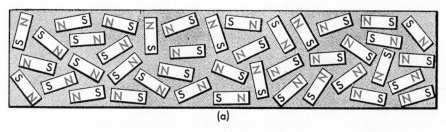

(a)

(b)

turned around and lined up parallel to each other. This is shown by the schematic representation in diagram (b). Lined up in this way, the small N and S poles are adjacent to each other and cancel each other's effect on external objects. At one end there are many free N poles and at the opposite end an equal number of free S poles.

When a magnet is broken at any point, *free S poles* are exposed at one side of the break and *free N poles* at the other. It is therefore clear why poles always exist in pairs and that no matter how many times a magnet is broken each piece will contain an N pole at one end and an S pole at the other.

When soft iron is magnetized by induction and the permanent magnet taken away, the elementary magnets return to their original random orientations; but when hardened steel becomes magnetized, they remain lined up after the magnetizing field is taken away.

Summary

Magnetism is exhibited largely by ores of very high iron content. Alloys that can be made into very strong, permanent magnets have been developed.

The attraction of iron by a magnet can act through wood, glass, paper, copper, aluminum, etc. Soft iron, however, acts as a relatively strong shield.

Magnets have regions of relatively strong attraction, and these have been called magnetic poles. Poles always exist in pairs and are of two kinds.

Like poles repel and unlike poles attract. When a bar magnet containing two poles near the ends is broken in the middle, new poles are created.

Many poles can be produced in a strip of magnetic material. This is the principle of magnetic tape recording.

When a piece of soft iron is brought close to a magnet, it becomes magnetized and behaves as if it too were a magnet. This is called magnetization by induction.

Magnetism is due to the magnetic properties of individual atoms and molecules within the metal.

Questions

1. What is a bar magnet? What is a horeshoe magnet?

2. What are magnetic poles? How many kinds of poles are there. What are their names? What is the origin of these names?

3. Can magnets be made strong enough to lift one another by repulsion?

4. Is a magnetic pole a point or a distributed area on the surface of a magnet? Can a magnet have one pole only? Can the two poles of a magnet be broken apart?

5. Can a magnet have more than two poles? Can a magnet have 1000 poles?

6. What is magnetic induction? How can it be demonstrated?

7. What is the molecular theory of magnetism? How does soft iron differ in behavior from steel?

8. Make a diagram of a bar magnet with five more or less equally spaced poles.

9. Do you think a magnet could be made with one **N** pole and three separated **S** poles? If so, how?

10. What inexpensive device can you make as a project for demonstrating some of the principles introduced in this lesson?

Electricity and Magnetism | **Lesson 13**

MAGNETIC FIELDS

The Magnetic Field. In the space surrounding every magnet there exists an imaginary something we call a magnetic field. Although this field cannot be seen, it can be demonstrated and mapped out in the following way.

If a very small compass is placed at some point near the **N** pole of a straight bar magnet and then moved always in the direction the compass is pointing, the center of the compass will trace out a smooth line called a magnetic line of force. Starting at various points many such lines may be drawn as shown in Fig. A. Each line starts at some point near the **N** pole and ends at a corresponding point near the **S** pole.

These magnetic *lines of force,* as they are called, do not really exist; they are but useful devices that may be used in describing the many different magnetic phenomena to

be taken up in later lessons. It should be noted that where the magnet exerts its strongest attraction near the poles, the lines are closest together and that each line points away from the **N** pole and toward the **S** pole. This latter is an arbitrary assignment, being the direction indicated by the **N** pole of the compass.

A close examination of the iron filings clinging to a magnet shows that each tiny needlelike piece of iron lines up in the direction of the magnetic lines of force. The reason for this is that each filing has become magnetized by the magnet, and having its own **N** and **S** poles, acts like a compass. An excellent demonstration of the field and its direction can be performed by laying a plate of glass or a sheet of paper over a magnet and then sprinkling iron filings over the top. By gently tapping the glass or paper the filings turn and line up as shown in the photographic reproduction given in Fig. B.

Fig. A. Diagram of the magnetic field and magnetic lines of force about a straight bar magnet, as obtained with a small compass needle.

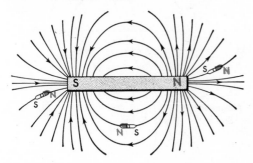

Fig. B. Photograph of the iron filings lined up by the magnetic field of a permanent straight bar magnet.

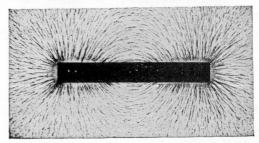

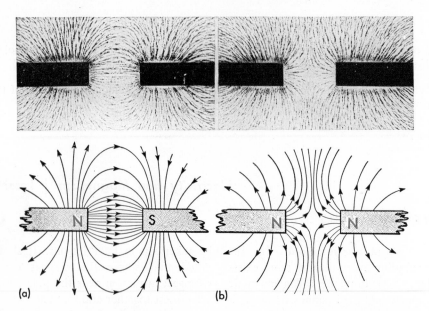

Fig. C. Diagrams and photographs illustrating the magnetic fields around pairs of magnetic poles.

The Field about Separate Poles. When two magnetic poles are brought close together, the mutual action of the two is such as to produce a complicated magnetic field. This is illustrated by compass-made drawings at the bottom in Fig. C and by photographic reproductions of the iron-filing method of observation at the top.

A simplified explanation of many electric and magnetic phenomena can be given by assuming that these imaginary *lines of force* are endowed with certain real but simple properties. Lengthwise along the lines they act as though they were stretched rubber bands under constant tension, whereas sideways they act as if they repelled each other. Both of these properties are illustrated in Fig. C. When the two poles are of different polarity as in diagram (a), the lines of force acting like stretched rubber bands tend to pull the poles together. In diagram (b) where the poles are alike, the lines repel each other, pushing the poles apart.

The Earth's Magnetic Field. To Sir William Gilbert we owe the view that the earth is a great magnet. To prove his theory Gilbert shaped a lodestone into a sphere and demonstrated that a small compass placed at any spot of the globe always pointed, as it does on the earth, toward the North Pole.

The earth, therefore, has been schematically pictured in Fig. D as a large magnetized sphere of iron or as though it contained a huge permanent magnet. Since the magnetic

Fig. D. Schematic diagram illustrating the earth as a huge magnet surrounded by a magnetic field extending far out into space.

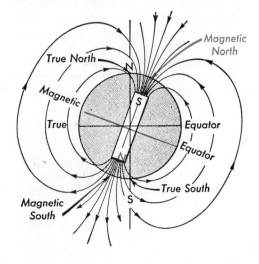

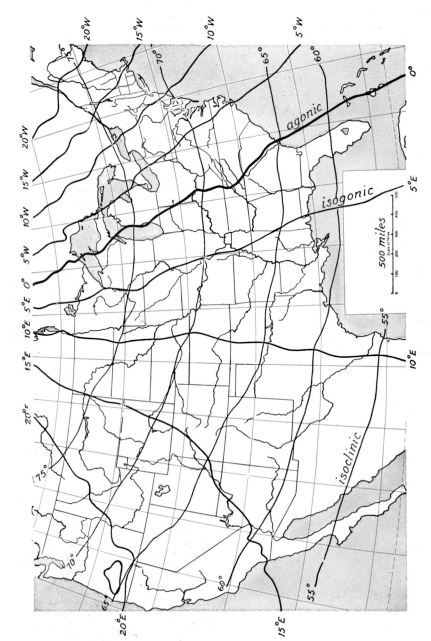

Fig. E. A magnetic map of the United States for the year 1954 showing the declination of a compass from true north and the angle of dip of a dip needle. Such maps are drawn from data assembled by the U.S. Coast and Geodetic Survey.

axis is at an angle with the polar axis, the earth's magnetic poles are not at the **true North** and **true South poles.** The true North and true South poles are points located on the earth's rotational axis.

The **North Magnetic Pole** is located in far northern Canada, while the **South Magnetic Pole** is located almost diametrically opposite in the Southern Hemisphere. As for polarity, the North Magnetic Pole is an **S** pole and the South Magnetic Pole is an **N** pole. This becomes apparent from the magnetic lines of force which always start from an **N** pole and are directed toward, and end at, an **S** pole.

Although the cause for the earth's magnetism is not completely understood, several reasonable theories have been proposed. The earth is known to contain large iron ore deposits, some of these deposits being almost pure iron. One theory proposes that during the ages past, all these iron deposits gradually became magnetized, in very nearly the same direction, and that together they act like one huge permanent magnet. Another theory, and a very plausible one, is that the magnetism is due to large electric currents which are known to be flowing around the earth, not only in the earth's crust but also in the air above. These earth currents seem to be connected in some direct way with the earth's rotation. This appears to be corroborated by the fact that the earth is magnetized in a direction almost parallel to the earth's polar axis.

Magnetic Declination. Since the earth's magnetic and polar axes do not coincide, a compass needle does not in general point toward True North. Because of the influence of the irregular iron deposits near the earth's surface, the magnetic field is not as regular as it is pictured in Fig. D and a compass needle may deviate considerably from magnetic north. The angle that a compass needle deviates from true north is called the **angle of declination.**

A map showing the angle of declination for

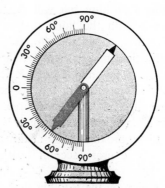

Fig. F. A magnetic dip needle.

the United States during the year 1954 is shown in Fig. E. The more or less vertical set of irregular lines are lines of equal declination and are called **isogonic lines.** At every point along the line marked 20°E, for example, a compass needle actually points 20° east of True North. In the region of San Francisco the declination is seen to be about 18°E, while in the region of New York it is about 11°W. The line through points where a compass points true north, 0°, is named the **agonic line.**

Magnetic Dip. If a compass needle is mounted free to turn about a horizontal axis as shown in Fig. F, it will not come to rest in

Fig. G. Arrows show the direction a dip needle takes at different parts of the earth's surface.

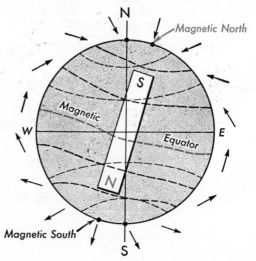

a horizontal position but will dip down at some angle with the horizontal as shown. This direction, called the **dip,** is the angle the earth's field makes with the earth's surface at the point in question. Referring to Fig. D it is seen that in the far north and south the angle of dip is quite large, whereas near the equator it is quite small. Fig. G indicates the approximate dip at different latitudes for one cross section of the entire globe.

At a region on the Boothia Peninsula just north of Hudson Bay and 20° from True North, a dip needle points straight down, perpendicular to the earth's surface, and locates the North Magnetic Pole. At a region about 18° from the true South Pole a dip needle points straight up, at 90° from the horizontal, and locates the South Magnetic Pole.

On maps of terrestrial magnetism all points that have equal dip angles are connected by a line called an **isoclinic** line. Such lines for different angles form a set of nearly parallel lines as shown on the map of the United States in Fig. E.

(In San Francisco, for example, the angle of dip is about 62°.)

Careful and accurate measurements of the **declination** and **dip** show that the earth's magnetic field is continually changing. Although these changes are extremely small, they are somewhat periodic and at times quite erratic. Within geologic time the earth's magnetic field has shifted greatly and actually reversed its direction completely.

Summary

Around every magnet there is an invisible something we call a magnetic field. Such a field is detected by means of small permanent magnets. It may be represented by lines which are everywhere parallel to a compass located there, and by arrows indicating the direction of the **N**-seeking pole.

The fields around magnets can also be demonstrated with iron filings.

The earth is magnetized with an **S**-pole in the Northern Hemisphere and an **N**-pole in the Southern Hemisphere. Because the earth's magnetic axis does not line up with the rotational axis, the compass does not point True North except in very special places.

The deviation of the compass from True North and South is called declination. Mounted free to turn around a horizontal, a dip needle lines up with the earth's magnetic field and indicates the angle of magnetic dip.

Questions

1. What is a magnetic field? Can it be seen? Can it be detected? Can a magnetic field be mapped out?

2. Can you draw from memory the magnetic field around a straight bar magnet with two poles?

3. Can you draw from memory the magnetic field between two magnets with two like-poles close together?

4. Can you draw from memory the magnetic field between two magnets with two unlike poles close together?

5. Can you draw from memory the earth's magnetic field? Can you label the four poles and two equators?

6. Does a compass point true north at all times? Does it ever point true north?

7. What is magnetic declination? Why does it arise?

8. What is meant by magnetic dip? How is it determined?

9. What is the agonic line? What is an isogonic line? What is an isoclinic line?

10. Does the earth's magnetic field remain always the same?

11. Why are the isogonic lines so irregular from point to point?

12. What would you propose as a project for the construction of an inexpensive device for demonstrating magnetic fields?

Electricity and Magnetism | **Lesson 14**

WHEATSTONE BRIDGE—*Laboratory*

In performing this experiment you will determine the resistance of a number of wires of different material with precision. From the recorded data the resistivity of three metals is determined. Details of the experiment are given in the accompanying LABORATORY EXERCISES.

Electricity and Magnetism | **Lesson 15**

EFFECTS OF ELECTRIC CURRENTS

Everyone is more or less familiar with the electrical appliances of the modern household: the electric light, electric toaster, iron, refrigerator, vacuum cleaner, washing machine, etc. All of these devices depend for their operation upon one or more of four general effects produced by electric currents; these are (1) **the heating effect,** (2) **the magnetic effect,** (3) **the mechanical effect,** and (4) **the chemical effect.** It is the purpose of this lesson to consider the first two of these different phenomena and to take up in some detail the important principles involved.

The Heating Effect of an Electric Current. When an electron current is sent through a wire, heat is generated and the temperature of the wire rises. If the current is increased, the rate at which heat is generated increases rapidly until the wire itself glows a deep red. A still further increase in current will heat the wire to a yellow or white heat. Beyond this point, if it has not already done so, the wire will reach a temperature where it will melt and become a liquid.

Whether a wire is only warmed by an electron current or heated to incandescence depends upon a number of factors, the principal ones of which are current and voltage. The electrical energy **E** consumed by a circuit is given by

$$E = VIt \qquad (1)$$

where **V** is in volts, **I** is in amperes, and **t** is in seconds. Electrical energy, like mechanical energy, is measured in joules. Heat energy is measured in calories.

By the law of conservation of energy each calorie of heat produced will require the expenditure of a definite amount of electrical energy. As an equation we can therefore write

$$E \propto H$$

or

$$E = JH \qquad (2)$$

where **J** is a proportionality constant and, as in mechanics, is found to have the value

$$J = 4.18 \frac{\text{joules}}{\text{calorie}} \qquad (3)$$

If we solve Eq. (2) for **H**,

$$H = \frac{1}{J} E$$

and substituting **E** from Eq. (1),

$$H = \frac{1}{J} VIt \qquad (4)$$

or

$$H = 0.24 \, VIt \qquad (5)$$

If Ohm's law is introduced in the form **V = IR**, we can substitute **IR** for **V** and obtain

$$H = 0.24 \, I^2Rt \qquad (6)$$

This is known as **Joule's law.**

Example. If the heating element of an electric toaster draws an electron current of 5 amps when applied to a 110-volt line, how much heat will be generated in one minute?

Solution. By direct substitution in Eq. (5)

$$H = 0.24 \times 5 \times 110 \times 60 = 7920 \text{ cal}$$

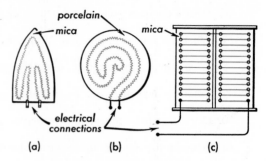

Fig. A. Diagrams of the heating elements of various electrical appliances found in many modern homes: (a) electric iron, (b) electric stove, and (c) electric toaster.

For some electric appliances heating is a desired effect, while in others it is a source of trouble and even danger. In an electric iron, hot plate, or toaster, for example, heat is the main objective of the device. In such appliances a relatively large current of several amperes is sent through a coil or element of special wire having a resistance of several ohms. As a rule the wire is of some alloy, such as nichrome, and of such a size that the heat developed will not raise the temperature higher than red hot. Diagrams of typical heating elements used in three different household appliances are shown in Fig. A.

Magnetic Effect, Oersted's Experiment. The first discovery of any connection between electricity and magnetism was made by Oersted* in 1820. Often during his lectures, at the University of Copenhagen, Oersted had

* Hans Christian Oersted (1777-1851), Danish scientist. Born the son of an apothecary, Oersted spent part of his boyhood teaching himself arithmetic. At the age of twelve he assisted his father in his shop and there became interested in chemistry. Passing the entrance examinations at the University of Copenhagen at the age of seventeen he entered the medical school to graduate six years later with his doctorate in medicine. At twenty-nine he came back to the university but this time as professor of physics. It was at one of his demonstration lectures on chemistry and metaphysics that he discovered the magnetic effect bearing his name. The discovery not only brought him many endowments and prizes but made him one of the most eminent personalities in his own country.

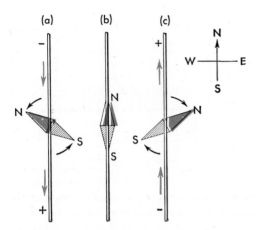

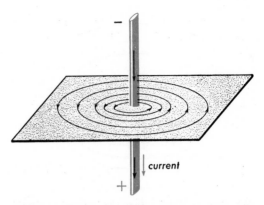

Fig. C. Experiment demonstrating the magnetic field about a straight wire carrying an electric current.

Fig. B. Diagram of Oersted's experiment illustrating the effect of an electric current upon a compass needle.

demonstrated the nonexistence of a connection between electricity and magnetism. His usual custom was to place a current-carrying wire at right angles to and directly over a compass needle and show that there was no effect of one on the other. On this one occasion at the end of his lecture, when several of the audience came up to meet him at the lecture room desk, he placed the wire parallel to the compass needle and, not the least expecting it, saw the needle move to one side (see Fig. B). Upon reversing the current in the wire the needle, to his amazement and perplexity, deviated in the opposite direction. Thus this great discovery was made quite by accident, but, as Lagrange once said of Newton on a similar occasion, "such accidents come only to those who deserve them."

The Left-Hand Rule. Oersted's experiment is interpreted as demonstrating that *around every wire carrying an electric current there is a magnetic field.* The direction of this field at every point, like that around a bar magnet, can be mapped by means of a small compass or by iron filings. If a wire is mounted vertically through a hole in a plate of glass or other suitable nonconductor and then iron filings sprinkled on the plate, there will be a lining up of the filings parallel to the magnetic field. The result shows that the mag-

netic lines of force or **lines of induction** are concentric circles whose planes are at right angles to the current. This is illustrated by the circles in Fig. C.

The left-hand rule used in electromagnetism can always be relied upon to give the direction of the magnetic field due to an electron current in a wire. *If the current-carrying wire were to be grasped with the left hand, the thumb pointing in the direction of the electron current, (−) to (+), the*

Fig. D. Diagram of the magnetic field through and around a single loop of wire carrying an electric current.

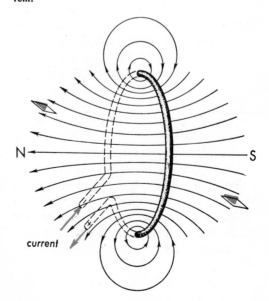

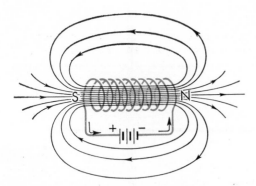

Fig. E. Diagram of the magnetic field around a solenoid carrying an electric current.

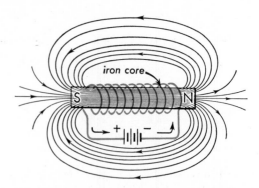

Fig. F. Diagram of an electromagnet and the field surrounding it when a current flows through the coil.

fingers will point in the direction of the magnetic induction.

In other books, using the older convention that current in a wire is from (+) to (−), the **right-hand rule** is used to give the magnetic field the same direction that it has here.

Magnetic Properties of a Solenoid. Not long after the announcement of Oersted's discovery of the magnetic effect of a current-carrying wire, Ampère found that a loop or coil of current-carrying wire acted as a magnet. This is illustrated by a single loop of wire in Fig. D, and by a coil of several turns of wire, in Fig. E. A coil of wire of this kind is sometimes referred to as a **solenoid** or as a **helix**. In either case the magnetic lines of force are such that one side or end of the coil acts like an **N** magnetic pole and the other side or end like an **S** magnetic pole.

At all points in the region around a coil of wire carrying a current the direction of the magnetic field, as shown by a compass, can be predicted by the left-hand rule. Inside each loop or turn of wire the lines point in one direction, whereas outside they are oppositely directed.

Outside the coil the lines go from **N** to **S** in quite the same way they do about a per-

manent bar magnet, whereas inside they go from **S** to **N**.

Not only does one coil of wire act like a magnet but two coils may be used to demonstrate the repulsion and attraction of like and unlike poles.

Another left-hand rule which must not be confused with the one in the preceding section, but which follows directly from it, is the following:

If the solenoid were to be grasped with the fingers pointing in the direction of the electron current, around the coil from (−) to (+), the thumb would point in the direction of the internal field as well as toward the N pole.

The Electromagnet. Five years after Oersted's discovery and Ampère's demonstration of the magnetic properties of a solenoid, William Sturgeon filled the center of a coil of wire with soft iron and thereby produced a powerful magnet. This is illustrated in Fig. F. As long as the electron current continues to flow, the addition of the iron core produces a magnet hundreds of times stronger than does the solenoid alone. A nearby compass needle if set oscillating will demonstrate this by vibrating quickly with the iron core in place and slowly with it removed.

Summary

When an electric current flows through a wire, heat is produced. Electrical energy is converted into heat. The amount of electrical energy converted is given by the product VIt, where V is in volts, I in amperes, and t in seconds.

The heat produced is given by

$$H = 0.24 \, VIt$$

This is one form of the law of conservation of energy. The product VIt gives the expended electrical energy in joules, and H is the heat energy produced in calories.

The discovery that a magnetic field exists around every current-carrying wire was discovered by Oersted. The field forms continuous lines around the conductor, while the direction is given by the left-hand rule for electron flow.

If a current-carrying wire is wrapped up into a coil, the magnetic field becomes more nearly like the field around a bar magnet.

When soft iron is inserted through a solenoid, the magnetic field is greatly intensified and an electromagnet is formed.

Questions

1. What are the four effects of electric currents? What, specifically, is the heating effect?

2. Does the same amount of electrical energy always produce the same amount of heat? What is Joule's law?

3. What three factors determine the electrical energy converted into heat? What are the units of heat energy? What are the units of electrical energy?

4. If V in Eq. (1) is replaced by the Ohm's law value of IR, what would the equation become? If I is replaced by V/R, what would the equation become?

5. Who discovered the magnetic effect of an electric current? What did he do? What happens when the current is reversed?

6. To what kind of current does the left-hand rule apply? How does the rule apply to a straight wire?

7. How does the left-hand rule apply to a coil of wire?

8. What effect does a soft iron core have upon the strength of the magnetic field around a solenoid? Does a current have to flow to produce the field?

9. What would you consider as a good project for the demonstration of the heating or magnetic effect of an electric current?

Problems

1. An electric toaster draws a current of 4 amps when connected to the house-lighting circuit of 120 volts. How many calories of heat are produced in 1 min?

2. The heating element of an electric heater draws a current of 10 amps when connected to 110 volts. How many calories of heat are produced in one hour?

3. An electric toaster with a resistance of 25 ohms draws a current of 5 amps when connected to a house-lighting circuit. If it takes 2 min running to make dark toast, how many calories are required?

4. The heating element of an electric stove connected to a 220-volt line draws an electron current of 5 amps. Find the amount of heat produced in 10 min.

5. An electric iron having a resistance of 15 ohms is connected to a 110-volt supply. Find the heat developed in 5 min.

6. Calculate the heat developed by an electric soldering iron in 10 min if it draws 3.5 amps on a 120-volt line.

7.* A teakettle containing 1 gallon of water (3785 cm³) at a temperature of 10°C is heated on an electric stove. If the heating element draws an electron current of 8 amps from a 220-volt line, and one-half of the heat generated goes to heat the water, how long will it take for the water to reach the boiling point?

8.* An electric coffee pot containing 1000 cm³ of water at 15°C is connected to a 110-volt line. If the electron current drawn is 4.5 amps and 65% of the heat developed goes into the water, how hot will the water be in 8 min?

9.* Three resistors, 5 Ω, 8 Ω, and 12 Ω, respectively, are connected in series to a battery. If these resistors are immersed in a glass containing 500 cm³ of water and a current of 5 amps sent through them, how long will it take to raise the water from 25°C to the boiling point of 100°C?

Electricity and Magnetism | **Lesson 16**

ELECTRICAL EQUIVALENT
OF HEAT—*Laboratory*

By immersing an electrical heating element in a vessel of water and sending a current through it, you will determine the electrical equivalent of heat. The measurements required in this experiment are described in the accompanying LAB-ORATORY EXERCISES.

Electricity and Magnetism | **Lesson 17**

ELECTRIC MOTORS

Mechanical Effects of Electric Currents. It was on Christmas, 1821, that Michael Faraday discovered that when a wire carrying a current is placed in the field of a magnet, a mechanical force is exerted on the wire. This is the principle upon which the modern electric motor is based.

A demonstration of Faraday's discovery

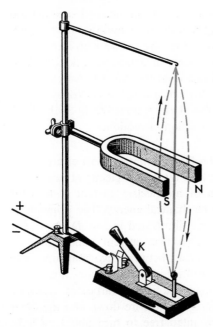

Fig. A. Demonstration of the mechanical effect of an electric current in a magnetic field.

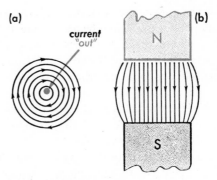

Fig. B. Magnetic fields (a) due to an electron current and (b) due to magnetic poles.

is shown in Fig. A, where a flexible copper wire about one meter long is suspended from a support. A U-shaped magnet straddles the wire somewhere near the middle.

Upon closing the switch **K** an electron current flows up through the wire and the wire moves to the left. If the battery connections are reversed, thereby reversing the electron current, the deflection of the wire will be to the right.

If the magnet is turned over, thereby interchanging **N** and **S** poles, the deflection of the wire will again reverse. In other words, the reversing of either the magnetic field or the direction of the electron current will reverse the direction of the force acting on the wire. The reversal of both will make it the same.

Interaction Between Magnetic Fields.

To gain some understanding of this mysterious invisible force acting on a current-carrying wire in a magnetic field, consider the diagrams in Fig. B.

The circles in diagram (a) represent the circular magnetic lines of force around a straight wire carrying a current. The directions of the arrows are given by the left-hand rule, shown here for an electron current up and out of the page.

The lines of force in diagram (b) represent the magnetic field between two opposite poles of a magnet.

If we now place the current-carrying wire between the poles of the magnet, the two fields interact on each other. The interaction is such that a newly formed field like that shown at the right in Fig. C is obtained. Imagining that the magnetic lines of force act like stretched rubber bands, one can predict from this diagram that the wire should experience a force **F** to the left.

To understand how such a field can arise out of two interacting symmetrical fields it

Fig. C. Diagrams of two interacting magnetic fields.

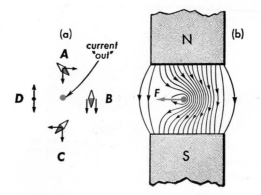

should be remembered that the field direction at any point is that taken by a small magnetic dipole placed there. Consider as examples the points **A**, **B**, **C**, and **D** of diagram (a). At **A** the field due to the current in the wire is to the right, and that due to the magnet poles is down. If the two fields exert equal torques on the tiny compass needle, it will point along a direction halfway between the two.

At **B** the field due to the wire is down, and so is the field due to the magnet. A compass at this point would point down. At **C** the fields are again at right angles, and the compass points down and to the left. At **D** the fields are oppositely directed and, if they are equal in magnitude, cancel each other's effect. This process repeated for many other points will lead to the field shown in diagram (b).

It is important to note that the direction of the current *I* in the wire, the direction of the magnetic field *B* at the wire due to the magnet, and the direction of the force *F* acting on the wire are all at right angles to each other. Furthermore, the direction of the force *F* can be quickly ascertained by applying the left-hand rule to the electron current in the wire. If the wire were to be grasped with the left hand, the thumb pointing in the direction of the electron current ($-$ to $+$), the force is toward the weakened field, that is, toward the region where the fingers are oppositely directed to the field of the magnet.

It should be emphasized here that this force is exerted on the electrons, the moving charges in the wire, and that they, being confined to the wire, cause it to move. An electron at rest in a magnetic field experiences no force from the magnet. An electron moving across magnetic lines of force experiences a force at right angles to both the field and the direction of motion.

The Electric Motor. An electric motor is a device by which electrical energy in the form of an electric current is transformed into mechanical energy. The principle of the motor is illustrated in Fig. D. A wire carrying an electron current is bent into a loop and placed between two magnetic poles as shown. In this horizontal position the resultant magnetic field is warped as shown in Fig. E, forcing one wire down and the other up.

Mounted free to turn about an axis, the loop rotates until it is in a vertical plane. At this point the current in the loop is reversed in direction by means of **sliding contacts** and a **split-ring commutator**. The reversal of the electron current reverses the forces so that the side of the loop which was previously pushed up is now pushed down and the side previously pushed down is now pushed up. The loop therefore rotates through half a turn more where the current again reverses.

A repetition of this reversing process at each half turn gives rise to a continuous rotation, the left side of the coil or loop always moving down and the right side always moving up.

Fig. D. Principal elements for demonstrating the principles of an electric motor.

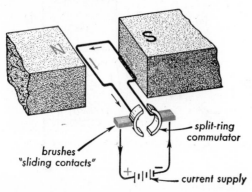

Fig. E. Diagram of the magnetic field around a current-carrying loop as found in the electric motor.

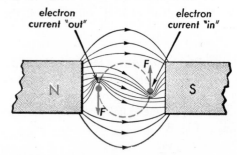

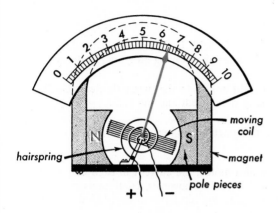

Fig. F. Diagram of the essential parts of an ammeter or voltmeter.

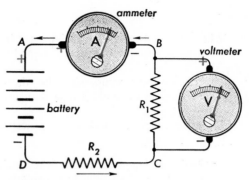

Fig. G. Circuit diagram showing the connections for an ammeter and voltmeter.

Ammeters and Voltmeters. Electrical instruments designed to measure an electric current are called *ammeters,* and those designed to measure potential difference are called *voltmeters.* The principle upon which both of these devices operate is essentially the same as that of the electric motor as shown in Fig. D. They differ from the motor, however, in the delicateness of their construction and the restrained motion of the rotating armature.

A coil of fine copper wire is so mounted between the two poles of a permanent magnet that its rotation, as shown in Fig. F, is restrained by a hairspring. The farther the coil is turned from its equilibrium or zero position, the greater is the restoring force. To this coil is fastened a long pointer at the end of which is a fixed scale reading amperes if it is an ammeter or volts if it is a voltmeter.

Upon increasing the current through the moving coil of an ammeter or voltmeter, the resultant magnetic field between coil and magnet is distorted more and more. The resulting increase in force therefore turns the coil through a greater and greater angle, reaching a point where it is just balanced by the restoring force of the hairspring.

Whenever an ammeter or voltmeter is connected to a circuit to measure electron current or potential difference, the ammeter must be connected in series and the voltmeter in parallel. As illustrated in Fig. G, the ammeter is so connected that all of the electron current passes through it. To prevent a change in the electron current when such an insertion is made, all ammeters must have a low resistance. Most ammeters therefore have a low resistance wire, called a **shunt,** connected across the armature coil inside.

A voltmeter, on the other hand, is connected across that part of the circuit for which a measurement of the potential difference is required. If the potential difference between the ends of the resistance R_1 is wanted, the voltmeter is connected as shown. If the potential difference across R_2 is desired, the voltmeter connections are made at **C** and **D**; whereas if the potential difference maintained by the battery is desired, they are made at **A** and **D**. In order that the connection of a voltmeter to a circuit does not change the electron current in the circuit, the voltmeter must have a relatively high resistance. If the armature coil does not have a large resistance of its own, additional resistance is added in series.

Very delicate ammeters are often used for measuring very small currents. A meter whose scale is calibrated to read thousandths of an ampere is called a **milliammeter.** One whose scale is calibrated in millionths of an ampere is called a **microammeter** or **galvanometer.**

Summary

When a current-carrying wire is placed in a magnetic field, it experiences a mechanical force acting upon it. This action is due to the force on the moving electrons in the wire.

The greatest force occurs when the wire is at right angles to the magnetic field. Under these conditions the force is at right angles to both the current and the field.

The electric motor, as well as many electrical instruments, is based upon this mechanical force.

To obtain continuous rotation of the armature of a motor, the current in each coil must be reversed every half turn. In the voltmeter and ammeter, however, continuous rotation is not required, and a coil spiral spring supplies a restoring force proportional to the angle turned through.

An ammeter has a low resistance and a voltmeter a high resistance.

Questions

1. Who discovered the mechanical effects of electric currents? What are the necessary conditions for producing the mechanical effect of an electric current?

2. Can you apply the left-hand rule to find the direction of the force on a wire?

3. If a current-carrying wire is parallel to the magnetic induction, is there a mechanical force?

4. How is the mechanical effect used in the electric motor? What is the split ring used for? Why are sliding contacts needed?

5. How is an ammeter constructed? What is the spiral spring for? Why are the poles curved?

6. Can an ammeter be converted into a voltmeter? If so, how?

7. In what general way does a voltmeter differ from an ammeter?

8. Why should an ammeter have a low resistance? Why should a voltmeter have a high resistance?

9. What simple and inexpensive device would you propose as a project utilizing the principles introduced in this lesson?

Problems

1. A voltmeter having a resistance of 100 Ω shows a full-scale reading when 5 volts is applied to its terminals. What resistance connected to this instrument will give it a full-scale reading when connected to 120 volts?

2. A voltmeter with a resistance of 200 Ω shows a full-scale reading when 1 volt is applied to its terminals. What resistance connected to this instrument will give it a full-scale reading of (a) 5 volts, (b) 50 volts, and (c) 150 volts?

3. A voltmeter with a resistance of 5000 Ω shows a full-scale reading at 25 volts. What resistance should be connected to this instrument to have it give a full-scale reading of 500 volts?

4. If the voltmeter in Problem 1 is used as a milliammeter, what current will give a full-scale deflection?

5.* What shunt resistance across the voltmeter in Problem 1 will make it into an ammeter with a full-scale deflection for 5 amps?

6.* What shunt resistance across the voltmeter in Problem 2 will make it into an ammeter with a full-scale deflection for 5 amps?

7.* What shunt resistance across the voltmeter in Problem 3 will make it into an ammeter with a full-scale deflection of 25 amps?

8.* A voltmeter having a resistance of 500 ohms shows a full-scale reading when an electron current of 10 milliamperes flows through it. What shunt resistance across this instrument will enable it to be used as an ammeter indicating 5 amps on full-scale deflection?

Electricity and Magnetism | **Lesson 18**

MAGNETIC INDUCTION

We have seen in the preceding lessons how an electron current gives rise to a magnetic field surrounding the conductor, and also how a current-carrying wire placed in a magnetic field experiences an unbalanced force tending to move it across the field. The mathematical formulation of the principles involved in these magnetic and mechanical effects depends primarily upon a quantitative account of the magnetic field strength.

The strength of the magnetic field at any point in and around any electrical equipment is represented by the letter **B** and is called the *magnetic induction.* As a simple illustration, the magnetic induction around a long, straight wire is everywhere perpendicular to the wire, and the magnetic lines of force representing **B** are drawn as concentric circles as shown in Fig. A. While the direction of **B**, as repre-

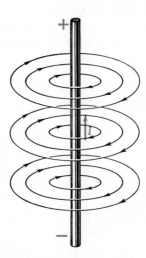

Fig. A. The magnetic field around a long, straight conductor.

sented by the arrowheads, is given by the left-hand rule, the magnitude of **B** at any point is given by

$$B = \mu_o \frac{I}{2\pi r} \qquad (1)$$

for long straight wire

where I is the electron current in amperes, r is the perpendicular distance from the point in question in meters, and μ_o is a proportionality constant whose value is

$$\mu_o = 12.57 \times 10^{-7} \frac{\text{weber}}{\text{ampere meter}} \qquad (2)$$

See Fig. B.

Example 1. A current of 75 amperes flows through a long straight wire. Find the magnetic induction 1 cm from the wire.

Solution. By direct substitution in Eq. (1), we obtain

$$B = \left(12.57 \times 10^{-7} \frac{\text{weber}}{\text{amp m}}\right) \frac{75 \text{ amp}}{2\pi \times 0.01 \text{ meter}}$$

$$B = 0.0015 \frac{\text{weber}}{\text{meter}^2}$$

Magnetic induction **B** is measured in webers/meter², and having both magnitude and direction, is a vector quantity.

In the cgs system of units magnetic induction is measured in maxwells/cm², and these have the name of gauss.

Fig. B. Magnetic induction B around a straight conductor carrying an electron current.

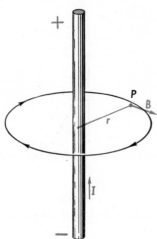

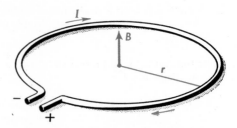

Fig. C. Magnetic induction B in a current-carrying loop of wire.

$$1 \frac{\text{weber}}{\text{m}^2} = 10,000 \text{ gauss} \qquad (3)$$

Circular Turns of Wire. As the current I flows through a circular loop of wire, as shown in Fig. C, each part of the wire contributes to the magnetic induction **B** at every point in the space inside or outside the loop. The direction of **B** at all points in the surrounding space is shown in Fig. D of Electricity and Magnetism, Lesson 15, and the closeness of the lines in any region is a measure of the magnitude of **B**.

The field strength is greatest at the center of a circular turn of wire and is given by

$$B = \mu_o \frac{I}{2r} \qquad (4)$$

The magnetic induction **B** is in webers/meter², the current I is in amperes, r is the radius in meters, and μ_o is given by Eq. (2).

If instead of a single loop of wire, the coil has a number of turns, each turn contributes the same field at the center, and the resultant magnetic induction will be given by **N** times that of Eq. (4). Hence,

Fig. D. Magnetic induction B in a coil of N turns of wire.

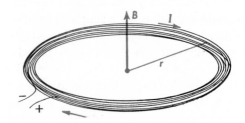

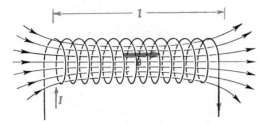

Fig. E. A solenoid of N turns of wire.

$$B = \mu_o \frac{NI}{2\,r} \qquad (5)$$

for flat coil

N in this equation represents the number of turns (see Fig. D), and the product **NI** represents what is called the **ampere turns.**

Magnetic Induction Inside a Solenoid. The general shape of the magnetic field in a solenoid is shown in Fig. E. The magnetic induction is fairly uniform throughout the center of the solenoid, and its magnitude at the center is given by

$$B = \mu_o \frac{NI}{l} \qquad (6)$$

for long solenoid

were **l** is the length of the solenoid in meters.

Fig. F. Force on a charge moving across a magnetic field.

Force on a Moving Charge. In Lesson 17 it was shown how a current-carrying wire, when placed in a magnetic field, experiences a mechanical force tending to move it across the field. This mechanical force is due directly to the force exerted by the magnetic induction **B** upon the individual moving electrons within the conductor. See Fig. F.

A charge **Q**, moving with a velocity **v** through a magnetic field at right angles to **B**, experiences a force **F** given by

$$F = QvB \qquad (7)$$

In the mks system, **F** is in newtons, **B** is in webers/meter^2, **v** is in meters/sec, and **Q** is in coulombs. The vectors **B**, **v**, and **F** are all mutually perpendicular to each other.

If the velocity vector **v** makes an angle θ with **B**, as indicated in Fig. G, the magnitude of the force **F** is proportional to the component of the velocity perpendicular to **B**.

$$F = QvB \sin \theta \qquad (8)$$

If the charge **Q** in Fig. G is positive, the force **F** is opposite in direction to the one shown. When a charged particle moves parallel to the field, that is, along the magnetic lines, $\sin \theta = 0$, there is no force.

Fig. G. Force on a negative charge moving at an angle to a magnetic field.

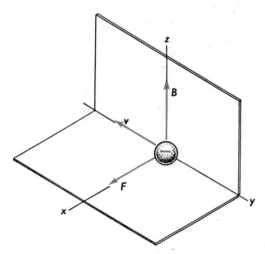

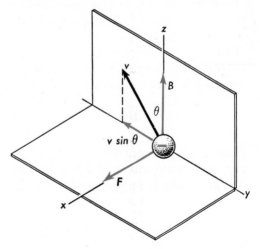

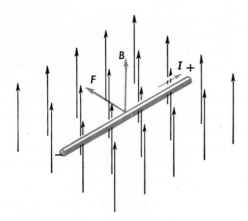

Fig. H. The force on a current-carrying wire in a magnetic field.

Force on a Current-Carrying Wire. To find the force on a current-carrying wire in a magnetic field we make use of the above Eq. (7), $F = QvB$. See Fig. H. A single moving charge Q constitutes a current $I = Q/t$. Moving with a velocity v, it will, in a time t, travel a distance $l = vt$. Substituting It for Q and l/t for v in Eq. (7), we obtain

$$F = It \times \frac{l}{t} \times B$$

or

$$F = IlB \qquad (9)$$

(In the mks system F is in newtons, B is in webers/meter², I is in amperes, and l is in meters. In the cgs system F is in dynes, B is in maxwells/cm², I is in abamperes, and l is in cm. One abampere $= 10$ amps, and 1 maxwell/cm² $= 1$ gauss.)

Like a moving charge in Fig. G, a current-carrying wire making an angle θ with the field experiences a force proportional to sin θ.

$$\boxed{F = IlB \sin \theta} \qquad (10)$$

Example 2. A wire 40 cm long and carrying an electron current of 2.5 amps is located in a uniform magnetic field in which $B = 10^{-2}$ weber/meter². Calculate the force on the wire when it makes an angle of 60° with the field direction.

Solution. Since θ is measured from the direction of **B**, $\theta = 60°$, and substitution in Eq. (10) gives

$$F = 2.5 \times 0.40 \times 10^{-2} \times 0.866$$
$$= 8.66 \times 10^{-3} \text{ newton}$$

Total Magnetic Flux and Flux Density. In this and preceding lessons the magnetic field over a region of space is graphically represented by what are called **lines of force**. In order to specify the **strength** or **intensity** of a magnetic field at any point in space, the vector quantity called **magnetic induction B** has been defined. Since lines of force are frequently used as graphical representations of the variations in the magnetic induction from point to point, they are also called **lines of induction**.

The direction of the magnetic induction **B** at any point is tangent to the line of induction passing through that point, and its magnitude is given by the number of lines per unit area. The unit area is so chosen that it includes the point in question and is everywhere perpendicular to all lines passing through it.

In the mks system, a line of induction is called a **weber**, while in the cgs system a line of induction is called a **maxwell**.

The total number of lines of induction passing through a surface is called the magnetic flux and is represented by ϕ. In a region where the field is uniform and the surface area **A** is normal to the lines of induction,

$$\boxed{\phi = BA} \qquad (11)$$

Since **B** is measured in **webers/meter²** and **A** is in **meters²**, the total flux ϕ is in **webers**. **B is often called the flux density.**

Summary

The strength of the magnetic field at any point in the free space surrounding a current-carrying wire is measured in webers per square meter and is called the magnetic induction **B**.

Relatively simple equations for the value of **B** are given for a straight wire, a coil, and a solenoid.

When an electric charge moves across a magnetic field, it experiences a mechanical force acting upon it. This force depends upon the charge **Q**, its velocity **v** with respect to the field, and the magnetic induction **B**.

When a current-carrying wire is placed in a magnetic field, the force on the moving electrons gives rise to a force on the wire itself. This force depends upon the current **I**, the length of the wire **l**, and the magnetic induction **B**.

The total number of lines of induction passing through a surface of area **A** is given by the product **BA** and is called the magnetic flux.

Questions

1. What is meant by magnetic induction? In what units is **B** measured? Does **B** have direction? Is **B** a vector quantity?

2. How does the magnetic induction **B** at a point vary with distance from a long straight wire carrying an electron current?

3. How does **B** at the center of a circular coil vary with the current? How does **B** vary with the radius? How does **B** vary with the number of turns?

4. How does **B** at the center of a long solenoid vary with the current? How does **B** vary with the radius?

5. Upon what factors does the mechanical force on a current-carrying wire in a magnetic field depend?

6. If a negatively charged particle enters a uniform magnetic field moving parallel to the magnetic induction **B**, what will be the shape of its path?

7. If a current-carrying wire is placed in a uniform magnetic field parallel to the magnetic induction **B**, what force acts upon it?

8. How will the magnetic induction **B** at the center of a coil be altered if (a) the current is doubled and (b) the current is reversed in direction?

9. What is a weber? What is magnetic flux? What is meant by flux density?

10. What demonstration experiment would you propose for illustrating one or more of the principles introduced in this lesson?

Problems

1. Calculate the magnetic induction at a distance of 1 cm from a long straight wire carrying an electron current of 200 amps.

2. Two long straight parallel wires 6 cm apart each carry an electron current of 40 amps. Calculate the magnetic induction at a point between the wires, 2 cm from one and 4 cm from the other, when the currents are (a) in the same direction and (b) in opposite directions.

3. A wire 100 ft long is wound into a flat coil 2 in. in diameter. If an electron current of 5 amps flows through the coil, what is the magnetic induction at the center?

4. A flat coil of 50 turns has a diameter of 4 in. and carries an electron current of 15 amps. Find the magnetic induction at the center.

5. If the magnetic induction at the center of a solenoid 25 cm long is to be 2×10^{-2} w/m^2 when an electron current of 6 amps is flowing through it, how many turns must it have?

6. A solenoid 60 cm long has 1000 turns of wire. What electron current is required to produce a magnetic induction of 2×10^{-2} w/m^2 at its center?

7. A straight wire 6 in. long and carrying an electron current of 25 amps is placed in a field where the magnetic induction is 1 w/m^2. If the wire and the field are perpendicular to each other, find the force on the wire.

8. An electron current of 50 amps flows through a straight wire 15 cm long. If this wire is placed in a field of 2×10^{-2} w/m^2 making an angle of 90° with the field direction, what is the force on the wire?

9. An electron with its charge of 1.6×10^{-19} coulomb moves with one-tenth the speed of light across a magnetic field of 0.01 w/m^2. Find the magnitude of the mechanical force acting on the electron.

Electricity and Magnetism | **Lesson 19**

A STUDY OF MOTORS—*Laboratory*

The simplest elements of an electric motor are assembled in this experiment, and qualitative observations of the resultant speeds and directions of rotation are made. The different combinations of parts and connections are described in the accompanying LABORATORY EXERCISES.

Electricity and Magnetism | **Lesson 20**

INDUCED ELECTRIC CURRENTS

Induced Electric Currents. The discovery of induced electric current goes back more than one hundred years to 1831 and the well-planned experiments of Michael Faraday.* A straight bar magnet plunged into a coil of wire was found to produce an electric current. The experiment is illustrated in Fig. A. As the **N** pole of the magnet is plunged into the coil, a galvanometer needle deflects to the *right;* when it is withdrawn, the needle deflects to the *left,* indicating a current in the opposite direction. If the **S** pole is moved down into the coil, the needle de-

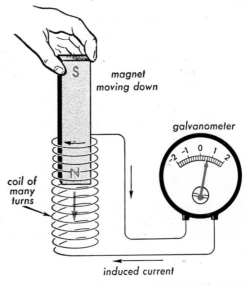

Fig. A. Diagram of Faraday's experimental discovery of induced electric currents.

* Michael Faraday (1791-1867), English experimental physicist. Born the son of a blacksmith, Faraday's early life was spent earning his living as a bookbinder's apprentice. Taking time from his work to read some of the books passing through his hands, Faraday became intensely interested in science. With a passionate desire to make science a life work, his chance finally came when he was made a valet and assistant to the great English scientist Sir Humphrey Davy of the Royal Institute. As a young man he openly proclaimed that women were nothing in his life, and even wrote and published a poem in criticism of falling in love. At the age of twenty-nine he saw, fell desperately in love with, and married Sarah Barnhard, who became a devoted and inspiring companion for the nearly fifty remaining years of his life. Four months after his marriage he made the famous discovery of the motion of a wire carrying a current in the field of a magnet. Since a current-carrying wire would move in a magnetic field, should not the reverse be true and a magnet be made to produce current in a wire? For days he experimented with magnets and coils of wire until in desperation he plunged a magnet down into a coil and observed that a current was generated in the coil. Why had he not discovered this before? The motion was the thing; it was the connecting link he had failed to realize. For this discovery the whole scientific world sought to honor him. So many universities gave him honorary degrees that he soon had to turn down such honors. He refused the presidency of both the Royal Institute and the Royal Society of London, and also refused to be knighted. Like all great scientists he loved his work more than these honors.

flects to the *left;* and as it is withdrawn, the deflection is to the *right.*

The relative motion of the coil and magnet is what produces the current, and it makes no difference whether the coil alone moves, whether the magnet alone moves, or whether they both move. In either case, when the relative motion ceases, the current stops. A "somewhat old-fashioned" way of describing the action is to say that only when a wire is cutting the lines of force is there an induced emf. A somewhat more acceptable statement at the present time is, in effect, that only when the total magnetic flux linking a closed electrical circuit is changing is there an induced emf. To demonstrate this concept, a simple experiment like that shown in Fig. B may be performed.

A flexible wire connected to an ammeter, and held in the hands, is moved in various

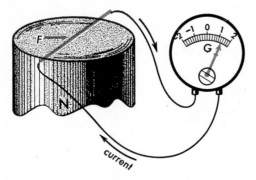

Fig. B. Experimental arrangement for demonstrating induced electron currents.

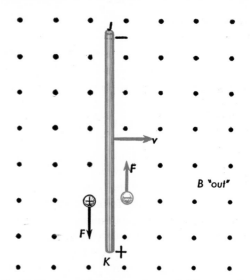

Fig. C. Forces on the charges in a conductor moving through a magnetic field.

ways across the pole of a magnet. When a straight section of the wire is held over the **N** pole and moved to the right, an electron current flows in the direction shown by the arrows. If the wire is moved in the opposite direction, the induced emf and current reverses direction. If the wire is moved vertically upward or downward, parallel to the magnetic induction, no current flows. In other words, *there is an induced emf only when the total number of lines of induction through the closed circuit is changing.*

The *left-hand rule* may be used to predict the direction of the induced emf in any section of wire. If we imagine grasping the wire in the left hand, as it moves through the magnetic field, the fingers pointing in the direction of the magnetic induction immediately in front of it, the thumb will point in the direction of the induced emf.

Induced Electromotive Force. It was shown in Electricity and Magnetism, Lesson 18, how an electric charge **Q**, moving with a constant velocity **v** through a magnetic field where the flux density is **B**, experiences a force **F** upon it given by

$$F = QvB \qquad (1)$$

where **F**, **B**, and **v** are all mutually perpendicular to each other.

When, therefore, a single wire is made to cross magnetic lines of induction, as shown in Fig. C, every atomic charge within the

metal experiences a force upon it parallel to the conductor. The direction of the force on the (+) charges is from **J** to **K**, while the force on the (−) charges is from **K** to **J**. Since only the electrons are free to move in a metallic conductor, the negative charges migrate along the wire building up a negative potential at one end and a positive potential at the other.

Consider the straight conductor sliding along a U-shaped conductor to form a closed circuit as shown in Fig. D. The potential difference created between the ends forces electrons through and around the circuit in the direction indicated. In other words the mov-

Fig. D. Inducing a current by the motion of a conductor.

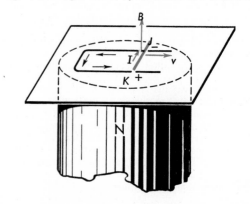

ing conductor becomes the source of an **electromotive force.**

The electromotive force developed within a moving conductor of length **l** is defined as the work per unit charge done in carrying any charge from one end to the other. From mechanics we draw upon the principle that work done **W** is equal to **force times distance moved.** With the force given by Eq. (1) and the distance moved by **l,** the work done on a charge **Q** is

$$W = QvBl \qquad (2)$$

If we now divide both sides of the equation by **Q,** the work per unit charge becomes

$$\boxed{V = vBl} \qquad (3)$$

where **V** is the **emf,** or work per unit charge done on the charges in this section of the moving conductor.

In the mks system **B** is in **webers/meter²,** **v** is in **meters/second, l** is in **meters,** and **V** is in **volts.** It should be pointed out that it makes no difference in the above treatment whether the wire moves through a stationary magnetic field or whether the field moves across a stationary conductor. It is the relative motion giving rise to crossing of lines of induction that produces the **emf.**

The Electric Generator. An electric generator is constructed the same as an electric motor, with a rotating armature containing coils of wire, pole pieces, field windings, brushes, and a commutator. Instead of supplying an electron current to obtain mechanical rotation, mechanical work is done to turn the armature thus producing an electron current.

If, in the construction of a generator, two solid rings are used as a commutator, as shown in Fig. E, the current delivered to the brushes flows first in one direction, then in the other. The reversal of current with each half turn of the armature is due to the fact that each wire moves up across the field at one instant and down at the next. At one

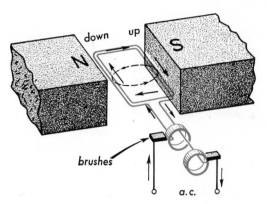

Fig. E. Illustrating the principles of the electric generator.

instant the one terminal is positive and the other negative; at the next instant the first terminal is negative and the second positive. This periodically reversing emf produces what is called **an alternating emf.**

If a direct current is desired, the commutator of the generator must be of the split-ring type illustrated in Fig. F. It can be seen with this arrangement that one brush is at all times in contact with wires moving up across the field while the other is in contact with wires moving down across the field. This produces a unidirectional electron current and the whole machine is called a **direct-current (d.c.) generator.**

Fig. F. Split-ring commutator for a direct-current generator.

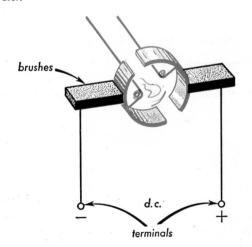

It is important to note that a generator does not make electricity. The electricity, or electric charge, is always in the wire, and a generator sets it into motion. A generator produces an electric current.

Alternating Current. The magnitude of the voltage induced in a generator coil rotating as shown in Fig. E is given by the relation

$$V = NBA\omega \sin \omega t \qquad (4)$$

where N is the number of turns in the coil, B is the magnetic induction in webers/meter^2, A is the area of the coil in meters^2, ω is the angular speed in radians/second, and t is the time in seconds.

If f represents the frequency of rotation

$$\omega = 2\pi f \qquad (5)$$

A 60-cycle, 110-volt alternating emf, for example, is one in which the potential difference reverses direction 120 times per second. The rating of 110 volts, as shown in Fig. G, specifies a sort of average voltage called the **root mean square** voltage and not the so-called **peak voltage** of 155 volts.

The maximum voltage is obtained when the plane of the coil is parallel to the field ($\omega t = 90°$ or $270°$) and zero when it is perpendicular ($\omega t = 0°$ or $180°$). When $\omega t = 90°$, $\sin \omega t = 1$, and Eq. (3) gives

$$V_{\max} = NBA\omega \qquad (6)$$

The root mean square voltage is given by

$$V_{\mathrm{rms}} = .707\, V_{\max} \qquad (7)$$

Fig. G. Voltage graph for an alternating-current generator coil.

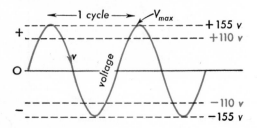

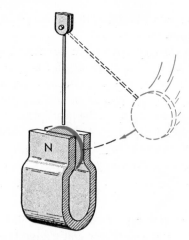

Fig. H. Induced currents in the copper-disk pendulum quickly stop it from swinging through.

and the root mean square current supplied to any circuit is given by

$$I_{\mathrm{rms}} = .707\, I_{\max} \qquad (8)$$

Lenz's Law. When a conductor moves through a magnetic field, the induced current in the wire is in such a direction that its own magnetic field generated by that current acts on the original magnetic field in a way opposing the motion. Stated for the first time by H. Lenz in 1833, this is known as Lenz's law. The action of the two magnetic fields upon each other is always such as to oppose the motion or any change in conditions already existing, for if they assisted the change we would have perpetual motion and a violation of the law of conservation of energy.

Fig. I. Slotted copper disks for the demonstration of induced eddy currents.

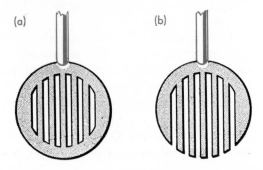

(a)   (b)

If the **N** pole of a straight bar magnet is approaching a solenoid as shown in Fig. A, the induced electron current in the coil is in such a direction as to produce an **N** pole near the top of the coil. The two **N** poles therefore repel each other, tending to stop the motion. To keep the current flowing a force **F** must continually be supplied to the moving magnet. It is this force **F** moving through a given distance that determines the amount of mechanical work done in producing a given current.

If now the **N** pole is withdrawn from the solenoid, the induced current in the coil reverses in direction and produces an **S** pole at the top end. The opposite poles therefore attract each other, tending to stop the motion. Again to keep the current flowing a force **F** must be continually supplied and thus work is done.

There are numerous ways of demonstrating Lenz's law. One common experiment is to move a flat copper or aluminum plate rapidly through a strong magnetic field as shown in Fig. H. As each part of the plate enters the field between the poles of the magnet a strong opposing force tends to stop it. What happens electrically is that strong eddy currents of electricity are produced in the metal. The magnetic field arising from these eddy currents opposes the field through which it is moving. If the plate is held in the hand the sensation is that of movement through thick molasses.

If the solid disk is replaced by a slotted disk, as shown in Fig. I(a), strong currents are induced in the vertical bars as they enter the field, and the disk stops quickly. If the slots are open at one end as in diagram (b) each bar is an open circuit and no large induced currents can be produced. Consequently the disk is not strongly retarded but swings through the magnetic field rather freely.

Summary

When a wire is made to move through a magnetic field, cutting across lines of induction, each charged atomic particle within the wire experiences a force tending to make it move. Since only electrons can move, an electron current will be developed in the wire.

The electromotive force developed between the ends of a wire moving across a magnetic field is proportional to the velocity of the wire, the length of the wire, and the magnetic induction **B**,

$$V = vBl$$

If a coil of wire is rotated in a magnetic field, an alternating current may be developed within it. The emf developed from such a coil is proportional to the number of turns **N**, the area of the coil **A**, the magnetic induction **B**, and the angular velocity ω,

$$V = NBA\omega \sin \omega t$$

The magnetic field produced by an induced current in a wire is always in such a direction as to oppose the original field and the motion. This is known as Lenz's law.

Questions

1. Who discovered induced electric currents? How was the phenomenon produced?

2. What are the basic principles of induced currents?

3. Can a current be induced in a wire that is stationary?

4. Can a current be induced in a wire by a stationary magnetic field?

5. If a wire moves through a magnetic field parallel to the lines of induction, is there an emf developed within the wire?

6. Upon what three factors does the induced emf in a wire depend?

7. How can an alternating current be induced in a wire?

8. How are alternating currents generally produced?

9. Upon what four factors does the emf produced by an alternating current generator depend?

10. What is Lenz's law? How can the law be demonstrated?

11. Make a diagram of an experiment you might perform to illustrate induced currents.

Problems

1. A wire 20 cm long moves with a speed of 25 m/sec through a uniform magnetic field where the magnetic induction is 0.3 w/m². If the wire, field, and motion are all mutually perpendicular, what emf is produced in the wire?

2. A wire 10 meters long is located in the wing of an airplane making 720 km/hr. If the magnetic induction due to the earth's field has a value of 5×10^{-4} w/m², what is the maximum possible induced emf?

3. A wire one meter long moves with a speed of 15 m/sec through a uniform magnetic field where the flux density **B** is 0.2 w/m². If the wire, field, and motion are all perpendicular to each other, what emf is produced in the wire?

4. A wire 20 cm long is moved with a speed of 4 m/sec through a uniform magnetic field where the magnetic induction **B** is 0.25 w/m². Find the emf produced in the wire.

5. At what speed should a wire 50 cm long be moved through a magnetic field where **B** = 0.5 w/m² if it is to produce an emf of 1 volt?

6. A flat rectangular coil, 10 cm by 20 cm, and 50 turns of wire is rotating at the constant speed of 3000 rpm in a magnetic field where the magnetic induction is 0.2 w/m². Calculate (a) the maximum voltage and (b) the root mean square voltage.

7. A flat circular coil 20 cm in diameter and containing 100 turns of wire is rotating at 2400 rpm in a magnetic field where **B** = 0.25 w/m². Find (a) the maximum emf produced and (b) the root mean square voltage.

8.* A rectangular coil of 100 turns is 10 cm wide and 20 cm long. What is the speed at which this coil should rotate in the earth's magnetic field (**B** = 5×10^{-4} w/m²) to produce a peak emf of 0.10 volt?

9.* A flat circular coil of 50 turns is 20 cm in diameter. If this coil is to be rotated in a uniform magnetic field to produce a root mean square voltage of 100 volts at 1000 cycles/sec, what must be the value of the magnetic induction?

10. An electrical appliance with a resistance of 30 ohms is connected to a house lighting outlet of 120 a.c. Find (a) the peak voltage and (b) the peak current.

TRANSFORMERS

Electricity and Magnetism | **Lesson 21**

COULOMB'S LAW—*Laboratory*

By means of special dumbbell-shaped magnets you will test Coulomb's law of attraction and repulsion of magnetic poles. The use of the Hibbert balance designed for this experiment is described in the accompanying LABORATORY EXERCISES.

Electricity and Magnetism | **Lesson 22**

TRANSFORMERS

Because of the widespread use of transformers in long-distance power transmission as well as in telephones, radio transmitters and receivers, television, etc., it is of interest to consider the elementary principles upon which these instruments operate. A transformer is an electrical device by which the **electromotive force** of a source of alternating current may be increased or decreased.

The Primary Circuit. To study the actions and principles of a transformer we must return to the **solenoid,** or **electromagnet,** treated in Electricity and Magnetism, Lesson 18. Before an electron current is started through the coil of an electromagnet, no magnetic field whatever exists. This is illustrated by the diagram in Fig. A. When

the switch **K** is first closed, completing the electric circuit, the electron current does not rise immediately to its full value but requires a certain amount of time to build up (see Fig. B). Starting at zero at the time the switch is closed, the current increases rapidly at first, then more slowly, reaching finally its full value, the value given by Ohm's law.

During the time the electron current is increasing, the magnetic induction **B**, in and around the solenoid, is increasing as shown in Fig. C. This field continues to grow in strength until the current reaches its maximum value, whereupon both current and field become constant. In most circuits this whole process requires but a small fraction of a second. A constant current is indicative, therefore, of a constant unchanging magnetic field.

When the switch is opened, the current

Fig. A. Electromagnet on open circuit. No current and no field.

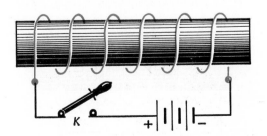

Fig. B. Current-time graph for an electromagnet as illustrated in Fig. A.

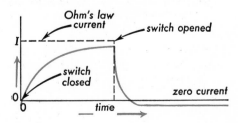

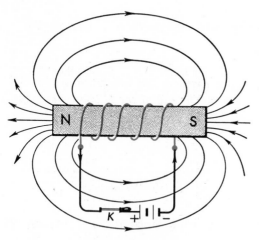

Fig. C. Electromagnet field on closed circuit.

will not stop instantly, nor will the surrounding field vanish instantly. The current will decrease with time, as shown in the graph of Fig. B, and the magnetic induction will decrease accordingly. When the current reaches zero, once more the field will simultaneously vanish as in Fig. A. Thus, by opening and closing a switch, a magnetic field of increasing and decreasing strength is produced.

The Secondary Circuit. If a loop of wire is placed around an electromagnet, as shown in Fig. D, and the switch in the circuit is

Fig. D. Diagram illustrating an electron current induced in a loop of wire placed in the changing field of an electromagnet.

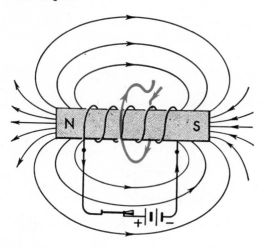

closed and opened as described in the preceding section, an electromotive force, and hence an electron current, will be induced in the loop. Immediately after the switch has been closed and the current and magnetic induction begin to rise, the total flux through the loop increases and we obtain an induced emf. An induced emf means that if the loop ends are connected together, or to something else, to form a closed circuit, a current will flow in the loop as shown by the arrows in the diagram.

When the electromagnet current reaches a steady state, the field becomes constant. This means that the total flux through the loop is no longer changing and the loop emf has dropped to zero.

If the switch **K** is opened at this time, allowing the electromagnet current to decrease, the magnetic induction will decrease, and the total flux through the loop will fall. This decreasing flux, linking the loop circuit, induces an electron current opposite in direction to that shown in the diagram. When the current in the electromagnet winding drops to zero, the field vanishes and so does the induced emf. The properly timed closing and opening of a switch can, therefore, induce in a loop of wire one complete cycle of an alternating current.

To increase the emf in the outside circuit, many loops of wire are usually employed. Such an arrangement becomes similar to that shown in Fig. E and is called an **open-core**

Fig. E. Diagram of an open-core transformer.

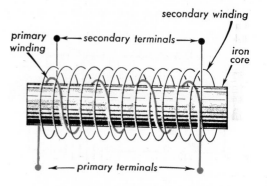

transformer. The inside winding is called the *primary* and the outside winding is called the *secondary.* As the magnetic induction increases, the total flux through each loop of the secondary increases, and approximately the same emf is induced in each turn of the coil. Since the turns are all in series with each other, the total emf between the outside ends is the sum of the individual emf's for each turn.

It is customary for both the primary and secondary windings of a transformer to be wound with well-insulated copper wire and for both windings to be electrically insulated from each other.

Alternating Current.   To operate a transformer on a direct current supply, as from a battery, the primary circuit must be opened and closed at a rapid rate.

Rather than do this by some mechanical means like a vibrator, it is convenient and practical to connect the primary winding to a source of alternating current. In this way the rapidly increasing and decreasing field induces a corresponding alternating emf in the secondary.

As a consequence, most transformers operate from alternating-current sources, rather than from batteries or d.c. generators.

Step-Up and Step-Down Transformer. Nearly all transformers come under one of the two following classes: (a) *step-up,* or (b) *step-down transformers.* As shown in Fig. F, the step-up transformer is one in which the secondary winding has more turns of wire than the primary. In the step-down transformer the reverse is true. The importance of this distinction is based upon the general and well-established principle that the ratio of the number of turns of wire in the primary and secondary windings is the same as the ratio of the respective voltages in each. This may be stated as an equation.

$$\frac{\text{no. of primary turns}}{\text{no. of secondary turns}} = \frac{\text{primary voltage}}{\text{secondary voltage}} \quad (1)$$

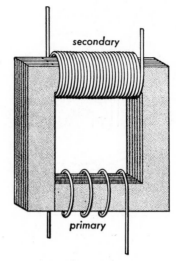

step-up transformer

Fig. F. A step-up transformer with a closed core.

Thus, if a transformer has 100 turns in the primary and 100,000 turns in the secondary, the voltage delivered at the secondary terminals will be 1000 times the voltage impressed upon the primary. If this same transformer were connected to the ordinary house lighting circuit of 110 volts a.c., the voltage at the secondary terminals would be 110,000 volts a.c.

The step-down transformer is just the reverse of this: the secondary voltage is lower than the primary voltage. As an illustration, suppose the primary of a transformer has

Fig. G. Shell-type transformer.

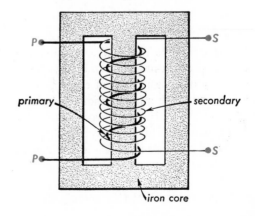

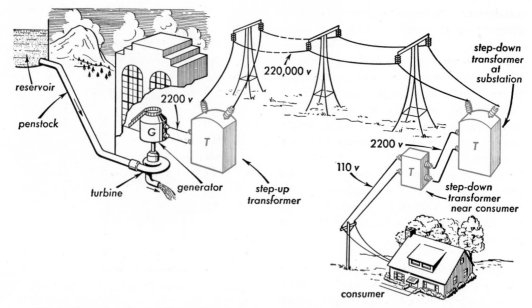

Fig. H. Illustrating the use of transformers in the transmission of electrical energy from the power house in the mountains to the consumer in the distant city.

2000 turns of fine wire and the secondary has 100 turns. Having a turn ratio of 20 to 1, this transformer connected to the 110 volt a.c. line will deliver at its secondary a difference of potential of one-twentieth of 110 volts, or 5.5 volts. Such transformers are used in electric welding, for the ringing of door-bells, for the operation of toy electric trains, for lighting the filaments in radio tubes, etc.

Transformers used in the construction of modern radio and television receivers and transmitters are of the **shell type** shown in Fig. G.

Power. The increase in voltage of an alternating current by means of a step-up transformer appears at first sight to be a violation of the law of conservation of energy, i.e., it appears as though a large amount of energy could be obtained at the expenditure of a smaller amount. This is really not the case, for when the voltage is increased, the current is simultaneously decreased by the same proportion.

The power developed in any electric circuit is given by the product of voltage times current.

$$P = VI \qquad (2)$$

If V is in volts and I is in amperes, the power P is in watts. One thousand watts is called one **kilowatt.**

When, for example, a transformer is used to step up the voltage to 100 times that supplied to the primary, the current in the secondary becomes only one one-hundredth of the current in the primary. In keeping with the law of conservation of energy, therefore, the power supplied at the primary ($V_p I_p$) is just equal to that delivered at the secondary ($V_s I_s$). In general, when the voltage is stepped up by a transformer the current is stepped down by the same proportion.

In practice this is not exactly true, because a transformer is not quite 100 per cent efficient. A small amount of electrical energy is continually expended, principally in the form of heat. In a well-designed transformer such losses do not exceed 2 or 3%; so that a transformer is often considered as almost 100% efficient.

Power Transmission.   In the transmission of electrical energy over wires for long distances, transformers are practically indispensable. At the power house in the distant mountains, for example, electric current is generated by huge a.c. generators at the relatively low voltage of several thousand volts. If an attempt were made to transmit this electrical energy, at a voltage of say 2200 volts, over many miles of wire cable to a distant city, the current would be so large that nearly all of the energy would be consumed in heating the power line. The heat generated is, according to Eq. (6), Electricity and Magnetism, Lesson 15, proportional to the square of the current. (**Heat = kI^2Rt.**)

To avoid large heat losses, transformers at the power house (see Fig. H) step the voltage up to some 220,000 volts before switching the current onto the power line. Since the voltage in the case cited is increased one-hundred fold, the current drops by the same proportion to one one-hundredth. Since the square of 1/100 is 1/10,000, the heat loss along the transmission line is only one ten-thousandth of what it would have been had the transformer not been used.

At the city end of the power line a transformer substation steps the voltage down to something like its original value of 2200 volts. From there branch lines distribute the power to various sections of the city where smaller transformers, one near each group of several houses, steps it down again to the relatively safe voltage of 110 and 220 volts.

Summary

The principal function of a transformer is to increase or decrease the voltage available from a given source of alternating current.

A transformer is composed of three parts: a primary coil, a secondary coil, and a core. The core, frequently composed of iron, links the primary and secondary together by acting somewhat as a conductor of magnetic lines of induction.

A step-up transformer is one in which the alternating emf supplied by the secondary is greater than the emf supplied by the primary. In a step-down transformer the secondary voltage is lower than the primary voltage.

While a transformer may raise or lower the available emf, the law of conservation of energy is not violated. When the voltage is raised, the current drops in the same proportion, so that the power consumed is the same.

The power consumed or developed by any circuit is given by the product voltage $\times$ current

$$P = VI$$

In alternating-current circuits both V and I must be the root mean square values.

Power loss due to the resistance of any electric circuit is given by I^2R. High voltages are therefore applied to the transmission of power over long distances by rasing the input voltage to the power line. By raising the voltage, the current is lowered and power losses are greatly reduced.

Questions

1. What is a transformer? What are its three principal components?

2. Can direct current be applied to a transformer? If so, how?

3. What advantages are there in applying an alternating current to a transformer rather than a direct current?

4. What is a step-up transformer? What is a step-down transformer?

5. If a transformer increases the voltage tenfold, how does the secondary current compare with the primary current?

6. How is the power supplied to a circuit computed? What is a watt? What is a kilowatt?

7. Why are high voltage transformers used in power transmission?

8. Why are the high voltages from power lines reduced to lower voltages in the city? What kind of transformers are used?

9. What is the relation between transformer voltages and the windings of the primary and secondary coils?

10. How could you demonstrate the principles of a transformer, and what would you need in the way of materials to make the component parts of the apparatus?

Problems

1. A step-up transformer has 125 turns in the primary coil and 25,000 turns in the secondary coil. If the primary is connected to a 110-volt a.c. line, find the voltage delivered at the secondary terminals.

2. The primary of a step-up transformer having 150 turns is connected to a house lighting circuit of 115 volts a.c. If the secondary is to deliver 15,000 volts, how many turns must it have?

3. The secondary of a step-down transformer has 25 turns of wire, and the primary is connected to a 110-volt a.c. line. If the secondary is to deliver 2.5 volts at its output terminals, how many turns should the primary have?

4. The primary of a step-down transformer has 300 turns and is connected to a 120-volt a.c. line. If the secondary is to supply 5 volts at its terminals and an electron current of 3.5 amps, find (a) the number of turns in the secondary and (b) the electron current in the primary.

5.* A step-up transformer with 175 turns in the primary is connected to a 120-volt a.c. line. The secondary delivers 10,000 volts at its terminals and a current of 40 milliamperes. (a) How many turns are in the secondary? (b) What is the current in the primary? (c) What power is drawn from the line?

6.* The primary of a step-up transformer is connected to a 110-volt a.c. line. The secondary with 8600 turns delivers 10,000 volts and a current of 20 milliamperes. Calculate (a) the number of turns in the primary and (b) the current drawn from the line.

7.* One end of a power transmission line of 6 ohms is connected to a 220-volt line and the other end to a load resistance of 16 ohms. Find the power consumed by (a) the line and (b) the load. (Each of the two wires is 3 ohms.)

8.* If by means of transformers the source voltage in problem 7 is stepped up to 2200 volts, and then down to 160 volts at the load, find the power consumed by (a) the line and (b) the load. Assume both transformers to be 100% efficient.

Electricity and Magnetism | **Lesson 23**

ALTERNATING CURRENT THEORY

Self-Induction. When a battery is first connected to the ends of a long straight copper wire, the electron current rises quickly to the value given by Ohm's law as shown by curve (a) in Fig. A. When the same wire is wound into a coil or solenoid, however, the current rises more slowly as shown by curve (b). If an iron core is inserted to make of the solenoid an electromagnet, the current rises much more slowly as shown in curve (c).

The cause for this lagging of the current is attributed to an emf induced in the wire which is opposed in direction to the rising current. This **back emf,** as it is sometimes called, is extremely small if the wire is straight, is large if it is a coil, and still larger if a soft-iron core is inserted. To explain the existence of a back emf, consider a small section of one turn of wire in a solenoid of many turns. As the current rises in this section, the growing magnetic induction developing around it threads through neighboring loops of wire inducing in them an emf. These induced emf's and their corresponding currents run counter to the impressed emf and current. This property is called **self-induction.**

The unit by which one measures the self-induction of a coil is called the **henry** in honor of the American scientist, Joseph

Henry.* *A coil having an inductance of one henry is one in which a change in the current of one ampere per second produces a back emf of one volt.* A coil with a large number of turns is one that has a large inductance **L**, whereas one with but a few turns has a small inductance. The higher the inductance the more slowly does the current rise or fall within the coil.

The establishment of a steady current in an inductance requires work, since the back emf's must be overcome. Not all of the electrical energy expended in reaching the steady-current state is lost. Some is stored up in the form of a magnetic field. When the source emf is disconnected from the circuit, the magnetic induction decreases, thereby inducing an oppositely directed emf and corresponding current.

An experiment demonstrating the property of self-induction is illustrated in Fig. B. A solenoid of many turns of wire is connected in parallel with an electric light to a 110-volt battery **B**. When the switch **S** is closed, the light flashes brightly for an instant and then becomes dim. When the switch is opened, the

* Joseph Henry (1797-1878), American physicist and scientific administrator, was born in Albany, New York, in 1797. Henry attended a country school, but quit at the age of thirteen. Later he attended the Albany Academy. Becoming interested in electricity and magnetism he invented the magnetic telegraph, the electric relay, and discovered the phenomenon of self-induction. In 1832 he became professor of natural philosophy at Princeton and in 1842 was elected by Congress as first secretary of the Smithsonian Institution in Washington, D. C. In this capacity he founded the U. S. Weather Bureau and inaugurated the idea of distributing scientific publications to libraries and scientific bodies all over the world. He was the principal figure in the organization of the National Academy of Sciences of which he was the second president. By general agreement Henry was the foremost American physicist of his time.

Fig. A. Current-time graph for a long copper wire in the form of (a) a straight wire, (b) a coil, and (c) a coil with an iron core.

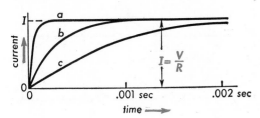

inductance

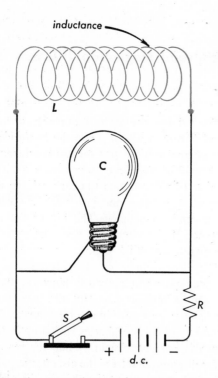

L

C

R

S

+ d.c. −

Fig. B. An experimental demonstration of the self-induction of a coil of wire.

$$L = \mu \frac{N^2 A}{l} \qquad (1)$$

where **N** is the number of turns of wire, **A** is the cross-sectional area of the core in **square meters**, μ is the permeability of the core in **webers/ampere-meter**, and **l** is the length of the coil in meters.

Example.   A round iron bar 4 cm in diameter and 20 cm long is wrapped with one layer of copper wire to form a solenoid. The coil has 200 turns and the permeability of the iron is 2×10^{-3} **w/amp-m**. Find the inductance.

Solution.   The given quantities are just those occurring on the right in Eq. (1). **N** = 200, $\mu = 2 \times 10^{-3}$, **l** = 0.20 m, and **A** $= \pi r^2 = 0.00126$ m².

$$L = \frac{2 \times 10^{-3} \times (200)^2 \times 0.00126}{0.2}$$

$$= 0.504 \text{ henry}$$

Without the iron core the solenoid above would have a very much smaller inductance. For an air core, μ would be equal to $\mu_o = 12.57 \times 10^{-7}$, and the inductance would be only 0.316 millihenry. **The millihenry (abbr. mh) is a smaller unit of inductance and is equal to one-thousandth of a henry,** while a still smaller unit, **the microhenry (abbr. μh) is equal to one-millionth of a henry.**

It should be noted that if the core is air,

light again flashes brightly for a moment and then goes out. When the switch was closed, the back emf in the inductance prevented the current from building up rapidly through the inductance. The inductance therefore acted as though it had a very high resistance, so that practically all of the current went through **C**. When the current became steady, there was no back emf in **L**, and part of the current flowed through **C** and part through **L**. When the switch was opened, the magnetic field rapidly diminished, inducing a current in **L**. This current flowing through the lamp **C** caused it to light up momentarily to full brightness.

Calculation of Inductance.   In many instances the inductance of a solenoid can be calculated from its geometry. For a long solenoid of uniform cross section (see p. 417) the inductance **L**, in **henries**, is given by

Fig. C. Series circuit containing inductance and resistance.

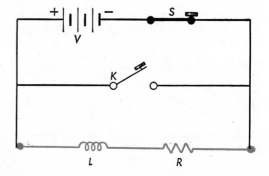

+   −   S

V

K

L   *R*

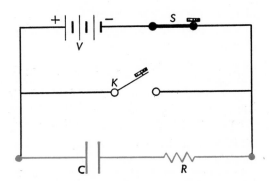

Fig. D. Series circuit containing capacitance and resistance.

or a vacuum, **L** is a constant independent of the electron current and magnetizing field **H**. If the core is a ferromagnetic material, however, **L** will vary because the permeability varies.

Inductance and Capacitive Reactance. When an inductance **L** is connected in series with a resistance **R** and a battery **V** (see Fig. C), it takes time for the electron current **I** and the accompanying magnetic field to build up to a steady state. When the switch **S** is opened and the switch **K** closed, the field decreases and the electron current falls, approaching zero as **t** approaches infinity.

When a capacitor **C** is connected in series with a resistor **R** and a battery **V** (see Fig. D), an electron current flows for a short period of time because it takes time for the plates of the capacitor to acquire their full charge **Q**. If now the switch **S** is opened disconnecting

Fig. E. Series circuit containing inductance, capacitance, and resistance.

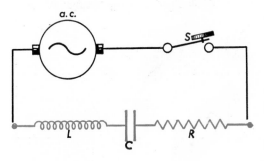

the battery, and then the switch **K** is closed, the capacitor will discharge, and again an electron current will flow through **R**.

All electrical devices connected to a source of alternating emf contain a certain amount of **resistance, inductance,** and **capacitance.** If the total inductance and capacitance of the circuit are small compared with the resistance, Ohm's law can be applied to find the current in the various parts.

If the inductance and capacitance are not relatively small, they will introduce phase differences, or time lags, between current and voltage, and Ohm's law will not apply in the ordinary way. Such a circuit is shown schematically in Fig. E.

Since an **emf** suddenly applied to an inductance requires a certain time for the electron current to build up to a fixed value (see Fig. A), the application of an **alternating emf** finds the current lagging behind the voltage in its rapid changes and reversals. Furthermore, if the frequency is very high, there isn't time enough for the electron current to rise very far from zero toward its Ohm's law value.

Because the inductance effect reduces the electron current, it may be thought of as something analogous to a resistance. The measure of this effect is called **inductive reactance,** to distinguish it from a true resistance where electrical energy is converted into heat.

inductive reactance

$$X_L = 2\pi fL \qquad (2)$$

where **f** is the frequency or cycles per second.

When a capacitor is inserted into a **d.c. circuit,** the plates charge up, and the electron current drops to zero. The capacitor thereafter acts as though it has an infinite resistance. Connected to an alternating emf, however, it may act quite differently. As the frequency **f** rises in an **a.c. circuit,** the resistive effect of a capacitor decreases. The reversing of the **emf** reverses the flow of electrons to and from the plates of the capacitor, and the alternating flow of charge constitutes an **alternating current**. Because a capacitor differs from a pure resistance in that it stores electrostatic energy, its resistive effect is called **capacitive reactance.**

capacitive reactance

$$X_C = \frac{1}{2\pi fC}$$ (3)

A.C. Series Circuit. When an inductance **L**, capacitance **C**, and a resistance **R** are connected in series to an a.c. generator as shown in Fig. E, the electron current in the circuit can be determined by the following equation,

$$I = \frac{V}{\sqrt{R^2 + (X_L - X_C)^2}}$$ (4)

where **I** and **V** are the electron current and voltage respectively. The quantity $X_L - X_C$ in this equation is often called the **reactance** and is represented by **X**,

$$X = X_L - X_C$$

so that

$$I = \frac{V}{\sqrt{R^2 + X^2}}$$

The whole denominator is called the **impedance** and is represented by **Z.**

$$Z = \sqrt{R^2 + (X_L - X_C)^2}$$ (5)

and

$$I = \frac{V}{Z}$$ (6)

Note the identical form of this last equation to Ohm's law for direct currents. The resistance **R** in Ohm's law has here been replaced by the impedance **Z.**

Phase Relations Between I and V. The effect of an inductance and a capacitance on an **a.c. series circuit** is such as to alter the phase of the electron current **I** with respect to the applied alternating voltage. If the inductive reactance X_L is greater than the capacitive reactance X_C, the electron current will lag behind the impressed voltage, while if X_C is greater than X_L the electron current will lead the impressed voltage.

The amount the electron current lags or leads is given by what is called **the phase angle** θ, where θ is given by

$$\tan \theta = \frac{X}{R}$$ (7)

In one complete cycle of either the current or voltage the phase angle has changed by 2π radians, so that a phase lag of 45 degrees means that the electron current is one-eighth of a cycle behind the voltage. A graphical representation of this example is given in Fig. F.

Power Factor. With direct current circuits the power is given by the product **V** × **I**, and is measured in **volt-amperes**, or **watts**. In alternating current circuits the instantaneous rate at which energy is supplied is equal to the product of the instantaneous voltage and the instantaneous current. Since both of these are sometimes zero, it is clear that the power consumption varies over each cycle and that some sort of average power must be taken.

The average useful power delivered by any a.c. circuit is equal to the rms voltage times the rms electron current multiplied by the cosine of the angle of lag.

Fig. F. Graph showing current lagging 45° behind voltage.

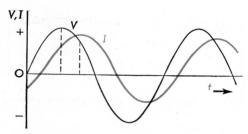

$$P = VI \cos \theta \qquad (8)$$

The quantity cos θ is called the **power factor**. A low power factor in **a.c. circuits** is to be avoided since for a given supply voltage **V** a large current would be needed to transmit appreciable electrical energy. Because heat losses are given by I^2R currents should be held to a minimum by making the power factor as near unity as possible. This means that θ should be as near zero as possible.

Levitation. The phenomenon known as levitation is another illustration of Lenz's law. A metal bowl **B**, as in diagram (a) Fig. G, is supported in stable-equilibrium in the mid-air just above an electromagnet **M** of special design. Top and side views of the iron core and coil windings are shown in diagrams (b) and (c). Excited by an alternating current, the raised iron knobs labeled **N** and **S** reverse their polarity periodically with the current. As the electron current builds up in the direction indicated in diagram (b), the magnetic induction grows as in diagram (c). With the aluminum bowl in place as in diagram (c), the growing field induces strong eddy currents in the aluminum conductor. These currents in turn give rise to opposing fields. Since the primary field being created by an alternating current increases and decreases rapidly, the bowl always experiences an upward force.

Should the bowl move to one side, as for example to the left in diagram (c), the changing field at **A** will induce stronger elec-

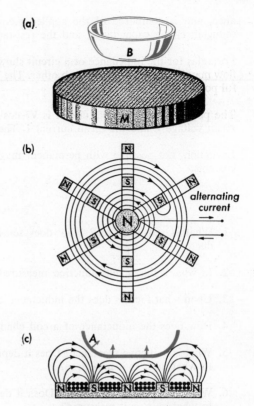

Fig. G. A metal bowl is suspended in mid-air.

tron currents on that side of the bowl and give rise to an increased repulsion, pushing the bowl back toward the center as indicated. The strong induced currents give rise to so much heat that the bowl soon becomes hot.

Because the coil windings of a levitator have a relatively large inductive reactance, a fairly large capacitance must be inserted in the a.c. circuit to keep the current in the levitator coils in step with the voltage supplied by the source.

Summary

When an emf is suddenly applied to any electric circuit, the current does not immediately rise to its maximum value because of self-induction. The rising magnetic induction from any one part of the circuit links other parts of the crcuit, and the resulting induced emf opposes the rising current. For any given circuit the self-induction or the inductance is a constant and is generally represented by **L**.

When an alternating emf is applied to a circuit, Ohm's law must be modified when it is to be applied to find the current flow. The circuit resistance in ohms is called the impedance, and is composed of the applied a.c. frequency and three circuit elements: the inductance, the capacitance, and the resistance.

Formulas for the impedance of a circuit show that the applied emf and resultant current flow may be out of step with each other. The more they are in step the greater is the useful power delivered by a circuit.

The power in an electrical circuit is $VI \cos \theta$, where θ is the phase angle between the mean voltage V and the mean current I. The power factor is given by $\cos \theta$.

Levitation, not possible with permanent magnets, can be accomplished with alternating currents.

Questions

1. What is self-induction? How does self-induction depend on the shape of a conductor?

2. In what units is self-induction measured?

3. Upon what factors does the inductance of a long solenoid depend?

4. How does the inductance of a coil change when an iron core is inserted?

5. What is inductive reactance? Does it depend upon the frequency of the applied emf? In what units is it measured?

6. What is capacitive reactance? Does it depend on the frequency of the applied emf? In what units is it measured?

7. What is the reactance of a circuit?

8. What is impedance? Upon what circuit factors does it depend? In what units is it measured?

9. What is meant by the power factor? What is its significance?

10. Upon what three factors does the useful power delivered by an a.c. circuit depend? What is the formula for power? What are the units of power?

11. Can levitation be established with permanent magnets? Is levitation possible at all? Explain.

Problems

1. An oscillator coil is wound on a glass tube 4 cm in diameter and 20 cm long. How many turns of copper wire must it have to give it an inductance of 250 μh?

2. A round iron bar 4 cm in diameter and 20 cm long is wound with copper wire to form a solenoid. If the iron has a permeability of 12.57×10^{-4} w/amp-m, and the inductance is 0.45 h, how many turns of wire does it have?

3. A solenoid 2.0 cm in diameter and 50 cm long has 420 turns of wire. Find its inductance when it has (a) an air core and (b) an iron core of permeability 2.5×10^{-3} w/amp-m.

4. A small solenoid 1 cm in diameter and 10 cm long has 500 turns of fine wire. Calculate its inductance when it has (a) an air core and (b) an iron core of permeability 2263×10^{-7} w/amp-m.

5. An inductance of 60 μh is connected to a 60-cycle a.c. line. Calculate the inductive reactance.

6. A capacitance of 250 μf is connected to a 60-cycle a.c. line. Find the capacitive reactance.

7. An inductance of 240 μh is connected to a 500-cycle/sec a.c. line. Calculate the inductive reactance.

8. A capacitance of 180 μf is connected to a 500-cycle/sec a.c. line. Find the capacitive reactance.

9.* A 60-ohm resistor is connected in series with a 0.25 henry inductor, a 50 μf capacitor, and an a.c. generator delivering 110 volts (rms) at 60 cycles. Find (a) the reactance, (b) the impedance, (c) the electron current in the circuit, (d) the power factor, and (e) the power.

10.* An inductance of 60 mh is connected in series with a resistance of 90 ohms, a capacitance of 50 μf, and a generator delivering a 60-cycle rms voltage of 30 volts at its terminals. Find (a) the reactance, (b) the impedance, (c) the rms current, (d) the phase angle, (e) the power factor, and (f) the useful power developed.

Electricity and Magnetism | **Lesson 24**

TRANSFORMERS—*Laboratory*

Measurements of the primary and secondary voltages are made with a transformer having removable coils. Detailed steps using fixed, multiple, and tapped secondaries are given in the accompanying LABORATORY EXERCISES.

ATOMIC PHYSICS

The main result of our investigations and of those of other scientists during these years, was to make known the nature of the rays emitted by radium, and to prove that they belonged to three different categories. Radium emits a stream of active corpuscles moving with great speed. Certain of them carry a positive charge and form the Alpha rays; others, much smaller, carry a negative charge and form Beta rays. The movements of these two groups are influenced by a magnet. A third group is constituted by the rays that are insensible to the action of a magnet, and that, we know today, are a radiation similar to light and to X-rays.

Marie Curie, *Pierre Curie*, Macmillan, New York, 1923, p. 103.

After long consideration of the experiments it seemed to me that there was no escape from the following conclusions:

(1) That atoms are not indivisible, for negatively electrified particles can be torn from them by the action of electrical forces, impact of rapidly moving atoms, ultra-violet light or heat.

(2) That these particles are all of the same mass, and carry the same charge of negative electricity from whatever kind of atom they may be derived, and are a constituent of all atoms.

(3) That the mass of these particles is less than one-thousandth part of the mass of an atom of hydrogen.

I at first called these particles corpuscles, but they are now called by the more appropriate name "electrons."

J. J. Thomson, *Recollections and Reflections*, Macmillan, New York, 1937, pp. 338-339.

← A heavy ion linear accelerator built at the University of California. With this accelerator an isotope of element 102 was definitely discovered.

University of California

Discovery of the Electron

ALTHOUGH no one has ever seen an atom there is no doubt in the mind of the true scientist that such particles really exist. To the physicists and chemists who have built up and established the present-day theories of the structure of matter, atoms are as real as any material objects large enough to be seen with the eyes or to be felt with the hands. Their reality is evidenced by hundreds of laboratory experiments that can be planned and executed in the research laboratory.

Electrical Discharge Through a Gas. In 1853, an obscure French scientist by the name of Masson sent the first electric spark from a high-voltage induction coil through a partially evacuated glass vessel and discovered that instead of the typical spark observed in air the tube was filled with a bright glow.

Several years later, Heinrich Geissler, a German glass blower in Tübingen, developed and began the manufacture of gaseous discharge tubes. These tubes, made in diverse sizes, shapes, and colors of glass, and resembling the modern neon and argon signs used in advertising, attracted the attention of physicists in the leading scientific institutions and universities of the world, who purchased many of these "Geissler tubes" and used them for study and lecture demonstrations.

In 1869 W. Hittorf of Munster, with improved vacuum pumps, observed a dark region near one electrode of the electrical discharge which grew in size as the exhaustion was continued. This is but one of a number of phases of the study of electrical discharge through gases observed and studied a few years later by Sir William Crookes.*

In Fig. A a long glass tube about 4 cm in diameter and 150 cm long is shown connected to a mercury diffusion pump and a mechanical vacuum pump. The purpose of the pumps is to enable one to observe continuously the changes in the electrical discharge as the air is slowly removed from the tube. The purpose of the *trap* is to freeze out

* Sir William Crookes (1832-1919), English physicist and chemist. At twenty-two he became an assistant at the Radcliff Observatory in Oxford. He was knighted in 1897, received the Order of Merit in 1910, and was president of the Royal Society from 1913 to 1915. He invented and made the first focusing type of X-ray tube. His experiments with electrical discharges through rarefied gases led to his discovery of the dark space which now bears his name.

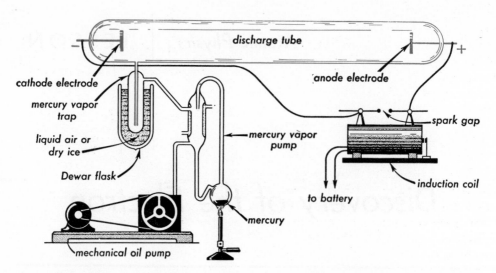

Fig. A. Diagram of a gaseous discharge tube showing the electrical connections as well as the vacuum pumps and accessories.

any mercury vapor and prevent it from reaching the discharge. High voltage from an induction coil is shown connected to the two electrodes, one at either end of the tube.

Although an induction coil does not deliver direct current, its characteristics are such that the potentials are higher on half of the alternations than they are on the other half and that the two electrodes act nearly the same as if a high-voltage direct current were used. The negative electrode under

Fig. B. Sketches of the general appearance of a high-voltage electric discharge through rarefied air at various stages of evacuation.

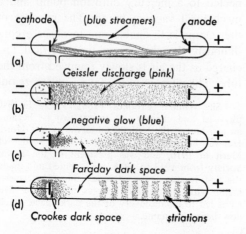

these circumstances is called the **cathode** and the positive electrode the **anode.**

As the long tube is slowly pumped out, an emf of 10,000 to 15,000 volts will produce the first discharge when the pressure has dropped to about one one-hundredth of an atmosphere, i.e., at a barometric pressure of about 10 mm of mercury. This first discharge, as illustrated in diagram (a) of Fig. B, consists of long thin bluish-colored streamers. As the gas pressure drops to about 5 mm of mercury, sometimes called a Geissler-tube vacuum, the discharge changes to pink and at the same time widens until it fills the whole tube as shown in diagram (b). At a still lower pressure of about 2 mm a dark region called the **Faraday dark space** appears in the region of the cathode, dividing the bright discharge into two parts, a long pinkish section called the **positive column** and a short bluish section called the **negative glow.**

As the pressure drops still further the Faraday dark space grows in size and the negative glow moves away from the cathode, producing another dark space between it and the cathode. With the appearance of this second dark region, called the **Crookes dark space,** the positive column divides into a number of equally spaced layers called **stria-tions.**

As the pumping proceeds, the striations and the negative glow grow fainter, and the Crookes dark space widens until finally at a pressure of about 0.01 mm it fills the whole tube. At this point a new feature appears: the whole glass tube itself glows with a faint greenish light.

Cathode Rays. The green glow in the final stage of the gaseous discharge just described was soon found to be a **fluorescence of the glass produced by invisible rays emanating from the cathode itself.** These **cathode rays,** as they are called, believed by Sir William Crookes to be an "ultra gaseous state" and by Johann W. Hittorf to be a "fourth state" of matter, turn out to be tiny corpuscles which we now call **electrons.** In the relatively free space of a highly evacuated tube, cathode particles, torn loose from the atoms of the cathode, stream down the length of the tube, seldom colliding with a gas molecule until they hit the glass walls.

The first important discovery concerning the nature of cathode rays was that they travel in straight lines. This was first revealed by Hittorf in 1869 by casting shadows of objects placed inside the discharge tube. This is usually demonstrated by a tube of special design as shown in Fig. C.

Fig. C. A Crookes' discharge tube for demonstrating that cathode rays travel in straight lines.

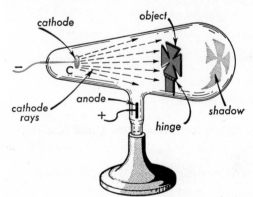

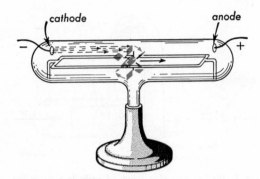

Fig. D. Demonstration of experiment showing that cathode rays have momentum and energy. Cathode rays striking the vanes of a small pinwheel cause it to roll from one end of the tube to the other.

Where the rays strike the walls of the tube the glass fluoresces green, while in the shadow it remains dark. Under continuous bombardment of the walls by cathode rays the fluorescence grows fainter because of a fatigue effect of the glass. This is demonstrated by tipping the object down on its hinge, permitting the rays to strike the fresh glass surface. Where the shadow appeared previously, a bright green image of the object is clearly visible.

That **cathode rays have momentum and energy** was first demonstrated by Crookes in 1870 using a tube of special design as illustrated in Fig. D. Leaving the cathode and acquiring a high speed on their way toward the anode, the rays strike the mica vanes of a small pinwheel and exert a force, causing it to turn and thus roll along a double track toward the anode. When it reaches the end of the track a reversal of the potential, making the right-hand electrode the cathode, will send it rolling back toward the anode, now at the left. From this experiment Crookes concluded that cathode particles have **momentum,** and that therefore they have **mass, velocity,** and **kinetic energy** $\frac{1}{2}mv^2$.

That **cathode rays are negatively charged particles** was first discovered in Paris in 1895 by Jean Perrin. A discharge tube of special design usually used to demonstrate this property is illustrated in Fig. E. A

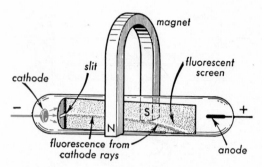

Fig. E. The bending of a beam of cathode rays in the field of a magnet demonstrates that cathode rays are negatively charged particles.

magnet over the outside of the tube as illustrated, the path of the cathode rays is bent down. If the polarity of the magnet is reversed, the path is bent up. The bending shows they are charged, and the direction of bending shows the kind of charge. Being charged, a stream of particles is like an electric current. From the direction of the magnetic field, the direction of the current, and applying the left-hand rule, the charge is found to be **negative.** (Remember that the left-hand rule applies to a current from $(-)$ to $(+)$.)

beam of cathode rays is narrowed down to a thin pencil or ribbon of rays by a narrow slit near the cathode. The path of the rays is made visible by allowing them to strike a long strip of metal painted with zinc sulfide, a fluorescent paint. By placing a horseshoe

The penetrating power of cathode rays was first demonstrated by Heinrich Hertz and his assistant P. Lenard by passing cathode rays through thin aluminum foils. Out in the air the rays were found to retain sufficient power to cause fluorescence and phosphorescence.

Summary

When a high-voltage spark discharge is made to occur in a partially evacuated tube, many changes in the general appearance of the emitted light take place as the pressure is altered.

At very low pressures, rays given off by the cathode (the negative electrode, or terminal inside the discharge tube) produce fluorescence where they strike the glass walls.

By a special discharge tube containing a Maltese cross, cathode rays are found to travel in straight lines. By another tube containing a pinwheel cathode rays are shown to have momentum and energy.

By the bending of a beam in a magnetic field cathode rays are found to carry a negative charge. Cathode rays are electrons.

Questions

1. What is a cathode? What is an anode?

2. What is the general appearance of the first vacuum discharge in a tube when the pressure is lowered?

3. What is the negative glow? What is the positive column?

4. What are striations? What is the Faraday dark space? What is the Crooke's dark space?

5. How can it be shown that cathode rays travel in straight lines? Where do cathode rays originate?

6. How can it be shown that cathode rays have momentum and energy? Do cathode rays have mass?

7. How can it be shown that cathode rays (a) are charged particles and (b) that the charge is negative?

8. Do cathode rays have penetrating power?

9.* What evidence is there in the experiments described here that cathode rays probably are all alike and have the same mass and charge?

10.* Upon what does the color of the light from the positive column of an electrical discharge tube depend? How is this related to present-day "neon signs"?

Atomic Physics | Lesson 2

ELECTRONIC CHARGE AND MASS

When, in 1895, it was discovered that cathode rays were negatively charged particles, the question immediately arose as to whether or not they were all alike. It was clear from the beginning that two things would have to be done: one was to measure the amount of charge on the particles and the other was to measure the particles' mass.

Although the first attempts to measure the electronic charge and mass were not entirely successful, J. J. Thomson* did succeed, in 1897, in determining the velocity of the rays and in measuring the ratio between their charge and mass.

The discharge tube designed for these experiments is shown in Fig. A. Cathode rays, originating at the left-hand electrode and limited to a thin pencil of rays by two pin-

* Sir Joseph John Thomson (1856-1940), English physicist, educated at Owens College, Manchester, and at Trinity College, Cambridge. He was appointed Cavendish professor at Cambridge in 1884, and professor of physics at the Royal Institution, London, in 1905. He was awarded the Nobel Prize in physics in 1906, was knighted in 1908, and elected to the presidency of the Royal Society in 1915. He became master of Trinity College in 1918 and helped to develop at Cambridge a great research laboratory attracting scientific workers from all over the world.

holes in diaphragms **DD**, are made to pass between two parallel metal plates and the magnetic field of two external solenoids to a fluorescent screen at the far end.

When the two metal plates **P** are connected to a high potential, the particles experience a downward force and their path curves to strike the screen at **N**. Without a charge on the plates the beam passes straight through undeviated and strikes the screen at **S**.

When the magnetic field alone is applied so that the magnetic lines are perpendicular to the plane of the page, the path of the rays curves upward to strike the fluorescent screen at some point **M**. If both the electric field and the magnetic field are applied simultaneously, a proper adjustment of the strength of either field can be made so that the deflection downward by the one is exactly counteracted by the deflection of the other upward. When this condition is attained a measurement of the magnetic induction **B** and the electric intensity **E** permits a calculation of the velocity of cathode rays.

Deflection in an Electric Field. In Electricty and Magnetism, Lesson 8, on the

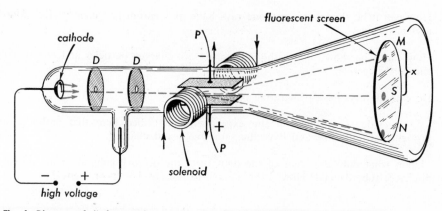

Fig. A. Diagram of discharge tube used by J. J. Thomson to measure the velocity of cathode rays.

theory of electricity it is shown that if e is the charge on a body located in an electric field of strength E, the force exerted on the particle is given by

$$F_E = eE \qquad (1)$$

As a charged particle like an electron enters the electric field between two charged plates, as shown in Fig. B, this force acts straight downward parallel to the field lines at all points. The net result is that the particle traverses a parabolic path in much the same way that a projectile follows a parabolic path in the earth's gravitational field.

Deflection in a Magnetic Field. In Electricity and Magnetism, Lesson 18, it is shown that if e is the charge on a body moving through a magnetic field, the force acting upon it is given by

$$F_B = evB \qquad (2)$$

Since this force is always at right angles to both the magnetic induction B and the di-

rection of motion v, the particle will traverse a circular path as shown in Fig. C. The force F_B is simply the centripetal force, and we can make use of the mechanics relation for centripetal force, and write

$$F_B = m\frac{v^2}{r} \qquad (3)$$

or

$$evB = m\frac{v^2}{r} \qquad (4)$$

Transposing, this relation can be written

$$\boxed{\frac{e}{m} = \frac{v}{Br}} \qquad (5)$$

Fig. C. Electrons in a uniform magnetic field B follow a circular path.

Fig. B. Electrons in a uniform electric field E follow a parabolic path.

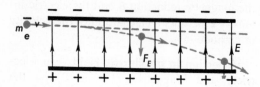

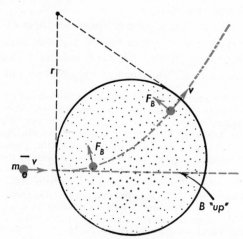

Electron Velocity. When both the electric and magnetic fields act on the stream of electrons as in Thomson's experiment, Fig. A, the two opposing forces are adjusted until the beam travels straight through. Under these conditions the two forces F_E and F_B are equal in magnitude, and we can write

$$eE = evB$$

By canceling the charge e on both sides of this equation, we obtain

$$E = vB$$

from which

$$v = \frac{E}{B} \tag{6}$$

where E is in volts per meter, B is in webers per square meter, and v is in meters per second. Inserting the known values of E and B, the velocity v can be calculated. Thomson's early results showed that cathode rays travel with a speed of several thousand miles per second, about one-fifth the velocity of light. Furthermore, the velocity is not always the same but depends upon the voltage applied between the anode and cathode. By increasing this voltage the velocity of the rays is increased.

The equation giving the velocity of the cathode rays, acquired as the result of the applied voltage V, is

$$Ve = \tfrac{1}{2} mv^2 \tag{7}$$

It is of interest to point out here that the picture tubes used for television receivers are quite similar in shape and principle to J. J. Thomson's cathode-ray tube of Fig. A.

The Ratio of Charge to Mass. Having found the velocity of electrons, Thomson next proceeded to measure the deflection of the beam produced by the magnetic field alone, and to calculate the radius of their path r. See Fig. C.

Upon substitution in Eq. (5) of the velocity v, the magnetic induction B, and the radius r (all measurable quantities), Thomson found a value for the ratio e/m.

This ratio is called the electronic charge to mass ratio. The most probable value today of this important constant for electrons is

$$\frac{e}{m} = 1.7589 \times 10^{11} \frac{\text{coulomb}}{\text{kg}} \tag{8}$$

Such a large number means that the mass of an electron in kg is extremely small as compared with the charge it carries in coulombs.

Millikan's Oil-Drop Experiment. Millikan* began his experiments on the electronic charge e in 1906. His apparatus is illustrated by a simple diagram in Fig. D. Minute oil drops from an atomizer are sprayed into the region just over the top of one of two circular metal plates E^+ and E^-. Shown in cross section, the upper plate is pierced with a tiny pinhole P through which an occasional oil drop from the cloud will fall. Once between the plates such a drop, illuminated by an arc light from the side, is observed by means of a low-powered microscope.

With the switch S in the up position, the capacitor plates are grounded so that they are not charged. Under these conditions the oil drop falling under the pull of gravity has a constant velocity. This **terminal velocity,** as it is called, is reached by the drop

---

* Robert Andrews Millikan (1868-1953), American physicist, educated at Oberlin College and Columbia University, for twenty-five years professor of physics at the University of Chicago and for thirty years president of the Norman Bridge laboratory at the California Institute of Technology in Pasadena. He served during World War I in the research division of the Signal Corps with the rank of lieutenant colonel. His principal contributions to science have been his measurement of the charge on the electron, his photoelectric determination of the energy in a light quantum, and his precision study of cosmic rays. He was the second American to be awarded the Nobel Prize in physics (1923). He has also been awarded the Edison Medal, the Hughes Medal of the Royal Society, the Faraday Medal, and the Mattenci Medal.

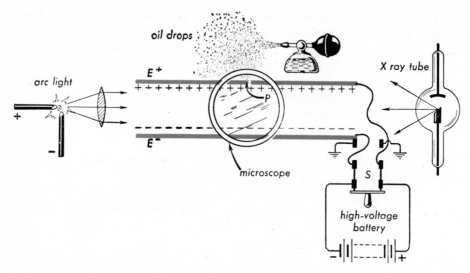

Fig. D. Schematic diagram of Millikan's oil-drop experiment. From this experiment the charge of the electron was determined.

before it enters the field of view and is of such a value that the downward pull of gravity F_G is exactly equalized by the upward resisting force of the air. By measuring this velocity of fall, the force F_G can be calculated and from it the mass of the oil drop determined. The velocity of the drop can be determined by using a stop watch and measuring the time required to fall the distance between the two cross hairs illustrated in Fig. E.

As the drop nears the bottom plate, the switch **S** is thrown down, charging the two parallel plates positive and negative. If now the drop has a negative charge, as illustrated in Fig. F, there will be an upward electro-

static force F_E acting to propel the drop up across the field of view. The drop will move upward with a constant velocity if F_E is greater than the gravitational force F_G. Again using the stop watch, this time to measure the velocity of rise, the upward force F_E can be calculated. Knowing the force, and the voltage on the condenser plates, the charge on the drop can be computed.

As the drop nears the top plate, the switch **S** is thrown up and the plates are again grounded. Under these conditions the drop falls again under the pull of gravity alone.

Fig. F. Diagrams of oil drop with extra electronic charges.

Fig. E. Microscope field of view showing oil drop.

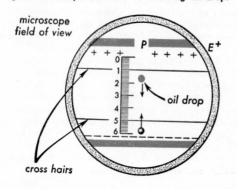

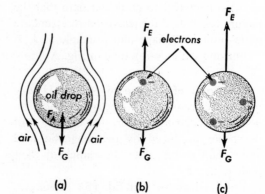

Upon nearing the bottom plate the switch is again thrown down and the drop rises once more. When this process is repeated, a single drop may be made to move up and down many times across the field of view. Each time it falls, the velocity is measured and the mass of the oil drop computed; while each time it rises, the velocity is measured and the charge computed.

Millikan found that if X rays were allowed to pass through the apparatus while an oil drop was being observed, the charge on the drop could be increased or decreased almost at will. One time on rising, the velocity would be low due to a small charge, see diagram (b) in Fig. F, while the next time the velocity would be high due to a larger change, as in diagram (c). Regardless of the amount of charge, the rate of fall for a given drop is always the same. The reason for this is that the total mass of a number of electrons is so small compared with the mass of the oil drop that their added mass is not perceptible.

Millikan, and numerous other experimenters who have repeated these experiments, have found that the charge on a drop is never less than a certain minimum value, and is always some integral multiple of this value. In other words, any one electron is like every other electron, each carrying this minimum charge called **e**.

$$e = -1.6019 \times 10^{-19} \text{ coulomb} \qquad (9)$$

This is the most recent and probable value of the electronic charge.

The Mass of the Electron. From Millikan's determination of the charge on the electron and Thomson's measurement of **e/m**, the mass of the electron can be calculated by dividing one value by the other. Using the most accurately known values for both **e** and **e/m**, we obtain

$$m = \frac{e}{e/m} = \frac{1.6019 \times 10^{-19} \text{ coulomb}}{1.7589 \times 10^{11} \text{ coulombs/kg}}$$

$$m = 9.1072 \times 10^{-31} \text{ kg}$$

This mass is unbelievably small; yet its value has been determined many times and by many experimenters, and it is always the same.*

* For a more complete and elementary treatment of these early experiments see "Electrons + and −," by R. A. Millikan, University of Chicago Press.

Summary

When cathode rays, as negatively charged particles, pass through a uniform magnetic field perpendicular to the lines of induction, they are bent in the arc of a circle. When these same particles enter and traverse a uniform electric field, they traverse a parabolic path.

By applying electric and magnetic fields to a beam of cathode rays in a tube of special design, J. J. Thomson found that the particles travel with a speed of about one-fifth the speed of light.

By measuring the beam deflection in a magnetic field alone, Thomson found a value for the ratio of charge to mass, **e/m**, for electrons.

Millikan's oil-drop experiment made it possible to determine the charge e on the electron. This was accomplished by finding the various charges held by an oil drop as it was forced up and down in an apparatus of special design.

The charge on the electron is found to be

$$e = -1.6019 \times 10^{-19} \text{ coulomb}$$

and the electron's mass to be

$$m = 9.1072 \times 10^{-31} \text{ kg}$$

Questions

1. What is the path taken by a charged particle in traversing a magnetic field at right angles to **B**?

2. What is the path taken by an electron as the result of entering a uniform electric field perpendicular to the electric lines of force?

3. What was the approximate speed of the cathode rays in J. J. Thomson's experiment?

4. What is meant by the expression "**e** over **m**"?

5. What is Millikan's oil-drop experiment? What was its purpose?

6. What determines the speeed of fall of an oil drop? Is the velocity of fall constant?

7. What determines the speed of rise of an oil drop? Is the velocity the same each time the same drop rises?

8. What is determined by the rate of fall of an oil drop? What is determined by the rate of rise?

9. What was the purpose of the X rays in the oil-drop experiment?

10. What conclusions can be drawn from J. J. Thomson's experiment? What conclusions can be drawn from the Millikan oil-drop experiment?

Problems

1. Electrons with a velocity of one-tenth the velocity of light enter a uniform magnetic field at right angles to the magnetic induction. What will be the radius of their circular path if $B = 2.0 \times 10^{-3}$ w/m²?

2. Electrons entering a uniform magnetic field in a direction at right angles to the lines of induction where $B = 4 \times 10^{-4}$ w/m² have a velocity of 6.5×10^8 cm/sec. Calculate the radius of their circular path.

3. In J. J. Thomson's experiment, a magnetic induction field of 1.9×10^{-2} w/m² is employed. If electrons entering this field have a velocity of 2×10^9 cm/sec, what potential difference applied to the parallel plates will keep their path straight? Assume the plate to be 0.5 cm apart.

4. Electrons moving in a uniform magnetic field where $B = 1 \times 10^{-3}$ w/m² follow a circular path of 46.5 cm radius. Calculate their velocity.

5. Electrons moving in a uniform magnetic field $B = 4.5 \times 10^{-4}$ w/m² follow a circular path of 20 cm radius. Find their velocity.

6. Electrons are injected with a speed of 5×10^6 m/sec into a uniform magnetic field at right angles to the lines of induction. If the flux density is 2×10^{-3} w/m², find the diameter of their circular path.

7. If a beam of electrons with a speed of 3×10^7 m/sec enters a uniform magnetic field at right angles to **B** and describes a circular path of 10 cm radius, what is the value of **B**?

8.* A 100-volt battery is connected to two parallel metal plates 15 cm long and 2 cm apart. If electrons enter this field from one end, moving with a constant velocity of 3×10^7 m/sec, how far will they be deviated from their original straight line path when they reach the other end?

Atomic Physics | Lesson 3

THE ELEMENTS AND THEIR ISOTOPES

The Discovery of Positive Rays. During the latter part of the nineteenth century, when many physicists were investigating the various properties of cathode rays, Goldstein designed a special discharge tube and with it discovered new rays called **canal rays**. The name canal rays is derived from the fact that the rays, traveling in straight lines through a vacuum tube in the opposite direction to cathode rays, pass through and emerge from a canal or hole in the cathode. A tube designed to illustrate this is shown in Fig. A.

Shortly after the measure of the electronic charge by J. J. Thomson in 1896, W. Wien deflected a beam of canal rays in a magnetic field and came to the conclusion that the rays consisted of positively charged particles. Be-

cause of this and other experiments, canal rays have become more commonly known as **positive rays.**

Since the time of Goldstein's discovery, positive rays have been found to be charged atoms of different weights. The origin of the charge carried by such atoms is explained briefly as follows. As the electrons from the cathode stream down the tube toward the anode, they occasionally collide with the atoms and molecules of the small quantity of remaining gas, knocking electrons from them.

This process, called **ionization**, is illustrated by a schematic diagram of a single oxygen atom in Fig. B. Before the collision, the atom as a whole, with its eight electrons and eight equal positive charges on the nucleus, has no net charge. After one of the

Fig. A. Experiment illustrating canal rays discovered by Goldstein.

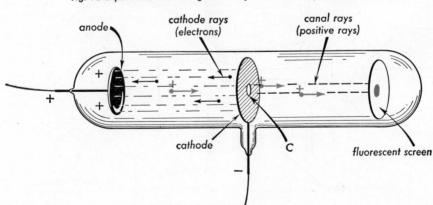

anode   cathode rays (electrons)   canal rays (positive rays)

cathode   C   fluorescent screen

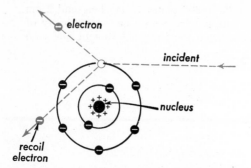

Fig. B. Schematic diagram of an oxygen atom in the process of becoming ionized by a collision with a high-speed electron.

electrons is removed by collision, it has but seven electrons and therefore a net positive charge equivalent in amount to the charge of one electron.

Since the atom is now positively charged, the anode repels and the cathode attracts such atoms, accelerating them toward the cathode. There exists, therefore, between the anode and cathode, two streams of particles: electrons moving toward the anode and positively charged atoms or molecules moving toward the cathode.

Any process by which an electron is removed from an atom or molecule is called *ionization,* and the resulting charged particle is called a *positive ion.*

The Thomson Mass Spectrograph. In 1911 J. J. Thomson developed a method of measuring the relative masses of different atoms and molecules by deflecting positive rays in a magnetic and an electric field. The apparatus he developed for doing this is shown schematically in Fig. C and is called *Thomson's mass spectrograph.*

The entire spectrograph, enclosed in an airtight glass chamber, is first thoroughly evacuated, and then a small quantity of the gas, the masses of whose atoms are to be measured, is admitted to the bulb at the left. When a high voltage is applied to this chamber, electrons from the cathodes ionize atoms and molecules in the region between the anode **A** and the cathode **C**. Traveling to the right, many of these positively charged particles pass through the narrow hole in the cathode, thus forming a very narrow pencil of rays. Leaving the cathode with a constant velocity, they then pass between the poles of an electromagnet and the parallel plates of a capacitor, and thence to a fluorescent screen at the far end of the chamber.

The two capacitor plates, when charged, exert an upward force on the particles, deflecting them from the point O toward **E**. The magnetic field, on the other hand, with its magnetic lines vertically downward and in

Fig. C. Diagram of J. J. Thomson's mass spectrograph.

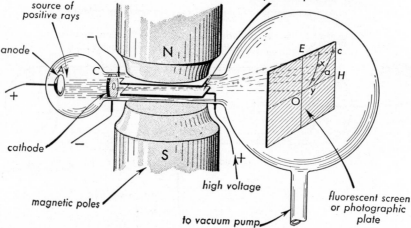

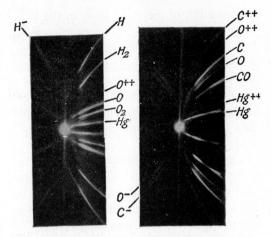

Fig. D. Reproductions of the photographs of parabolas made with Thomson's mass spectrograph.

the plane of the page, exerts a force at right angles to this, deflecting the particles into the page from the point **O** toward **H**.

If the gas in the apparatus is not pure but contains two kinds of atoms, the positive ions passing through the cathode will have two different masses. Although each ion will contain the same positive charge and will therefore experience the same electric and magnetic forces when passing through the fields, the heavier particles will not be deflected as much as the lighter ones. The net result is that the heavier particles form one curved line and the lighter particles another.

By substituting a photographic plate for the fluorescent screen and exposing it to the rays for several minutes, photographs like those reproduced in Fig. D are obtained. The continual bombardment of the photographic plate by atoms and molecules has the same effect as does light, and images are produced upon development. The upper half of each picture is taken with the connections as shown in Fig. C and the lower half by reversing the polarity of the electromagnet, and exposing for an equal length of time.

When this photograph was taken, the spectrograph contained **hydrogen, oxygen,** and **mercury,** and the magnetic field was relatively weak. From the known strengths of both the electric and magnetic fields and the assumption that each atom carries a unit positive charge, the mass of the atoms producing each parabola can be calculated. The results of these calculations show that the two largest parabolas are due to ionized hydrogen atoms (H^+) of mass 1 and ionized hydrogen molecules (H_2^+) of mass 2. The next three are due to ionized atoms (O^+) of mass 16, ionized oxygen molecules of mass 32, and ionized mercury atoms (Hg^+) with a mass of approximately 200.

Thomson's Discovery of Isotopes. In 1912 Thomson, in comparing the mass of the neon atom with the known masses of other elements, discovered two parabolic curves for neon in place of one. Upon computing the masses of the particles involved, the stronger of two parabolas was found to be due to particles of mass 20 and the other, a fainter parabola, to particles of mass 22.

Since the atomic weight of neon was then known to be 20.2, Thomson expressed the belief that neon is composed of two kinds of atoms, 90% of which have a mass of 20 and the other 10% a mass of 22. Because these two kinds of atoms exist as a mixture and cannot be separated chemically, their atomic weight, when measured by chemical methods, is found to be their average value 20.2.

The discovery of two kinds of neon atoms, identical chemically but differing in atomic weight, suggested the possibility that all other elements whose atomic weights were not whole numbers might also be mixtures of atoms which do have whole number weights. Not only has this been confirmed by experiment but a large majority of the elements have been found to be mixtures of from two to ten different kinds of atoms.

To all atoms of different weight belonging to the same element Soddy gave the name *isotopes.* The external structures of all isotopes of a given element are identical. The two atoms Ne-20 and Ne-22, shown in Fig. E, are neon isotopes. Each of these neutral

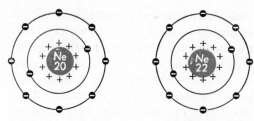

Fig. E. Schematic diagrams of the two different kinds of neon atoms, one of mass 20 and the other of mass 22. The external electron structure of two such isotopes are identical.

atoms, before it is ionized to become a positive ray, has ten external electrons and ten positive charges on the nucleus. They differ only in the weight of the nucleus.

Atoms having different weights but belonging to the same chemical element have the same atomic number and are called isotopes.

Aston's Mass Measurements. Immediately following World War I in 1919, F. W. Aston developed a new and improved type of mass spectrograph. Employing both electric and magnetic fields, the device presented an improvement over Thomson's mass spectrograph by focusing the rays of different

velocities but of the same mass to the same point on the screen or a photographic plate. This had two important effects: (1) it made it possible to observe rare isotopes which might otherwise escape detection and (2) it produced sharper images of the different masses on the photographic plate, so that their masses could be more accurately measured.

An Aston mass spectrogram is reproduced at the top of Fig. F. In taking this particular photograph Aston had introduced into his apparatus, among other things, a little **hydrochloric acid** (HCl), **carbon monoxide** (CO), and **sulfur dioxide** (SO_2). Being close together in the periodic table, these elements furnish an excellent demonstration of the linear shift of atoms and molecules differing in mass by one unit. It is found from this and other photographs that sulfur has three isotopes with masses 32, 33, and 34, and that chlorine has two isotopes of mass 35 and 37.

Since the atomic weight of chlorine is 35.46, then for every atom of mass 37 in a given quantity of chlorine gas there are four of mass 35. Mixed together in these proportions they give an average mass of 35.4.

Fig. F. Drawings based on photographs taken with a mass spectrograph illustrating the linear shift of atoms differing by one unit of mass. (a) Carbon monoxide, sulfur, chlorine, and argon lines. (b) and (c) Isotopes of mercury, tin, and lead.

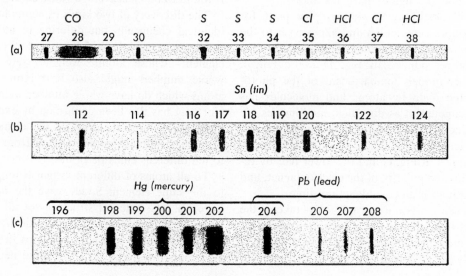

The photographic lines corresponding to masses 28, 36, and 38 are due to diatomic molecules CO and HCl, each molecule having the combined weight of its constituent atoms. Since there are two relatively abundant chlorine isotopes, there are two kinds of HCl molecules. One type, H^1Cl^{35}, has a mass of 36, and the other type, H^1Cl^{37}, a mass of 38.

So successful was Aston with his mass measurements and his determination of isotopes of different elements that he attempted an investigation of the entire periodic table. All of the known elements are listed in Appendix II, with all of their observed isotopes. In each case the most abundant isotope is given in heavy type, while the very rare isotopes, i.e., those present to less than 1%, are given in parentheses. Where more than one isotope is given in heavy type the isotopes occur with almost equal abundance. The isotopes given in italics represent unstable atoms which are responsible for **radioactivity**, the subject of another lesson. Recent developments in mass spectroscopy have made it possible to detect exceptionally rare isotopes. In neon, for example, an isotope of mass number 21 has been found, making three in all, with relative abundances as follows:

isotope	Ne-20	Ne-21	Ne-22
abundance, %	90.4	0.6	9.0

Isobars. *Atoms having the same atomic weight but belonging to different chemical elements are called isobars.*

The first pair of isobars, see Appendix II, occurs in argon and calcium. The principal isotope of argon, atomic number 18, has a mass of 40, as does also the principal isotope of calcium, atomic number 20. Other examples are Cr54 and Fe54, Ge76 and Se76, Rb87 and Sr87, Zn92 and Mo92. The isobars

Hg204 and Pb204 are illustrated in Fig. F(c).

To compare the masses of atoms with the mass of an electron, it is convenient to know the mass of the atom in kilograms. This mass can be calculated by knowing its equivalence in atomic mass units, **unit atomic mass being defined as one-sixteenth the mass of an oxygen sixteen atom.** Unit atomic mass is found by experiment to be

$$M = 1.660 \times 10^{-27} \text{ kg} \qquad (1)$$

This number multiplied by the "atomic weight" of any atom will give its mass in kilograms.

Compared with the mass of the electron, namely,

$$m = 9.1072 \times 10^{-31} \text{ kg} \qquad (2)$$

an atom of unit mass would be 1824 times as heavy. The hydrogen atom is slightly heavier than one unit mass and is about 1840 times as heavy as the electron. This latter number is convenient to remember for it is often quoted to illustrate the enormous difference between the mass of the nucleus of a hydrogen atom and the mass of its one and only electron.

Atomic number is defined as that number ascribed to an element specifying its position in the periodic table of elements. See the first column of Appendix II.

Mass number is defined as that whole number nearest the actual mass of an isotope measured in atomic mass units. See column four of Appendix II.

Atomic weight is defined as the average weight of all the isotopes of an element weighted according to relative abundance and expressed in atomic mass units.

Summary

In any high voltage discharge, electrons moving through the gas collide with and knock electrons from the atoms and molecules. These atoms with their net positive charge are called positive ions.

The existence of positive ions in an electrical discharge was first discovered by Goldstein and were called canal rays.

By deflecting positive rays in magnetic and electric fields J. J. Thomson found the high-speed particles are atoms and molecules of whatever gas is present in the apparatus.

Atoms having the same atomic number but different mass number are called isotopes. Some atoms have but two isotopes, while others may contain three, four, five, six, etc.

Atoms of different atomic number but the same mass number are called isobars.

Questions

1. What are canal rays? Who discovered them? How are they detected?

2. What is a mass spectrograph? Make a diagram of one and explain how it operates.

3. Who discovered isotopes? What are isotopes?

4. What is meant by (a) atomic number, (b) mass number, and (c) atomic weight?

5. How do isotopes of any given element differ from each other?

6. What is meant by relative abundance?

7. What are isobars? Give an example.

8. How much greater is the mass of a hydrogen atom than the mass of an electron?

9. What do the more or less equal spacings of the mass spectrograms shown in Fig. F suggest regarding the relative masses of atoms?

10. Name five members of each of the following classifications: (a) alkali metals and (b) alkaline earths. See Appendix.

11. What chemical element has the greatest number of isotopes? See Appendix II.

12. Make a list of elements having (a) atoms of one mass only and (b) only two isotopes. See Appendix II.

Problems

1. The atomic weight of aluminum is 26.97. Find the mass in grams of one aluminum atom.

2. If the atomic weight of cobalt is 58.94, how many atoms are there in one gram of cobalt metal?

3. The atomic weight of manganese is 54.94. How many atoms are there in one gram of manganese metal?

4. If the atomic weights of carbon and oxygen are 12.00 and 16.00 respectively, find the mass in grams of a carbon dioxide molecule. See Fig. A, Mechanics, Lesson 44.

5. The atomic weights of hydrogen, carbon, and oxygen are 1.01, 12.00, and 16.00 respectively. How many ethyl alcohol molecules are there in one gram of ethyl alcohol? See Fig. A, Mechanics Lesson 44.

6.* The two isotopes of lithium have masses of 6 and 7 atomic mass units. If the normal mixture of these atoms has an atomic weight of 6.94, what is the relative abundance of the two isotopes?

7.* The normal mixture of chlorine found in nature has an atomic weight of approximately 35.5. What is the relative abundance of the two chlorine isotopes 35 and 37?

8.* Boron has two stable isotopes 10 and 11. Find their relative abundance in a normal mixture if the atomic weight is 10.82.

Atomic Physics | Lesson 4

ELECTRONIC CHARGE TO MASS
RATIO—*Laboratory*

A beam of electrons from an electron gun is projected into the uniform magnetic field at the center of Helmholz coils. By measuring the radius of their circular beam path the ratio e/m can be determined as described in the accompanying LABORATORY EXERCISES.

Atomic Physics | Lesson 5

LIGHT SOURCES AND THEIR SPECTRA

Classification of Spectra. *A spectrum may be defined as an array of the different colors, or wave lengths, of radiant energy emitted by a light source.* As illustrated in Fig. A, a spectrum is frequently produced by sending white light through a glass prism. Different light sources produce different colors, and different wave lengths, and hence reveal different spectra.

All spectra may be grouped into four classes:

    (a) continuous emission spectra
    (b) line emission spectra
    (c) continuous absorption spectra
    (d) line absorption spectra

Continuous Emission Spectra. When a block of metal like iron or copper is heated slowly to incandescence, the first noticeable change in its appearance occurs at a temperature of about 1000°K. At this temperature the metal has a dull red glow. As the temperature continues to rise, the color changes slowly to orange, then to yellow, and finally to white.

If the white hot metal is observed through a prism, one sees a band of pure spectrum colors, red, orange, yellow, green, blue, and violet.

What the prism has done in such an experiment is to separate all of the light waves ac-

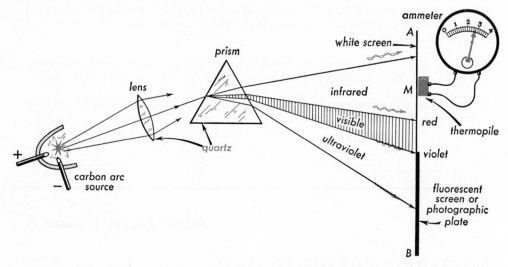

Fig. A. Experiment demonstrating the existence of the ultraviolet and infrared rays beyond the visible spectrum.

cording to their wave lengths, the longest waves of red light at the one side, the shortest waves of violet light at the other, and the intermediate waves at their proper places in between.

The fact that the color is continuous from red through violet is characteristic of the spectrum of all solids and liquids and means that there is a continuous set of different wave lengths present.

To demonstrate the existence of an ultraviolet and infrared spectrum, an experiment of the type illustrated in Fig. A may be performed. The visible light from a carbon arc lamp is made to pass through a quartz lens and prism to be focused on a nearby screen.

If at the violet end of the spectrum the screen is painted with luminous paint, a bright fluorescence will be observed for some little distance beyond the visible violet. When the screen is replaced by a photographic plate, the exposed and developed picture will again show the extension of the spectrum into the ultraviolet.

To detect the presence of the infrared radiations, a thermopile as shown is conveniently used at the top of the screen. Connected to an ammeter, a thermopile measures the

amount of light energy falling upon its front face. If the thermopile is first placed to receive ultraviolet light and slowly moved across the visible spectrum and out into the infrared region beyond, the ammeter will show a steady rise in current. The current will continue to rise until a maximum is reached at a point in the region of **M**, and then it will drop off slowly as the thermopile approaches the end of the screen at **A**.

If a graph of the radiated energy is plotted against the wave length of the light, a curve similar to that shown in Fig. B is obtained. If the source temperature is increased this curve will rise at all points but the peak will

Fig. B. Graph of the energy emitted by a hot solid.

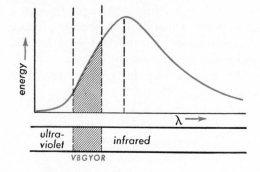

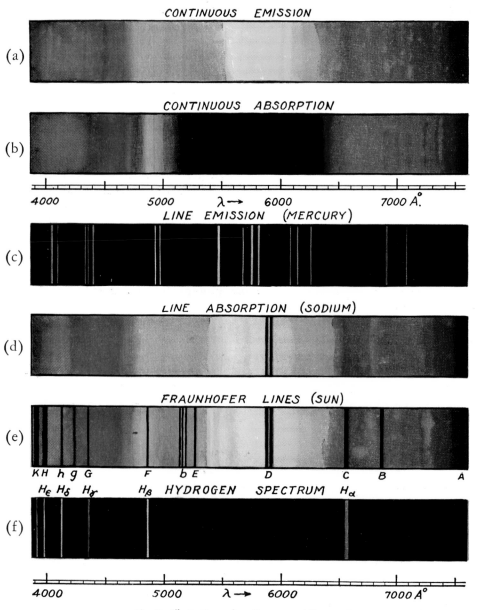

(a) CONTINUOUS EMISSION

(b) CONTINUOUS ABSORPTION

4000   5000   λ —→   6000   7000 Å.

(c) LINE EMISSION (MERCURY)

(d) LINE ABSORPTION (SODIUM)

(e) FRAUNHOFER LINES (SUN)

KH h g G   F   b E   D   C   B   A
H$_\epsilon$ H$_\delta$ H$_\gamma$ H$_\beta$ HYDROGEN   SPECTRUM   H$_\alpha$

(f)

4000   5000   λ —→   6000   7000 Å°

Fig. D. Illustrations of continuous and line spectra.

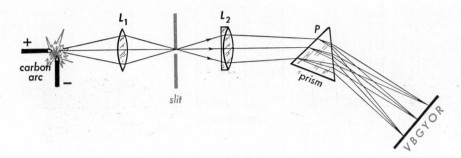

Fig. C. Experimental arrangement used in demonstrating spectrum lines in emission.

shift to shorter wave lengths. When the sun's temperature of 6000°K is reached the peak is located in the yellow green part of the visible spectrum.

Line Emission Spectra. When the slit of a prism spectrograph (see Fig. C) is illuminated by the light from a mercury arc, sodium lamp, neon discharge tube, or the flame of a carbon arc, a number of bright lines appear on the screen or photographic plate in place of a continuous spectrum. See Fig. D.

It is important to realize that **line spectra** derive their name from the fact that, before entering the prism, the light passes through a narrow slit, and it is the different colored images of this slit, formed by the lens, that constitute the lines. If a small circular opening were used in place of a slit, a disk image would appear in the place of each line in Fig. D.

The most intense sources of spectrum lines are obtained from metallic arcs and sparks.

The flame of a carbon arc may be used for demonstration purposes by previously soaking the **positive carbon rod** in various chemicals. (The arrangement shown in Fig. C may also be used for projecting the spectrum on a large screen.) Common salt water (sodium chloride in solution) gives a brilliant yellow line characteristic of sodium. Solutions of strontium or calcium chloride will show other strong spectrum lines in the red, green, and blue.

While a continuous emission spectrum arises from hot solids, **a line spectrum always arises from a gas at high temperatures.** It is the free atoms of the element used which are in the gas flame of the carbon arc that give rise to the line emission spectrum, in the above experiment.

Continuous Absorption Spectra. Continuous absorption spectra are usually produced by passing a continuous emission spectrum through matter in the solid or liquid state.

Fig. E. Experimental arrangement for demonstrating the line absorption spectrum of sodium vapor.

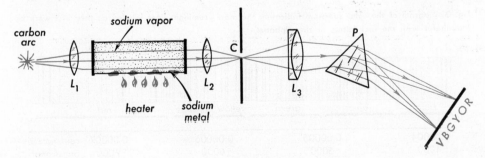

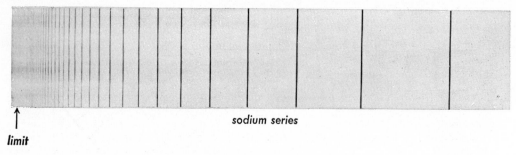

sodium series

↑
limit

Fig. F. Absorption spectrum of sodium vapor. The principal series of sodium. (After Jenkins)

Good demonstrations can be performed by allowing white light to pass through colored glass. When the light is later dispersed by a prism, the missing colors will in general cover a wide band of wave lengths. See spectrum (b) in Fig. D.

Line Absorption Spectra. Line spectra in absorption are produced by sending continuous white light through a gas. Experimentally the gas is inserted in the path of the light as shown in Fig. E. Light from a carbon arc, after passing as a parallel beam through a glass tube containing sodium vapor, is brought to a focus at the slit **C**. From there the light passes through a lens L_3 and a prism P to form a spectrum on the observing screen.

Sodium is chosen as an example for demonstration purposes because of its convenience. The vapor is produced by inserting a small amount of metallic sodium in a partially evacuated glass tube and heating it with a small gas burner. As the metal vapor-

izes, filling the tube with sodium vapor, a dark line will appear in the yellow region of the spectrum (see color plate (d) in Fig. D).

If a photograph is taken of this absorption, and the photographic plate is long enough to extend into the ultraviolet, many absorption lines, as shown in Fig. F, are detected. A systematic array of absorption lines like this occur only with a few elements, principally with the alkali metals, lithium, sodium, potassium, rubidium, and cesium. All elements in the gaseous state, however, give rise to a number of absorption lines, usually in the ultraviolet region of the spectrum.

The Sun's Spectrum. The solar spectrum, consisting of a bright colored continuous spectrum interspersed by thousands of dark lines, was first observed by Wollaston in 1802 and independently discovered and studied by Fraunhofer in 1817. Fraunhofer mapped out several hundred of these lines and labeled eight of the most prominent lines by the first

Fig. G. Diagram of the solar spectrum indicating the most prominent lines labeled as they first were by Fraunhofer with the first letters of the alphabet.

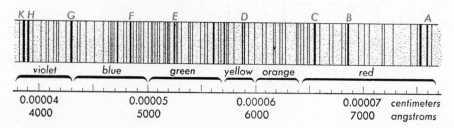

letters of the alphabet. The strongest of these lines, now called **Fraunhofer lines,** are illustrated in Fig. G.

These lines are explained as being due to the absorption of light by the solar atmosphere. The surface of the sun at a temperature of 6000°K emits light of all wave lengths, i.e., a continuous emission spectrum. As this light passes out through the cooler gas layers of the solar atmosphere (see Fig. H) certain wave lengths are absorbed. Because the absorbing medium is in the gaseous state, the atoms and molecules there do not absorb all wave lengths equally but principally those wave lengths they would emit if heated to a high temperature. Thus the atoms of one chemical element with their own char-

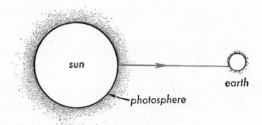

Fig. H. Light from the sun must pass through the solar atmosphere and the earth's atmosphere before reaching an observer on the earth's surface.

acteristic frequencies absorb certain wave lengths, whereas the atoms of other elements absorb certain other wave lengths. Some of the dark lines are known to be due to absorption by the earth's atmosphere.

Summary

Light sources may be characterized by the general appearance of the spectrum of light they emit.

Hot solids give rise to a continuous band of color extending beyond the red into an invisible part of the spectrum called the infrared and beyond the violet into an invisible region called the ultraviolet.

Hot gases are composed of isolated atoms which emit discrete wave lengths of visible and invisible light. When observed or photographed with a spectrograph, these different wave lengths appear as lines. In the visible spectrum these observed lines are colored.

When a continuous light spectrum from a hot solid passes through a cold solid or gas a continuous absorption or line absorption spectrum, respectively, may be produced.

The sun's spectrum is composed of a line absorption spectrum, the lines corresponding to light absorbed by atoms in the sun's atmosphere.

Questions

1. What is a spectrum? What are the four classes of spectra called?

2. How is infrared light detected? How is ultraviolet light detected? What is the color of infrared light?

3. From what kind of light source does one obtain (a) a continuous emission spectrum and (b) a line emission spectrum?

4. What are spectrum lines? Why are they in the form of lines?

5. From what kind of source does one obtain the most intense line emission spectrum?

6. How can one produce a line absorption spectrum in the laboratory?

7. What kind of spectrum does sunlight exhibit? To what process are the dark lines attributed?

8. How can we prove that the same elements existing on the earth are to be found in the sun as well?

9. If white light is allowed to pass through a piece of crimson or magenta colored glass and then into a prism, what kind of spectrum is produced?

10. What kind of experiment might you readily perform in the laboratory to demonstrate a line emission spectrum?

Atomic Physics | **Lesson 6**

WAVE LENGTHS OF SPECTRUM LINES—*Laboratory*

A diffraction grating is used to dispense the light from a mercury vapor lamp into a line emission spectrum. The measurements and wave length determinations are described in the accompanying LABORATORY EXERCISES.

Atomic Physics | **Lesson 7**

X RAYS

One of the most interesting episodes in the history of modern science began with the accidental discovery of X rays by Wilhelm Röntgen* in 1895. While studying the green fluorescent stage of an electrical discharge in a Crookes tube, Röntgen observed the bright fluorescence of some nearby crystals of barium platino-cyanide. Even though the discharge tube was in a darkened room and entirely surrounded with black paper to prevent the escape of visible light, a distant screen covered with crystals would fluoresce brightly, when the discharge was turned on. Röntgen reasoned, therefore, that some kind of invisible yet penetrating rays of an unknown kind were being given out by the discharge tube. These rays he called **X rays,** the letter **X** meaning, as it so often does in algebra, an unknown.

In the short series of experiments that followed his discovery, Röntgen found that the

* Wilhelm Konrad von Röntgen (1845-1923). Born at Lennep on March 27, 1845, Röntgen received his education in Holland and Switzerland. His scientific career began at the age of twenty-five when he became an assistant in the physics laboratory at Würzburg, Germany. After a teaching period extending over a period of twenty-five years, which carried him to the University of Strasbourg, then to Hohenheim, back to Strasbourg, then to Giessen and finally to Würzburg again, he discovered X rays in his laboratory at Würzburg in 1895. For this discovery he received the Rumford Medal of the Royal Society in 1896 and the first Nobel Prize in physics in 1901. Röntgen also conducted researches in light, heat, and elasticity, but none of these works compare in importance with his discovery of X rays.

unknown rays were coming from the glass walls of the tube itself and, in particular, from the region where the most intense part of the cathode-ray beam was striking the glass. So great was the importance of this discovery that, within but a few weeks of Röntgen's announcement, X rays were being used as an aid to surgical operations in Vienna. This, along with other practical applications and uses to be made of a single scientific discovery, is a good example of the role played by modern science in the rapid advancement of civilization.

X-ray Tubes. The Crookes tube with which Röntgen made his discovery bears very little resemblance to the modern X-ray tube. In form it had somewhat the appearance of the tube shown in Fig. C, Atomic Physics, Lesson 1. Within a short period of time after Röntgen's discovery quite a number of noteworthy improvements upon tube design were made.

The biggest improvement in X-ray tube design was made by Coolidge, an American physicist, in 1913. In the Coolidge tube (see Fig. A), a tungsten wire filament is placed at the center of the cathode and heated to incandescence by a storage battery or low-voltage transformer. This filament, being a copious source of electrons, gives rise at the target to a far more intense source of X rays than was previously possible with a cold cathode. Under the terrific bombardment of

Fig. A. Diagram of a Coolidge X-ray tube employing a hot cathode.

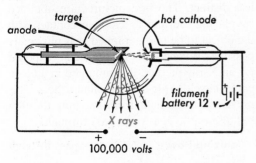

the target by so many electrons, most metals will melt. To overcome this difficulty a metal, with a high melting point, like tungsten or molybdenum, is imbedded in the face of a solid copper anode to become the target. Copper, being a good heat conductor, helps to dissipate the heat.

The early sources of high voltage applied to the anode and cathode of X-ray tubes were supplied by induction coils of various descriptions. Although some of these sources are still in use, they have been almost entirely supplanted by a more efficient high-voltage transformer. The emf generated by these transformers varies between 50,000 and 2,000,000 volts. The normal emf used for surgical work is about 100,000 volts, whereas for the treatment of diseases the higher emf's are employed. The high-voltage alternating emf supplied by a transformer is not applied directly to the X-ray tube but is first changed into direct current by means of rectifier tubes.

Penetration of X Rays. Four useful and important properties of X rays are their ability (1) to penetrate solid matter, (2) to cause certain chemical compounds to fluoresce, (3) to ionize atoms, and (4) to affect a photographic plate. The penetration of X rays depends upon two things: first, the voltage applied between the anode and cathodes of the X-ray tube; and second, the density of the substance through which the rays must travel. The higher the voltage applied to the tube, the greater is the penetration. *X rays of great penetrating power are called hard X rays, whereas those having little penetrating power are called soft X rays.*

The relation between density and penetration may be illustrated in several ways. When X rays are sent through a block of wood containing nails, or a closed leather purse containing coins, a clear and well-defined image of the nails, or coins, can be formed and observed on a fluorescent screen. The experimental arrangement is the same as that shown

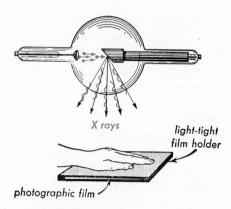

X rays

light-tight
film holder

photographic film

Fig. B. Arrangement for taking X-ray photographs of the bones of the hand.

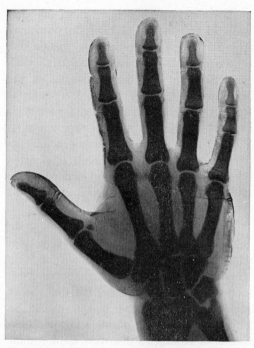

Fig. C. X-ray photograph of the hand and wrist bones. Lead oxide ointment was spread on the hand to show the flesh. (Courtesy of the Stamford Research Laboratories, American Cyanamid Co.)

in Fig. B. When X rays are sent through the hand or any part of the body to obtain photographs of the bones, it is the difference in penetration between the flesh and the bones that permits a picture to be made. Materials like paper, wood, flesh, etc., composed principally of light chemical elements like those at the beginning of the periodic table, are readily penetrated by X rays. In other words they are poor absorbers of X rays. For materials like brass, steel, bone, gold, etc., composed partly of heavy elements, like those farther along and near the end of the periodic table, the penetration of X rays is very poor. Hence heavy elements, or dense substances, are good absorbers.

The bones of the body, containing large amounts of calcium, are relatively good absorbers of X rays, whereas the flesh, composed principally of much lighter elements— hydrogen, oxygen, carbon, and nitrogen— are poor absorbers. This explains the general appearance of X-ray photographs. X-ray pictures like the ones in Fig. C are similar to shadows cast by the objects being photographed. The focus point on the X-ray target, being bombarded by high-speed electrons, acts as a point source of rays. These spread out in straight lines as shown in Fig. B. On passing through the hand to the photographic film, more X rays are absorbed by the bones than by the flesh. The shadow cast by the

bones is therefore very weak in X rays and the photographic film develops out clear.

Where only flesh is traversed, the X rays penetrate through to the photographic film, causing it to develop out black. The bones therefore appear white against a darker background. If this "negative film," as it is called, is printed on paper as in Fig. C, it becomes a "positive" with the bones appearing black.

If the photograhic film is placed farther away from the hand than shown in the diagram, the shadow picture will be larger and less distinct. The best pictures are obtained by placing the film as close in contact with the object to be photographed as is physically possible. Whenever a film is being exposed for an X-ray picture, it is mounted in a black paper envelope or thin aluminum box. This prevents visible light from reaching the film but allows the X rays to pass through.

Ionizing Power. As X rays pass through

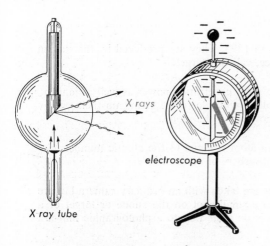

Fig. D. X rays discharge an electroscope.

matter in the solid, liquid, or gaseous state, they are found to *ionize* atoms and molecules. This can be shown by charging a gold-leaf electroscope positively or negatively and placing it some 10 to 15 ft away from an X-ray tube. When the X-ray tube is turned on (see Fig. D), the gold leaf falls, showing discharge.

The explanation of this experiment is as follows: X rays pass through the electroscope and ionize the air by removing electrons from many of the oxygen and nitrogen molecules. Leaving these particular molecules with a net positive charge, the freed electrons move about until they are picked up by other neutral molecules, thus giving them a net negative charge. The result is that the passage of X rays through matter produces both *positively charged* and *negatively charged ions*. If the electroscope is negatively charged, it attracts the positively charged ions to the gold leaf, neutralizing the charge and re-pelling the negatively charged ions to the "grounded" walls where they, too, become neutralized. If the electroscope is positively charged, it attracts the negative ions to it, again neutralizing the charge. The positive ions in this case are repelled to the walls. In either case, whether the electroscope is positively or negatively charged, the gold leaf falls, showing discharge.

It is the ionization of atoms and molecules in a substance that limits the penetrating power of X rays. Heavy elements contain more electrons than light elements, thus placing more electrons in the path of the X rays to stop them. The stopping power of a thin sheet of lead, for example, is equivalent to the stopping power of a sheet of aluminum several times thicker. Lead atoms each contain 82 electrons, whereas aluminum atoms each contain only 13.

X Rays Are Waves. The discovery that X rays are electromagnetic waves of extremely high frequency, and not high speed particles, was made by von Laue in 1912. With the assistance of Friedrich and Knipping, X rays were diffracted by a zinc sulfide crystal.

The equally spaced layers of atoms within such a crystal behave like the rulings of a diffraction grating and produce what is called an X-ray spectrum. X-ray wave lengths are, on the average, some ten thousand times shorter than visible light.

The effect of increasing the voltage applied to an X-ray tube is to shorten the wave length and increase the penetrating power of the X rays produced.

Summary

X rays were discovered by William Röntgen in 1895. They are produced by the sudden impact of high-speed electrons on any surface, called a target.

Sometimes called Röntgen rays, X rays have great penetrating power as well as ionizing power. In passing through matter X rays collide with electrons, giving up their energy to remove such electrons from their bound position in the atoms.

Since the number of electrons confined to an atom is equal to the atomic number, elements of higher atomic number are better absorbers of X rays.

X-ray photographs are not focused pictures as are taken with an ordinary camera but are shadowgraphs. X-ray sources are confined to a small spot on the anode or target of a tube and in passing through different materials on their way to a photographic film are absorbed in varying amounts.

X rays are electromagnetic waves like visible light and have an extremely short wave length.

Questions

1. Who discovered X rays? How were they discovered?

2. What contribution did Coolidge make to the design and construction of X-ray tubes?

3. What are hard X rays? What are soft X rays? How is hardness or softness related to X-ray wave lengths?

4. How are X-ray photographs made? Why do the bones of the body absorb more X rays than the flesh?

5. How is X-ray absorption related to the periodic table of elements?

6. Which of the following materials is the best absorber of X rays: (a) beryllium, (b) magnesium, (c) calcium, (d) copper, (e) gold, (f) lead, and (g) uranium?

7. What is the process of ionization by X rays? What happens to the liberated free electrons?

8. Why does the skin show so clearly in the X-ray photograph in Fig. C?

9. If a small child swallowed a safety pin, why would an X-ray photograph clearly show the location of the pin?

10. Can you name three important properties of X rays?

11. Make a list of specific places in which X rays would prove to be of considerable use.

12. How is the penetrating power of X rays related to the voltage applied to the tube?

RADIOACTIVITY

Radioactivity may be defined as a spontaneous disintegration of the nucleus of one or more atoms. The phenomenon was discovered originally by Becquerel* in 1896 and is confined almost entirely to the heaviest elements in the periodic table, from elements 83 on. What Becquerel discovered was that uranium, element 92, gave out some kind of rays that would penetrate through several thicknesses of thick black paper and affect a photographic plate on the other side. When the same phenomenon was confirmed several months later by Pierre and Marie Curie, these rays became known as Becquerel rays.

Discovery of Radium. Unlike the discovery of many new phenomena, the discovery of radium by Pierre and Madame Curie in 1898 was brought about intentionally by a set of carefully planned experiments. Having found that pitchblende was active in emitting Becquerel rays, the Curies treated chemically a ton of this ore in the hope of isolating from it the substance or element responsible for the activity. The first concentrated radioactive substance isolated was called **polonium** by Madame Curie, a name chosen in honor of her native country, Poland. Five months later came the isolation of a minute quantity of **radium,** a substance which was a powerful source of Becquerel rays. Continued experiments by the Curies, and others, soon

led to the isolation of many other substances now recognized as radioactive elements. Some of the more common of these are **ionium, radon,** and **thorium.**

The Properties of Becquerel Rays. It is to the experimental genius of Rutherford** that we owe the complete unraveling of the mystery surrounding the nature of Becquerel rays. As the result of an extensive series of experiments, Rutherford and his co-workers discovered that these penetrating rays are of three quite different kinds. A simplified experiment demonstrating this is illustrated in Fig. A.

A small sample of radium is dropped to the bottom of a small drill hole made in a block of lead. This produces a narrow beam of rays emerging from the top of the block since those rays entering the walls of the lead are absorbed before reaching the surface. When electrically charged plates are placed at the side of this beam, the paths of some rays are bent to the left, some to the right, and some not at all. Those paths bending to the left indicate positively charged particles called α **rays,** or α **particles,** those bending to the right indicate negatively charged

* Antoine Henri Becquerel (1852-1908), French physicist. Born in Paris on December 15, 1852, Antoine succeeded to his father's chair at the Museum of Natural History in 1892. In 1896 he discovered radioactivity, the phenomenon for which he is most famous. The invisible but penetrating rays emitted by uranium and other radioactive elements are now called Becquerel rays. For these researches he was granted the Nobel Prize in physics in 1903.

** Lord Rutherford (1871-1937), British physicist, was born in New Zealand where he attended the university. In 1898 he became Macdonald professor of physics at McGill University, Montreal, Canada, and in 1907 professor of physics at Manchester University. In 1919 he became professor and director of experimental physics at the University of Cambridge, and in addition held a professorship at the Royal Institution in London. He is most famous for his brilliant researches establishing the existence and nature of radioactive transformations and the electrical structure of the atom. For this work and until the time of his death in 1937, he was acclaimed by many as the greatest living experimental physicist. He was awarded the Nobel Prize in chemistry in 1908 and was knighted in 1914.

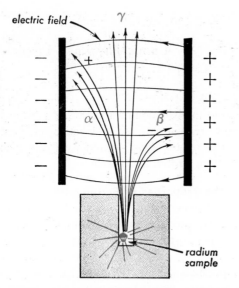

Fig. A. Becquerel rays are of three kinds: α, β, and γ.

particles called β **rays,** or β **particles,** and those going straight ahead indicate no charge and are called γ **rays,** or **photons.**

Rutherford, by a series of experiments, was able to show that each α **ray** is in reality a **doubly ionized helium atom,** i.e., a helium atom with both of its electrons gone. Such a particle is nothing more than a bare helium nucleus with double the positive charge of a hydrogen nucleus or proton, and a mass number or atomic weight four times as great. The β **rays** he found are ordinary electrons with a mass of 1/1840 the mass of a **proton** or 1/7360 the mass of an α **particle,** while γ **rays** are electromagnetic waves of about the same or a little higher frequency than X rays. Although γ rays all travel with exactly the velocity of X rays and visible light, α rays are ejected with a speed of from one tenth to one hundredth the velocity of light. β particles move faster than α particles, some of them traveling with 99 percent the velocity of light.

Ionizing Power. When Becquerel rays penetrate matter in the gaseous, liquid, or solid state, they do not continue to move indefinitely, but are brought to rest slowly

by ionizing atoms all along their path. Being ejected from their radioactive source with tremendously high speeds, all three types of rays collide with electrons and knock them free from atoms. They are, therefore, **ionizing agents.** The relative number of ionized atoms created along the path of an α particle, however, is much greater than the number created by a β particle or γ ray. If, in traveling the same distance in a given material, a γ ray produces one ionized atom, a β particle will, on the average, produce approximately one hundred, and an α particle will produce about ten thousand. Thus α particles are powerful ionizing agents, while γ rays are not.

Penetrating Power. At each collision with an atom, Becquerel rays lose on the average only a small part of their initial energy. Usually an α particle or β particle will make several thousand collisions before being brought to rest. At each collision some of the kinetic energy is expended in ionizing the atom encountered while giving that same atom a certain amount of kinetic energy. Since α particles produce the greatest number of ions in a given path, they penetrate the shortest distance and therefore have the poorest penetrating power. The penetrating powers of the three kinds of rays are roughly inversely proportional to their ionizing power.

	α	β	γ
relative ionizing power	10,000	100	1
relative penetrating power	1	100	10,000

Methods of Detecting Becquerel Rays. There are several well-known methods for detecting and measuring radioactivity; the most common of these are

electroscopes
cloud chambers
bubble chambers
Geiger-Mueller counters

scintillation counters
ionization gauges
Photographic emulsions

We have already seen in Lesson 7 of Atomic Physics how X rays passing through an electroscope cause the charge to disappear and the gold leaf to fall. This same action may be demonstrated with α, β, and γ rays. The stronger the source of rays or the nearer the sample is brought to the electroscope, the more rapid is the discharge. Experiments show that if the walls of the electroscope are too thick, only the γ rays get through to produce ionization on the inside. For this reason, specially designed electroscopes made with thin windows of light material like aluminum are used for measuring α and β rays.

The Wilson Cloud Chamber. In 1912 C. T. R. Wilson devised a method by which one may actually observe the paths of α and β particles. As will be seen in the following lessons this method is used extensively in modern atomic physics as a means of studying many different atomic processes. The de-

Fig. C. Photograph of α particle tracks in a Wilson cloud chamber. (After C. T. R. Wilson)

vice by which this is accomplished consists of an expansion chamber in which water vapor is made to condense upon ions produced by the high-speed particles that have previously passed through it.

A diagram of a laboratory type of Wilson cloud chamber is shown in Fig. B. The arrangement is made from an ordinary flat-bottomed flask with a rubber bulb attached to the neck. A tiny deposit of radium or polonium is inserted in the end of a thin-walled glass tube as indicated. When the rubber bulb is squeezed to compress the air in the top, and then released to cause an expansion, fogdrops will form on the ions created by the α particles. See Fig. C. The battery and the wires leading to the wire ring in the top of the chamber and the water below are for the purpose of quickly removing ions previously formed in the chamber. This clears the field of view for newly formed tracks.

Gamma rays are never observed in a cloud chamber since they produce so few ions. In passing through several feet of air a single γ ray will, on the average, produce only one or two ions. This is not enough to produce a recognizable cloud track. If a very strong source of γ rays is available, however, their presence can be observed in a cloud chamber by the chance collisions some of them make with electrons. These recoiling electrons are called **Compton electrons.**

Fig. B. Diagram of a small laboratory type of Wilson cloud chamber.

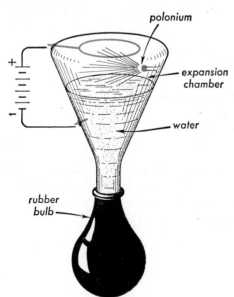

Transmutation by Spontaneous Disintegration. A careful study of radioactivity indicates that α, β, and γ rays originate from within the nucleus of the atom. When a radium atom disintegrates by ejecting an α particle, the nucleus loses a net positive charge of two. Since the number of positive charges on the nucleus determines the exact number of electrons outside of the atom and this in turn determines the chemical nature of an atom, the loss of an α particle, with two positive charges, leaves a new chemical element. Thus a **radium atom,** for example, in disintegrating, changes into a new atom called **radon.** We say there has been a **transmutation.** Not only does a nucleus lose a double charge by emitting an α particle and thereby **drops down two places in atomic number** but it also loses a weight of four units and thus **drops down four units in atomic weight,** or **four units in mass number.**

When a nucleus like **radium B** disintegrates by ejecting a β particle (an electron) to become **radium C,** the nuclear positive charge **increases by one unit.** Such a transmutation yields a new element one atomic number higher in the chemical table. Since an electron weighs only 1/1840 part of a hydrogen atom or proton, the change in mass due to a β particle leaving a nucleus is too small to change the mass number. Although the loss in weight is measurable, it changes the atomic weight so slightly that for most purposes of discussion it can be and is neglected. A γ ray, like the β ray, changes the weight of a nucleus by a negligible amount and, since it has no charge, it does not alter either the atomic number or the mass number.

Half Life. *The half life of a radioactive element is the time required for half of a given quantity of that element to disintegrate into a new element.* For example, it takes 1600 years for half of a given quantity of radium to change into radon. In another 1600 years half of the remainder will have disintegrated, leaving one quarter of the

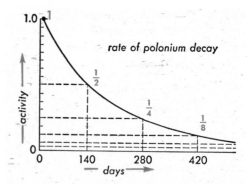

Fig. D. Typical graph of the decay of a radioactive element.

original amount. The half life of radium is therefore said to be 1600 years.

The rate at which a given quantity of a radioactive element disintegrates, that is, **decays,** is found by observing the activity of a given sample over a period of time and plotting a graph of the type shown in Fig. D. Here for **polonium** the activity drops to half of its original value in 140 days. In another 140 days it again drops to half value, etc. The term activity may be defined as the number of rays given off per second of time, or as the number of ionized atoms produced each second by the rays.

The only difference between the decay curve of one element and that of another is the horizontal time scale to which they are plotted. To turn Fig. D into a decay curve for radium, the **times** 140, 280, 420 days, etc., need only to be changed to read 1600, 3200, 4800 years, etc., respectively. Since, therefore, all radioactive decay curves follow the same law, one does not have to wait for half of a given sample to disintegrate to be able to calculate the half life. This would require too many years of waiting for some elements.

Range. *The range of any nuclear particle is defined as the distance such a particle will travel through dry air at normal atmospheric pressure.* In a partial vacuum where there are fewer air molecules per centimeter

Fig. E. Wilson cloud-chamber tracks from thorium C and C'. (After Rutherford, Chadwick, and Ellis; courtesy of Cambridge University Press)

to bump into, the distance traveled before coming to rest will be greater, whereas in air under higher than normal atmospheric pressure there are more molecules per centimeter and the distance will be diminished. Experiments show that some radioactive elements eject α particles with a higher speed than others. The higher the initial speed the greater is the range. The range of the α particles from *radium* is 3.39 cm, whereas the range of those from *thorium C'* is 8.62 cm.

The ranges of α particles in general have been determined in three different ways: **first,** by the Wilson cloud chamber; **second,** by the number of ions produced along the path; and **third,** by scintillations produced on a fluorescent screen.

In the Wilson cloud-chamber photograph of Fig. E, α particles of two different ranges

are observed. The radioactive sample used to obtain this picture was a mixture of **thorium C** and **thorium C'**. The shorter tracks with a 4.79 cm range are due to the α particles from **thorium C** disintegrating to become **thorium C''**, and the longer tracks of 8.62 cm range are due to the α particles from **thorium C'** disintegrating to become **lead.**

It is common practice among physicists to designate all atomic nuclei in an abbreviated form. The nucleus of radium, for example, is written $_{88}Ra^{226}$. The subscript to the left of the chemical symbol gives the **atomic number,** i.e., the number of positive charges on the nucleus, and the superscript on the right gives the **mass number,** or weight.

The disintegration of radioactive nuclei may be written in the form of simple equations called **nuclear reactions.**

for radium,
$$_{88}Ra^{226} \rightarrow {}_{86}Rn^{222} + {}_{2}He^{4} \tag{1}$$
for polonium,
$$_{84}Po^{210} \rightarrow {}_{82}Pb^{206} + {}_{2}He^{4} \tag{2}$$
and for radium B,
$$_{82}RaB^{214} \rightarrow {}_{83}RaC^{214} + {}_{-1}e^{0} + \gamma \text{ ray} \tag{3}$$

In each reaction the sum of the subscripts on the right side of the arrow is equal to the subscript on the left. The same is true for the superscripts. The designation $_{2}He^{4}$ represents the α particle, and $_{-1}e^{0}$ represents the β particle. In nearly all radioactive disintegrations where a β particle is emitted, one finds a γ ray also. In such cases, as shown by the example in Eq. (3), **radium B** ejects a β particle and a γ ray to become **radium C,** a nucleus higher in atomic number by unity but with the same mass number.

Summary

Radioactivity was discovered by Becquerel in 1896. In seeking the origin of the penetrating rays the Curies discovered radium, polonium, ionium, radon, and thorium. Many elements are now known to be radioactive, that is, to spontaneously emit high-speed atomic particles.

Rutherford discovered the rays were of three kinds, α, β, and γ. The α rays are helium nuclei, β rays are electrons, and γ rays are electromagnetic waves of extremely high frequency and therefore exactly like X rays.

Because of their double positive charge, α rays readily ionize atoms as they pass through matter, whereas β rays with their single negative charge do not ionize as readily and therefore have greater penetrating power.

Gamma rays seldom ionize atoms and therefore have the greatest penetrating power.

The spontaneous emission of α, β, and γ rays from atomic nuclei automatically changes them into different elements. This is transmutation.

The half life of a radioactive element is the time required for half of any given quantity of that element to disintegrate into a new element.

The range of any nuclear particle is defined as the distance such a particle will travel through dry air at normal atmospheric pressure.

Questions

1. Who discovered radioactivity? What were the circumstances?

2. Who discovered radium, polonium, and thorium?

3. What names are given to the different radioactive rays? Who unraveled this mystery?

4. What are α rays, β rays, and γ rays?

5. What are the relative ionizing powers and penetrating powers of the different rays?

6. What is a Wilson cloud chamber? How does it work?

7. What kinds of particles do not leave tracks in a Wilson cloud chamber? Why not?

8. What is spontaneous disintegration?

9. What is transmutation? What change takes place in the nucleus of an atom when an α particle is emitted? What change takes place when a β particle is emitted?

10. What is meant by the half life of a radioactive isotope?

11. What is meant by the range of radioactive rays? Which of the three kinds of rays should have the greatest range?

12. What is the abbreviated designation for atomic nuclei?

Problems

1. Write down the nuclear reaction, in the abbreviated form, for the emission of an α particle by an ionium nucleus (atomic number 90). See Appendix II.

2. Write down the nuclear reaction for the emission of an α particle by radium A (atomic number 84). See Appendix II.

3. Write down the nuclear reaction for α particle emission by uranium-238. See Appendix II.

4. Write the nuclear reaction for the emission of a β particle by actinium-227. See Appendix II.

5. Write the nuclear reaction for the emission of a β particle by radium B. See Appendix II.

6. If the activity of a radioactive sample drops to ⅛ of its initial value in 2 hr and 15 min, what is its half life?

7. If the activity of a radioactive sample drops to 1/32 of its initial value in 7.5 hr, find its half life.

8.* How long will it take a sample of radon to decrease to 10% if its half life is 3.82 days? Find your answer by plotting a decay curve.

9.* How long will it take a sample of radium D to decrease to 10% if its half life is 22 years?

Atomic Physics | Lesson 9

RADIOACTIVITY MEASUREMENTS—
Laboratory

The detection characteristics of a Geiger counter for radioactivity are determined in this experiment. The counter is then used to study the radiation fall-off with distance from a radium source, as described in the accompanying *LABORATORY EXERCISES*.

ELECTRONICS

*The young Italian observed a marked difference between Hertzian oscillations
and ordinary alternating currents which had attracted the attention of several experimenters. This was the Marconi explanation:*

*An analogy may be found in the case of a sound wave in the air. The swing
of a bell in a church steeple to and fro will produce no wave and further no
sound. But if the rim of the bell is struck with a hammer, it affects the air with
sufficient suddenness to make a sound.*

*Hence it appears absolutely clear to me that there is no Hertzian wave teleg-
raphy without the essential feature for producing Hertzian waves, which is the
Hertzian spark.*

Orrin E. Dunlap, Jr., *Marconi—The Man and His Wireless*,
New York, Macmillan Co., 1937, pp. 10-11.

*". . . To Mr. Hertz, of course, belongs the distinction of having discovered
the electric waves, and by his experiments he proved that electricity in its progress through space, follows the law of optics," said Signor Marconi. "Many
others have made experiments in the same direction as I, but so far no one has
obtained such results at anything approaching the distances I have done with
these Hertzian waves. Fog has no effect upon the signals, nor has even the
most solid substance. The waves can penetrate walls, and rocks without being
materially affected."*

The New York Times, December 15, 1901.

*Both the two- and three-electrode thermionic valves have become instruments of
prime importance in the arts of radiotelegraphy and radiotelephony, and without
them radiotelephonic broadcasting would not exist as we have it at present.*

*The invention of the two-electrode rectifying thermionic valve by the author in
1904 made an entirely new departure in wireless telegraphy and telephony, and the
subsequent development from it of the hard three-electrode valve marked an equally
important era.*

John A. Fleming, *The Thermionic Valve*, 2nd ed., London,
Iliffe & Sons, 1924, p. vii.

← The reflector bowl and aerial of the radio telescope at Jodrell Bank, Cheshire, England. It can penetrate deeper into space than any other form of telescope, to "hear" radio signals emitted a distance
millions of light years away.

British Information Service

Electromagnetic Waves

The **Leyden Jar.** A cross section of a Leyden jar of the type invented by the Dutch scientist Musschenbroek in 1746 is shown in Fig. A. Two metallic conductors forming the plates of a capacitor are separated by a glass bottle as a dielectric insulator. When such a capacitor is connected to a source of high potential, one plate will become positively charged and the other will be negative. If the source voltage is high enough, an electric spark will jump between the terminals indicating a sudden discharge of the capacitor, and an electron current will surge first one way then the other around the circuit.

This oscillatory current was first postulated by Joseph Henry, then derived from theory by Lord Kelvin, and later proved experimentally by Fedderson. Fedderson, looking at a spark discharge with a rotating mirror, observed that each initial breakdown spark was followed by a succession of fainter sparks. The initial spark ionizes the air making of it a good conductor and of the entire system **ABCDEFGA** a complete electrical circuit.

The Oscillatory Circuit. The Leyden jar circuit in Fig. A contains, in addition to a *capacitance,* an *inductance* and *resistance* as well. The single loop **FGABCD** and **E** forms practically one turn of a coil. An inductance, capacitance, and resistance, connected as shown in simplest schematic form in Fig. B, form the elements of all oscillating circuits. If initially the capacitance is charged as

Fig. A. The discharge of a Leyden jar is oscillatory.

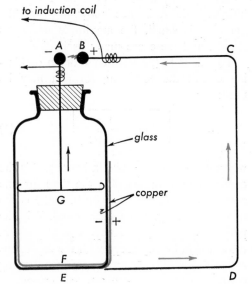

to induction coil

glass

copper

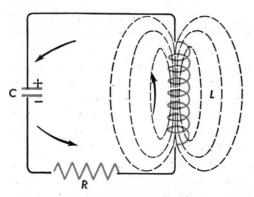

Fig. B. Schematic diagram of an oscillating circuit.

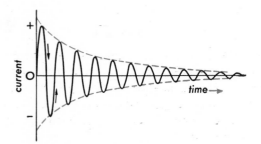

Fig. D. Graph of the damped oscillations of an electrical circuit.

indicated, the surplus electrons on the plate below cause a surge of negative charge counterclockwise around the circuit to neutralize the positives and, in so doing, set up a magnetic field in and around the inductance. When the positives become neutralized and the electron current tends to cease, the magnetic flux linking the circuit decreases and keeps the current flowing in the same direction. Once this field has vanished and the current has ceased, the capacitance is found to be in a charged condition, the upper plate negative and the lower plate positive.

Having reversed the charge on the capacitance, the above process will repeat itself, this time the electron current surging clockwise around the circuit. Thus the current

rushes first in one direction then the other, oscillating back and forth in an electrical way just as any spring pulled to one side and released vibrates in a mechanical way (see Fig. C).

When a straight spring is pulled to one side and released the kinetic energy it gains upon straightening keeps it moving and it bends to the other side. Just as the vibration amplitude of the spring slowly decreases because of *friction,* so also does the current in the electrical circuit decrease because of **electrical resistance.** A graph showing how current slowly dies out in an electric circuit is given in Fig. D. These are called **damped vibrations,** or **damped oscillations.** If the resistance of the circuit is high, the damping is high and the current quickly dies out after but few oscillations. If the resistance is low, however, the damping is small, the amplitude decreases slowly, and there are many oscillations.

To calculate the frequency of an oscillating circuit the following formula may be used:

Fig. C. A vibrating spring is like an electrical oscillating circuit.

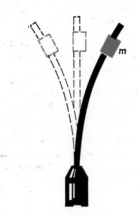

$$f = \frac{1}{2\pi\sqrt{LC}} \qquad (1)$$

where **L** is the inductance in henries, **C** is the capacitance in farads, **T** is the time for one complete oscillation in seconds, and **f** is the number of oscillations per second. **T** is the period and **f** the frequency. The formula at the left is to be compared with the analogous formula for the frequency of a vibrating spring.

$$f = \frac{1}{2\pi\sqrt{m/k}} \qquad (2)$$

The mass **m** for the spring is analogous to the inductance **L** for the circuit, and the stiffness $1/k$ is analogous to the capacitance **C**. An increase of the inductance **L**, or capacitance **C**, or both, decreases the frequency of the oscillating circuit.

Example. A Leyden jar with a small capacitance of 0.01 μf is connected to a single turn of wire (about 6 in. in diameter) having an inductance of 1 microhenry. Calculate the natural frequency of the circuit.

Solution. Since 1 henry $= 10^6$ microhenries and 1 farad $= 10^6$ microfarads, direct substitution for **L** and **C** in Eq. (1) gives

$$f = \frac{1}{2\pi\sqrt{LC}} = \frac{1}{2\pi\sqrt{1 \times 10^{-6}\,h \times 1 \times 10^{-8}\,f}}$$

$$= 1{,}590{,}000 \text{ cyc/sec}$$

or

$$1.59 \text{ megacycles/sec}$$

Electrical Resonance. One of the earliest experiments on electrical resonance is due to Sir Oliver Lodge, and is known as Lodge's experiment. The phenomenon is analogous to the sympathetic vibrations of two tuning forks demonstrated with sound on p. 263. Two similar electrical circuits, each containing a Leyden jar of the same capacity, are set up parallel to each other and some 5 to 10 ft apart as shown in Fig. E. The circuit **T** on the left acts as a source of oscillations, or transmitter, and the circuit **R** on the right acts as a resonator, or receiver.

Connected to a source of high potential, the capacitance C_1 charges, and sparks are seen jumping the gap **AB**. If the crossbar **S** of the receiver is moved to position **M**, resonance will occur and small sparks will also be observed jumping the gap **ab**. If **S** is moved toward **L** or **N**, however, no sparks are observed at **ab**. In other words, to respond to the oscillations the receiver **R** must be tuned to the same frequency of the transmitter **T**.

With the first rise of the current in the transmitting circuit, a magnetic field develops in and around the loop **T**. With each reversal of the current the field falls off and builds up again in the opposite direction just as it does with the primary winding of a transformer. Reaching out in all directions from **T**, this changing field induces a weak but alternating current in **R**. If the natural vibration frequency of **R** is the same as that of the induced current, the amplitude of the oscillations will quickly rise to a high value and cause sparks to jump the gap **ab**.

Hertzian Waves. In 1888 a young German scientist, Heinrich Hertz,* began a series of experiments in which he not only produced and detected electromagnetic waves but also demonstrated their properties of re-

* Heinrich Rudolf Hertz (1857-1894), German physicist born at Hamburg, February 22, 1857. Studied physics under Helmholtz in Berlin, at whose suggestion he first became interested in Maxwell's electromagnetic theory. His researches with electromagnetic waves that made his name famous were carried out at Karlsruhe Polytechnic between 1885 and 1889. As professor of physics at the University of Bonn, after 1889, he experimented with electrical discharges through gases and narrowly missed the discovery of X rays described by Röntgen a few years later. By his premature death science lost one of its most promising disciples.

Fig. E. Diagram of experiment demonstrating electrical resonance.

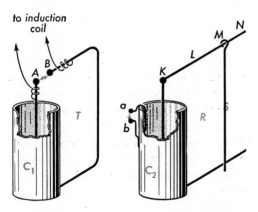

to induction coil

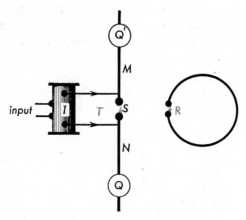

Fig. F. Schematic diagram of the apparatus with which Hertz produced and detected the first radio waves.

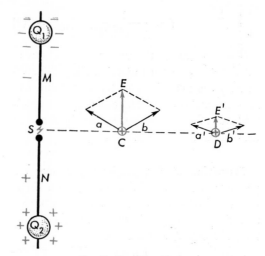

Fig. G. Hertzian dipole.

flection, refraction, and interference. One of his experimental arrangements is diagramed in Fig. F.

The transmitter consists of two spheres **QQ'** located near the ends of two straight rods **MN** separated by a spark gap **S**. With the two rods connected to transformer **I**, sparks jump across the gap **S**, giving rise to oscillating currents in **MN**. That such a generator is an oscillating circuit can be seen from the fact that the spheres **QQ'** form the plates of a capacitor and the rods form the inductance.

The receiver, or detector, consists of a single loop of wire with a tiny spark gap at **R**. This circuit too is an oscillating circuit with the spark gap as a capacitance **C** and the loop as an inductance **L**. Tuning the transmitter frequency to that of the receiver is accomplished by sliding the spheres **Q** along the rods **MN**, resonance being indicated by the appearance of sparks at **R**.

Electromagnetic Waves. To visualize the production of waves by an Hertzian oscillator, consider the schematic diagram in Fig. G. Let the rods **MN** and spheres **Q₁** and **Q₂** be charged initially as indicated and consider the electrostatic action of the charges on a small charge **C** located some distance away. The negative charge **Q₁** attracts **C** with

a force **a** and the positive charge **Q₂** repels it with a force **b**. Since by symmetry these two forces are of equal magnitude, their resultant **CE** is parallel to **MN**. If the isolated charge is farther away as at **D**, the resultant force is also parallel to **MN** but weaker. In other words, the electric field **E** at points **C** and **D** is up and parallel to **MN**, decreasing in intensity as the distance from the transmitter increases.

Suppose that a spark jumps the gap **S** and oscillation sets in. One-half cycle after the condition shown in Fig. G, electrons have surged across the gap charging **Q₁** positively and **Q₂** negatively. With reversed charges the resultant force on **C** and **D** will be down instead of up. Thus it is seen how oscillations in the transmitter, which constitute a surging of electrons back and forth between **M** and **N** give rise to a periodically reversing electric field at distant points.

In addition to an electric field at **C** and **D** the surging electrons in **MN** give rise to a magnetic field as well. When the electron current is down (using the conventional left-hand rule), the magnetic induction **B** at **C** or **D** is perpendicular to and into the plane of the page; when the electron current is up, the magnetic induction is out from the page. The surging of the charges therefore gives

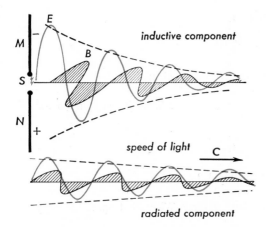

well (and this has been confirmed by numerous experiments) is the same as the speed of light. The changing **E** and **B** fields at **C** therefore lag behind the oscillating charges in **MN**, and those at **D** lag behind still farther.

Fig. H is a graph of the instantaneous values of the electric and magnetic fields as they vary with distance from the transmitter. At certain points the fields are a maximum and at other points they are zero. As time goes on, these electric and magnetic waves move away from the transmitter with a speed of 186,300 mi/sec.

The mathematical theory of electromagnetic radiation shows that close to the transmitter the **E** and **B** fields, called the **inductive components,** are 90° out of phase and that their magnitudes fall off very rapidly with distance. Farther out, however, the two get in step with each other and their amplitudes fall off more slowly as shown in the lower diagram. The latter are called the **radiated components** and are the ones detected at great distances. These waves are used in radio, radar, and television.

rise to a periodically reversing magnetic induction, the direction of which is at right angles to the electric intensity at the same points.

According to Maxwell's theory, the **E** and **B** fields do not appear instantly at distant points; time is required for their propagation. The speed of propagation, according to Maxwell

Summary

The Leyden jar is the earliest form of capacitor, and with it the oscillatory nature of a spark discharge was discovered.

An oscillating electrical circuit contains an inductance, a capacitance, and a resistance.

If the resistance of an oscillatory circuit is exceedingly low, its natural frequency of oscillation is given by

$$f = \frac{1}{2\pi\sqrt{LC}}$$

Two circuits having the same natural frequency may be used to demonstrate resonance or sympathetic oscillations.

Electromagnetic waves are emitted by every oscillating circuit. Traveling outward with the speed of light, these waves may be detected by a distance oscillating circuit tuned to have the same frequency.

Hertzian dipoles are frequently used as transmitters and receivers of high-frequency electromagnetic waves. These are the waves used in radio, radar, and television.

Questions

1. What is a Leyden jar? What is it used for?

2. What is an oscillatory circuit? What are its three principal elements?

3. Upon what does the natural frequency of a circuit depend? What is the formula for the frequency?

4. What is electrical resonance? Under what conditions does it arise?

5. What are Hertzian waves? What is a Hertzian dipole?

6. What are electromagnetic waves? What is their nature? With what speed do they travel?

7. What are damped oscillations? How can damping be reduced?

Problems

1. Calculate the frequency of an oscillating circuit composed of a 1 μf capacitor and a 1 μh inductor.

2. Calculate the frequency and period of an oscillating circuit containing two 3 μf capacitors and an inductance of 3.4 μh if all three are connected in parallel.

3. What inductance connected to a capacitor of 0.25 μf will give the circuit a natural frequency of 4 megacycles/sec?

4. What capacitance if connected in parallel to an inductance of 6 μh will give an oscillating circuit a frequency of 250 kilocycles/sec?

5. Determine the frequency of an oscillating circuit composed of two capacitors and one inductor, all connected in parallel: $C_1 = 2$ μf, $C_2 = 3.5$ μf, and $L = 6.6$ μh.

6. Two capacitors of 10 μf each are first connected in series and then the combination connected across an inductor of 2 μh. Calculate the frequency of the oscillating circuit.

7. What capacitance in parallel with an inductance of 0.1 μh will have a frequency of 1 megacycle/sec?

8.* A capacitance of 0.1 μf is connected to an inductance of 8×10^{-8} henry. Find (a) the frequency and (b) the wave length of the electromagnetic waves emitted.

9.* What capacitance should be used with an inductance of 0.09 μh to produce electromagnetic waves having a wave length of 10 cm?

10.* What inductance should be used with a capacitance of 0.04 μf to produce electromagnetic waves of wave length 1 meter?

VACUUM TUBES

Early in the summer of 1895 a young Italian inventor, Guglielmo Marconi,* happened upon a scientific article describing Hertz's experiments with electromagnetic waves (see Electronics, Lesson 1, p. 481). After reading the article with great interest, Marconi, then only twenty-one years of age, conceived the idea of using Hertzian waves as a means of communication. Beginning experiments immediately, he soon found that (1) by increasing the power of the transmitter, (2) by stretching a wire high in the air for an antenna, and (3) by improving upon Hertz's methods of detection, distances over which signals could be transmitted and received could be greatly increased. So successful was he with these improvements that by 1898 he had spanned a distance of 12 mi and by 1900 had communicated successfully with another station 200 mi away.

The first authentic broadcast of the human voice by wireless waves took place on Christmas day in 1906. The feat was accomplished by Prof. F. A. Fessenden of the University of Pittsburgh. Using the continuous oscillating currents from a high-frequency electrical generator of his own design, instead of the damped oscillations of a discharging condenser circuit, he was able to broadcast music from an experimental station at Brant

* Guglielmo Marconi (1874-1939), Italian inventor, famous for establishing wireless telegraphy on a commercial basis, was born at Bologna on April 25, 1874. Privately educated, he became interested in electrical phenomena at the age of twenty. During his lifetime he initiated many new ideas in wireless telegraphy, each one of which contributed to greater and greater range. In World War I he served in the Italian Army and Navy as a technical expert. In 1909 Marconi, jointly with Ferdinand Braun, was awarded the Nobel Prize in physics, the Albert Medal of the Royal Society of Arts and, in the United States, the Franklin and the John Fritz Medals.

Rock, Massachusetts, and have it heard by U. S. naval warships nearby. It is a most incredible fact that the importance of this great event and its future possibilities were not generally recognized.

The Vacuum Tube Rectifier. While the great American inventor, Thomas A. Edison, was striving by a process of trial and error to produce a satisfactory electric light bulb, he made an accidental discovery, the importance of which was first recognized and used successfully by Sir John Fleming. Now called a vacuum tube rectifier or diode, the Fleming valve is used in nearly every radio and television transmitter and receiver to change alternating current into direct current.

The Fleming valve, as shown in Fig. A, consists of a highly evacuated glass bulb containing a wire filament that is heated electrically to incandescence. Surrounding the fila-

Fig. A. Diagram of a Fleming valve, or rectifier tube. Such tubes are now called diodes.

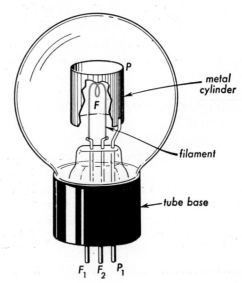

metal cylinder

filament

tube base

F_1 F_2 P_1

fleming valve

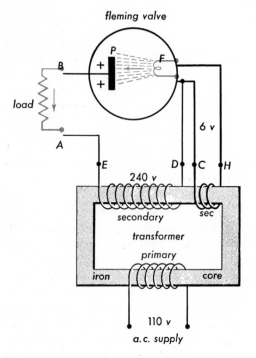

Fig. B. Circuit diagram of a Fleming valve rectifier.

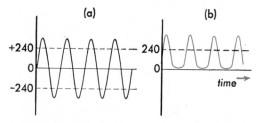

Fig. C. Alternating current as rectified by a Fleming valve, or diode.

filament **F** is negatively charged, the electrons from **F** are attracted to the plate **P** and constitute a current flowing across the vacuum space **PF** and through the load from **B** to **A**. One-half cycle later, when the potential is reversed and **P** becomes negatively charged and **F** positively charged, the electrons from **F** are repelled by **P** and very little current flows.

The emfs in each part of the rectifier circuit are shown by graphs in Fig. C: the secondary emf of 240 volts in (a) and the **rectified**, or **pulsating emf**, through the load **AB** in (b).

Fig. D. Drawing of a full-wave rectifier tube.

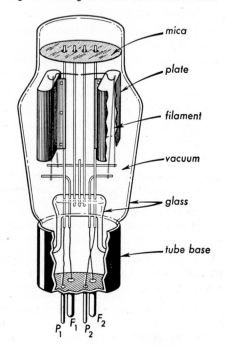

ment and connected to the outside through the tube base and a prong P_1 is a cylindrical metal plate **P**. When the filament is heated to incandescence, it gives off large quantities of electrons by thermionic emission.

The principal action of the **filament F** and **plate P** is explained by means of a typical electric circuit shown schematically in Fig. B. The circuit consists of a **transformer** having **two secondary windings**, a **Fleming valve**, and a **load**. The latter, shown as a resistance, represents any electrical device requiring unidirectional current for its operation. With an alternating current of 110 volts supplied to the primary, a high voltage, 240 volts for example, is delivered by one secondary to the terminals **ED** and a low voltage of 6 volts alternating current is delivered by the other secondary to the terminals **CH**. The latter, called the **filament winding**, is for the purpose of heating the filament.

When for a fraction of a second the plate **P** of the tube is positively charged and the

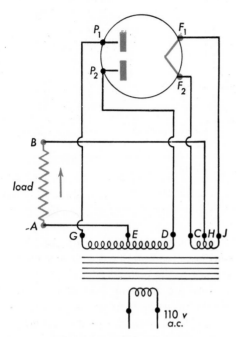

Fig. E. Diagram for a full-wave rectifier circuit.

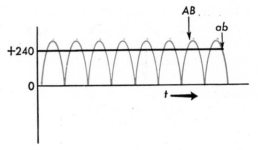

Fig. F. Rectified voltage from a full-wave rectifier circuit.

Full-Wave Rectifier. A full-wave rectifier tube, sometimes called a **duo-diode,** is essentially a double Fleming valve with two plates and two filaments. (See Fig. D.) The two prongs F_1 and F_2 in the base are connected to both filaments in series while the prongs P_1 and P_2 are connected one to each plate.

A schematic diagram of a rectifier circuit employing such a tube is shown in Fig. E. Here an iron-core transformer with one primary and two secondary windings is used, differing from the single-phase rectifier in Fig. B in that the center of each secondary winding is now connected to the load. **CHJ** is the filament winding and supplies current to both filaments (shown as one bent wire), while **GED** is the high-voltage winding. The latter supplies an alternating potential to the plates so that when P_1 is + and P_2 is −, electrons from the filament are attracted to P_1, and when a moment later P_1 is − and P_2 is +, electrons from the filament are attracted to P_2.

In the first instance a current flows around

the circuit $F_1P_1GEABHJF_1$, and in the second it flows around the circuit $F_2P_2DEABHCF_2$. In each case the current has gone through the load **AB** in the same direction and has pulsating characteristics as shown in Fig. F.

A Filter Circuit. If such a pulsating current were used to supply the direct current needed in every radio receiver, a loud objectionable hum with a frequency of 120 cycles would be heard. To make this current a steady, smooth direct current as illustrated by the straight line in the same graph, and thus eliminate the hum, a **filter circuit** as shown in Fig. G is used. The terminals **A** and **B** are connected to and replace the load **A** and **B** in Fig. E. **K** is an iron-core inductance, and C_1 and C_2 are capacitors of large capacitance.

As the current through **AabKB** starts to flow, the condensers become charged as shown and a magnetic field is created around **K**. This has a retarding action and prevents the current from reaching its otherwise peak

Fig. G. Electrical filter circuit for "smoothing out" pulsating direct current.

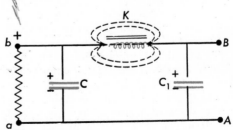

value. When a moment later the filament to plate current drops to near zero, the capacitors discharge and the field around **K** collapses, thus sending a current through **AB.** This process is repeated with each pulse of electrons from either plate of the tube, and the current through **ab** remains steady. Large capacities and large self-inductance deliver more constant voltage.

De Forest's Audion. Although the Fleming valve was originally developed for the purpose of detecting wireless waves, its operation as such did not prove to be very satisfactory until, in 1906, De Forest* invented the **audion.** By inserting a **grid** wire between the **plate** and **filament** of a Fleming valve, he created a device capable not only of detecting wireless waves but of amplifying the signals

* Lee De Forest (1873-   ), American scientist; Ph.D. from Yale University, 1899. Most famous for the audion, considered by many to be the most important invention ever made in radio. He designed and installed the first five high-power radio stations for the U. S. Navy. After 1921 he devoted his time to the development of talking motion picture film. He was awarded gold medals at the St. Louis exposition in 1904, the Panama Pacific Exposition in San Francisco in 1915, and the Institute of France in 1923. He received the Cresson Medal of the Franklin Institute in 1921 for his important contributions to wireless.

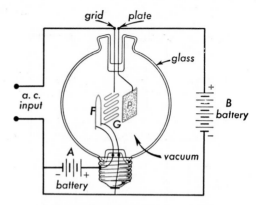

Fig. H. Diagram of the De Forest audion.

as well. The purpose of the grid (see Fig. H) is to control the flow of electrons from the hot filament **F** to the plate **P.**

During the time the grid **G** is negative, electrons from the filament are repelled and are unable to reach the plate **P.** When the grid is positive, however, the electrons from the filament are accelerated toward the plate and constitute a flow of current.

Not only does the grid act as a rectifier valve and let the electron current flow in one direction only, from filament to plate, but it acts as an amplifier, allowing large currents from the high voltage **B**-battery to flow through when it is slightly positive and practically no current when it is slightly negative.

Summary

The first successful attempt to send messages for any distance by means of wireless telegraphy was made by Marconi in 1895.

The first vacuum tube to be used as a rectifier of alternating current was employed by Fleming several years later. The Fleming valve was used to convert alternating current into unidirectional current.

A full-wave rectifier is essentially two Fleming valves and makes use of both half cycles in converting alternating current into unidirectional current.

To smooth out pulsating direct current into one of constant value, a filter circuit is frequently used. A filter circuit employs capacitance and inductance.

The first radio vacuum tube using a grid, along with the customary plate and filament, was the audion. The audion, invented by De Forest, not only rectifies an alternating current but amplifies it as well.

Questions

1. Who is credited with the invention of wireless telegraphy? What kind of waves were used?

2. What is a Fleming valve? What is a rectifier? Make a diagram of a rectifier and show how it is used.

3. What is a full-wave rectifier? What is a half-wave rectifier? Make a diagram of a full wave rectifier and explain how it operates.

4. What is a filter circuit? What is its purpose? Make a circuit diagram of a full-wave rectifier and a filter circuit.

5. What is an audion? What are the three elements of such a vacuum tube? Who invented the tube?

6. Draw from memory a schematic wiring diagram of a full-wave rectifier showing the vacuum tube, transformer, and load.

7. Make a schematic diagram combining a full-wave rectifier with a filter circuit consisting of a transformer, vacuum tube, choke coil, two capacitors, and a load.

Electronics | **Lesson 3**

CHARACTERISTICS OF VACUUM TUBES—*Laboratory*

In performing this exercise you will determine the grid-voltage vs plate-current curve for a typical three element vacuum tube. The simplified circuit used and the steps taken in making the measurements are described in the accompanying LABORATORY EXERCISES.

Electronics | **Lesson 4**

OSCILLATORS, AMPLIFIERS, AND RADIO

Vacuum Tube Oscillator. To broadcast the human voice by radio, a generator of alternating current of extremely high frequency and constant amplitude is required. In commercial broadcasting stations and amateur transmitters this function is performed by a vacuum tube and circuit of relatively simple design.

One type of oscillator circuit is shown in Fig. A. When the switch S is closed connecting the B-battery to the plate of the tube, an electron current from the cathode K to the

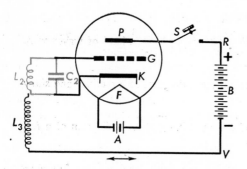

Fig. A. Vacuum tube oscillator circuit for generating radio waves of constant amplitude.

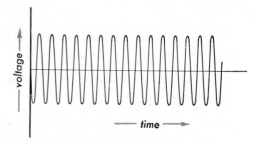

Fig. B. Continuous oscillations in a vacuum tube oscillator circuit like Fig. A.

plate **P** starts a current in the circuit **PRVL₃K**. This growing current in **L₃** creates a growing magnetic field, which cutting across **L₂** induces a current in the grid circuit in such a direction that the grid becomes negative. A negative charge on the grid causes the plate current to decrease. This decreasing current causes the field about **L₃** to diminish, thus inducing a reversed current in the grid circuit and therefore a positive charge on the grid. Such a charge increases the plate current and the above process is repeated.

If the two circuits **L₂C₂** and **PRVL₃** are properly tuned by adjusting **C₂**, resonance will occur and energy from the **B**-battery will be continuously supplied to keep the oscillations going with constant amplitude. The graph of the continuous oscillations shown in Fig. B represents the voltage across **L₃** as

it varies in time. The **L₂C₂** circuit controls the frequency by controlling the grid potential while the large voltage and current fluctuations take place in the **L₃** circuit.

Radio Transmitter. To use an oscillating tube circuit, of the kind described above, as part of a radio transmitter, the high-frequency oscillations in the **L₂C₂** circuit must be modified by sound waves and then applied to an antenna and ground system for broadcasting as electromagnetic waves. A simplified circuit diagram showing one of the many ways of doing this is given in Fig. C. There are three parts to this particular "hook up": (1) *the microphone circuit* containing a battery **D** and a transformer **T**, (2) *the oscillator circuit* in the middle, and (3) *the antenna circuit **C₁L₁G*** at the left.

By talking or singing into the microphone,

Fig. C. Radio transmitter employing a microphone and only one tube as an oscillator.

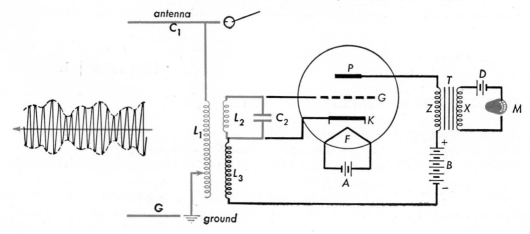

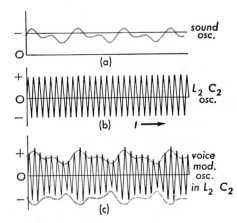

Fig. D. Graphs of (a) sound waves, (b) continuous oscillations in L_2C_2, and (c) voice-modulated oscillations in L_2C_2.

the diaphragm inside moves back and forth with the sound vibrations, thus altering the steady current previously flowing around the circuit **DMX**. An illustration of the pulsating current is shown in Fig. D(a). Current pulsations in **X**, the transformer primary, cause similar pulsations in **Z**, the secondary circuit carrying the plate current. The effect of the relatively low-frequency audio currents on the high-frequency oscillations already there is to alter their amplitude as shown in diagram (c).

Through the **coupling** of L_3 with L_1 the modulated oscillations are induced in the antenna circuit by resonance and are radiated as electromagnetic waves of the same frequency and form. The continuous wave produced by the radio-frequency oscillations

alone is called the **carrier wave,** and the alteration of its amplitude by **audio frequencies** is called **modulation.** Although radio transmitters with one vacuum tube have been used by radio amateurs, it is customary to find transmitters with half a dozen or more tubes. The principal function of additional tubes in receivers as well as transmitters is to amplify currents wherever they are needed and thereby give greater transmitting range and clearer reception.

Vacuum Tube Amplifier. One of the most important functions of the vacuum tube is its use as an **amplifier** of radio-frequency or audio-frequency currents as shown in Fig. E. The **input** resistor represents some part of any circuit in which a weak but varying current is flowing, and the **output** resistor represents another circuit to which a stronger current of the same form is delivered. In some cases these are resistors as shown, but in others they are the primary and secondary windings of separate transformers. The source of the additional energy is the **B**-battery plate supply.

In amplifying any given signal current a faithful reproduction of the **wave form** must be carried out, otherwise **distortion** will re-

Fig. F. Graph showing amplifier operation.

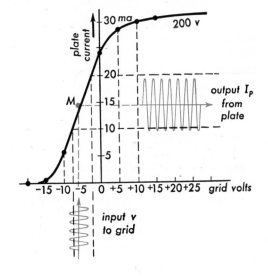

Fig. E. Amplifier circuit with one vacuum tube.

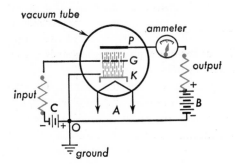

sult; musical sounds from a radio will be harsh or pictures from a television receiver will be blurred. To amplify without distortion, a tube must be used that has a long straight section in its **characteristic curve** (see Fig. F), and it should be operated at the center of this straight portion. Such operation is shown by the graph. To make the tube operate at **M**, a small battery, called a **C**-battery or **C**-bias, is inserted in the grid circuit to maintain the grid at a negative potential. For the curve and tube shown this requires −5 volts, while for other types of tubes it might well require greater or smaller potentials.

When, in Fig. E, no input signal potentials are imposed, the grid is held at −5 volts and a steady current of 15 milliamperes flows through the plate and output circuit. If now an alternating current like a radio frequency of constant amplitude is impressed across the input terminals, the grid potential will rise and fall in the same way, and an undistorted but amplified current will flow in the plate and output circuit. The time variations in grid potential are shown above in Fig. F, and the corresponding plate current oscillations at the right and center. If the input radio frequency is voice modulated, the amplified current will also be voice modulated without distortion. It should be noted that if the impressed grid-voltage variations are too large, say −20 to +10 volts, the amplified currents will reach the curved portions of the curve above and below, and **distortion** of the **wave form** will result. As long as the tube is operated on the straight portion of the curve, plate current is directly proportional to the impressed grid potential, and faithful amplification takes place.

The Dynamic Loud-Speaker. A loudspeaker of conventional design is shown in cross section in Fig. G. Its function is the same as that of a telephone receiver: to change audio-frequency currents from the last amplifier in a radio receiver or public

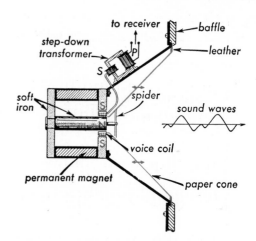

Fig. G. Cross-section diagram of dynamic loud-speaker.

address system into sound waves of the same form.

There are three main parts to every loudspeaker. First, there is a strong shell-type magnet whose function it is to provide a field radially outward from a central **N** pole, across a narrow air gap, to a ringlike **S** pole. In most speakers this field is provided by an **alnico permanent magnet.** The second element is a small cylindrical **voice coil** consisting of a dozen or so turns of wire fixed near the apex of a **paper cone** and centered in the narrow field gap by a springy fiber disk called a **spider.** The third is a **step-down transformer,** the low-voltage, high-current winding of which is connected by flexible wires to the voice coil.

When a varying current from the output transformer passes through the voice coil, varying forces are exerted which cause it to vibrate back and forth along its axis. As the cone is driven back and forth, it acts like a plunger, its large area setting considerable air into vibration. The walls of the room or cabinet behind which the speaker is mounted acts as a **baffle,** preventing sound waves from the back surface of the cone from getting around to interfere destructively with the waves from the front surface. A good demonstration is to be had by removing a speaker from its normal mounted position and listening to the distorted sounds it seems to produce. The low-pitched sounds in particular are noticeably absent.

Large-sized speakers with a suitably large baffle area are particularly good at reproducing and dispersing low-pitched sounds. Because of **diffraction** and **interference,** however, high-pitched sounds are emitted in a narrow beam and in a forward direction only. Speakers with small cones, on the other hand, are particularly good on the high-pitched notes but are generally poor at reproducing the lows.*

* For a detailed treatment of the principles of radio see "Basic Radio," by J. Hoag, D. Van Nostrand Co., Inc.

Summary

A three element vacuum tube, a triode, may be used to produce a continuously oscillating circuit. Such circuits are used in radio, television, radar, and many other electronic systems.

A triode vacuum tube may be used as an amplifier of low-, medium-, and high-frequency currents. An alternating emf of constant or varying magnitude is applied to the grid and cathode of the tube, and an alternating emf of greater magnitude is delivered by the plate and cathode.

The increased energy output of a vacuum tube amplifier is supplied by the **B**-battery.

A radio transmitter generates a very high-frequency emf of constant amplitude, and this is made to vary in amplitude by sound vibrations. The modulated oscillations are radiated as electromagnetic waves from the antenna and ground.

A dynamic loud-speaker consists of a paper cone set into vibration by the voice modulations developed in a radio receiver. A small winding called a voice coil fastened to the apex of the cone is located between the poles of a strong magnet. Audio currents in the voice coil drive it back and forth, thus setting the cone vibrating.

Questions

1. What is a vacuum tube oscillator? What does it produce? What determines the oscillation frequency?

2. Where does the energy come from that keeps the amplitude of the oscillations constant?

3. Name the basic elements of a simple radio transmitter?

4. What is a carrier wave? What is an audio frequency? What is a radio frequency?

5. What is a vacuum tube amplifier? Where does the added electrical energy come from?

6. What is modulation? What is distortion?

7. What are the principal elements of a dynamic loud-speaker?

Problems

1. Draw a circuit diagram for a vacuum tube oscillator for generating radio frequencies of constant amplitude.

2. Draw from memory an amplifier circuit with one vacuum tube.

3. Make a diagram of a radio loud-speaker from memory. Show in detail the three main parts: the magnet, the voice coil, and the output transformer.

THE PHOTOELECTRIC EFFECT

Photoelectrons. The photoelectric effect in its simplest form is demonstrated in Fig. A. Light from a carbon arc is focused by means of a quartz lens onto a freshly polished plate of zinc metal. When the plate is charged negatively and the light is turned on, the gold leaf of the attached electroscope slowly falls. It falls because the electrons, under the action of the light, leave the zinc plate at the illuminated spot **P.** When the plate is positively charged, the gold leaf does not fall, showing that the plate retains its charge. The same result of no discharge is observed if the zinc plate is negatively charged and a sheet of glass is inserted as shown in the figure. When the glass is removed the gold leaf again falls. Since common glass transmits visible and infrared light but not ultraviolet, we conclude that elec-

trons are liberated only by ultraviolet light. This is also generally true for nearly all of the known metals.

Although these electrons are the same negatively charged particles that constitute cathode rays, they are called **photoelectrons** because they are liberated by means of light.

A few elements—namely the alkali metals **lithium, sodium, potassium, rubidium,** and **cesium**—are exceptions to this, for they will eject photoelectrons when visible light falls on them. For this reason the **alkali metals** are often used in the manufacture of photoelectric cells.

The Photoelectric Cell. Photoelectric cells are usually made by depositing a thin layer of an alkali metal on the inner surface of a small vacuum tube (see Fig. B). If the

Fig. A. Experimental arrangement for demonstrating the photoelectric effect. When the glass plate is inserted, the effect stops.

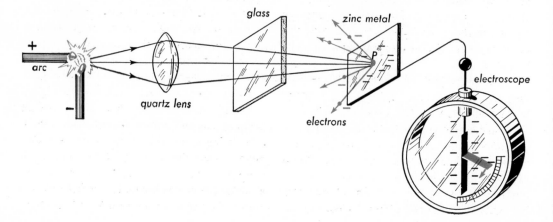

glass
zinc metal
+
arc
quartz lens
electrons
electroscope

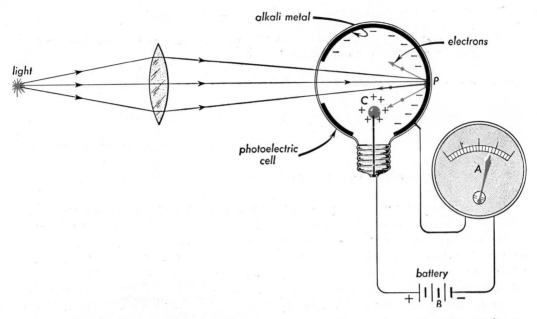

Fig. B. Diagram of a photoelectric cell showing the light beam and electrical connections necessary for its operation.

cell is to operate in ultraviolet light it is made of quartz, whereas if it is to be used in visible light it is made of common glass. The cell must be thoroughly evacuated as the oxygen content of the air will combine chemically with the active metal layer, contaminating its surface and making it insensitive to visible light. A small section of the cell is always left clear to serve as a window for the incoming light. Photoelectrons, upon leaving the metal surface, are attracted and collected by the positively charged electrode **C.** The negative charge on the metal film and the positive charge on the central collector electrode are maintained at a constant potential by the battery **B.**

A beam of light shining through the window of a photoelectric cell acts like a switch which completes an electric circuit. When the light strikes the metal **P**, there is a flow of electrons to the collector **C**, thus causing a current to flow around the circuit. This current can be measured by means of an ammeter at **A.** If the intensity of the light increases, the number of photoelectrons in-

creases and the current therefore rises. When the light is shut off, the photoelectric action ceases and the current stops. If the metal film is positively charged, the cell becomes inactive to light since electrons attempting to leave the plate are held back by electrostatic attraction. All of these factors are readily demonstrated by a simple electrical circuit arranged as shown in the figure.

Sound Over a Light Beam. The sending of voice and musical sounds for several miles over a light beam is readily accomplished with a suitable light source as transmitter and a photoelectric cell as a receiver. A convenient laboratory demonstration can be made by using a small $\frac{1}{4}$ watt neon glow lamp as a source of light, as shown in Fig. C.

Sound waves entering the microphone **M** produce electric current fluctuations which, after being strengthened by a two-stage amplifier, cause the intensity of the neon glow lamp **N** to fluctuate accordingly. Made into a parallel beam by a lens L_1, the light travels across the room to a second lens L_2 and a

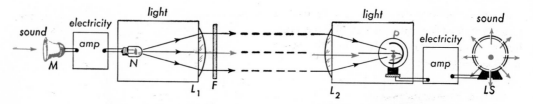

Fig. C. Voice and musical sounds can be sent long distances over a beam of light.

photoelectric cell where the light is changed back into a varying electric current. This faint signal is then amplified by a two-stage amplifier before it is delivered to the loud-speaker.

If the microphone is replaced by a phonograph "pick-up," records can be played at the transmitter end and excellent reproduction can be obtained from the loud-speaker. The light beam can be made completely invisible by placing an infrared filter in the light beam at **F.**

The Velocity of Photoelectrons. The first measurements of the velocity of photoelectrons led to the very startling discovery that the velocity does not increase as the intensity of the light increases. *Increasing the intensity of the light increases the number of photoelectrons but not their velocity.* This discovery, as we shall see later, has had far reaching implications in its result, for it has played an important role in the development of our modern concepts of light and atomic structure.

Lenard's experiments, performed as far back as 1902, showed that to increase the velocity of photoelectrons one must increase the frequency of the light, i.e., use shorter wave lengths. The shorter the wave length of the light used, the higher are the velocities of the electrons.

Einstein's Photoelectric Equation. Following an earlier idea of Planck's that light waves consist of tiny bundles of energy called **photons** or **quanta,** Einstein proposed an explanation of the photoelectric effect as early as 1905. His ideas are expressed by one

simple relation, an algebraic equation, destined to become famous in the annals of physics. Two Nobel Prizes, one to Einstein in 1921 and one to Millikan in 1923, have been granted on this, the photoelectric equation,

$$h\nu = W + \tfrac{1}{2}mv^2 \qquad (1)$$

The first term $h\nu$ represents the total energy content of a single quantum of light incident on a metal surface, as shown in Fig. D. The letter h is a constant called **Planck's constant of action,** which has the same value for all light waves regardless of the frequency ν. At or beneath the surface of the metal this **light quantum,** better known as a **photon,** is completely absorbed and, in disappearing, imparts its total energy to a single electron. Part of this energy **W** is consumed in getting the electron free from the atoms and away from the metal surface, and the remainder is used in giving the electron kinetic energy $\tfrac{1}{2}mv^2$, and therefore a velocity. For some metals like platinum the energy required to

Fig. D. A light quantum (photon) of energy $h\nu$, incident on a metal surface, ejects an electron with a velocity v given by Einstein's equation.

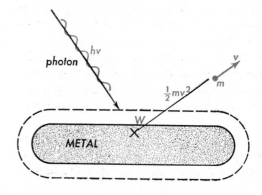

pull an electron away from the surface is large, whereas for other metals like the alkalies it is quite small. **W** is called the **work function** of the metal.

Millikan's Measurement of h. The letter **h** in Einstein's photoelectric equation is important because it is fundamental to the structure of all matter and therefore *a universal constant*. Having first been introduced by Planck in 1901, the name **Planck's constant** has become firmly attached to this symbol **h**. The first experimental confirmation of Einstein's photoelectric equation came in 1912 when A. L. Hughes, and independently O. W. Richardson and K. T. Compton, observed that the energy of photoelectrons increased proportionately with the frequency. The constant of proportionality they found to be approximately equal to a constant, Planck's constant **h**.

Subsequently Millikan carried out extensive experiments which established the photoelectric equation so accurately that his work is now considered to give one of the most trustworthy values for **h**.

To do this it was necessary to measure the three factors **v**, **W**, and $\frac{1}{2} mv^2$, and calculate **h** as the unknown quantity in Eq. (1). The most recent value obtained for this universal constant, is

$$h = 6.62 \times 10^{-34} \text{ joule sec} \qquad (2)$$

Since the frequency of visible light is about 6×10^{14} vib/sec, the energy in a single photon or quantum of visible light is the product of these two numbers, or 3.936×10^{-19} joule.

It should be pointed out in passing that the photon, in ejecting an electron from a metal surface as in the photoelectric effect, disappears completely, i.e., it is annihilated.

Secondary Electrons. When electrons strike the surface of a metal plate, they knock additional electrons free from the surface.

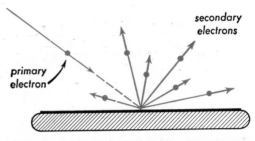

Fig. E. The impact of a single electron liberates additional electrons from a metal surface.

These are called **secondary electrons,** and the process is called **secondary emission** (see Fig. E). As the speed of a primary or incident electron increases from zero to a few hundred volts, the number of secondaries increases toward a definite maximum. For most metal surfaces this maximum is in the neighborhood of two, while for certain alkali metal films it may be as great as eight or ten. In general it is greatest for surfaces having a **low work function.**

Photo-Multiplier Tubes. The process of secondary electron emission is widely used in a special type of photoelectric cell used most effectively in detecting faint light. A

Fig. F. Photo multiplier tube with six stages. Cesium-oxide silver-coated photo cathode.

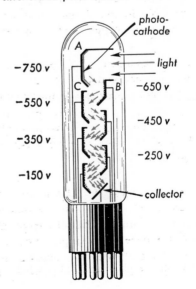

cross-section diagram of such a photo-multiplier tube is given in Fig. F.

The number of photoelectrons from the photocathode **A** is proportional to the intensity of the incident light. These are attracted toward the next dynode **B**, more positive by 100 volts, where upon impact additional electrons are liberated. Attracted to the next more positive dynode **C**, still more electrons are liberated. By the time the collector plate has been reached, a small avalanche of electrons has developed and a correspondingly large charge and current are led off through that electrode to a suitable recording device.

If each electron on impact releases **n** secondaries, then in a tube with **k** stages, the number arriving at the collector would be n^k. For example, if **n** = 6, and if **k** = 5, then n^k = 7776 electrons. This is an enormous gain over the signal obtained from a standard photo tube. Photo-multiplier tubes have been used most successfully with faint light, not only with visible light but with infrared and ultraviolet as well.

Summary

When light of sufficiently high frequency falls on a metal plate, electrons are ejected from the surface. Such a process is called the photoelectric effect, and the emitted electrons are called photoelectrons.

While most metals require ultraviolet light to liberate electrons, some elements and compounds exhibit the phenomenon with visible light. Such elements as the alkali metals are good examples.

The velocity **v** with which photoelectrons are ejected from a surface is given by the Einstein photoelectric equation

$$h\nu = W + \tfrac{1}{2} mv^2$$

where ν is the frequency of the incident light, **W** is the energy necessary to free an electron from the metal surface, and **m** is the electron mass.

The so-called Planck's constant **h** was first measured by Millikan and is now known to have the value

$$h = 6.62 \times 10^{-34} \text{ joule sec}$$

Electrons, too, on striking the surface of some metals are found to liberate several more electrons. These are called secondary electrons. The operation of photo-multiplier tubes is based upon this principle.

Questions

1. What is the photoelectric effect? What are photoelectrons? How do they differ from cathode rays?

2. What is a photoelectric cell? What can it be used for?

3. What determines the velocity of photoelectrons? What is the Einstein photoelectric equation?

4. What is a photon? What is a light quantum?

5. What is Planck's constant? What is its significance?

6. What are secondary electrons? How is the principle employed in a photo-multiplier tube?

7. How can sound be transmitted over a beam of light? Where is the photoelectric cell used in this application? Could this device be made to operate an invisible light?

8. What is the work function of a metal? Is the work function for alkali metals larger than for most other metals or smaller?

9. How would you go about the problem of sending sound waves, like those from your voice, over a beam of ultraviolet light?

Problems

1. Find the energy equivalent to a light wave of wave length 5×10^{-7} meter. Such light is in the green region of the visible spectrum.

2. Calculate the energy in joules of ultraviolet light of wave length 3×10^{-7} meter.

3.* If X rays with a wavelength of 5.0×10^{-10} meter fall on a metal plate, what would be the maximum velocity of the photoelectrons emitted? (Assume the work function to be negligibly small, $W = 0$.)

4. Assuming the work function of sodium to be negligibly small, what will be the velocity of photoelectrons emitted as the result of incident light of wave length 3×10^{-8} meter? This is ultraviolet light.

5. Find the over-all gain of a ten-stage photo-multiplier tube if the average number of secondary electrons produced by each primary electron is five.

6. A six-stage photo-multiplier tube has an over-all gain of 15,625. Find the average number of secondary electrons produced by each primary electron.

7. Make a diagram showing how a photoelectric cell could be used to count the number of cars passing a given point on a highway in a single day.

Electronics | **Lesson 6**

ELECTROMAGNETIC WAVES—*Laboratory*

Electromagnetic waves in the VHF range are used to study the polarization of waves. The wave length of microwaves from a transmitter is measured by setting up and detecting the nodes and antinodes of standing waves. This experiment is described in the accompanying LABORATORY EXERCISES.

RADAR AND TV

Radar is one of the most important electronic developments of World War II and may be defined as the art of determining by means of **radio echoes** the presence, distance, direction, and velocity of distant aircraft, ships, land masses, cities, and other objects. RADAR derives its name from the longer title "RAdio Detection And Ranging."

The Fundamental Principle. Basically a complete radar station consists of a **transmitter**, a **receiver**, and an **indicator**. As shown by a schematic diagram in Fig. A, the transmitter sends out high-frequency radio waves which, traveling outward with the velocity of light, are reflected from a distant object. That small portion of the reflected waves returning toward the station is picked up and amplified by the receiver. The signal is then fed into any one of a number of indicating devices, some of which are so complete as to give continuously the instantaneous **distance**, **direction**, and **relative velocity** of the object. With one type of air-borne unit, ground objects can be observed on the screen of a kinescope even though fog or clouds intervene. Such systems are extremely useful in reduc-

ing flying hazards always present during inclement weather.

The wave lengths of the waves used in radar are in the **microwave** region of the electromagnetic spectrum. They have wave lengths in the range of 1 cm to 10 cm.

The Pulsed System. Since a powerful transmitter must operate side by side with a supersensitive receiver, some provision is always made whereby the power from the transmitter is blocked out of the receiver. In most radar equipment this is accomplished by means of intermittent transmission commonly called the **pulsed system.** According to this system the transmitter is turned **on** for only a fraction of a second to send out a train of waves while the receiver is made very insensitive. When the transmitter goes **off,** the receiver is turned **on** to full sensitivity to receive the faint echo signal returning. When the receiver goes **off,** the transmitter comes **on** again to send out another wave train and repeat the above process hundreds of times per second.

A graph of the received pulses from an object 9 mi away is shown in Fig. B. Since the velocity of radio waves is 186,300 mi/sec,

Fig. A. Illustrating the principles of radar detecting and ranging.

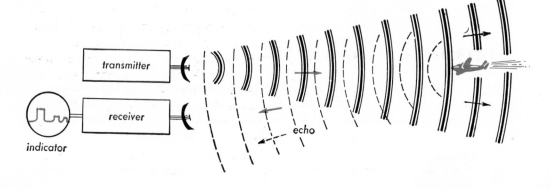

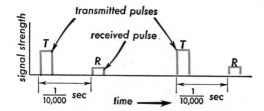

Fig. B. Graph of transmitted pulses showing received pulse, or echo, from an object 9 mi distant.

the same as light, the time interval between each transmitted pulse **T** and its echo **R** returning is a direct measure of the distance. If a frequency of 30,000 megacycles is used, the wave length is 1 cm and each pulse will contain thousands of waves. Rectified by the receiver, an entire wave train appears as a voltage pulse as in the graph.

One type of **indicator** used for determining this time interval is a **cathode-ray oscilloscope**, or **kinescope**, of the type shown in Fig. G of this lesson. While the scanning spot is kept at constant intensity, a saw-tooth potential is applied to the horizontal sweep to make it move with constant speed across the fluorescent screen.

Electrical circuits are so arranged that the spot starts at the left just prior to the trans-

Fig. C. Trace of spot on cathode-ray tube as used in radar ranging.

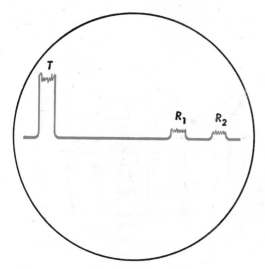

mitter's emission of a pulse. When, a fraction of a second later, a pulse is initiated, a small part of the energy is applied as a vertical deflection of the spot, thereby producing a trace **T** as shown in Fig. C. When the returning echo signal arrives at the receiver, it too is applied as a vertical deflection, and a peak like the one at **R₁** is produced. Upon reaching the right-hand end of the screen the spot is extinguished and returned to the left, where it is again turned on and the above process repeated. As the spot retraces the same line many times every second, persistence of vision gives rise to the appearance of a steady trace.

If several different objects reflect waves of sufficient intensity to be picked up by the receiver, several peaks **R₁**, **R₂**, etc., will be seen on the indicator screen. In radar parlance, each such peak on the trace is called a **pip**, and its distance along the horizontal line from **T** is a direct measure of the time required for the signal to go out and return and is therefore a measure of the range of the object that caused it. Various methods of accurately measuring the distance interval have been developed.

If an object is coming toward or receding from a radar station, the frequency of the waves reflected from it will be increased or decreased respectively as in the Doppler Effect. Hence by measuring the frequency change between the waves going out and those coming back, the velocity of approach or recession becomes known.

Wave Guides. The term wave guide is generally applied to a special class of metallic conductors having the property of conducting high-frequency oscillations from one place to another. To be more specific it is a radio transmission line by which power generated at an oscillator can be transmitted to some utility point with little or no loss along the line.

Two types of wave guide commonly used at present are shown in Fig. D. The first,

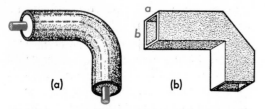

Fig. D. Wave guides commonly used in radar and television transmission lines: (a) coaxial cable and (b) hollow conductor.

called a **coaxial cable** or **concentric line,** consists of a wire conductor insulated from and running lengthwise through the center of a tubular conductor. Power from any high-frequency source, when connected to the central wire and tubular sheath, is propagated as waves through the dielectric between the two conductors.

The second is a hollow rectangular pipe called a **wave guide.** Power introduced as electromagnetic waves at one end is guided by the conducting walls to the other end. Each conductor is shown with a 90° bend to show that waves can be guided around corners.

While there is no limit to the frequency transmitted by coaxial lines there is a lower limit for hollow wave guides. This lower limit, called the **cut-off frequency** or critical frequency, is the limiting case of a so-called

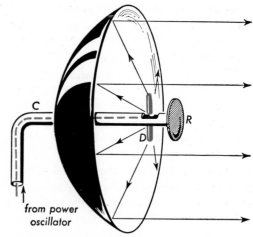

Fig. E. Radar antenna system for producing a parallel beam.

dominant mode of vibration inside the guide and is analogous in some respects to the **fundamental vibration** of a given air column in sound. The dominant mode occurs in a rectangular pipe when the wider of the two dimensions **b** is one-half a wave length. The narrow dimension of the latter is not critical but in practice is made to be about $\frac{1}{2}$ **b.**

Since wave guides are comparable in cross section to the waves they propagate, and a coaxial cable will transmit any frequency no matter how low, the latter is generally used for waves longer than 10 cm, whereas hollow

Fig. F. Illustrating the process of picture scanning.

object at sending station

exploring spot

picture seen at receiver

reproducing spot

pipes are used with waves shorter than 10 cm. The power capacity of a hollow pipe, transmitting at its dominant mode, is greater than a coaxial cable of the same size.

Fig. E shows an arrangement in which the high-frequency oscillations from an oscillator tube source (not shown) are fed through a coaxial cable **C** to a single dipole, or Hertzian doublet **D**. Radiated waves from the doublet are reflected into a parallel beam by the mirror. Since the over-all length of a dipole must be equal to one-half a wave length, the two small rods for 10 cm waves would each be 2.5 cm, or 1 in., long.

The Scanning Process in Television. For years the sending of pictures by wire or radio has been an everyday occurrence. The fundamental principle involved in this process, which is illustrated in Fig. F, is known as *scanning*. Every picture to be transmitted is scanned by an *exploring spot* which, starting at the top, moves in straight lines over the entire picture. The spot first moves from **A** to **B**, then from **C** to **D**, then **E** to **F**, etc., until the entire picture has been covered. Each time the spot reaches the right-hand side it jumps back to the left and starts on the next line. This process is called *field sequential scanning*.

The exploring spot in any scanning device

is so constructed that it generates an electric current proportional to the brightness of its instantaneous position. Such a pulsating current, called the *video signal*, is transmitted over wires or radio waves to the receiving station. There in a specially designed instrument a *reproducing spot*, whose brightness is proportional to the video signal amplitude, moves over a viewing screen in a path similar to that of the exploring spot. In this way the reproducing spot reconstructs the original picture.

It will be realized that the smaller the scanning and reproducing spots and the greater the number of lines, the better will be the details of the scanned picture being reproduced at the receiving end. The diagram shown here includes only 50 lines per picture as compared with 525 lines used in some standard (black and white) broadcasts.

To avoid spurious shadows and images, the process of *interlacing* is employed. By this process each picture is scanned twice, first by running the exploring spot over the odd numbered lines 1, 3, 5, 7, etc., and then over the even numbered lines 2, 4, 6, 8, etc.

The Kinescope. In many respects the construction of a television receiver and its operation is similar to an ordinary radio receiver. After being tuned in, detected, and

Fig. G. Diagram of a kinescope or television picture tube.

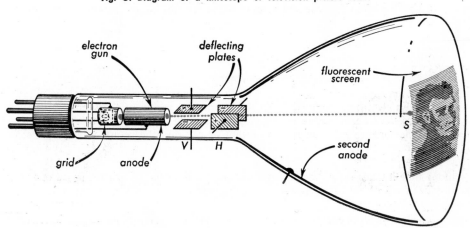

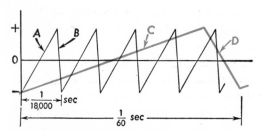

Fig. H. Saw-tooth potentials applied to plates of the television tube to produce horizontal scanning A and B, and vertical scanning C and D. A, horizontal deflection; B, horizontal return; C, vertical deflection; and D, vertical return.

amplified with conventional radio tube circuits, the carrier wave from a nearby transmitter is fed as a video signal into a kinescope in place of a loud-speaker. A kinescope is a large vacuum tube used for scanning and viewing the transmitted pictures.

A kinescope using electrostatic deflection plates for scanning is shown in Fig. G. Electrons from an electron gun at the left travel down the length of the tube to where, impinging upon a fluorescent screen, they produce a bright luminescent spot **S**. The purpose of the deflecting plates **V** and **H** is to deflect the electron beam with the identical frequency and scanning motion of the transmitting station. Two special oscillator tubes and circuits in the receiver supply saw-tooth potentials (see Fig. H) to these plates; the high-frequency potentials to the **H-plates** for horizontal scanning and the lower frequency potentials to the **V-plates** for vertical scanning.

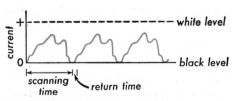

Fig. I. Video signal current for three lines of a single picture.

The proper fluctuations in the intensity of the luminescent spot are brought about by applying the video signal shown in Fig. I to the **grid** of the electron gun. This grid controls the flow of electrons through to the anode in the same way that the grid controls the current to the plate in an ordinary three-element radio tube.

For a small fraction of a second, between successive pictures being scanned for transmission, current pulses of a certain type and frequency are sent out from the sending station as part of the video signal. These, picked up by the receiver, act as a triggerlike mechanism to bring the reproducing spot to the top left of the screen at the proper time to start the next picture. In other words the transmitter sends out signals that enable the receiver to automatically keep "in step" with the pictures as they are sent.

The wave lengths used in transmitting TV signals lie in the VHF and UHF regions of the electromagnetic spectrum. These two wave-length bands extend from 10 cm to 10 m.

Summary

Radar employs electromagnetic waves in the microwave region of the spectrum. Waves sent out from the transmitter, in the form of a Hertzian dipole at the focal plane of a parabolic reflector, are reflected from a distant object, and the return wave is detected by a sensitive receiver.

From the time it takes the waves to travel out and back, at the rate of the speed of light, the distance from object to receiver can be computed with considerable accuracy.

Television employs electromagnetic waves in the VHF and UHF region of the spectrum.

Each picture to be transmitted is scanned at the transmitter. The varying intensity of the scanning spot as it crosses the picture becomes the signal that modulates the radio waves being transmitted.

At the TV receiver a similar scanning procedure is carried out by a spot produced on a fluorescent screen by a focused beam of electrons. The scanning process is accomplished by deflecting the beam with proper magnetic fields.

Questions

1. What is RADAR? What do the letters stand for?

2. What is a pulsed radar system? Why is the operation intermittent?

3. How is the distance of an object determined? How is the velocity of a moving object determined?

4. What is a wave guide? How many kinds are there?

5. What is the process called scanning? What is a video signal?

6. What is a kinescope? How is the electron beam deflected for scanning the screen of the picture tube?

7. What is meant by field sequential scanning? What is interlacing?

Problems

1. Radar waves of frequency 5×10^3 megacycles per second are reflected from a paraboloidal metal reflector. Calculate the over-all length of the dipole used at its focal plane.

2. The dipole of a radar transmitter has an over-all length of 1.63 cm. Calculate the frequency in Mc/sec.

3. Find the time required for a radar signal to go out and return from an object 15 miles away.

4. What is the minimum microwave frequency that can be transmitted through a rectangular tube wave guide if the inside cross section is 1 cm by 0.5 cm?

5. If each scanned picture in TV requires 325 lines and 30 pictures per second are used, how many times per second does the electron beam sweep across the picture tube?

6.* If the video signal for each line of a TV picture requires 10,000 waves of the carrier wave, and each picture requires 350 lines, what minimum frequency is required to send 30 pictures per second?

GEIGER-MUELLER AND SCINTILLATION
COUNTERS—*Laboratory*

Geiger and scintillation counters used as detectors of penetrating radiation are operated at different counting rates. By measuring differences in counting rates their respective resolution times can be determined. The methods used are described in the accompanying LABORATORY EXERCISES.

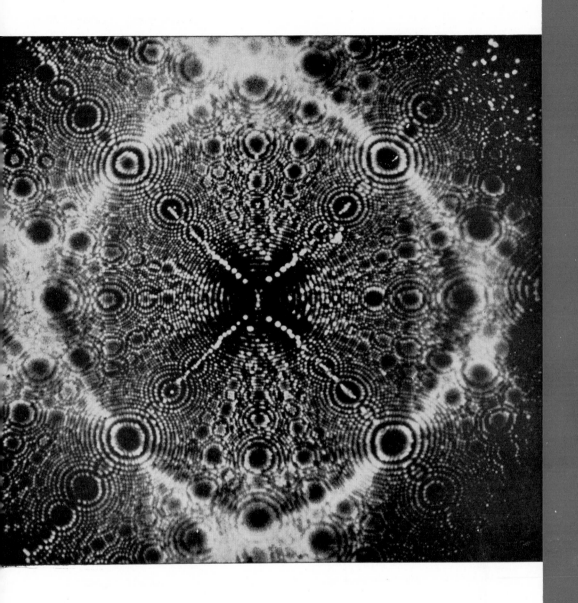

QUANTUM OPTICS

The present state of atomic theory is characterised by the fact that we not only believe the existence of atoms to be proved beyond a doubt, but also we even believe that we have an intimate knowledge of the constituents of the individual atoms.

According to our present conceptions, an atom of an element is built up of a nucleus that has a positive electrical charge and is the seat of by far the greatest part of the atomic mass, together with a number of electrons, all having the same negative charge and mass, which move at distances from the nucleus that are very great compared to the dimensions of the nucleus or of the electrons themselves. In this picture we at once see a striking resemblance to a planetary system, such as we have in our own solar system. Just as the simplicity of the laws that govern the motions of the solar system is intimately concerned with the circumstance that the dimensions of the moving bodies are small in relation to the orbits, so the corresponding relations in atomic structure provide us with an explanation of an essential feature of natural phenomena in so far as these depend on the properties of the elements.

To the first class belong most of the ordinary physical and chemical properties of substances, such as their state of aggregation, colour, and chemical reactivity. These properties depend on the motion of the electron system and the way in which this motion changes under the influence of different external actions. . . . On the other hand, the structure of the nucleus will be responsible for the second class of properties that are shown in the radioactivity of substances. In the radioactive processes we meet with an explosion of the nucleus, whereby positive or negative particles, the so-called α- and β-particles, are expelled with very great velocities.

Prof. Niels Bohr: "The Structure of the Atom," *Nature,* vol. 112, 1923, p. 29.

← The atomic lattice structure of a platinum crystal is shown by means of a photograph taken with a field ion microscope.

Professor Erwin Muller,
Pennsylvania State University

The Bohr Atom

DURING the years 1905-1913 Sir Ernest Rutherford, and his collaborators H. Geiger and E. Marsden, performed in England a series of ingenious experiments on the scattering of α particles, the results of which implied that the positive charge and mass of every atom is confined to a particle smaller than 10^{-12} cm in diameter. Historically this marks the beginning of the idea of a nuclear atom proposed formally by Niels Bohr several years later. A schematic diagram of the scattering experiments is given in Fig. A.

Fig. A. Diagram of the Rutherford scattering experiments.

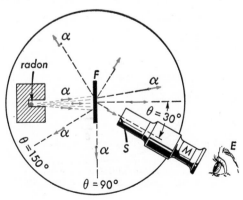

High-speed α particles from the radioactive element radon, confined to a narrow beam by a hole in a lead block, were made to strike a very thin gold foil **F**. While most of the α particles go straight through the foil as if there were nothing there, some of them collide with atoms of the foil and bounce off at some angle. The latter phenomenon is known as **Rutherford scattering.**

The observations and measurements made in the experiment consisted of counting the number of particles scattered off at different angles θ. This was done by the scintillation method of observation. Each α particle striking the fluorescent screen **S** produces a tiny flash of light, called a **scintillation,** and is observed as such by the microscope **M**. With the microscope fixed in one position the number of scintillations observed within a period of several minutes was counted, then the microscope was turned to another angle and the number again counted for an equal period of time.

In the schematic diagram of Fig. B, α particles are shown passing through a foil three atomic layers thick. Although the nuclear atom was not known at the time the experiments were performed, each atom is drawn in the figure with the positively charged nu-

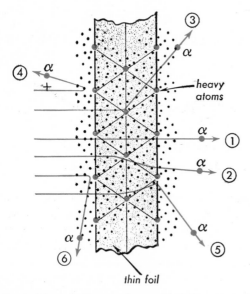

Fig. B. Schematic diagram of α particle being scattered by the atomic nuclei in a thin metallic film.

pelled by the heavy positively charged nucleus and deflected in such a way as to make it follow a curved path. The magnitude of the repulsive force is at all times given by Coulomb's law.

$$F = k \frac{QQ'}{r^2} \qquad (1)$$

The potential energy between electric charges is analogous to the potential energy of a body in mechanics, for just as we multiply the force **F** by the distance moved **d** to get potential energy in mechanics, so in electrostatics we multiply the force **F** by the distance **r** between the charges to get the potential energy **PE**. Multiplying Eq. (1) by **r** gives

potential energy

$$PE = k \frac{QQ'}{r} \qquad (2)$$

cleus at the center and surrounded by a number of electrons. Since most of the film is **free space,** the majority of the α particles go through with little or no deflection as indicated by ray (1). Other α's like (2) passing relatively close to an atom nucleus are deflected at an angle of a few degrees. Occasionally, however, an almost **head-on collision** occurs as shown by (4) and the incoming α particle is turned back toward the source.

Repeated experiments with different films made of light and heavy elements like copper, silver, and gold showed that the relative number of the wide-angled deflections increases with atomic weight. From all of these results and numerous calculations, Rutherford came to the following conclusions: **(1) that all of the positive charge of an atom is confined to a particle smaller than 10^{-12} cm in diameter; (2) that practically all of the weight of an atom is confined to this same particle; and (3) that the amount of positive charge in atomic units is approximately equal to half the atomic weight.**

As an α particle approaches an atom, as represented by ray (6) in Fig. B, it is re-

The reason for giving this equation, and the potential energy curve in Fig. C, is that from it an interesting mechanical model for demonstrating Rutherford scattering can be derived. Such a model is illustrated in Fig. D, where the circular peak at the right represents the nucleus of an atom and has a form generated by rotating the curve of Fig. C, about its vertical axis at **r** = 0.

Marbles, representing α particles, roll down a chute and along a practically level

Fig. C. Potential energy curve for two positive charges at close range.

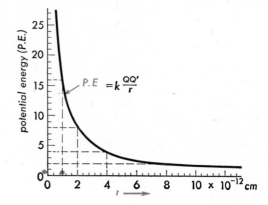

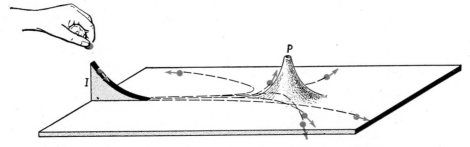

Fig. D. Mechanical model of an atomic nucleus for demonstrating Rutherford scattering.

plane where they approach the potential hill. Approaching the hill at various angles the marbles roll up to a certain height and then off to one side or the other. The paths they follow, if watched from above, are hyperbolic in shape. Approaching the hill in a head-on collision, the ball rolls up to a certain point, stops, then rolls back again. Thus the potential energy of the α particle close to the nucleus is analogous to the potential energy of a marble on the hillside, and the electrostatic force of repulsion is analogous to the downhill component of the downward pull of gravity. In a later lesson this same model is used to demonstrate the disintegration of atomic nuclei.

Bohr's Theory of the Hydrogen Atom. In 1913 Niels Bohr* proposed a theory of the hydrogen atom which marked the begin-

* Niels Bohr (1885-   ), Danish physicist, was born at Copenhagen, the son of Christian Bohr, professor of physiology at the University of Copenhagen. After taking his Ph.D. degree at Copenhagen in 1911 he studied for one year under J. J. Thomson at Cambridge, and one year under Ernest Rutherford at Manchester. Returning to Copenhagen in 1913, with the results of the Rutherford scattering experiments fresh in his mind, he worked out and published his now famous theory of the hydrogen atom. In 1920 Bohr was appointed head of the institute for theoretical physics at the University of Copenhagen. In 1921 he was awarded the Hughes Medal of the Royal Society and in 1922 the Nobel Prize in physics. Today he is the most honored Danish scientist and the father of a fine family. In 1937 he proposed the waterdrop theory of the atomic nucleus, which, at the time this is being written, is meeting with considerable experimental confirmation.

ning of a new era in the history of physics. With his theory Bohr gave not only a satisfactory explanation of the Balmer series of hydrogen but a model for the structure of all other atoms as well.

Starting with what should be the simplest of all atoms, Bohr assumed that a hydrogen atom, $Z = 1$, consists of a nucleus with one positive charge $+e$ and a single electron of charge $-e$ revolving around it in a circular orbit of radius r (see Fig. E). Because it is 1840 times heavier than the electron, the nucleus could be assumed at rest.

To keep the electron in its orbit and prevent it from spiraling in toward the nucleus, or away from it to escape, Bohr next assumed that the inward centripetal force is due to and, therefore, is the inward electrostatic force E. From Eq. (7), p. 140, the centripetal force is mv^2/r, and from Cou-

Fig. E. Orbital diagram of the hydrogen atom according to the Bohr theory.

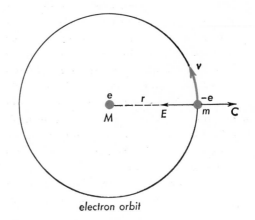

electron orbit

lomb's law, Eq. (1), p. 366, the electrostatic force is kee/r^2. Equating these two, we obtain

$$m\frac{v^2}{r} = k\frac{ee}{r^2} \qquad (3)$$

At this point Bohr introduced his second assumption, **the quantum hypothesis.** The electron, he assumed, cannot move in any sized orbit, stable under the conditions of the equation above, but in just certain **definite and discrete orbits.** The sizes of these orbits are governed by Eq. (3) and the rule that **the angular momentum of the electron in its orbit is equal to an integer n times a constant h divided by 2π.**

$$mvr = n\frac{h}{2\pi} \qquad (4)$$

In this equation **n** is called the principal **quantum number** and, because it can take only whole number values 1, 2, 3, 4, etc., it fixes the sizes of the allowed orbits. To find the radii of these "Bohr circular orbits," Eq. (4) is solved for **v**, then squared and substituted in Eq. (3) to give

$$r = \frac{n^2h^2}{4\pi^2me^2k} \qquad (5)$$

Putting into this equation the known values of the constants **e, m, h,** and **k,**

$$e = -1.60 \times 10^{-19} \text{ coulomb}$$
$$m = 9.10 \times 10^{-31} \text{ kg}$$
$$h = 6.62 \times 10^{-34} \text{ joule sec}$$
$$k = 9 \times 10^9 \text{ newton meters}^2/\text{coulomb}^2$$

the orbits shown in Fig. F are calculated. The innermost orbit, with **n** = 1, has a radius **r** = 0.000,000,000,0528 m, or 0.528 A, and a diameter of 1.06 A. A stands for a very small unit of length called the **angstrom.**

$$1 \text{ meter} = 10^{10} \text{ angstroms}$$

The second orbit is four times as large, and

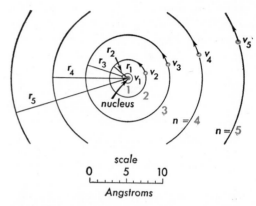

Fig. F. Scale diagram of the Bohr circular orbits of hydrogen.

the third is nine times, etc. The constant **h** is **Planck's constant.**

The velocity of the electron, when it is in any one orbit, can be determined from Eq. (4). In the innermost orbit, **n** = 1, the velocity **v** is 1/137 the velocity of light. In the second orbit the speed is only half as great, and in the third only one-third as great, etc. With such small orbits and such high velocities, the number of revolutions per second becomes very high. In the second orbit the frequency is calculated to be 10^{15} rps. This, by comparison with the frequency of vibration of visible light waves, is of the same order of magnitude.

It should be noted that the one and only electron in each hydrogen atom can occupy only one orbit at any one time. If the electron changes its orbit, it must move to one of the allowed orbits and never stop in between.

Fig. G. Schematic diagram of Bohr's quantum hypothesis of the radiation of light from an hydrogen atom.

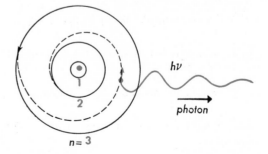

Electron-Jumps. Bohr's third and final assumption regarding the hydrogen atom concerns the emission of light. Bohr postulated that light is not emitted by an electron when it is moving in one of its fixed orbits, but only when the electron jumps from one orbit to another, as illustrated in Fig. G. The frequency of this light, he said, is not determined by the frequency of revolution but by the difference in energy between the initial and final orbit,

$$E_2 - E_1 = h\nu \qquad (6)$$

where E_2 is the energy of the **initial orbit, E_1** the energy of the **final orbit, h** is Planck's constant, and ν is the frequency of the light.

To illustrate this, let E_1, E_2, E_3, E_4, etc., represent the total energy of the electron when it is in the orbits $n = 1, 2, 3, 4$, etc., respectively. When, for example, the electron is in orbit $n = 3$ where its energy is E_3, and it jumps to orbit $n = 2$ where the energy is E_2 (see Fig. G), the energy difference $E_3 - E_2$ is ejected from the atom in the form of a light wave of energy $h\nu$ called a **photon.** Here then is the origin of light waves from within the atom.

Summary

The Bohr model of the hydrogen atom consists of a nucleus with a single electron revolving around it in a circular orbit.

The centripetal force necessary to keep the electron in its orbit is attributed to the attractive force of the positively charged nucleus (a single proton) for the negatively charged electron.

The electron cannot move in just any size of orbit; it must move in definite and discrete orbits only. These allowed orbits are given by the quantum condition that the orbital angular momentum is exactly equal to a whole number n times unit angular momentum $h/2\pi$.

The quantum number $n = 1, 2, 3, 4$, etc., for the different orbits.

For a hydrogen atom to emit light its single electron must jump from a larger orbit to a smaller one. The difference in energy between the two orbits is radiated as a light quantum, or photon $h\nu$.

Questions

1. What were the Rutherford scattering experiments? What conclusions were drawn from these early experiments?

2. Can you describe a mechanical device or experiment that simulates the scattering of alpha particles by an atomic nucleus?

3. What was Bohr's first assumption regarding the structure of a hydrogen atom?

4. What was Bohr's assumption regarding the centripetal force of an electron in a circular orbit?

5. What was Bohr's second assumption? What is the principal quantum number?

6. What are the relative diameters of the Bohr circular orbits given by $n = 1, 2, 3$, and 4?

7. What is an electron jump? How is such a process related to the emission of light?

8. If an electron jumps from orbit $n = 2$ to orbit $n = 1$ and the emitted light meets an-other hydrogen atom with its electron in orbit $n = 1$, what would happen in this second atom?

Problems

1. Find the diameter of the first four circular orbits of hydrogen according to the Bohr theory.

2. What would be the approximate quantum number n for a circular orbit of hydrogen 0.0001 mm in diameter? This would be just big enough to see under a microscope.

3. What would be the approximate quantum number n for a circular orbit of hydrogen 1 mm in diameter?

4.* (a) Solve Eq. (3) for r as the only unknown.
    (b) Solve Eq. (4) for r as the only unknown.
5.* Set the right-hand sides of the equations obtained in Problem 4 equal to each other and solve for v as the unknown quantity.
6.* Using this equation for v and the known values of e, m, h, and k, calculate the electrons' velocity in the first Bohr circular orbit.

Quantum Optics | **Lesson 2**

ELECTRON SHELL STRUCTURE

The success of Bohr's theory is not to be attributed so much to the mechanical picture or model of the atom just proposed but rather to the development of an equation which agrees exactly with experimental observations.

By continuing the equations presented in the preceding lesson, Bohr derived an equation for the frequency v of the light waves, or photons, emitted by hydrogen atoms. This equation is

$$v = 3.28810 \times 10^{15} \left(\frac{1}{n_1^2} - \frac{1}{n_2^2} \right) \quad (1)$$

where n_1 and n_2 represent the **principal quantum numbers** of two orbits.

If we introduce the wave equation, valid for all waves,

$$c = v\lambda \quad (2)$$

and replace v by c/λ, where c is the speed of light, Eq. (1) can be written

$$\lambda = 9.1176 \times 10^{-6} \left(\frac{n_2^2 \times n_1^2}{n_2^2 - n_1^2} \right) \quad (3)$$

where λ is the wave length of the light in **centimeters**, n_2 is the quantum number of any orbit of the hydrogen atom in which an electron is confined, and n_1 is the quantum number of the orbit to which the electron jumps to emit light of wave length λ.

Bohr found that if in Eq. (3) he placed $n_1 = 2$ and $n_2 = 3$, the calculated wave length $\lambda = 0.000065647$ cm is exactly equal to the measured wave length of the red spectrum line of hydrogen. See Fig. D, p. 461. If he placed $n_1 = 2$ and $n_2 = 4$, the calculated wave length agreed exactly with the meas-

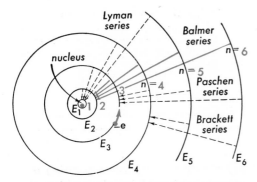

Fig. A. Diagram of the Bohr circular orbits of hydrogen showing the various electron jumps giving rise to the emission of light waves of different frequency.

observing the light through a spectroscope one may observe the entire Balmer series of lines.

Bohr's Predicted Series. Bohr's orbital model of the hydrogen atom not only accounts for the Balmer series of hydrogen, but also for many other observed lines as well.

By substituting $n_1 = 1$ and $n_2 = 2, 3, 4$, etc., in Eq. (3), one obtains a series of spectrum lines in the ultraviolet region of the spectrum. These lines were first photographed by T. Lyman of Harvard University, and the wave lengths are found to check exactly with calculations. This series, now called the Lyman series, which can only be photographed in a vacuum spectrograph, is reproduced in Fig. B. On the orbital picture of Fig. A, the Lyman series of lines arises from electron jumps from any outer orbit directly to the innermost orbit, the **normal state.**

If in Eq. (3), n_1 is set equal to 3 and n_2 to 4, 5, 6, etc., the calculated frequencies predict spectrum lines in the infrared spectrum. These lines were first looked for and observed, exactly as predicted, by F. Paschen, and the series is now known by his name. Another series of lines arising from electron jumps, ending on orbit $n = 4$, was predicted and observed in the far infrared by Brackett.

ured wave length of the blue-green spectrum line of hydrogen.

In fact the entire series of lines in the hydrogen spectrum are exactly represented by Eq. (3), by setting $n_1 = 2$ and $n_2 = 3, 4, 5$, 6, etc. This series of lines, so prominently displayed by the sun and stars, as well as by any hydrogen discharge tube in the laboratory, is known as the **Balmer series.**

These quantum number changes correspond, as shown in Fig. A, to an electron jumping from any outer orbit n to the next to the smallest orbit $n = 2$. In any high-voltage electrical discharge in a glass tube containing hydrogen gas, many thousands of atoms may each have their one and only electron jumping from orbit 3 to 2, while in many other atoms the electron may be jumping from other orbits to $n = 2$. Hence, upon

Normal and Excited Atoms. When the single electron of an hydrogen atom is in the

Fig. B. Photograph of the extreme ultraviolet series of hydrogen predicted by Bohr's theory and first observed by Lyman.

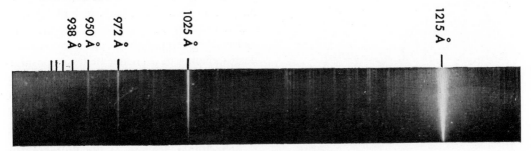

Lyman series of hydrogen

innermost orbit, $n = 1$, the atom is said to be in its normal state. As the name implies, this is the condition of most free hydrogen atoms in a gas under normal room temperature and pressure. If an electrical discharge is sent through a vessel containing hydrogen gas, cathode rays (electrons) moving at high speed make frequent collisions with electrons, knocking some of them out of the atom completely and some of them into one of the outer allowed orbits, $n = 2, 3, 4$, etc.

When the electron is completely removed from the atom, the atom is said to be **ionized;** whereas when it is forced into an outer orbit, the atom is said to be excited. Once in an excited state an atom will not remain that way long, for the electron under the attraction by the nucleus will jump to an inner orbit. By jumping to an inner orbit the electron loses all or part of the energy it had gained.

When an electron is in an excited state, it does not necessarily return to the innermost orbit by a single jump, but may return by several jumps, thereby emitting several different light waves, or quanta.

The Thomson Atom. Early in the twentieth century, while Rutherford, Geiger, and Marsden were doing their experiments on the scattering of α rays by thin metallic films, J. J. Thomson proposed a type of electron shell structure for all atoms. His model structures were worked out by mathematics from

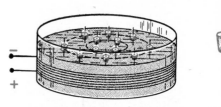

Fig. D. Floating needles in magnetic field demonstrating electron shell structure of Thomson atom.

Coulomb's law for charged particles and soon became known as the **plum-pudding atom.**

Thomson visualized all the positive charge of an atom as being spread out uniformly throughout a sphere about 10^{-8} cm in diameter, with the electrons as smaller particles distributed in shells somewhat as shown in Fig. C. While the net force exerted by the positively charged sphere on each electron is toward the center of the sphere, the electrons mutually repel each other and form rings.

An excellent demonstration of the tendency to form rings can be obtained as shown in Fig. D. A glass dish 15 to 20 cm in diameter is wound with about 30 turns of No. 14, insulated copper wire. The most common steel sewing needles are then mounted in small corks (8 mm diam. and 8 mm long) as shown at the left, and magnetized by stroking from top to bottom with the **N** pole of a strong Alnico magnet.

With water in the dish, and a current of 1 to 2 amperes through the coil, a single needle is placed upright in the water. Released it will migrate to the center where the magnetic field is strongest. The addition of needles, one after another, near the edge of the dish will result in the formation of geometrically symmetrical patterns and rings.

An increase or decrease in current will cause any given pattern to shrink or expand, corresponding to a greater or lesser positive charge. The stability of such ring patterns undoubtedly influenced the later extension by Bohr and Stoner of the quantized orbit model of the hydrogen atom to all atoms.

Bohr-Stoner Scheme of the Building Up of Atoms. Bohr and Stoner proposed an

Fig. C. Diagram of the Thomson atom model.

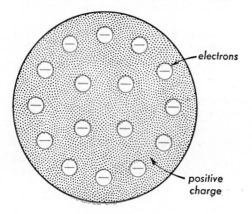

electrons

positive charge

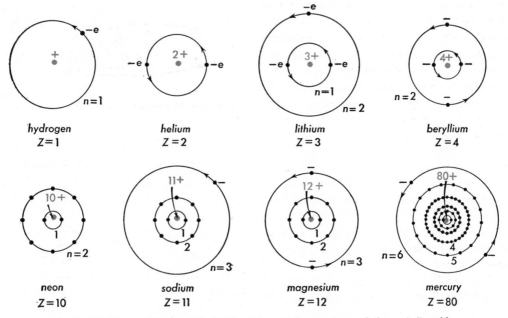

hydrogen
Z=1

helium
Z=2

lithium
Z=3

beryllium
Z=4

neon
Z=10

sodium
Z=11

magnesium
Z=12

mercury
Z=80

Fig. E. Bohr-Stoner orbital models for the light and heavy atoms of the periodic table.

extension of the orbital model of hydrogen to include all of the chemical elements. As shown by the examples in Fig. E, each atom is composed of a positively charged nucleus with a number of electrons around it.

Although the nucleus is a relatively small particle less than 10^{-12} cm in diameter, it contains almost the entire mass of the atom, a mass equal in **atomic mass units** to the **atomic weight**. *The positive charge carried by the nucleus is equal numerically to the atomic number, and it determines the number of electrons located in orbits outside.* A helium atom, atomic number **Z** =2, has two positve charges on the nucleus and two electrons outside. A lithium atom, atomic number **Z** = 3, contains three positive charges on the nucleus and three electrons outside. A mercury atom, atomic number 80, contains 80 positive charges on the nucleus and 80 electrons outside.

The orbits to which the electrons are confined are the Bohr orbits of hydrogen with **n** = 1, 2, 3, etc., and are called electron shells. Going from element to element in the

atomic table, starting with hydrogen, electrons are added one after the other, filling one shell and then another. A shell is filled only when it contains a number of electrons given by 2 n^2. To illustrate this, the first shell **n** = 1 is filled when it has 2 electrons, the second shell **n** = 2 when it has 8 electrons, the third shell **n** = 3 when it has 18 electrons, etc. 2 $\times$ $1^2 = 2$, 2 $\times$ $2^2 = 8$, 2 $\times$ $3^2 = 18$, etc.

quantum number	$n = 1$	$n = 2$	$n = 3$	$n = 4$
number of electrons	2	8	18	32

Among the heavier elements there are several departures from the order in which the shells are filled. Although these departures are not important from the present standpoint, their nature is illustrated by the mercury atom, Fig. E. The four inner shells **n** = 1, 2, 3, and 4, are entirely filled with 2, 8, 18, and 32 electrons, respectively, while the fifth shell contains only 18 electrons and the sixth shell 2 electrons. The reasons for such departures are now well understood and are indicative of the chemical behavior of the heavy elements.

It is important to note that, as the nuclear charge increases and additional electrons are added in outer shells, the inner shells, under the stronger attraction by the nucleus, shrink in size. The net result of this shrinkage is that the heaviest elements in the periodic table are not much larger in diameter than the lighter elements. The schematic diagrams in Fig. E are drawn approximately to the same scale.

The experimental confirmation of these upper limits to the allowed number of electrons in each shell is now considered one of the most fundamental principles of nature. A sound theoretical explanation of this principle of atomic structure was first given by W. Pauli in 1925 and is commonly referred to as the **Pauli exclusion principle.**

Spinning Atomic Particles. Careful studies of the spectrum lines arising from various kinds of atoms led to the proposal in 1925, by the two Dutch physicists Goudsmit and

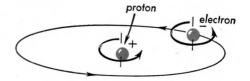

Fig. F. The electron and proton both spin around an axis through their center.

Uhlenbeck, that all electrons are spinning like a top. Now it is known that both electrons and protons spin about an axis, much the same as the earth spins about its polar axis, and that each one has angular momentum.

$$\text{angular momentum} = \frac{1}{2}\frac{h}{2\pi}$$

where

$$h = 6.62 \times 10^{-34} \text{ joule sec}$$

A schematic diagram of the spinning proton and electron of the hydrogen atom is shown in Fig. F.

Summary

Bohr's theory of circular electron orbits for the hydrogen atom results in an equation for the frequencies and wave lengths of the light hydrogen atoms can emit.

By simply inserting two whole numbers, called quantum numbers, into his equation the wave length of any and all of the observed spectrum lines of hydrogen can be calculated with extremely high precision.

Bohr's formula for the hydrogen spectrum not only accounted for the Balmer series of lines but predicted other lines in the ultraviolet and infrared spectrum. These lines were looked for and found later, exactly as predicted.

The single electron in a normal hydrogen atom is in the innermost allowed orbit, or state, for which the quantum number $n = 1$. By collision in an electrical discharge the electron may be made to occupy momentarily one of the outer orbits, $n = 2, 3, 4$, etc. When the electron jumps back toward the innermost orbit, its normal state, light is emitted.

The assignment of electrons to the different quantized orbits to build up the structure of the other elements of the periodic table is similar to the Thomson shell model. According to the Bohr-Stover scheme the various shells are limited by fixed numbers of electrons.

Every electron and every proton spins around an axis through its center, with a fixed angular momentum

$$\frac{1}{2}\frac{h}{2\pi}$$

Questions

1. What is the Balmer series of hydrogen? What particular electron jump gives rise to the red spectrum line?

2. What is the Lyman series of hydrogen? Are these wave lengths in the visible spectrum? What electron jump is responsible for the longest wave length of the series?

3. What is the Paschen series of hydrogen? Are these wave lengths of light in the visible spectrum?

4. What is an excited atom? What is an ionized atom? What is the normal state of hydrogen?

5. What was the form of the Thomson atom? Where did he locate the positive charges? Where did he locate the negative charges?

6. What is a spinning electron? What is a spinning proton? Should such particles produce a magnetic field?

7. What is the Bohr-Stoner scheme of the building up of atoms? How does it differ from the Thomson atom?

8. How many electrons can each shell have? What is the formula?

Problems

1. Calculate the wave length of the third line of the Balmer series of hydrogen.

2. Find the wave lengths of the fourth and fifth lines of the Balmer series of hydrogen.

3. Compute the wave lengths of the first three lines of the Lyman series of hydrogen.

4. Find the wave lengths of the first three lines of the Paschen series of hydrogen.

5. Make a diagram of a zinc atom (atomic number 30) according to the Bohr-Stoner scheme.

6. Make a diagram of a krypton atom (atomic number 36) according to the Bohr-Stoner scheme.

7. Calculate the angular momentum of a spinning electron.

Quantum Optics | **Lesson 3**

PHOTON COLLISIONS AND ATOMIC WAVES

In the preceding lessons we have seen that light waves consist of small finite bundles of energy called **quanta** or **photons,** and that they too, like atomic particles, may be made to collide with atoms of one kind or another. This was the case both in the **photoelectric effect,** Electronics, Lesson 5, p. 494, and in the production of **X rays,** Lesson 7, p.

464. The first part of the present lesson deals with the **corpuscular nature of light** and the last part with the **wave nature of atomic particles.**

This last statement suggests a sort of "Dr. Jekyll and Mr. Hyde" existence for light waves as well as for atoms. Under some conditions light and atoms may both act as though they were waves, whereas under other conditions they may both act like small particles.

The Photoelectric Effect with X Rays. When a beam of X rays is allowed to shine on the surface of a thin sheet of metal, like gold, an interesting phenomenon may be observed to take place. Acting like particles, they may collide with atoms and eject electrons as in the photoelectric effect.

Even though a beam of X rays may contain waves with the same frequency, not all of the ejected photoelectrons acquire the same velocity, but are divided into several well-defined groups. These groups are illustrated schematically by the lengths of the arrows in Fig. A.

Careful measurements of the velocities of the photoelectrons, first made by Robinson and his collaborators in 1914, have shown that each velocity group is to be associated with the various shells of electrons within the

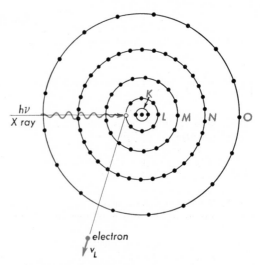

Fig. B. Detail of an X ray ejecting an electron from the **L** shell in a heavy atom.

atoms. The slowest electrons, all with the same velocity v_K, are ejected from the innermost or **K**-shell, the next faster group with a velocity v_L from the second shell out, the **L**-shell, the next group with a velocity v_M from the **M**-shell, etc. See Fig. B.

The closer an electron is to the nucleus, the greater is the attracting force and the greater is the force and energy necessary to liberate it from the atom. The velocity of the electrons in each group is given by Einstein's photoelectric equation,

$$h\nu = W + \tfrac{1}{2}mv^2 \qquad (1)$$

where **W**, the work function, is the energy necessary to free an electron from any one of the different electron shells.

The Compton Effect. While making a spectroscopic study of scattered X rays in 1923, A. H. Compton discovered a new phenomenon now known as the Compton effect. After considerable controversy with other experimenters Compton proved quite conclusively that an X ray may collide with an electron and bounce off with reduced energy in another direction. This is analogous to the collision between two billiard balls.

Fig. A. The photoelectric effect with X rays experimentally establishes the existence of electron shells.

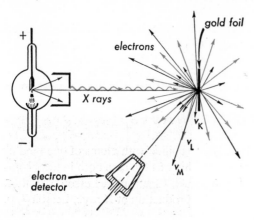

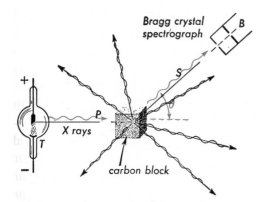

Fig. C. Diagram of Compton's experiment with X rays.

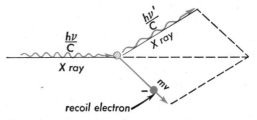

Fig. D. Momentum diagram for the collision between an X-ray photon and an electron. The Compton effect.

Compton's historic experiment is illustrated in Fig. C. X rays from a tube **T** were made to strike one face of a small carbon block and scatter out in various directions. With an X ray spectrograph at one side of the block he measured the wave length of the X rays **S** scattered in a direction θ. These wave lengths he then compared with those of the incident beam **P** and found that some of the scattered X rays have changed their wave length whereas others have not. He also found that as the angle increased, the change in wave length of the modified rays increased.

To explain the modified wave lengths, Compton invoked the quantum theory of light and proposed that a single X-ray photon acting as a material particle may collide with an electron and recoil as though it were a perfectly elastic sphere.

The fact that a beam of light has the equivalent of a momentum **mv**, and can exert a pressure on a wall on which it falls, has long been known. According to the quantum theory the momentum of a single photon is given by its energy **hν** divided by the velocity of light **c**,

$$\text{momentum of a photon} = h\nu/c \qquad (2)$$

Compton's experiment is considered a proof of this equation. The momentum of the X ray before impact is **hν/c**, while its momen-

tum after impact is **hν'/c**, and the momentum of the electron is **mv**. See Fig. D.

The discovery and early observations of the Compton effect were confined to the change in wave length of the scattered X rays and not to the recoiling electrons predicted by theory. Compton's success is to be attributed to the exact agreement he found between the wave-length shift calculated from his application of the quantum theory and the values measured by experiment.

The first discoveries of the recoil electrons from the Compton effect were made by C. T. R. Wilson, and by Bothe and Becker. The existence of these collision products is readily shown by sending a beam of X rays through a Wilson cloud chamber just prior to its expansion. The result is a photograph similar to the one reproduced in Fig. E.

De Broglie's Electron-Waves. In 1924 De Broglie, a French theoretical physicist, derived an equation predicting that all atomic particles have associated with them waves of a definite wave length. In other words, a beam of electrons or atoms should, under the proper experimental conditions, act like a

Fig. E. Recoil electrons from X rays passing through the air in a Wilson cloud chamber. The Compton effect. (After C. T. R. Wilson)

X-ray

beam

train of light waves or a beam of photons. The wave length of these waves, as predicted by De Broglie, depends upon the mass and velocity of the particles according to the following relations:

$$\lambda = \frac{h}{mv} \tag{3}$$

This is known as **De Broglie's wave equation.** For an electron moving at high speed the denominator **mv** is large and the wave length is small. In other words, the faster an electron moves, the shorter is the wave length associated with it.

The Davisson-Germer Experiment. The first experimental proof of the wave nature of atomic particles was demonstrated in 1927 by two American physicists, C. J. Davisson and his collaborator, L. H. Germer. Their experiment is illustrated schematically in Fig. F. Electrons from a hot cathode are accelerated toward an anode, where, upon passing through a system of pinholes, they

Fig. F. The Davisson-Germer experiment. Electrons striking the surface layers of a crystal are diffracted at different angles just as if they were waves with a very short wave length.

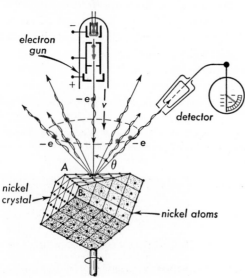

emerge as a narrow beam as indicated. This source acts as an **electron gun** from which electrons of any desired velocity may be obtained by applying the proper potential **V.**

Upon striking one of the polished faces of a nickel crystal, the equally spaced rows of atoms in the crystal act like the lines of a diffraction grating, and the electrons, acting like waves, are diffracted off in certain preferred directions. The electron wave length is given by Eq. (3) and the preferred directions by $\lambda = 2\,d\,\sin\,\theta$. These preferred directions are located by means of a detector in which the electrons are collected and their accumulated charge measured. The detector is mounted so that it may be turned to any angle θ and the crystal is mounted so it may be turned about an axis parallel to the incident beam.

Electron Waves Within the Atom. The most recent development in the theory of atomic structure has shown that the Bohr picture of the atom with sharply defined electron orbits is not correct. The new theory does not discard the Bohr theory entirely but only modifies it to the extent that the electron does not behave as though it were a particle. The electron behaves as if it were made up of waves of the type described in the previous sections.

One method of representing the electron in the atom is to picture an electron wave as one having a considerable length so that it extends around the atom far enough to overlap and form standing waves. These may be illustrated schematically as shown in Fig. G.

Fig. G. Schematic diagram of the waves of the orbital electron in a hydrogen atom.

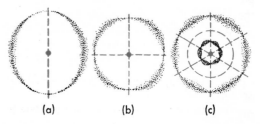

(a)   (b)   (c)

In the first figure there are two radial nodes, in the second four radial nodes, and in the third six radial nodes and one spherical node. In this representation the electron is not thought of as a particle located at some point within the atom but as though its mass and charge were spread out symmetrically throughout the space immediately surrounding the nucleus of the atom. It is interesting to point out that while the Bohr circular orbits were confined to a plane, the wave model allows the electron distribution to be three-dimensional.

To set up these standing waves, the length of the path of an electron around the hydrogen nucleus must be a whole number of wave lengths. The circumference of a circle is $2\pi r$,

$$\text{circumference} = 2\pi r \qquad (4)$$

Since this distance must be exactly equal to λ, 2λ, 3λ, etc., or $n\lambda$, we can write

$$n\lambda = 2\pi r$$

where $n = 1, 2, 3$, etc. Upon substituting the De Broglie wave length, Eq. (3), we obtain

$$n\frac{h}{mv} = 2\pi r \qquad (5)$$

which upon transposing, gives

$$\boxed{2\pi r \times mv = nh} \qquad (6)$$

This is exactly the condition proposed by Bohr in his orbital theory presented in Eq. (4), p. 512. It is not surprising, therefore, that the new theory also gives exactly the Bohr equations for the wave lengths and the frequencies of the hydrogen spectrum.

Summary

In some experiments light waves behave like particles with a definite amount of momentum, and upon collision with atomic particles like electrons they exert impulses. In other experiments atomic particles behave like waves of definite wave length and exhibit diffraction.

The photoelectric effect produced by X-ray waves as they pass through a solid material reveals the shell-like structure of atoms by the grouped velocities of the ejected electrons.

X rays colliding with free electrons rebound much the same as in the collision between two billiard balls. Having lost some energy by the collision the recoiling X ray has a lower frequency. The momentum of a photon is $h\nu/c$.

The wave length associated with every moving atomic particle is given by the De Broglie wave equation,

$$\lambda = \frac{h}{mv}$$

A beam of atomic particles passing through a crystal is diffracted and produces a pattern similar to those produced by X rays.

The orbital electrons in atoms have wave properties. The overlapping of these waves set up standing waves with nodes and loops with definite spacings.

Questions

1. What experiments are considered proof of the shell structure of atoms?

2. What happens to the X-ray wave that ejects a photoelectron from a solid?

3. What happens to the X ray that ejects a Compton electron from a solid?

4. Do light waves have momentum? Could you write down the formula for such a momentum?

5. What is the De Broglie wave equation? Write down the equation.

6. What was the Davisson-Germer experiment?

7. In what way do the wave properties of electrons modify the Bohr theory of circular orbits in hydrogen?

Problems

1. Calculate the momentum of an X ray having a wave length of 1×10^{-10} meter.

2. Compute the wave length associated with an electron moving with one-tenth the speed of light.

3. Compute the wave length of a proton moving with one-tenth the speed of light.

4.* If the electron beam in a TV picture tube is accelerated by 10,000 volts, what is the De Broglie wave length?

5. What would be the De Broglie wave length of a 2000-kg car moving along the highway at 30 m/sec?

6. Draw standing wave diagrams to scale for the first three Bohr orbits of hydrogen.

7.* (a) Find the De Broglie wave length for the electron in the first circular orbit of hydrogen. (b) How is this related to the orbit circumference?

8.* Derive an equation for the De Broglie wave length of the electron in the different Bohr circular orbits of hydrogen. (See Quantum Optics, Lesson 1, for orbit radii.)

Quantum Optics | **Lesson 4**

ELECTRON OPTICS

There exists a remarkable similarity between optical systems of prisms and lenses as they act upon light rays, and electric and magnetic fields as they act upon streams of electrons. It is the purpose of this lesson to consider some of these similarities and to treat several practical applications of **electron optics.**

Refraction of Electrons. When a moving electron, entering an electric field, makes an angle with the electric lines of force, it is bent in its path according to **Bethe's law of refraction** (see Fig. A). A correlation of this law with Snell's law in optics (see Fig. B) is indicated by the following parallel equations.

Snell's law

$$\frac{\sin i}{\sin r} = \frac{v_1}{v_2}$$

Bethe's law

$$\frac{\sin \alpha}{\sin \beta} = \frac{v_2}{v_1} \qquad (1)$$

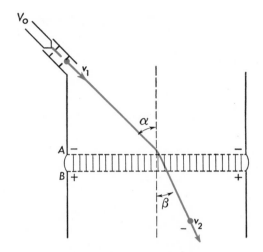

Fig. A. Refraction of electrons.

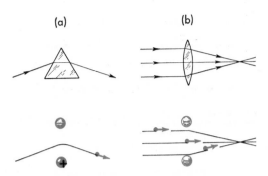

Fig. C. Comparison of light optics with electron optics.

electrons, keeping their speed the same, and they will retrace their paths exactly. Such a behavior is analogous to the very useful principle in geometrical optics that all light rays are retraceable.

Note the reverse order of the velocities v_1 and v_2. When a ray of light enters a more dense medium like glass it is slowed down and at the same time bent toward the normal. Electrons, on the other hand, are deflected toward the normal when, in crossing a potential layer, they are speeded up. If the grid potentials are reversed, the electrons will be retarded in crossing the potential layer and they will be deflected away from the normal. In other words, reverse the direction of the

To carry the refraction analogy a little further, consider the bending of electron paths by electrically charged bodies as shown above in Fig. C. Attraction by the positively charged wire and repulsion by the negative produces a prismlike action in case (a). A negatively charged metal ring produces a converging lenslike action in case (b).

Electron Lenses. An electron lens, known as a double-aperture system, is shown in Fig. D and is to be compared in its action to parallel rays of light incident on a converging glass lens as shown at the lower right. While both are converging systems, the essential difference between the two is that whereas

Fig. B. Refraction of light.

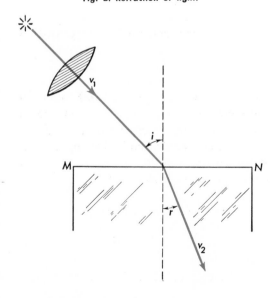

Fig. D. Double-aperture electron lens and its optical analogue.

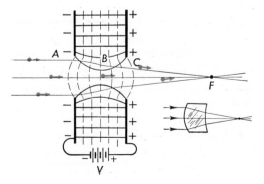

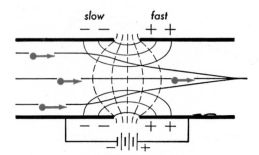

Fig. E. Symmetrical electron lens.

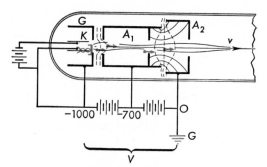

Fig. G. Electron gun.

light rays are bent only at the two surfaces, electrons are refracted continuously as they pass through the electric field between the two coaxial disks.

If the electrons are reversed in direction on the right, they will retrace their paths and emerge parallel at the left; but if the electric field is reversed in direction, the electron paths will not be the same but the system will still act as a converging lens.

A second type of electron lens, known as a double-cylinder system, is shown in Fig. E. In passing through the potential gap the electric field has a converging action for the first half of the distance and a diverging action during the second half. Because they spend a greater time in the first half of the converging field, and the force on a charged particle is independent of velocity, the impulse (force × time) is greater for the convergence interval than it is for the divergence interval.

By making the second cylinder larger than

Fig. F. Asymmetrical electron lens.

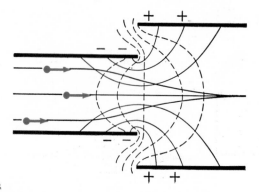

the first, as in Fig. F, the electric lines of force spread out more in the second cylinder. Such spreading weakens the field in the larger cylinder and reduces the divergent action to bring the electrons to a shorter focus.

An Electron Gun. A narrow beam of high-speed electrons, all having as nearly as possible the same velocity, has many practical applications in the field of electronics and atomic research. A device for producing such beams, mentioned in Electronics, Lesson 7, is called an *electron gun* (see Fig. G).

Electrons from a small filament-heated cathode **K** are accelerated by a difference of potential **V** applied to the cylinders of an electrostatic lens system A_1 and A_2. The purpose of the guard ring maintained at the potential of the cathode is to improve the properties of the lens action of the first aperture and thereby collect a maximum number of emitted electrons into the collimated beam.

The function of the second lens is to converge the bundle toward a focus and then introduce enough divergence to straighten the beam out into a narrow pencil. The velocity of the emergent beam is given by Eq. (7), p. 449, where **V** is the over-all voltage from cathode **K** to anode A_2.

The Cathode-Ray Oscilloscope. One of the simplest applications of an electron gun is to be found in every *cathode-ray oscilloscope,* an instrument whose purpose it is to reveal the detailed variations in rapidly

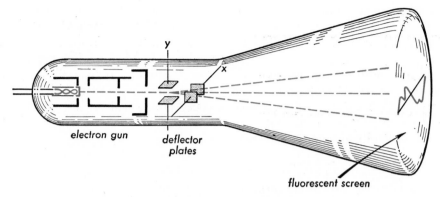

Fig. H. Cathode-ray oscilloscope.

changing electric currents, potentials, or pulses (see Fig. H). In appearance this device looks like J. J. Thomson's cathode-ray tube (see Fig. A, p. 448), and is actually the important element in one type of television picture tube.

A cathode-ray oscilloscope is a vacuum tube containing **an electron gun** at one end, two pairs of **deflector plates** (or magnetic coils) near the middle, and a **fluorescent screen** at the other end. When an alternating potential is applied to the **x-plates,** the electron beam bends back and forth from side to side and, when applied to the **y-plates,** it bends up and down. The luminous spot produced where the beam strikes the fluorescent screen traces out a horizontal line in the first instance and a vertical line in the second.

Magnetic Lenses. When electrons cross a magnetic field, and their paths make an angle with the magnetic lines, they are deflected in spiral-like paths which, if properly controlled, may bring them to a focus. Such focusing properties of magnetic fields, illustrated by the cross section of a flat-coil in Fig. I, were first demonstrated and proved mathematically by Busch in 1926. It can be shown that the focal length **f** of such a lens, the magnetic induction **B**, and the electron velocity **v**, fit into well-known formulas in optics.

By encasing a flat coil in a hollow iron ring the magnetic field becomes more concentrated and the refraction of electrons becomes more abrupt as they pass through the field. As a consequence the refraction more nearly resembles that of optical lenses. Still

Fig. I. Magnetic lens for electrons. (Optical analogue lower right.)

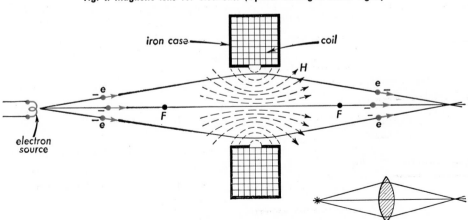

greater concentration is brought about by providing a small narrow gap on the inside of the iron casing as shown in the diagram.

Electron Microscope. The electron microscope, like the optical microscope, is an instrument used principally in the research laboratory for magnifying small objects to such an extent that their minutest parts may be observed and studied in detail.

Like the optical microscope it contains two principal lens elements: an objective lens for the initial magnification and an occular lens for the final magnification.

The importance of this device in the field of medical research cannot be overestimated. To illustrate, many viruses known to medical science as being responsible for certain human diseases lie beyond the range of the optical microscope. With the electron microscope, magnifications of from 10 to 100 times that of the finest optical microscopes make many of these viruses and some of their detailed structure observable. While the highest magnification obtained with the best optical microscope is about 2000X, electron microscopes have already been made that give magnifications as high as 100,000X.

Summary

The bending of electron beams as they cross an electric field is analogous to the refraction of light by an optically transparent medium.

Just as converging glass lenses are capable of bringing light rays to a focus, so electric fields can be designed to bring electrons to a focus. Such devices are called electron lenses.

Electron lenses are of two general types: (1) coaxial cylinders placed end to end and (2) coaxial disks, with circular holes, placed side by side.

Combinations of electron lenses are used to produce narrow intense beams of electrons by what is called an electron gun.

The cathode-ray oscilloscope is a frequently used electronic device in which a beam of electrons from an electron gun is deflected back and forth across a fluorescent screen with predetermined frequency. Varying electrical potentials to be studied are made visible on the screen by applying them to the vertical deflecting plates of the beam.

The electron microscope, capable of magnifications 10 to 100 times that of the best optical microscope, employs electron lenses.

Some electron lenses employ magnetic fields for their focusing action.

Questions

1. What is Bethe's law? In what way is it like Snell's law in optics? In what way is it different?

2. What kind of electric field will deviate an electron beam the way a glass prism deviates a light beam?

3. What are electron lenses? How are they made?

4. What is an electron gun? What can it be used for? Does it employ electron lenses?

5. What is a cathode ray oscilloscope? What is its purpose?

6. What are the principles of a magnetic lens?

7. What is an electron microscope? Is it capable of magnifying very small objects?

8. Can you think of some practical application for an electron gun other than its use in an oscilloscope?

Problems

1. Make a diagram of an electron gun, using two hollow tubes of the same diameter. Show the electric field and the paths of electrons in passing through.

2. Make a diagram of an electron gun, using two hollow tubes of different diameter. Show the electric field and electron paths. Reverse the potentials and assume a parallel beam again coming in from the left.

3. Make a diagram of an electron gun. Label the principal elements. Briefly describe its action.

4. Make a diagram of a cathode ray oscilloscope. Label the principal parts. Briefly describe its action.

5. Make a diagram of your idea of an electron microscope. Label the principal elements.

NUCLEAR PHYSICS

During the last few years Dr. Chadwick and I have obtained definite evidence that hydrogen nuclei or protons can be removed by bombardment of α particles from the elements boron, nitrogen, fluorine, sodium, aluminum and phosphorus. In these experiments the presence of H nuclei is detected by the scintillation method, and their maximum velocity of ejection can be estimated from the thickness of matter which can be penetrated by these particles. The number of H nuclei ejected even in the most favorable case is relatively very small compared with the number of bombarding α particles, viz., about one in a million.

Sir Ernest Rutherford: "The Natural and Artificial Disintegration of the Elements," *Journal of the Franklin Institute,* vol. 198, 1924, p. 736.

Before leaving this subject it is desirable to say a few words on the important question of the energy relations involved in the formation and disintegration of atomic nuclei, first opened up by the study of radioactivity. For example, it is well known that the total evolution of energy during the complete disintegration of one gram of radium is many millions of times greater than in the complete combustion of an equal weight of coal. . . . Since it is believed that the radioactive elements are analogous in structure to the ordinary inactive elements, the idea naturally arose that the atoms of all the elements contained a similar concentration of energy, which would be available for use if only some simple method could be discovered of promoting and controlling their disintegration. This possibility of obtaining new and cheap sources of energy for practical purposes was naturally an alluring prospect to the lay and scientific man alike.

Sir Ernest Rutherford: "The Electrical Structure of Matter," *Nature,* vol. 112, 1923, p. 417.

← The Oak Ridge National Laboratory's thermonuclear experimental machine in operation. An intense direct-current carbon arc runs through the length of the machine. When a beam of molecular ions passes through the arc, the molecular ions are broken into atomic ions. These atomic ions, held by a magnetic field, circulate in a glowing ring which may be seen through the side window of the machine.

Oak Ridge National Laboratory
Operated by Union Carbide Corporation
For the U. S. Atomic Energy Commission

Nuclear Disintegration

THE DISCOVERY of the disintegration and transmutation of stable elements by controlled experiments is attributed to the great experimental genius of Lord Rutherford. Some might say that the discovery was an accident, but to those who knew him well it was the result of a long series of well-planned experiments. True, he did not predict the phenomenon and then discover it, but his long experience with radioactivity and his keen insight enabled him to recognize the meaning and importance of the phenomenon when it was first observed. Due credit must also be given to the admirable work of his collaborators and to experimenters in other laboratories who have since carried the work much further.

Elastic Collisions Between Atoms. Collisions between free atomic particles were first studied by Rutherford with apparatus as shown in Fig. A. A long glass tube, containing a small sample of radioactive material **R**, was first thoroughly evacuated by means of a vacuum pump and then filled with a gas of known constitution. Alpha particles from the radioactive source were then permitted to travel through the gas to the other end of the tube, where, upon passing through a thin aluminum foil to a fluorescent screen **S**, they could be observed as scintillations in the field of view of a microscope. This is exactly the arrangement used by Rutherford in measuring the range of α particles from different

Fig. A. Rutherford's apparatus used in observing atomic collisions between α particles from radium and the atoms of a gas like hydrogen, helium, nitrogen, oxygen, etc.

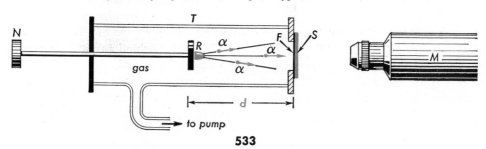

(a)   (b)

Fig. B. Wilson cloud-chamber photographs of collisions between α particles: (a) a hydrogen atom and (b) a helium atom. (After Rutherford, Chadwick, and Ellis)

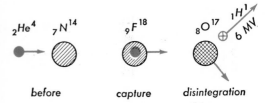

before   capture   disintegration

Fig. C. Illustrating the disintegration of a nitrogen nucleus by a high-speed α particle.

radioactive elements (see Atomic Physics, Lesson 8).

With air in the tube **T** and **radium C'** as a source of α particles, scintillations could be observed with the screen as far back as 7 cm. With hydrogen in the tube it was found that the distance **d** could be increased to 28 cm. The conclusion Rutherford drew from his result was that an α particle occasionally collides with a hydrogen atom, much the same as a large ball collides with a lighter one, imparting to it a greater velocity and hence a greater penetrating power.

A more convincing study of such atomic collisions can be made with a Wilson cloud chamber. Out of thousands of cloud chamber photographs of the ion tracks made by α particles from radioactive elements one occasionally observes forked tracks of the type reproduced in Fig. B. When each of these pictures was taken, the cloud chamber contained a different gas. For photograph (a), the cloud chamber contained hydrogen; for (b), it contained helium.

The Discovery of Nuclear Disintegration. Upon repeating the range experiments illustrated in Fig. A, with a heavy gas in the tube **T**, Rutherford in 1919 made a new and startling discovery. When nitrogen gas (atomic weight, 14) was admitted to the tube, scintil-

lations could be observed at a distance of 40 cm or more from the source.

Rutherford was not long in coming forward with the correct explanation of the phenomenon. An α particle, near the beginning of its range where its velocity is high, may make a "head-on" collision with a nitrogen nucleus and be captured. This capture is then followed immediately by a disintegration in which a proton is ejected with high speed. The process is illustrated in Fig. C, and the transformation can be represented by the following simple reaction.

$$_2He^4 + _7N^{14} = (_9F^{18}) = _8O^{17} + _1H^1 \qquad (1)$$

When the α particle with a charge of $+2$ and mass 4 collides with the nitrogen nucleus with a charge of $+7$ and mass 14, they form a single particle with a charge of $+9$ and mass 18. Since an atom with a nuclear charge of $+9$ would be expected to have all the chemical properties of **fluorine,** atomic number 9, the newly formed nucleus is labeled $_9F^{18}$.

An examination of the table of isotopes, however (see Appendix II), shows that no such isotope exists in nature. The reason becomes apparent when it is realized that such a combination of particles is not stable. A fluorine nucleus of mass 18 is unstable and disintegrates by discharging a proton, a particle with a charge of $+1$ and a mass of 1. This leaves behind a residual nucleus with a charge of $+8$ and a mass of 17. Under atomic number 8 in the same Appendix, an oxygen isotope of mass 17 is seen to have been found in nature.

Thus the above disintegration process

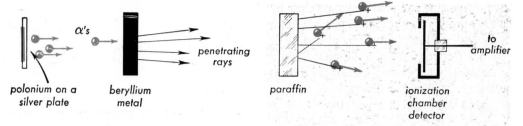

Fig. D. The experiment by which Chadwick discovered the neutron. The penetrating rays are neutrons and α rays.

started with two stable nuclei, **helium** and **nitrogen,** and out of them were created two new stable nuclei, **oxygen** and **hydrogen.** This is called a transmutation of elements. Because the intermediate step indicates but a momentary existence of a fluorine nucleus, $_9\mathbf{F}^{18}$, this step is often omitted from any discussion of the above process and the disintegration reaction simply written

$$_2\mathrm{He}^4 + _7\mathrm{N}^{14} = _8\mathrm{O}^{17} + _1\mathrm{H}^1 \qquad (2)$$

Such transformation reactions are like equations and must balance: first, the total amount of charge must remain the same, and second, the mass numbers must balance. The first of these is accomplished by having the sum of the subscripts on one side of the reaction equal to the sum of the subscripts on the other side, and the second by having the sum of the superscripts the same on both sides. In every known atom the subscript, representing the nuclear charge, is the sole factor determining the chemical element to which the atom belongs.

Chadwick's Identification of the Neutron. In 1932 Chadwick, in England, performed an experiment for which he was later awarded

the Nobel Prize in physics in 1935. As diagramed in Fig. D his experiment consisted of bombarding a beryllium target with α particles. Penetrating particles emerging from the beryllium were permitted to impinge upon a block of paraffin from which protons were found to emerge with high speed. From energy calculations he was able to show that the penetrating rays were uncharged particles with the mass of protons, and these he called **neutrons.** The disintegration taking place in the metal target is the following (see Fig. E):

$$_2\mathrm{He}^4 + _4\mathrm{Be}^9 = _6\mathrm{C}^{12} + _0\mathrm{n}^1 \qquad (3)$$

The α particle, $_2\mathbf{He}^4$, makes a collision and unites with a beryllium nucleus, $_4\mathbf{Be}^9$, causing a disintegration; whereupon a neutron, $_0\mathrm{n}^1$, is expelled with high velocity. The residual particle with a charge of $+6$ and mass of 12 units is a stable carbon nucleus such as found in nature.

The penetrating rays from the beryllium block in Fig. D are mostly neutrons which, in bombarding the paraffin block, collide elastically with some of the many hydrogen atoms, knocking them out on the other side. An elastic "head-on" collision between two particles of the same weight, like a neutron and proton, finds the entire velocity of one transferred to the other; the neutron is stopped and the proton goes on. The protons, having a positive charge, can be observed by their tracks in a Wilson cloud chamber, whereas neutrons cannot.

The reason fast neutrons have such a high penetrating power is that they are not slowed

Fig. E. Discovery of the neutron.

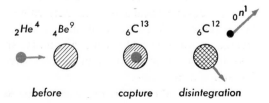

$_2\mathrm{He}^4 \quad _4\mathrm{Be}^9 \qquad _6\mathrm{C}^{13} \qquad _6\mathrm{C}^{12} \quad _0\mathrm{n}^1$

before   capture   disintegration

down by ionizing atoms as they pass close by them. A proton, electron, or α particle has a charge and can ionize atoms by attracting or repelling electrons from a distance, but a neutron without a charge cannot do this. It must make a direct collision with another particle to be slowed down or stopped.

The Nucleus Contains Neutrons and Protons. We now believe that the nucleus contains but two kinds of particles, neutrons and protons. Each neutron has a mass of one unit and no charge, whereas each proton has a mass of one unit and a positive charge of one unit.

Since only the proton has a charge, any given nucleus of atomic number Z and mass number M is now believed to have Z protons and $M-Z$ neutrons, and that in a neutral atom the number of protons is equal to the number of orbital electrons.

Schematic diagrams of the nuclei of five different atoms are given in Fig. F.

Mass Is a Form of Energy. Einstein, in working out the theory of relativity, arrived at a number of simple equations concerning the nature of the physical world. One of these equations has to do with mass as a form of energy. It is important at this point to consider this equation, since its proof can be demonstrated by, and is needed to explain, atomic disintegration experiments. The relation referred to is known as *Einstein's mass-energy equation.* In its simplest form it is written,

Fig. F. Diagrams showing the number of protons and neutrons in the nuclei of hydrogen, deuterium, helium, lithium, and oxygen.

$$_1H^1 \qquad _1H^2 \qquad _2He^4 \qquad _3Li^7 \qquad _8O^{16}$$

proton	deuteron	α particle	lithium	oxygen
$Z=1$	$Z=1$	$Z=2$	$Z=3$	$Z=8$
$M=1$	$M=2$	$M=4$	$M=7$	$M=16$

$$E = mc^2 \tag{3}$$

where m is the mass, c is the velocity of light, and E is the energy equivalence of the mass.

This relation would predict that mass can be turned into energy, or energy into mass. In other words, mass is a form of energy, for if a quantity of mass m could be annihilated, a definite amount of energy E would be available in some other form. To illustrate this, suppose that a 1-kg mass could be completely annihilated and the liberated energy given to another body in the form of kinetic energy.

$$\begin{aligned} E &= 1 \times 3 \times 10^8 \times 3 \times 10^8 \\ &= 9 \times 10^{16} \text{ joules} \end{aligned} \tag{4}$$

In foot-pounds of energy this is equivalent to 7×10^{16} ft-lb, or enough energy to propel the largest battleship around the world.

The annihilation of mass then is a source of undreamed-of energy. Disintegration is one means, however, whereby mass can be annihilated or created more or less at the will of the experimenter.

If an atom, a part of an atom, or an electron is annihilated, the energy may either be transformed into kinetic energy and given to another atomic particle in the form of a velocity or it may appear as a γ ray of specified frequency ν and energy $h\nu$. To find the equivalence between mass energy, γ-ray energy, and kinetic energy, all of the following quantities are equated to each other.

$$E = mc^2 = h\nu = \tfrac{1}{2}mv^2 = Ve \tag{5}$$

It is customary among physicists to express each of these energies in terms of V in volts. Thus one speaks of a million volt γ ray, a three million volt electron, or a 12.5 million volt proton, etc. This terminology is used for convenience only and denotes the value of V in the above equation which, with the electronic charge substituted for e, gives the energy of the γ-ray photon, or of the moving atomic particle.

To give an example, suppose that an electron were to be annihilated and we wished to express the liberated energy in volts. To calculate V we make use of the equality between the second and last terms of Eq. (5); that is,

$$mc^2 = Ve \qquad (6)$$

Substituting the known electronic mass $m = 9.1 \times 10^{-31}$ kg, $e = 1.60 \times 10^{-19}$ coulombs, and $c = 3 \times 10^8$ m/sec, we obtain $V = 500,000$ volts.

annihilation energy of 1 electron
$$= 0.5109 \text{ Mev} \qquad (7)$$

This means that if the energy liberated by the annihilation of an electron could be given to another electron in the form of kinetic energy, that electron would have a velocity equivalent to half a million volts. In other words, it would have the same velocity and energy as an electron which has been accelerated by a potential of 500,000 volts in a tube of the kind shown in Fig. G, Quantum Optics, Lesson 4.

A mass of one-sixteenth of the mass of the principal oxygen isotope $_8O^{16}$ is called the **atomic mass unit** (*abbr.* amu).

Summary

When α particles collide with other atomic nuclei, they sometimes perform perfectly elastic impacts by obeying the laws of conservation of kinetic energy and momentum.

Rutherford was the first to discover that high-speed α particles are sometimes captured by the other nucleus upon impact, with a subsequent disintegration of the compound nuclei.

Studying such processes of disintegration by α-particle capture, Chadwick discovered the neutron.

It is now quite certain that all atomic nuclei are composed of protons and neutrons. Within the atomic nucleus each of these particles has a mass of almost exactly 1 atomic mass unit, and each of the protons has a unit positive charge.

The number of protons in every nucleus is equal to the atomic number.

Mass is a form of energy. If mass is annihilated, the energy it produces is given by the Einstein equation

$$E = mc^2$$

Conversely, if energy in any form is converted into mass, this same equation applies.

In nuclear disintegration experiments energy is not measured in joules but in volts. The energy in joules divided by the electronic charge e in coulombs, gives the energy equivalent in volts.

Questions

1. What is meant by a perfectly elastic collision? Do atomic nuclei ever collide perfectly elastically?

2. Who discovered nuclear disintegration by α-particle collisions? What was the experiment? Can you write down the nuclear reaction?

3. Who discovered the neutron? What was the experiment? Why don't neutrons produce cloud chamber tracks?

4. How many protons are to be found in a given nucleus? How many neutrons are there?

5. What is the Einstein mass energy equation? What does it mean?

6. How can energy be expressed in volts? What is the basic relation between the various forms of atomic energy and the equivalent energy in volts?

Problems

1. Complete the following disintegration reactions:

$$_1H^2 + {_8}O^{16} \rightarrow {_7}N^{14} + ?$$
$$_2He^4 + {_{13}}Al^{27} \rightarrow {_{14}}Si^{30} + ?$$

$$_1H^2 + {_5}B^{10} \rightarrow {_6}C^{11} + ?$$
$$_1H^1 + {_3}Li^6 \rightarrow {_2}He^4 + ?$$

2. Complete the following disintegration reactions:

$$_1H^1 + {_4}Be^9 \rightarrow {_3}Li^6 + ?$$
$$_2He^4 + {_{13}}Al^{27} \rightarrow {_{15}}P^{30} + ?$$

$$_1H^2 + {_{15}}P^{31} \rightarrow {_{15}}P^{32} + ?$$
$$_1H^2 + {_6}C^{12} \rightarrow {_7}N^{13} + ?$$

3. The mass of 1 amu is equal to 1.66×10^{-27} kg. If such a mass were annihilated, what would be the converted energy in electron volts?

4. If an oxygen atom, atomic mass number 16, where annihilated, how much energy, in electron volts, would be liberated?

5.* What is the equivalent energy, in electron volts, of a γ ray whose frequency is 3×10^{18} vib/sec?

6.* What is the equivalent energy, in electron volts, of a proton moving with one-tenth the speed of light?

7. If one percent of a kilogram of uranium could be converted into energy, how many joules would be produced?

8.* If one percent of a gram of uranium could be converted into heat, how many calories would be produced?

Nuclear Physics | Lesson 2

COSMIC RAYS

Early Experiments. It has long been known that a charged electroscope, if left standing for some little time, will discharge regardless of how well the gold leaf is insulated. Realizing that the rays from radioactive materials can be stopped by a sufficient thickness of heavy matter, Rutherford and Cooke (in Canada, 1903) surrounded an electroscope with a thick wall of brick and found very little decrease in the rate of discharge. McLennan and his co-workers (also in Canada) lowered an electroscope into a lake hoping that the thick layer of water would screen off the rays. This experiment, like the other, failed.

In 1910 Glockel, with an electroscope, rose nearly 3 mi in a balloon in order to get away from the ground radiation, but to his astonishment he found that the rate of discharge did not decrease but increased the higher he went. The same effect was observed by Hess (in Austria, 1911) and Kolhörster (in Germany, 1914). Rising to heights as great as $5\frac{1}{2}$ mi, both of these observers independently found that the intensity of these unknown radiations became greater the higher they went.

Because in one of his scientific publications concerning these results Hess suggested the possibility that some kind of penetrating rays were entering the earth's atmosphere from outer space, he is usually credited with the discovery of cosmic rays. For this reason he was granted the Nobel Prize in physics for the year 1936.

Millikan and Bowen's Discovery. Soon after World War I (1922), R. A. Millikan, with the help of I. S. Bowen, constructed several small self-recording string electroscopes. Making use of their wartime experiences with sounding balloons, they sent these electroscopes high into the stratosphere by fastening each one to two sounding balloons.

On one of the best record flights only one of the balloons burst at a height of 10 mi and the other brought the instruments safely to earth. Like the earlier results obtained by other experimenters, Millikan and Bowen found the ionization to increase with increasing altitude. After extending the observations of previous workers to higher altitudes, Millikan and Bowen became convinced and announced their belief that the rays were coming from interstellar space.

The Penetration of Cosmic Rays. In order to determine the nature of the new rays, Millikan and his co-workers, Otis, Cameron,

Fig. A. Self-recording electroscopes lowered into deep snow-fed lakes are used to measure the absorption of cosmic rays.

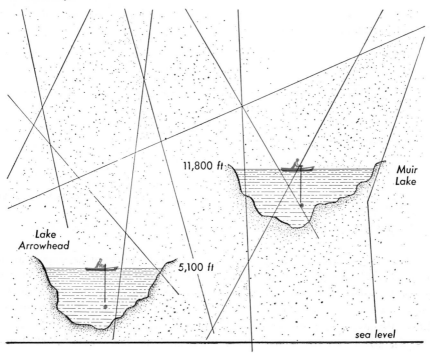

and Bowen, in the fall of 1922, began an extensive study of the penetrating power of cosmic rays. Since cosmic rays penetrate our atmosphere of many miles of air, how far might they penetrate into the earth?

Self-recording electroscopes were lowered to various depths in snow-fed lakes as illustrated schematically in Fig. A. Measurements taken at Arrowhead Lake in Southern California (at an elevation of 5100 ft) agreed approximately with those taken at Muir Lake near Mt. Whitney (at an elevation of 11,800 ft), provided one took into account the increased air path for the lower elevation. The extra mile and a quarter of air is equivalent in weight to 6 ft of water. As cosmic rays penetrate deeper and deeper below the surface of water, their number decreases until at a depth of 100 ft the intensity is reduced to about one ten-thousandth of that at the surface. With very sensitive electroscopes cosmic radiation capable of penetrating 2000 ft of water has more recently been detected. This is a far greater penetrating power than that possessed by any known X rays, or γ rays from radioactivity.

Cosmic Ray Detectors.   There are in general seven methods of observing and measuring cosmic rays. These are

>   electroscopes
>   cloud chambers
>   bubble chambers
>   Geiger-Mueller counters
>   scintillation counters
>   ionization gauges
>   photographic emulsions

Directional Effects.   To observe the direction of the greatest cosmic ray intensity, a cosmic ray telescope is used. Such a telescope is made by connecting two or more Geiger-Mueller tubes **in coincidence,** and mounting them on a common support some distance apart. Tubes in coincidence are so connected electrically that a current will flow in the accompanying electric circuit only

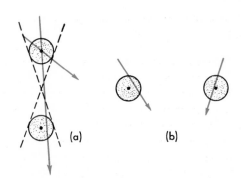

Fig. B. Diagram of two Geiger counters. Connected in coincidence, they form a cosmic-ray telescope.

when both tubes discharge at the same time. When the tubes are set one above the other, as shown in Fig. B(a), a single cosmic ray on going through both cylinders will cause a current to flow and a count to be made. If, however, a particle goes through one and not the other, no count is recorded. Experiments at sea level show that when the telescope is mounted in the horizontal position (b), few counts are made; whereas when it is mounted in a vertical direction, many more counts are recorded. The interpretation to be made, therefore, is that cosmic rays come principally from overhead.

As a verification of the telescope method, a Wilson cloud chamber is frequently inserted between two Geiger-Mueller tubes as shown in Fig. C and a photograph of each cosmic ray passing through both counters is taken. Thousands of such photographs are made automatically by having a single cosmic ray take its own picture. This is accomplished by allowing the sudden electric current from the counter tubes, produced by a ray in transit, to open and close a camera shutter, to cause the cloud chamber to expand, and to flash a light, illuminating the fog track that forms.

In the reproduction of Fig. C, either one of the two cosmic rays would have tripped the electrical devices and taken the picture. It should be noted that both rays passed right through a 0.5-in. lead plate without being deviated. Cloud-chamber pictures are not photographs of cosmic rays but of the path traversed by the rays.

Primaries and Secondaries. Experimental observations show that the cosmic rays entering our atmosphere are almost entirely composed of positively charged atomic nuclei. About two-thirds of these so-called *primary cosmic rays* are protons, and the other third (by mass) are about 90% α particles and 10% heavier nuclei like carbon, nitrogen, oxygen, iron, etc.

Fig. C. Wilson cloud-chamber photograph of two cosmic-ray tracks. Mounted between two Geiger-Mueller tubes connected in coincidence, the cosmic rays are made to take their own picture. *(After Brode)*

Geiger counter

Geiger counter

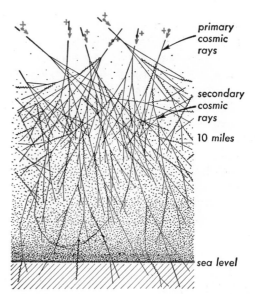

primary cosmic rays

secondary cosmic rays

10 miles

sea level

Fig. D. Schematic illustration of secondary cosmic rays produced from primaries entering the earth's atmosphere.

Upon entering the atmosphere, a high-energy primary particle soon collides with another atomic nucleus, splitting one or both particles into a number of smaller nuclear fragments, each one of which carries away some of the primary's energy. These high-speed particles in turn collide with other nuclei, further dividing their energy to produce other high-speed particles. All of these with the exception of the primary particle are called **secondary cosmic rays.** See Fig. D.

One of the results of cosmic ray collision processes is the creation of very high frequency and highly penetrating gamma rays. These photons, too, are included in the classification **secondary cosmic rays.**

Discovery of the Positron. The positron, or positive electron, was discovered by Anderson in 1932 by photographing the tracks of cosmic rays in a Wilson cloud chamber. Under the influence of a strong magnetic field applied perpendicular to the face of the cloud chamber, positively charged particles should bend to the right and negatively charged particles should bend to the left.

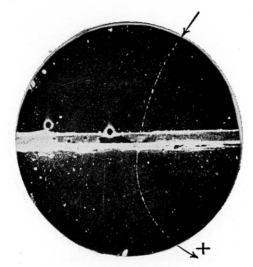

Fig. E. Wilson cloud-chamber photograph of a positron. *(After Anderson)*

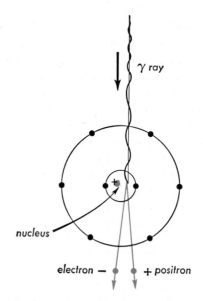

Fig. F. Schematic diagram of pair production.

In order to be certain that those bent one way were not all coming from above and those bent the other way were particles of the same kind and charge coming from below, Anderson inserted a block of lead in the chamber to slow down the particles. Under these conditions photographs similar to the one shown above in Fig. E were obtained. Here Anderson could be quite certain, from the curvature of the track on each side of the lead, that the particle entered from the side shown above, for in passing through the lead plate it could only have been slowed down and not speeded up.

Knowing the direction of motion, the direction of the field, and the direction of bending, Anderson concluded that such a particle had a positive charge. Comparing the track with well-known electron tracks and α particle tracks, he concluded that the new particle had about the same mass as the electron. Later experiments continued to give more positive proof of the existence of a positive electron. Now very strong beams of positrons can be produced in the laboratory.

Creation of Electron Pairs. Soon after Anderson's discovery of the positron several

people attempted to calculate the conditions under which a positron might exist in nature. An extension of the quantum theory of the electron, proposed earlier by P. Dirac, led him to the prediction that if a high-energy photon, i.e., a high-frequency γ ray, were to come close enough to the nucleus of

Fig. G. A γ **ray, entering the cloud chamber from above, creates a pair of electrons, one (+), the other (−).** *(After Lauritson and Fowler)*

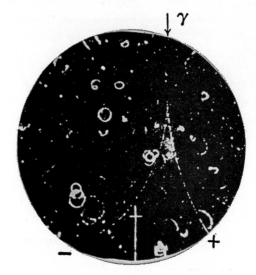

an atom, the electric field of the nucleus would be strong enough to annihilate the γ ray and create in its place a **pair of particles, an electron and a positron.** These two particles, the theory predicts, should have the same mass, and equal but opposite charges. A schematic diagram of pair production is given in Fig. F, and a photograph of such pair production is given in Fig. G.

The reason positrons were not discovered earlier in the history of physics is that they do not exist long in the free state. As soon as a positron meets an electron, the two are annihilated.

There is good evidence that when a positron and an electron come close together, they frequently combine by revolving around each other like a double star, with their spin axes parallel to one another. As such a pair they are called **positronium.** Positronium is very short lived for soon the two particles disintegrate completely and in their place two γ rays of half the original energy are created.

Cosmic Ray Showers. Out of hundreds and hundreds of cloud chamber photographs of cosmic rays, the experimenter is occasionally rewarded with a picture of a cosmic ray shower. Instead of one or two tracks in the picture in this instance one finds anywhere from half a dozen or more to several hundred. As shown by the photographs in Fig. H, most of the tracks of a shower seem to come from one localized region usually within a solid piece of matter like a lead plate or the wall of the cloud chamber. In photograph (a) a small shower of very high-energy particles enters the chamber from above, having been produced far above the cloud chamber in a shower-producing process, probably by a single particle of extremely high energy. As some of these secondaries pass through the lead, each produces a shower of its own.

Mesons. The presence in cosmic rays of

Fig. H. Cloud-chamber photographs of cosmic ray showers. (Courtesy of R. B. Brode, and C. D. Anderson and the Physical Review)

charged particles having a mass several hundred times that of an electron, yet considerably lighter than a proton, was discovered by Anderson and Nedermeyer in 1938. These particles, now called **mesons,** are of several kinds, and experimental data taken in balloons and airplanes show that most of them are produced high in the atmosphere by the collisions of primary cosmic rays with air nuclei.

Summary

Cosmic rays are composed of high-speed atomic particles entering the earth's atmosphere from the free space beyond. As these particles collide with the air molecules and atoms on their way down, they knock electrons free all along their path. When they occasionally collide with atomic nuclei, various kinds of transmutations and disintegrations occur.

Recoiling nuclear particles resulting from collisions of these incoming primary cosmic rays are called secondary cosmic rays. About two-thirds of the primaries are protons and one-third are α-particles and heavier atomic nuclei.

Positively charged electrons were discovered among cosmic rays by Anderson in 1932. Positrons are not normally found in atoms but are created when γ rays pass close to the nucleus of an atom. The γ ray disappears, and in its place a pair of electrons, one plus and the other minus, are produced.

A considerable number of different kinds of charged and uncharged particles are found in secondary cosmic rays that are not found in stable atoms. These elementary particles are called mesons.

Questions

1. Who discovered cosmic rays? How does the cosmic ray intensify as one goes up into the air above the earth's surface?

2. What kinds of detectors were used in the early cosmic ray experiments? Name six other detection and measuring devices.

3. How are cosmic rays made to take their own photographs?

4. What are primary cosmic rays? Of what are they composed?

5. What are secondary cosmic rays? Where do they come from? Of what are they composed?

6. What are positrons? Who discovered them? In what ways are positrons and electrons alike?

7. How are positrons produced? What is positronium?

8. What is a cosmic ray shower?

9. What are mesons?

10. What is a cosmic ray telescope? How is it made? How does it operate? What is its purpose?

Problems

1. Assuming all of the energy of a γ ray could be used in creating a pair of electrons (a positron and an electron), what must be its frequency? See Eq. (5), Nuclear Physics, Lesson 1.

2. What is the minimum energy, in volts, that a γ ray must have to produce an electron pair?

3. When a positron combines with an electron and the two are annihilated, what is the frequency of the two γ rays produced?

ATOMIC ACCELERATORS

The Cockcroft-Walton Experiment. Believing that the disintegration of atomic nuclei might be accomplished by using other than α particles as projectiles, Rutherford instigated in 1930 the construction of a high-voltage, direct-current generator at the Cavendish laboratory. The purpose of this **million-volt** source of potential was to accelerate hydrogen nuclei, **protons**, to high speeds and then cause them to strike known substances. In this way he hoped to produce new and various kinds of disintegrations.

Becoming impatient with the relatively slow progress of a difficult project, Rutherford suggested to Cockcroft and Walton that lower voltages be tried in the meantime to see if, by chance, disintegrations might occur. In 1932 Cockcroft and Walton announced that they had successfully disintegrated lithium atoms with protons accelerated by relatively low voltages. Their apparatus is schematically represented in Fig. A.

Electrons from a hot filament **F**, passing through hydrogen gas in the region of **A**, ionize many hydrogen atoms. These protons with their positive charge are then accelerated toward the other end of the tube by a potential **V** of 150,000 volts. Upon passing through the opening **C** and a window **W**, they emerge from the acceleration chamber as a narrow beam of protons.

This tube, acting as a **proton gun**, is aimed at a target consisting of lithium metal. Cockcroft and Walton observed α particles emanating from the metal with a range of 8 cm, an energy equivalent to 8.5 Mev. Considering the relatively low energy of the bombarding protons of only 0.15 Mev, this is a tremendous release in atomic energy. The transmutation taking place here is written as follows:

$$_1\text{H}^1 + {_3}\text{Li}^7 + E_1 = {_2}\text{He}^4 + {_2}\text{He}^4 + E_2 \quad (1)$$

This reaction, illustrated in Fig. B, shows a proton, $_1\text{H}^1$, of energy $E_1 = 0.15$ Mev entering a lithium nucleus, $_3\text{Li}^7$, to form a new but unstable beryllium nucleus, $_4\text{Be}^8$. Being unstable this compact structure of eight particles splits up into two α particles which are

Fig. A. Schematic diagram of the Cockcroft-Walton experiment. Lithium is disintegrated by 150,000-volt protons.

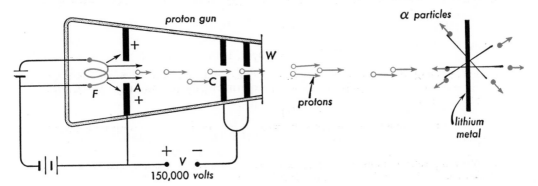

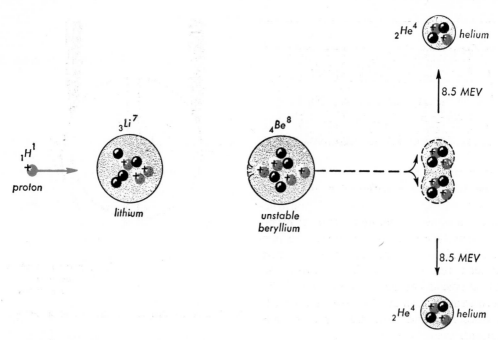

Fig. B. Disintegration of a lithium nucleus by a proton of 0.15 Mev. energy. The Cockcroft-Walton experiment.

driven apart with great violence. Since the measured energy of each α particle is equivalent to 8.5 Mev, each disintegration involves the liberation of 17.0-Mev energy. The source of energy is to be found in the annihilation of a part of the total atomic mass.

If we make use of the Einstein mass-energy relation as given by Eq. (6) in Nuclear Physics, Lesson 1,

$$Ve = mc^2 \qquad (2)$$

and substitute unit atomic mass

$$m = 1.66 \times 10^{-27} \text{ kg} \qquad (3)$$

as the mass to be annihilated, we find

$$V = 931{,}000{,}000 \text{ volts}$$

or

$$V = 931 \text{ Mev} \qquad (4)$$

We will now see how this important number is used.

The loss in mass in Eq. (1) can be calcu-

lated from the table of atomic weights, given in Appendix III. List the involved masses in two columns and add.

$$
\begin{array}{ll}
{}_1H^1 = 1.00814 & \\
{}_3Li^7 = 7.01822 & {}_2He^4 = 4.00387 \\
E_1 = 0.00016 & {}_2He^4 = 4.00387 \quad (5) \\
\hline
 8.02652 & \phantom{{}_2He^4 =} 8.00774
\end{array}
$$

E_1 in amu is the mass equivalent to the energy of the incident proton and is obtained by dividing 0.15 Mev by 931. The difference between the two sums, $8.02652 - 8.00774 = 0.01878$ mass unit, represents the loss in mass by the disintegration. When multiplied by 931, this gives 17.48 Mev as the liberated energy, a value in good agreement with the experimentally determined value of 17.0 Mev.

The Lawrence Cyclotron. At the time Cockcroft and Walton were performing their first disintegration experiments, E. O. Law-

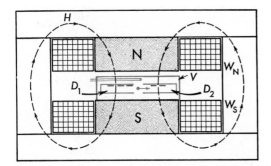

Fig. C. Cross-section diagram of a cyclotron.

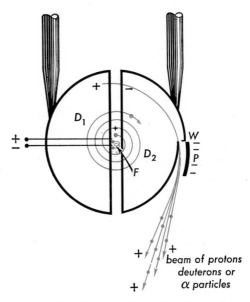

Fig. D. Detailed diagram of the D's of a cyclotron.

rence* and S. Livingston were developing a new type of atomic accelerator which soon attracted the attention of the leading physicists the world over. So successful was this "atomic machine gun" in producing high-speed atomic projectiles for disintegration experiments that a new and larger **cyclotron** was soon constructed and put into operation. Now a cyclotron of considerable size occupies a most prominent position in many of the leading physics laboratories of the world.

The very heart of the instrument, as shown in Figs. C and D, consists of two short, hollow, half cylinders D_1 and D_2 mounted inside a vacuum chamber **V** between the poles of a powerful electromagnet and connected on the outside to the two terminals of a high-frequency alternating current generator. It

* Ernest O. Lawrence (1901-1958), American experimental physicist. Deriving his early education in South Dakota, Lawrence obtained his Ph.D. degree at Yale University in 1925. In 1928 he was appointed associate professor of physics at the University of California, and in 1930 was made full professor. Having built up the Radiation Laboratory (now named in his honor), he became its director in 1938. In 1937 he was awarded the Comstock Prize of the National Academy of Sciences, the Cresson Medal of the Franklin Institute, and the Hughes Medal of the Royal Society of London. Lawrence is a member of the National Academy of Sciences and is noted principally for his development of the cyclotron and its application to the production of induced radioactivity. It is for these discoveries that he was awarded the Nobel Prize in physics for 1939. During World War II he directed one of the main research projects leading to the isolation of uranium 235, used in atomic bombs.

is interesting to point out that this generator is really a short-wave radio transmitter supplying energy to the dees (D_1 and D_2) instead of to the antenna.

When a trace of hydrogen gas is admitted to the evacuated chamber, the hot wire filament **F** ionizes some of the hydrogen atoms, thereby producing the protons to be used as atomic bullets. At the particular instant when D_1 is charged positively and D_2 is charged negatively, a proton in the neighborhood of **F** will be accelerated toward D_2. Moving through the strong magnetic field of the huge magnet, this positively charged particle traverses a circular path as shown in the diagram.

If, after making a half turn, the potential is reversed so that D_1 becomes negatively charged and D_2 positively charged, the proton will be attracted by one and repelled by the other, causing it to increase its speed. With added speed it therefore moves in the arc of a larger circle as shown. After this second half turn, the potential again reverses, making D_1 positive and D_2 negative, and again the proton speeds up. Thus, as the potential reverses periodically, the proton travels faster and faster, moving in everexpanding circles until, reaching the outer edge, it passes through a narrow open window **W.**

Upon leaving **W,** all protons must pass close to a negatively charged plate **P,** where, by attraction, their paths are straightened out and they become a separated beam of projectiles. Whatever substance is to be bombarded is then placed in this beam, and the disintegrated fragments are studied by means of various detecting devices.

The fundamental principle that makes the cyclotron work at all is the following fact:

The time required for a charged particle to make one complete turn within the cyclotron is the same for all speeds.

The faster a particle travels, the larger is the circle it must traverse, thus keeping the time constant. Hence with a constant frequency of the alternating current supply, some particles may be just starting their acceleration near the center, while others farther out have already acquired higher speeds. The result is a more or less continuous stream of protons emerging from the window **W.**

If the alternating current voltage applied between the **dees** of the cyclotron is 200,000 volts, with each half turn a particle obtains an added velocity equivalent to 200,000 volts. If a proton makes twenty-five complete revolutions before leaving the chamber at **W,** it will have acquired a velocity equivalent to 200,000 times 25 times 2, or 10,000,000 volts. Here, then, is a beam of 10-Mev protons acquired by the application of a potential only one-fiftieth as great.

When hydrogen in the evacuated chamber of a cyclotron is replaced by heavy hydrogen of mass 2, called **deuterium,** and the magnetic field strength is doubled, a beam of high-energy deuterons is obtained. Having twice the mass but the same charge as protons, these particles, called **deuterons,** acquire twice as much energy.

A photograph of an 11-Mev deuteron beam from the Harvard University cyclotron

Fig. E. Photograph of an 11 Mev deuteron beam from the Harvard University cyclotron. (*Courtesy of the Harvard University Press and A. K. Solomon*)

is shown in Fig. E. From the point where they emerge from the cyclotron window at the left center to where they come to rest in mid-air at the lower right, the high-energy particles ionize the air molecules and atoms, causing them to emit visible light.

The Van de Graaff Generator.   This machine, developed in 1931 by R. Van de Graaff at Princeton University, employs the principle of the electrostatic generator discovered many years ago. A typical installation, as shown in Fig. F, consists of a large hollow sphere supported on insulating columns and charged by a belt conveying electrical charges from a battery at ground potential, depositing the charges inside the sphere. The fabric conveyor belt, a foot or more in width, and running over well-aligned rollers, travels about 60 mi/hr.

As the belt passes between the metallic surface and row of needle points at **P,** electrons from the points jump toward the positive electrode and are caught by the belt. Upon entering the sphere at the top, the electrons jump to the needle points **Q,** where they go quickly to the outside surface of the sphere. The "spraying" of electrons **to** and **from** the points is assured by keeping the

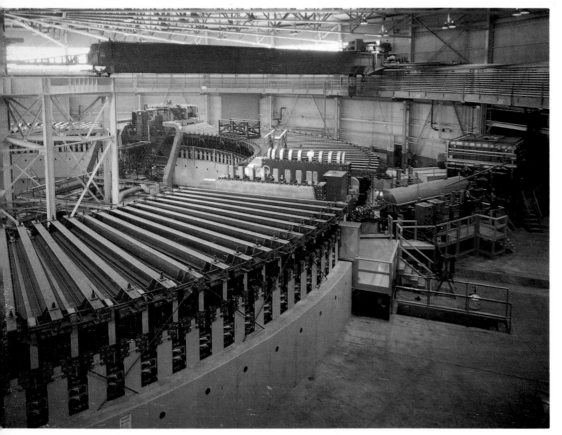

THE BEVATRON

Fig. G. A six-billion volt accelerator of atomic particles, located at the University of California, Berkeley. Photographed by K. Hildebrand and G. Kagawa. Courtesy of E. Lofgren, D. Cooksey, the Radiation Laboratory at the University of California, and the Atomic Energy Commission. Just behind the two men on the platform, at the far right and center, can be seen the rectangular housing of the atomic source and the Cockcroft-Walton accelerator. The cylindrical tank section containing the linear accelerator is clearly seen leading into the inflector assembly between quadrants 1 and 4. The main accelerating electrode assembly with the yellow colored ducts leading to it is seen farther back between quadrants 3 and 4. Note the overhead crane used for assembling, repairing, and the handling of massive apparatus and equipment.

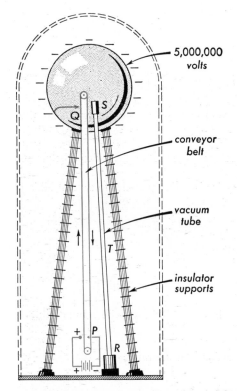

5,000,000 volts

conveyor belt

vacuum tube

insulator supports

Fig. F. Diagram of a Van de Graaff generator of high voltage.

able voltage, they are allowed to bombard whatever target is being studied. Where installations are designed for accelerating protons, deuterons, or α particles, the battery potential is reversed and the sphere acquires a high positive potential.

The Betatron. The **betatron,** invented in 1941 by D. W. Kerst at the University of Illinois, is an electron accelerator capable of producing electron beams of high energy as well as X rays of extremely high penetrating power. This ingenious device differs from the cyclotron in at least two fundamental respects: first, the electrons are accelerated by a rapidly changing magnetic field, and second, the circular orbit of the particles has a constant radius.

Billion Electron Volt Accelerators. The design and construction of an instrument capable of accelerating particles to energies of billions of electron volts (**Bev**) involves many problems. Not the least of these is the economic factor concerned primarily with the cost of such an instrument as well as its subsequent maintenance.

Five accelerators designed to reach the billion-volt energy mark are now in operation: (1) a 1-Bev **electron synchrotron** at the California Institute of Technology, in Pasadena, (2) a 1.3-Bev **proton accelerator** at Birmingham, England, (3) a 2- to 3-Bev proton accelerator at Brookhaven National Laboratory, Long Island, N. Y., and called a **cosmotron,** (4) a 6-Bev proton accelerator at the University of California, Berkeley, and called a **bevatron,** and (5) a 10-Bev **proton accelerator** in Russia.

battery potential high (about 50,000 volts) to maintain a "brush discharge." As more and more electrons arrive at the sphere, its negative potential rises higher and higher until leakage into the surrounding air and through the insulators becomes equally fast.

Atomic particles to be accelerated are generated inside a vacuum tube source **S** inside the sphere. Starting at the top of a long straight vacuum tube **T,** electrons are accelerated downward toward ground potential, where, acquiring the full energy of the avail-

Summary

The fact that atomic particles, like protons, can be accelerated by high voltage and then used to produce disintegrations was discovered in 1932 by Cockcroft and Walton.

Bombarding lithium metal with 0.15-Mev protons, helium nuclei are produced with each reaction resulting in a hundredfold increase in energy.

The purpose of an atomic accelerator is to produce ionized atomic particles and accelerate them to very high speeds. These high-speed particles are then used to bombard any given substance, called the target, to bring about nuclear collisions.

The design, construction, and existence of the many kinds of accelerators in use today began with the development of the first cyclotron by Lawrence in 1931.

Cyclotrons are used principally for accelerating protons and deuterons. Deuterons are the nuclei of hydrogen atoms of atomic mass 2.

The first high-energy electron accelerator was developed by Kerst and is called a betatron.

Large accelerators of modified types are capable of acclerating particles to several billion electron volts (*abbr.* Bev).

Questions

1. What was the Cockcroft-Walton experiment? What was the interaction?

2. Where does the energy come from that causes lithium to split up with a hundredfold increase in kinetic energy?

3. What is a cyclotron? What is its purpose? What does it accelerate?

4. What is deuterium? Is deuterium the same as hydrogen?

5. What is a Van de Graaff generator? What is it frequently used for? Can it be used to accelerate protons and electrons?

6. What is a betatron? Where do you think it got its name?

7. Approximately what is the highest energy to which atomic particles have been accelerated in the laboratory?

8. What does the abbreviation Mev stand for? What does the abbreviation Bev stand for?

Nuclear Physics | Lesson 4

RADIATION MEASUREMENTS—*Laboratory*

The rate at which atomic radiation is absorbed as it penetrates deeper and deeper into matter is measured with a Geiger counter. Graphs are plotted and absorption constants are calculated for β rays and γ rays in cardboard and aluminum absorbers. See the accompanying LABORATORY EXERCISES.

TRANSMUTATION

Proton and Deuteron Disintegrations. When high-energy protons or deuterons are used to bombard different known elements, various disintegration products are formed. An experimental arrangement in which the cyclotron acts as the source of high-speed particles is shown in Fig. A. To determine the nature of the disintegration taking place within the substance under bombardment, it is common practice to identify the penetrating rays emerging from the other side by the use of suitable detectors.

Numerous experiments have shown that the disintegration products to be looked for may be **protons,** α **particles, neutrons,** γ **rays,** or even **electrons, positrons,** and **mesons.** For some of these penetrating rays one kind of detector may be more suitable than another. The **Geiger and scintillation counters,** for example, are particularly useful in detecting γ rays and electrons, whereas the **Wilson cloud chamber** and **ionization chamber** are useful in detecting protons, α particles, and neutrons.

When a Wilson cloud chamber is used to identify disintegration products, charged particles can be identified with some degree of certainty by the density of their fog tracks, and their energy can be determined by the curvature of the tracks when a magnetic field is applied. (This is illustrated in Fig. E for positrons.) Once the nature of the emerging rays from a bombarded target is known, the recoil product of the disintegration also becomes known by writing down a reaction equation. Six examples of such reaction equations are given by the following:

$$
\begin{array}{llll}
{}_1H^1 + {}_9F^{19} = {}_8O^{16} + {}_2He^4 & Q = & 8.1 \text{ Mev} & (1) \\
{}_1H^1 + {}_5B^{11} = {}_6C^{12} + \gamma \text{ ray} & Q = & 15.8 \text{ Mev} & (2) \\
{}_1H^2 + {}_7N^{14} = {}_6C^{12} + {}_2He^4 & Q = & 13.6 \text{ Mev} & (3) \\
{}_1H^2 + {}_8O^{16} = {}_7N^{14} + {}_2He^4 & Q = & 3.1 \text{ Mev} & (4) \\
{}_1H^2 + {}_3Li^6 = {}_3Li^7 + {}_1H^1 & Q = & 5.0 \text{ Mev} & (5) \\
{}_1H^2 + {}_4Be^9 = {}_5B^{10} + {}_0n^1 & Q = & 4.4 \text{ Mev} & (6) \\
\end{array}
$$

It is customary to omit the **mass energy** of the bombarding particle from the left-hand side of all reaction equations and to designate the total energy liberated by the disintegration as shown at the right above. The values of **Q** given therefore represent the experimentally determined values of the liberated energy over and above that supplied by the incident projectile.

As an example, consider Eq. (6) in which deuterons, bombarding beryllium metal, produce high-speed neutrons and recoiling boron nuclei. This particular disintegration is important experimentally because it is used as a means of obtaining intense beams of neutrons for use as projectiles in other disintegrations. The nuclear changes are illustrated schematically in Fig. B. The available energy from the loss in mass alone is equivalent to 4.4 Mev, so that if deuterons with an energy of 7 Mev are used to bombard the beryllium target, the available energy becomes about 11.4 Mev, 1 Mev going to the recoil boron

Fig. A. Experimental arrangement generally used for bombarding known substances with high-speed deuterons from the cyclotron and for detecting the disintegration products with an ionization chamber as a detector.

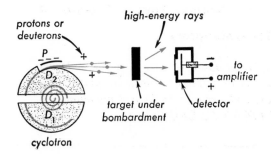

cyclotron

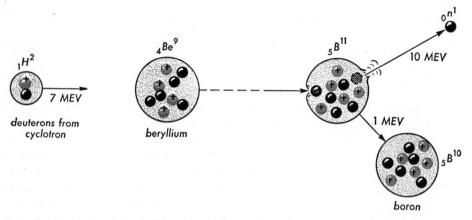

Fig. B. Deutron disintegration of a beryllium nucleus to produce high-speed neutrons.

nucleus and approximately 10.4 Mev to the neutron.

Multiple Disintegrations. A study of certain disintegration experiments shows that some of the unstable nuclei created by the capture of a proton or deuteron by a stable nucleus split up into more than two stable nuclei. Examples of this arise when boron is bombarded by protons and when nitrogen is bombarded by deuterons. In the case of boron (see Fig. C), the proton is first captured by a $_5B^{11}$ nucleus to form an unstable carbon nucleus, $_6C^{12}$. This composite structure disintegrates by the expulsion of an α particle with several million volts energy, leaving behind a beryllium nucleus, $_4Be^8$.

$$_1H^1 + _5B^{11} = _4Be^8 + _2He^4$$
$$= _2He^4 + _2He^4 + _2He^4 \quad (7)$$

This nuclear combination is still unstable and splits apart into two more α particles. When the phenomenon was first observed, it was thought that all three α particles came apart simultaneously, but further observations showed that first one and then two were ejected. The total energy liberated has been measured to be about 11 Mev and checks almost exactly with the value obtained from the loss in mass.

Fig. C. Diagram of the disintegration of a boron nucleus of mass 11 by a proton to produce three α particles.

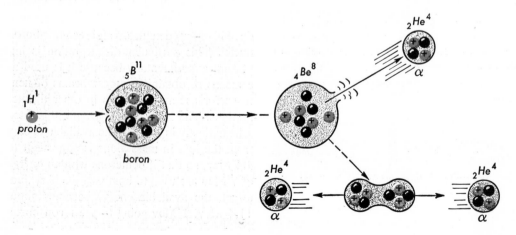

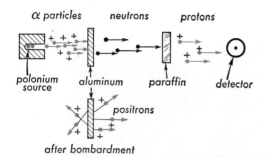

α particles   neutrons   protons

polonium source   aluminum   paraffin   detector

positrons

after bombardment

Fig. D. Experimental arrangement used by the Curie-Joliots when they discovered induced radioactivity.

Discovery of Induced Radioactivity.

The discovery of induced radioactivity was made in 1934 by F. Joliot and I. Curie Joliot.

For years these two researchers had been exposing various substances to the α rays from naturally radioactive elements and had been studying the various disintegrations that took place. In the specific instance referred to above, they bombarded aluminum with α *particles from polonium* and measured the energies of the ejected neutrons by the recoiling of protons from paraffin (see Fig. D). They observed that even after the polonium source was taken away, the detector continued to respond to some kind of penetrating radiation. Upon investigating the nature of these rays, they found positively charged electrons coming from the aluminum.

Repeating the experiments to make certain of the results, they came to the conclusion that, under the bombardment of α particles, the aluminum had become radioactive in its own right. What was happening has since been verified: α particles striking aluminum nuclei are captured, and the resulting nuclei disintegrate with the violent ejection of neutrons.

$$_2He^4 + {}_{13}Al^{27} = {}_{15}P^{30} + {}_0n^1 \qquad (8)$$

The newly created recoil particles, with a charge of $+15$ and mass 30, have been identified as phosphorus nuclei which are not stable but radioactive. Spontaneously disintegrating, these radioactive phosphorus nuclei $_{15}P^{30}$ shoot out positrons, leaving behind

them stable silicon atoms of charge $+14$ and mass 30.

$$_{15}P^{30} = {}_{14}Si^{30} + {}_1e^0 \qquad (9)$$

The *half life* of this activity, which measures the rate of decay of the phosphorus into silicon (for the meaning of half life see p. 472), is only 2.5 min.

Although the mass of the electron is not zero, it is so small compared with unit mass (the mass of one electron, it will be remembered, is $1/1840$ of one atomic mass unit) that e is written with a zero superscript. According to this notation, a positron is written $_1e^0$ and an electron $_{-1}e^0$.

Up to the present time more than two hundred different kinds of radioactive atoms have been produced in the laboratory. Three examples in addition to the one already given are illustrated by the following reactions:

$$_1H^2 + {}_{15}P^{31} = {}_{15}P^{32} + {}_1H^1, \quad {}_{15}P^{32} = {}_{16}S^{32} + {}_{-1}e^0 \quad (10)$$
$$_1H^2 + {}_6C^{12} = {}_7N^{13} + {}_0n^1, \quad {}_7N^{13} = {}_6C^{13} + {}_1e^0 \quad (11)$$
$$_1H^2 + {}_{11}Na^{23} = {}_{11}Na^{24} + {}_1H^1, \quad {}_{11}Na^{24} = {}_{12}Mg^{24} + {}_{-1}e^0 \quad (12)$$

A photograph of the positrons from radioactive nitrogen, Eq. (11), is shown in Fig. E.

Neutron Projectiles Produce Disintegrations.

The first disintegrations produced by high-speed neutrons as atomic projectiles were announced in 1932 by the English physicist, Feather. Immediately following

Fig. E. Photograph of the Wilson cloud-chamber tracks of positrons ejected by radio nitrogen, $_7N^{13}$.

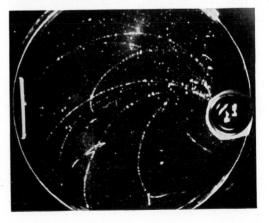

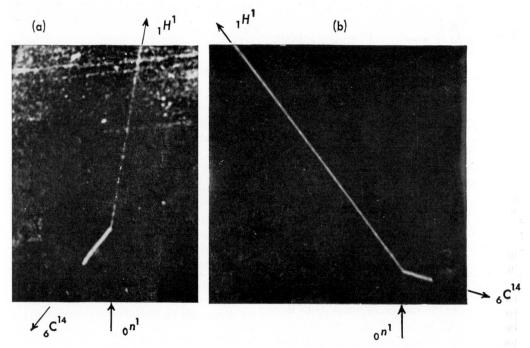

(a) $_1H^1$ $_1H^1$ (b)

$_6C^{14}$ $_0n^1$ $_0n^1$ $_6C^{14}$

Fig. F. Cloud-track photographs of neutron disintegrations of nitrogen. (After Feather and Rasetti)

Chadwick's discovery of these neutral particles, Feather allowed neutrons from beryllium to enter a Wilson cloud chamber containing pure nitrogen gas. Numerous expansions of the chamber and the simultaneous clicks of a camera shutter gave many photographs of the ion tracks left by recoiling nitrogen atoms.

Although most of the photographs indicated elastic collisions between nitrogen atoms and neutrons, an occasional photograph showed a forked track, indicating a disintegration of a nitrogen nucleus.

$$_0n^1 + {}_7N^{14} = {}_6C^{14} + {}_1H^1 \qquad (13)$$

Two photographs of such disintegrations are reproduced in Fig. F. Although hundreds of neutrons enter the cloud chamber every second, they do not ionize atoms as charged particles do, and hence leave no tracks. When a head-on nuclear collision occurs, however, the disintegrated nuclei, possessing as they do high speeds and positive charges,

leave a trail of ions behind them. The fork in each photo shows a proton track of considerable length originating at the same point as the more dense, short-ranged track of the recoiling carbon nucleus.

Strong sources of neutrons are produced by inserting a thin plate of beryllium metal in the intense beam of deuterons coming from the cyclotron as shown in Fig. G. The disintegration process, giving rise to the neu-

Fig. G. Experimental arrangement for producing intense beams of neutrons by bombarding beryllium with deuterons. The neutrons are then used as projectiles for further disintegrations as illustrated here for aluminum.

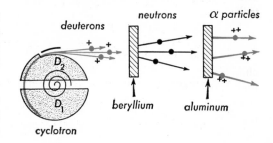

trons, is the reaction Eq. (6) and the diagram of Fig. B.

Into such a beam of chargeless particles
numerous substances of known chemical con-

stitution have been inserted and the disintegration products studied with suitable detectors.

Summary

High-speed protons or deuterons from an atomic accelerator will produce nuclear reactions when they are allowed to bombard a target composed of almost any element.

Some of the disintegration products of the reaction result in new but stable atoms, while
others produce nuclei that are radioactive. Such radioactive nuclei behave like the natural radioactive elements at the end of the periodic table, and possess a definite and
measurable half life.

While the natural radioactive elements emit α, β, and γ rays only, the laboratory-produced
radioactive isotopes emit protons, neutrons, and positrons in addition.

Neutrons moving at high speed may also make nuclear collisions, resulting in disintegration and transmutation.

Questions

1. What kinds of high-energy particles are commonly used in the bombardment of a
   target?

2. What kinds of high-speed particles might well be expected to be emitted as the result
   of various target bombardments?

3. What is induced radioactivity? What kinds of particles are given off by induced radioactive atoms?

4. Charged particles show their tracks in a Wilson cloud chamber. Neutrons and γ rays
   do not. Why?

5. How are strong beams of neutrons produced? Can neutrons be accelerated in a cyclotron?

6. What is a multiple disintegration? Give an example.

Problems

1. When nitrogen-14 is bombarded by deuterons, protons of considerable energy are
   observed being ejected. Write down the disintegration equation.

2. When beryllium-9 is bombarded by protons, α particles are observed being ejected.
   Write down the resultant reaction.

3. Nitrogen-14, bombarded by neutrons, liberates protons. Write down the reaction.

4. When magnesium-24 is bombarded by neutrons, protons are found coming from the
   target. Write down the resultant reaction.

5. When neutrons collide with oxygen-16 nuclei, α particles are observed to be given off. Write down the reaction.

6. If radioactive sulfur-35 is produced by the neutron bombardment of chlorine-35, what is the reaction equation?

7. When α particles with 7-Mev energy bombard sodium-23, protons are observed being given off. (a) Write down the reaction and (b) find the energy liberated.

8. Write down the multiple disintegration for deuterons bombarding nitrogen-14, in which α particles are produced.

Nuclear Physics | **Lesson 6**

INSIDE THE NUCLEUS

Nuclear Binding Forces. Although the disintegrations of different nuclei give rise to some half dozen different kinds of particles, it now seems quite probable that we need assume only two kinds of particles existing within the nucleus: **neutrons** and **protons**. If this is correct our task becomes the difficult one of explaining not only the disintegration mechanism of an unstable nucleus but the binding forces which hold a stable nucleus together. An attempt to find an answer to the latter question will serve as a starting point for the following presentations.

According to the **neutron-proton theory** of the atomic nucleus (see Fig. A), the deuteron nucleus contains but one neutron and one proton. Let us compare, therefore, the mass of one free proton and one free neutron with their mass when combined as a deuteron (for masses see Appendix III).

neutron mass,	$_0n^1$ =	1.00898
proton mass,	$_1H^1$ =	1.00814
	sum =	2.01712
deuteron mass,	$_1H^2$ =	2.01474

The difference in mass 0.00238 atomic mass unit (*abbr.* amu) is not due to inaccurate measurements of mass but is a real difference to be accounted for as the annihilation energy which binds the two particles together. When a neutron and proton come together to form a deuteron, a small part of their mass— namely 0.00238 amu (equivalent to 2.2-Mev energy)—is radiated from the newly formed nucleus. At close approach, in other words, the two particles attract each other so strongly that once together it takes the equivalent of a little more than two million volts of energy to pull them apart. This has been confirmed by a nuclear photoelectric effect, an experiment in which γ rays of 2.2-Mev energy or greater are found to break up deuterium nuclei into their constituent parts, while γ rays of lower energy have no effect. How neutrons and protons attract each other when very close together is a question of

Fig. A. Schematic diagram of the nucleus for (a) a deuterium atom and (b) a helium atom.

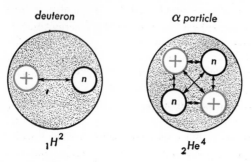

deuteron α particle

$_1H^2$ $_2He^4$

great importance for the stability of all the universe depends upon these forces.

To find the average binding energy of a single proton or a single neutron to the nucleus of a heavier atom, we need only compare the masses of two heavy nuclei differing from each other by only one proton or one neutron. Among the heavier atoms in Appendix III, it will be seen that consecutive nuclei differ from each other, on the average, by unity. Therefore, to remove a proton or neutron from the average nucleus, we must supply enough energy to increase the mass from 1.0000 to 1.0081 for a proton, or 1.0090 for a neutron. This means that in either case we must supply an energy equivalent to about 8 Mev.

The Nuclear Potential Barrier.   Early in the development of ideas concerning nuclear disintegration Gamow proposed a model by which one might represent the atomic nucleus. This model is based upon the forces acting between two positive charges.

Picture again a proton or α particle, with its positive charge, approaching a positively charged nucleus. As the two charges come closer and closer together, they repel each

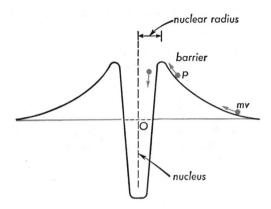

Fig. C. A graphical model of the atomic nucleus as proposed by Gamow. The potential barrier of a nucleus to an approaching positive charge is analogous to the crater of a volcano.

other with greater and greater forces as given by Coulomb's law. Graphically the increasing repulsion is represented by the potential curve shown in Fig. B. Such a curve represents what is called the **potential barrier** of the nucleus. The highest point of the barrier is frequently called the edge of the nucleus, which, for heavy atoms in the periodic table, occurs at and gives a nuclear radius of about 1×10^{-12} cm. For lighter nuclei the radius is several times smaller.

For want of a mechanical model of the nucleus we can pattern a surface having the form of the crater of a volcano similar to the surface obtained by rotating Fig. B around the vertical axis (see Fig. C). By such an analogy the electrical potential energy **V** between the two positively charged particles is analogous to the potential energy of a ball at any point on the crater model.

If now a small marble, representing a proton or α particle, approaches the nuclear barrier, it will roll up the hill as shown in the diagram. Experiencing a rapidly increasing opposing force, the ball may be turned back, or off to one side. If the initial velocity is high enough, however, the ball may go over the top of the barrier and drop down inside, representing a capture. What happens inside the nucleus and the disintegration that fol-

Fig. B. Potential energy curve for an α particle as it approaches a positively charged nucleus.

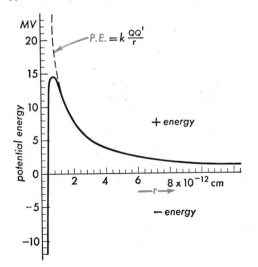

lows is the subject of the following sections of this lesson.

Bohr's Nuclear Model. In 1937 Niels Bohr, the famous Danish physicist, made another outstanding contribution to modern physics when he improved Gamow's model of the nucleus by extending what is sometimes called the *waterdrop model* of the nucleus. Bohr and his collaborator, Kalkar, imagine the many particles in a heavy nucleus as moving about within a spherical enclosure with motions analogous to the molecules in a drop of water. The surface of the spherical enclosure, which is the top of the potential barrier as represented in Fig. C, is analogous to the surface tension which holds a small waterdrop to its spherical form.

Just as the rapid motion of the molecules in water is a measure of the temperature, so Bohr speaks of the rapid motion of the neutrons and protons within the spherical boundary of the nucleus as a sort of *pseudotemperature*. See Fig. D. To explain disintegration, the analogy is drawn that *the ejection of a particle from the nucleus is like the evaporation of a water molecule from a drop of water.* Just as a rise in temperature brings about a more rapid evaporation of water, so an increase in the motions within the nucleus gives rise to a higher probability of disintegration.

In a stable nucleus, the particles within are moving about with very little kinetic energy and are in the analogous state of a relatively low temperature. When a high-speed particle from outside penetrates through the potential barrier, it is accelerated toward the center of the nucleus and acquires a very high kinetic energy before it collides with one or more of the particles inside. Soon the energy becomes divided among the many particles and the nucleus takes on a higher temperature state. Such a *pseudotemperature* corresponds to several million degrees.

Now as the particles move about inside, there is a certain probability or chance that,

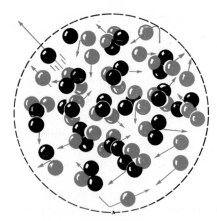

Fig. D. Nucleus in the act of ejecting a neutron, based upon the Bohr-Gamow waterdrop model.

within a given interval of time, some one particle will be hit by several particles, giving it a sufficiently high velocity in an outward direction to permit an escape through the potential barrier. This is illustrated in Fig. D by one of the neutrons in the upper left part of the diagram. The more rapid the internal motions, i.e., the higher the temperature, the greater is this chance of escape.

A direct disintegration may be described in this way: if upon entering the nucleus a high-speed particle like a proton adds sufficient energy to give the nucleus a high temperature, another particle like a neutron or α particle may be ejected immediately. Since such an ejected particle has to be supplied with a certain minimum energy to get free, the remaining particles will be slowed down, and the nucleus will return to a lower temperature.

Fig. E. Diagram representing an unstable nucleus.

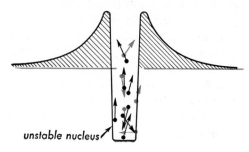

unstable nucleus

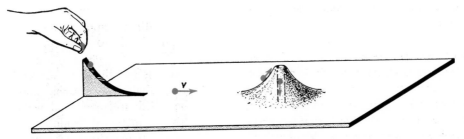

Fig. F. Mechanical model of a nucleus for demonstrating the capture of a high-speed proton, deuteron. or α particle, prior to disintegration.

A potential barrier model of an unstable nucleus is shown in Fig. E. For a stable atom the particles are moving slowly about at the bottom of the volcano pit. When a proton or α particle from outside comes over the barrier and drops down inside regaining its original speed, it collides with other particles and sets them into a more rapid state of motion as shown. If one of the particles near the outside is hit hard enough, it may acquire a sufficient energy to escape over the barrier. This is the analogue of disintegration and radioactivity.

Nuclear Demonstration Models. A demonstration model illustrating the capture of a high-speed proton or α particle by a nucleus, prior to disintegration, is shown in Fig. F. Marbles rolled down the incline represent the speeding up of atomic projectiles by an accelerator like the cyclotron. Approaching the potential barrier, a marble may roll part way up and then be deflected off to one side, illustrating an elastic collision without capture; or it may roll up the side and drop into the crater opening at the top, representing a capture prior to disintegration.

A demonstration of what happens inside the nucleus is illustrated by another model as shown in Fig. G. In this case the vertical scale of the barrier has, of necessity, been reduced, i.e., flattened out. When a marble is rolled down the incline and into the group of marbles at the center of the barrier, there may be several collisions before another par-

ticle usually goes bouncing out on the other side. This corresponds to a direct disintegration where one particle like a proton goes in and a neutron comes out.

If a single particle does not emerge, most of the particles inside take on random motions, colliding with each other much the same as do the molecules or atoms in a gas or liquid. To prevent friction from stopping them (there is no friction in an atom), the marbles are continually agitated by a small pin protruding from underneath the barrier. This pin is mounted slightly off center at the end of the shaft of a small electric motor. If the motor is left running for some time, a single marble will eventually be hit by several particles moving in the same direction and will recoil with sufficient speed to carry it over the barrier and out. This corresponds to a disintegration or radioactive decay, which takes place according to the laws of chance and to the resultant drop in temperature of the nucleus.

The faster the motor runs, the greater is

Fig. G. Mechanical model of a nucleus for demonstrating (a) the increased kinetic energy of nuclear particles after a capture and (b) the chance probability of radioactive decay or disintegration by the ejection of a particle.

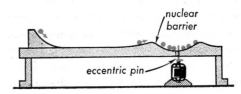

nuclear barrier

eccentric pin

the internal agitation and chance of ejection, and the shorter is the so-called **half life** of the element.

Nuclear Model for Neutron Disintegrations. When a neutron approaches a nucleus prior to a disintegration, it does not encounter a potential barrier of the type already described for protons and α particles. A neutron has no charge, so that at large distances it is not repelled by the positively charged nucleus. It may, therefore, approach a nucleus with very little speed of its own and be captured when it comes too close. At very close range a strong attractive force sets in, drawing the two together.

To an approaching neutron the nucleus acts as though it were a pit into which the particle will fall. This is illustrated by the flat potential curve in Fig. H. The marble rolling along the horizontal plane toward the pit represents the influence of the nucleus upon the neutron's motion, whereas the marble rolling up the hill (dotted line) represents the influence of the same nucleus upon the motion of a proton.

The Origin of Gamma Rays. It is often observed that the emission of α particles or β particles from a nucleus is accompanied by γ rays. The appearance of these high-frequency light waves, or photons, is now known to occur after the primary process of α or β disintegration and to represent a settling down of the excited residual nucleus to its normal state. The internal nuclear process

Fig. H. A graphical model of the nucleus as it is presented to an approaching neutron or proton.

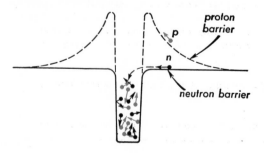

giving rise to γ rays has an explanation similar to that of the emission of visible light by the electrons in the outer structure of the atom.

The protons and neutrons within the nucleus are probably not moving about with quite the freedom pictured above but are very likely confined in their motions to shells analogous to the electron structure in the outer part of the atom.

When a projectile from the outside passes through the potential barrier and into the nucleus, it may supply the system with more than enough energy to emit an α particle. If this is the case and an α particle is ejected, one or more of the remaining particles may acquire a certain amount of energy and be held momentarily in an outer nuclear orbit. Then upon jumping into an orbit or shell nearer the center, the energy is given up and radiated as a γ ray. The energy $h\nu$ of this γ ray is equal to the difference in energy between the two energy states.

In some cases the capture of a particle from the outside is followed by the emission of a γ ray with all of the available energy, while in others it is divided between, for example, an α particle and a γ ray as described above.

The Origin of Beta Rays. For years the emission of electrons from radioactive elements has been a puzzle and a challenge to the best minds in physical science. Although many theories have been proposed, none appears to be entirely acceptable. From experimental evidence one thing seems quite certain and that is that the appearance of a high-speed electron is the result of some violent disruption of the nucleus. Among all of the heavy radioactive elements, natural or induced, electrons but no positrons are observed as a product of disintegration, whereas from the induced radioactivity of the lighter elements both positrons and electrons are found.

On numerous occasions it has been suggested that the neutron is a composite particle made up of one proton and one electron. The fact that the mass of a free neutron (1.00898) is slightly greater than the mass of a free proton (1.00814) and that the charge is zero would tend to confirm this. A β ray might therefore be explained as the result of a disintegration in which one of the neutrons in the nucleus splits apart with a violent ejection of an electron, the remaining particle, a proton, staying with the nucleus to increase its charge by unity.

A theory similar to this was proposed early to explain positron emission. According to this hypothesis, the proton is a composite particle, being made up of a positron and a neutron.

Since the difference in mass between the neutron and proton would seem to make one of these hypotheses wrong, it is assumed that both are incorrect. The difficulty is explained away by recalling that the average mass of neutrons and protons within the nucleus is unity and assuming that, so confined, both particles have the same mass and differ only in their charge. To explain electron or positron emission by a radioactive nucleus the electron has been assumed to be created at the expense of one-half million volts of energy.

Once a sufficient amount of energy is acquired by a certain nucleus, a neutron simply acts as an agent capable (1) of changing about $\frac{1}{2}$-Mev energy into a particle having the mass of an electron and (2) of creating a negative charge for the electron and itself absorbing an equal positive charge to become a proton. Similarly, in the nucleus of another type of atom, a proton may act as an agent capable of changing energy into a positron and itself becoming, by the absorption of the complementary negative charge, a neutron.

While the **half life** of a neutron in free space appears to be of the order of several minutes, its probability of capture by some nucleus when in solid matter reduces its life to about one thousandth of a second. In free space a neutron presumably disintegrates into a proton, an electron, and a neutrino.

Protons and neutrons, the fundamental "building blocks" of all atomic nuclei, are commonly called **nucleons.**

Since the neutrons and protons of a stable nucleus are bound together by strong forces, it must be assumed that Coulomb's law for the attraction of unlike charges and the repulsion of like charges becomes secondary to much stronger but short-range attractive forces.

Summary

Within the nucleus, neutrons and protons show strong attractive forces for each other, yet when they are separated, the protons with their positive charges repel each other and exert no forces upon neutrons.

As a proton, deuteron, or α particle approaches a nucleus, mutual repulsion occurs. If the velocity is high enough, however, and the two colliding nuclei come close enough, repulsion turns into attraction and the two come together. This is called capture.

According to the waterdrop model the protons and neutrons in a nucleus are in a state of motion and are like the molecules in a drop of water. In a stable nucleus the average velocity is low, while in a radioactive nucleus it is high.

The evaporation of water molecules is like the ejection of a proton or neutron from a nucleus.

The neutron may be thought of as a composite particle composed of a proton and an electron. Similarly a proton may be composed of a neutron plus a positron.

Questions

1. Does Coulomb's law of repulsion between like charges hold within the nucleus of an atom?

2. About how much energy is required to remove a nucleon from a nucleus?

3. What is a potential barrier? What equivalent mechanical model is sometimes used to represent such a barrier?

4. What is the waterdrop model of the nucleus? How is it used to explain stable nuclei on the one hand and radioactive nuclei on the other?

5. How is the waterdrop model of a nucleus carried over to the potential barrier model?

6. What mechanical model can be used to illustrate the conditions for the nuclear capture of a high-speed proton or α particle?

7. What mechanical model can be used to illustrate disintegration of a radioactive nucleus?

8. In what way does a radioactive nucleus of short half life compare with one of long half life?

9. What is the origin of γ rays within a radioactive nucleus?

10. What is the theory of the origin of β rays from radioactive nuclei?

Problems

1. Calculate the total energy in Mev required to separate a helium-4 nucleus into two deuterium nuclei.

2. How much energy in Mev is required to separate a helium-4 nucleus into two protons and two neutrons?

3. Calculate the total energy in Mev required to separate a lithium-7 nucleus into individual protons and neutrons.

4. How much energy in Mev would be liberated if the proper number of neutrons and protons could be brought together to make an argon-40 nucleus?

5. By what other name are each of the following known: (a) electron, (b) proton, (c) deuteron, (d) α particle, (e) positron, (f) X ray, (g) γ ray, and (h) photon?

6. Calculate the mass energy liberated when three neutrons and three protons combine to form lithium-6.

7. Draw a potential energy curve for a proton approaching a nucleus.

8. Draw a potential energy curve for a neutron approaching a nucleus.

NUCLEAR ENERGY

In 1937 Fermi, Segré, and their collaborators subjected uranium to the bombardment of neutrons, hoping that nuclear capture of the particles might produce elements heavier than uranium. At first, the experiments appeared to be successful, for after bombardment the uranium target was found to give off electrons with a number of different half lives.

Although similar observations were later made by others, an important discovery was made in 1939. After bombarding uranium with neutrons, Hahn and his collaborators in Germany performed a series of chemical separations of the uranium sample to determine the element to which the newly produced radioactivity belonged. To their amazement they found the radioactive atoms to be identical chemically to a number of different elements, nearly all of which are near the center of the periodic table. In other words, a uranium nucleus, after the capture of a single neutron, seemed to be splitting apart into two nearly equal fragments as illustrated in Fig. A.

In the few weeks that followed this discovery, many observers in different laboratories the world over not only confirmed the

results but extended the observations by studying in detail the products of the disintegrations. To explain the phenomenon in simple words, consider the details of the process illustrated in Fig. A. An original uranium nucleus, $_{92}U^{235}$, with its 92 protons and 143 neutrons is shown at the left as it captures a slow moving neutron.

In the center diagram (b) the newly formed nucleus is unstable and starts to separate into two nearly equal parts. This separation process is called **fission**. In coming apart the uranium nucleus, behaving like the analogous water drop, splashes out small drops, this time neutrons not needed by the two fragment nuclei. So great is the energy liberated by this explosion of the nucleus that each of the two heavy nuclei fly apart in opposite directions. That they do so has been confirmed by many Wilson cloud chamber photographs.

Uranium-235 as an Explosive. Not long after the discovery of fission it became evident to many scientific groups in America and in Europe that, if a sufficient quantity of pure uranium-235 (U-235) could be isolated from its more abundant isotope uranium-238 (U-238), it might have explosive powers many times greater than anything heretofore known. The reasons for believing this appeared at the time to be somewhat as follows. Suppose that a given mass of uranium metal, all composed of U-235 atoms, was brought together into one lump. The first cosmic ray that penetrated this mass and produced a neutron might well set off the chain reaction shown schematically in Fig. B. A U-235 nucleus would capture the neutron and, in splitting apart with great violence, liberate one or more additional neutrons. These in turn

Fig. A. Diagram illustrating the fission of a uranium nucleus into two almost equal parts.

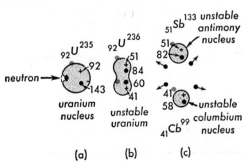

(a)   (b)   (c)

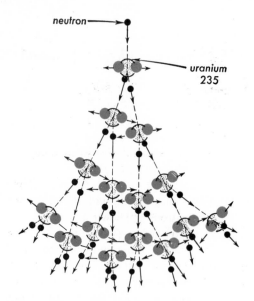

Fig. B. Schematic diagram of a chain reaction in pure uranium-235.

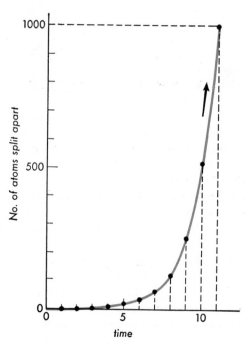

Fig. C. Growth curve of fission in pure uranium-235.

would be quickly absorbed by other nearby atoms, which in turn would split up and at the same time liberate other neutrons. Hence, a rapidly growing kind of avalanche might occur, a kind which, if fast enough, would have the characteristics of an explosion. A graph showing the rate of growth of such a chain process is given in Fig. C. Since even the slowest of neutrons in solid matter will have speeds of hundreds of thousands of centimeters per second, and since many neutron collisions will, on the average, occur within several millimeters, the graph shows how quickly the growth reaches gigantic proportions. (The *time* scale is of the order of microseconds.)

New Elements. Just prior to and during World War II, great strides were made in the study of nuclear structure and atomic energy. Not only were methods developed for separating large quantities of U-235 from natural uranium mixtures, but a number of new elements, among them neptunium (Np) and plutonium (Pu) 239, were produced and identified.

Neptunium (Np), element 93, was first detected and identified by Abelson and Mc-Millan* in 1939. A slow neutron captured by $_{92}U^{238}$ forms $_{92}U^{239}$ which is followed by β emission to give $_{93}Np^{239}$. This is but one of several known radioactive isotopes. Np^{237} is an α emitter with a half life of 2.2×10^6 years.

Plutonium (Pu), element 94, first identified by Kennedy, McMillan, Seaborg, Segré, and Wahl, arises from the spontaneous β emission of neptunium. Reactions giving rise to Pu-239, the isotope used in atomic bombs, are the following:

$$_0n^1 + {}_{92}U^{238} \rightarrow {}_{92}U^{239} + \gamma \text{ ray} \xrightarrow{23 \text{ min}} {}_{93}Np^{239} + {}_{-1}e^0$$

$$_{93}Np^{239} \xrightarrow{2.3 \text{ da}} {}_{94}Pu^{239} + {}_{-1}e^0 + \gamma \text{ ray}$$

Schematic diagrams of these processes are shown in Fig. D.

It is now known that all transuranium nuclei starting with Th-232 and through Cf-244

* For the discovery of neptunium and plutonium, E. M. McMillan and G. T. Seaborg were jointly awarded the 1951 Nobel Prize in chemistry.

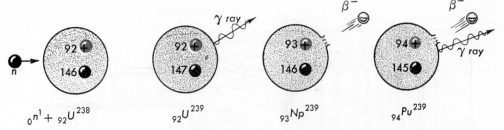

Fig. D. Neutron capture by uranium-238 produces, by radioactive β-decay, neptunium and plutonium.

are fissionable, i.e., under proper excitation conditions they split apart with great violence into almost equal pair fragments. Some of them, like U-233, U-235, and Pu-239, fission by the capture of a slow neutron; whereas others, like U-238 and Pu-241, fission only by the capture of fast neutrons. The capture of a slow neutron by U-238 is followed by β decay to produce Np-239 and Pu-239, whereas fast neutron capture is followed by fission.

The Uranium Pile. The uranium pile is a kind of atomic furnace in which U-235 is the "fuel burned" and many useful atomic by-products are produced. A schematic diagram of a pile constructed of solid carbon blocks is shown in Fig. E. Long cylindrical holes through the carbon blocks provide space for the insertion of all materials and controls needed for proper operation. Chemically pure uranium in tightly sealed aluminum containers is inserted in alternate rows

Fig. E. Uranium pile of carbon blocks used to produce plutonium-239 and many other radioactive atomic nuclei. (Concrete protective walls are not shown.)

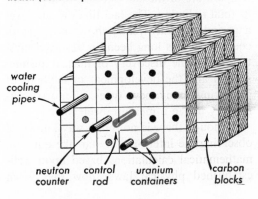

water cooling pipes

neutron counter   control rod   uranium containers   carbon blocks

of blocks, while water flows through pipes to keep the temperature of the entire mass from rising dangerously high.

When within the uranium metal a few U-235 atoms undergo fission, fast neutrons are liberated. Entering the surrounding medium, these neutrons collide frequently (about every 2.5 cm) with carbon atoms and are slowed down. Evenutally entering uranium metal again as slow neutrons, some are captured by U-235 nuclei to produce fission and hence more neutrons. Since each fission produces several neutrons, the total number in the pile will increase continuously and the temperature will rise from the recoiling energy of the carbon atoms. The whole process is a self-sustaining chain reaction only if a sufficient number of the neutrons produced find their way into U-235 nuclei before being lost or absorbed by some other process.

The other processes referred to are (1) absorption by U-238 nuclei to produce U-239 followed by β decay, (2) absorption by carbon atoms, (3) absorption by impurities, and (4) loss by escape through the furnace walls. The first of these, if not too large, is a desirable process as it leads to the production of Pu-239 (see previous section). The second is small since carbon is used as furnace material in preference to so many other substances because of its relatively low neutron capture probability. Small quantities of impurities initially present, as well as those resulting as fission fragments, are unavoidably present. The fourth loss is minimized by making the pile sufficiently large, thereby increasing the volume-to-wall-area ratio.

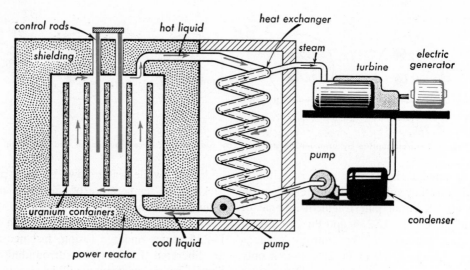

Fig. F. Schematic diagram of a proposed nuclear power plant.

Since cadmium atoms are strong absorbers of neutrons, a solid cadmium rod inserted into the pile will absorb many neutrons and, acting as a damper, limit the neutron density as well as the temperature within the pile. Activity within the pile is measured with a boron trifluoride counter inserted through one of the holes.

Power Reactors or Nuclear Power Plants. The idea that the natural heat developed in a uranium or plutonium pile might be utilized as a source of great power has long been recognized as a feasible enterprise. The basic principles of one type of **power reactor** are shown in Fig. F. A quantity of enriched uranium, or plutonium, in the form of a pure metal, or in the form of a solution of soluble salt in water, forms the center of the heat energy source.

The energy released by fission produces great quantities of heat and the rising temperature is regulated to a predetermined value by cadmium rods. To reduce the fission rate and thereby lower the temperature, the central rods are pushed in a little farther to absorb more neutrons, while to raise the temperature they are pulled out a little farther.

Because of the harmful effects of the intense neutron radiation to men and equipment, it is convenient to circulate a fluid through the shielded reactor and heat exchanger as shown in the diagram.

The hot liquid flowing through the heat exchanger vaporizes a more volatile liquid like water and the resulting hot gas or steam under pressure drives a turbine of special design. The turbine in turn drives an electric generator developing power that can be used to light our cities and factories, or to drive ships and submarines through the water and large planes through the air.

The Sun's Energy. Measurements of solar radiation reaching the earth each day not only make it possible to calculate the surface temperature of the sun but also to determine its total radiation. The fact that the sun, over a period of many years, shows no signs of cooling off, has long been an unsolved mystery. With the discovery of nuclear disintegration and the development of methods of producing many new types of atoms, this mystery has in a measure been solved.

Although there is no direct way known of observing the interior of a star like our sun, mathematical calculations based upon well-established physical laws show that down deep within such a mass the temperature is so extremely high that matter must be a conglomeration of atoms, electrons, and light waves all moving about at tremendously high speeds.

Near the center of the sun where the temperature is about 20 million degrees, the atoms are stripped of their electrons and the light waves produced there are of such high frequencies that they should be classified as γ rays and X rays. There, where the average particle velocity is so high, nuclear reactions must be taking place on a large scale and the liberated energy must be filtering up through to cooler and cooler layers as light waves of lower and lower frequency. At the surface most of the radiations escaping are of sufficiently low frequency to be classified as **visible, ultraviolet,** and **infrared.**

A careful study of all known nuclear reactions led Bethe in 1938 to propose the following set of chain processes as those most probably responsible for the generation of energy at the sun's central core.

$$
\begin{align}
&(1)\ _1H^1 + _6C^{12} = _7N^{13} + \gamma \text{ ray} \\
&(2)\ \phantom{_1H^1 + _6C^{12} =} _7N^{13} \to _6C^{13} + _1e^0 \\
&(3)\ _1H^1 + _6C^{13} = _7N^{14} + \gamma \text{ ray} \qquad (1) \\
&(4)\ _1H^1 + _7N^{14} = _8O^{15} + \gamma \text{ ray} \\
&(5)\ \phantom{_1H^1 + _7N^{14} =} _8O^{15} \to _7N^{15} + _1e^0 \\
&(6)\ _1H^1 + _7N^{15} = _6C^{12} + _2He^4
\end{align}
$$

By summing up the equations it will be seen that four hydrogen atoms are consumed and that two positrons, three γ rays, and one helium nucleus are created. The other nuclei cancel out since the original carbon atom in the first reaction is returned unaltered in the last reaction. Hence hydrogen is burned and helium is liberated. The loss in mass for each such cycle of reactions is, therefore, as follows:

$$4\ _1H^1 = 4.0326 \qquad _2He^4 = 4.0039$$
$$2\ _1e^0 = 0.0012$$

Subtracting gives

$$4.0326 - 4.0039 - 0.0012 = 0.0275 \text{ amu}$$

This is equivalent to about 27 Mev energy.

More recent experiments and calculations indicate that the **protonproton cycle,** Eqs. (2), (3), and (4), is of even greater importance in the creation of solar and stellar energy than the **carbon cycle,** Eq. (1).

$$
\begin{align}
_1H^1 + _1H^1 &\to _1H^2 + _1e^0 + 0.93 \text{ Mev} \qquad (2) \\
_1H^1 + _1H^2 &\to _2He^3 + \gamma \text{ ray} + 5.5 \text{ Mev} \qquad (3) \\
_2He^3 + _2He^3 &\to _2He^4 + 2\,_1H^1 + 12.8 \text{ Mev} \qquad (4)
\end{align}
$$

The net result is the same as before: four hydrogen atoms have been converted into one helium atom. Note that since two $_2\mathbf{He}^3$ nuclei are involved in the reaction Eq. (4), two proton-proton reactions of the type Eq. (2) are required to form one $_2\mathbf{He}^4$ nurleus.

The rates at which these reactions should take place are not only consistent with the temperature of 20 million degrees, calculated from other considerations, but hydrogen and helium are known to be the most abundant elements of which stars are made.

In order for the sun to radiate 3.8×10^{33} ergs of energy per second, Einstein's equation $E = mc^2$ shows that mass must be annihilated at the rate of 4.2×10^9 kg/sec (or 4,500,000 tons/sec). While this result indicates that the sun is losing mass at a tremendous rate, the amount is small when compared with the sun's total mass of 1.98×10^{30} kg. To illustrate, in one million years the sun should lose one ten-millionth of its total mass.

Fusion and the Hydrogen Bomb. We have just seen how the sun and stars, by means of certain nuclear reaction cycles, and temperatures of millions of degrees, are able to fuse hydrogen nuclei into helium with the simultaneous emission of great quantities of energy. While all of the elements needed in these reactions are plentiful on the earth's surface and can be purified and assembled in the research laboratory, the temperature of several million degrees required to cause them to fuse cannot be produced by any of the standard laboratory methods.

Here the atomic bomb with its heavy elements, employing the process of fission, comes to our aid and makes such tempera-

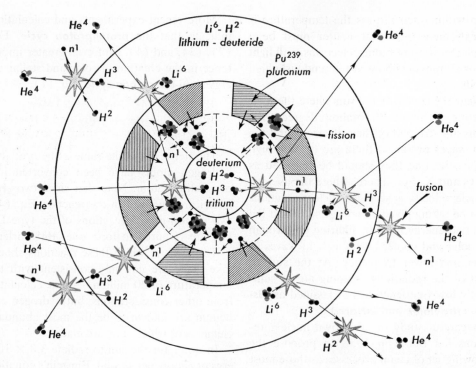

Fig. G. Schematic diagram of a hydrogen bomb.

tures possible. When an atomic bomb containing uranium-235 or plutonium-239 explodes, the temperature reached at the central core, though it may last for only a small fraction of a second, is comparable to that reached at the center of the sun.

Let us go along with some of those who are outsiders in this "top secret" process of building atomic weapons and make some guesses as to how a hydrogen bomb might be constructed. We may begin by writing down a number of well-established nuclear reactions involving the lightest of elements and from them select several that look promising from an energy standpoint. Among others we might select, for example, five reactions involving the three hydrogen isotopes as well as the two lithium isotopes.

$$_1H^2 + \,_1H^2 \rightarrow \,_2He^3 + \,_0n^1 \;\;+ \;\; 4.0 \; \text{Mev}$$
$$_1H^2 + \,_1H^3 \rightarrow \,_2He^4 + \,_0n^1 \;\;+ \; 17.6 \; \text{Mev}$$
$$_1H^2 + \,_3Li^6 \rightarrow \,_2He^4 + \,_2He^4 + 22.1 \; \text{Mev}$$
$$_1H^1 + \,_3Li^7 \rightarrow \,_2He^4 + \,_2He^4 + 17.5 \; \text{Mev}$$
$$_0n^1 + \,_3Li^6 \rightarrow \,_2He^4 + \,_1H^3 \;\;+ \;\; 4.6 \; \text{Mev}$$

Lithium is relatively abundant on the earth, and lithium-6 can be separated in reasonable quantities from its more abundant isotope lithium-7. Tritium, on the other hand, is not found in nature because of its relatively short half life of 31 years and is only produced in quantities at considerable expense.

Our hypothetical hydrogen bomb may now take the schematic form shown in Fig. G. A small concentrated core of hydrogen isotopes, deuterium and tritium, is surrounded by pellets of plutonium. Outside of this atomic bomb assembly, with its **booster core,** is a shell of deuterium and lithium-6 atoms in the concentrated chemical form of soild **lithium deuteride.**

We initiate the explosion process of the bomb by the sudden implosion, i.e., the sudden bringing together of isolated plutonium pellets into one spherical mass, whereupon a chain reaction of fission processes occur (see Fig. C), raising the temperature to several million degrees. At this high temperature the very active deuterium-tritium reaction takes place and the resulting boost to still higher temperatures makes possible the very energetic lithium-deuterium reactions. All this takes place in an extremely short period of time with a tremendous explosion.

Note in the schematic diagrams how neutrons on lithium-6 forms helium and tritium nuclei, thus regenerating the active tritium ingredient of the core, and how most of the fusion processes end up with stable helium nuclei. Considerable quantities of radioactive elements, however, are liberated as by-products of the plutonium. Since great quantities of neutrons are produced by the fissioning of plutonium, neutron reactions with lithium-6 to make tritium may eliminate the need for the expensive tritium ingredient as an initial booster.

Perhaps, too, the more abundant lithium-7 atoms could be used since considerable energy is there available (see Fig. B, p. 546).

The relative abundance of deuterium in ordinary hydrogen is about one in five thousand, and lithium-6 in ordinary lithium is about one in thirteen. See Appendix III. One pound of these two isotopes in a bomb should react with the explosive effect of 33,000 tons of T.N.T., and it would appear that any amount could be set off by an atomic blast.

The question of whether in the foreseeable future the fusion of the lightest elements such as hydrogen and lithium into helium can be controlled and used continuously as fuel in a power plant appears now to be more than just a possibility. Although a continuously high temperature of several million degrees cannot be maintained in the laboratory, the high atomic velocities needed to carry the reactions may be brought about by the intense radiations inside a power reactor or by intense beams from specially designed atomic accelerators.

It is the hope of every true scientist that the stock piles of powerfully destructive atomic weapons now on hand will never be used in warfare and that the knowledge gained from their test firings may be utilized in the design of power machines that can certainly be employed in peaceful ways to bring about a more abundant life for all mankind.

Summary

When a neutron is captured by a uranium-235 nucleus, the compound nucleus splits up into two nearly equal parts, with the liberation of several neutrons and considerable energy. This process, called fission, gives rise to an explosive chain reaction when confined to a sufficiently large quantity of uranium-235.

A uranium pile employing uranium metal as atomic fuel can be made to carry out a chain reaction under controlled conditions. Such piles convert some uranium-238 into plutonium-239 and at the same time produce quantities of useful radioactive isotopes.

Solar energy is attributed to the fusion of hydrogen nuclei into helium. Such fusion takes place near the center of the sun where the temperature is several million degrees.

The rapid fusion of hydrogn, as well as lithium, into helium is reported to take place in the hydrogen bomb where the fission explosion of uranium-235 or plutonium-239 produces the required high temperature.

It is hoped that methods will soon be found for the controlled fusion of hydrogen, lithium, and other light elements into helium.

Questions

1. What is fission? Are the two masses always equal?

2. What is a chain reaction? What are the conditions required for a chain reaction to be explosive?

3. By what reactions is plutonium-239 produced from uranium-238?

4. What is an atomic pile? What is the fuel? What is a moderator?

5. What controls can be applied to a pile reactor? How are operators protected from the intense neutrons in a pile?

6. What is the proton-proton cycle for solar energy?

7. What is the carbon cycle for solar energy? Write the reactions from memory.

8. How can fission be used to bring about the fusion of hydrogen or helium in an explosion?

9. Why is the controlled fusion of hydrogen into helium, as a continuous source of useful power, such a difficult problem?

10. Since the products of fission are composed of great quantities of radioactive elements, why do you think "fall-out" is an undesirable effect with fission bombs?

11. Since the products of fusion give rise to very little radioactivity, what do you think would be the constituents of a "clean bomb"?

12. How would you propose to cause the fusion of hydrogen or lithium, or both, under controlled conditions so that a more or less continuous source of heat energy is available?

Problem

1. If deuterium reacted fast enough with deuterium to produce a hydrogen bomb explosion, (a) how much energy in joules would be liberated by the complete transformation of 1 kg of deuterium into helium? (b) How many calories of heat would be produced?

Appendix I

TRIGONOMETRIC FUNCTIONS (*Natural*)

Angle	Sine	Cosine	Tangent	Angle	Sine	Cosine	Tangent
0°	0.000	1.000	0.000				
1°	.018	1.000	.018	46°	.719	.695	1.036
2°	.035	0.999	.035	47°	.731	.682	1.072
3°	.052	.999	.052	48°	.743	.669	1.111
4°	.070	.998	.070	49°	.755	.656	1.150
5°	.087	.996	.088	50°	.766	.643	1.192
6°	.105	.995	.105	51°	.777	.629	1.235
7°	.122	.993	.123	52°	.788	.616	1.280
8°	.139	.990	.141	53°	.799	.602	1.327
9°	.156	.988	.158	54°	.809	.588	1.376
10°	.174	.985	.176	55°	.819	.574	1.428
11°	.191	.982	.194	56°	.829	.559	1.483
12°	.208	.978	.213	57°	.839	.545	1.540
13°	.225	.974	.231	58°	.848	.530	1.600
14°	.242	.970	.249	59°	.857	.515	1.664
15°	.259	.966	.268	60°	.866	.500	1.732
16°	.276	.961	.287	61°	.875	.485	1.804
17°	.292	.956	.306	62°	.883	.470	1.881
18°	.309	.951	.325	63°	.891	.454	1.963
19°	.326	.946	.344	64°	.899	.438	2.050
20°	.342	.940	.364	65°	.906	.423	2.145
21°	.358	.934	.384	66°	.914	.407	2.246
22°	.375	.927	.404	67°	.921	.391	2.356
23°	.391	.921	.425	68°	.927	.375	2.475
24°	.407	.914	.445	69°	.934	.358	2.605
25°	.423	.906	.466	70°	.940	.342	2.747
26°	.438	.899	.488	71°	.946	.326	2.904
27°	.454	.891	.510	72°	.951	.309	3.078
28°	.470	.883	.532	73°	.956	.292	3.271
29°	.485	.875	.554	74°	.961	.276	3.487
30°	.500	.866	.577	75°	.966	.259	3.732
31°	.515	.857	.601	76°	.970	.242	4.011
32°	.530	.848	.625	77°	.974	.225	4.331
33°	.545	.839	.649	78°	.978	.208	4.705
34°	.559	.829	.675	79°	.982	.191	5.145
35°	.574	.819	.700	80°	.985	.174	5.671
36°	.588	.809	.727	81°	.988	.156	6.314
37°	.602	.799	.754	82°	.990	.139	7.115
38°	.616	.788	.781	83°	.993	.122	8.144
39°	.629	.777	.810	84°	.995	.105	9.514
40°	.643	.766	.839	85°	.996	.087	11.43
41°	.656	.755	.869	86°	.998	.070	14.30
42°	.669	.743	.900	87°	.999	.052	19.08
43°	.682	.731	.933	88°	.999	.035	28.64
44°	.695	.719	.966	89°	1.000	.018	57.29
45°	.707	.707	1.000	90°	1.000	.000	∞

Appendix II

At. No.	Element	Sym.	Isotopes, Mass. No.	At. Wt.
1	hydrogen	H	1, (2)	1.0078
2	helium	He	4, (3)	4.002
3	lithium	Li	6, 7	6.940
4	beryllium	Be	9	9.02
5	boron	B	10, 11	10.82
6	carbon	C	12, (13)	12.01
7	nitrogen	N	14, (15)	14.008
8	oxygen	O	16, (18), (17)	16.000
9	fluorine	F	19	19.000
10	neon	Ne	20, (21), 22	20.183
11	sodium	Na	23	22.997
12	magnesium	Mg	24, 25, 26	24.32
13	aluminum	Al	27	26:97
14	silicon	Si	28, 29, 30	28.06
15	phosphorus	P	31	31.02
16	sulfur	S	32, 33, 34	32.06
17	chlorine	Cl	35, 37	35.457
18	argon	Ar	(36), (38), 40	39.944
19	potassium	K	39, (40), 41	39.096
20	calcium	Ca	40, (42), (43), 44	40.08
21	scandium	Sc	45	45.10
22	titanium	Ti	46, 47, 48, 49, 50	47.90
23	vanadium	V	51	50.95
24	chromium	Cr	50, 52, 53, 54	52.01
25	manganese	Mn	55	54.93
26	iron	Fe	54, 56, 57, (58)	55.84
27	cobalt	Co	59	58.94
28	nickel	Ni	58, 60, 61, 62, (64)	58.69
29	copper	Cu	63, 65	63.57
30	zinc	Zn	64, 66, 67, 68, (70)	65.38
31	gallium	Ga	69, 71	69.72
32	germanium	Ge	70, 72, 73, 74, 76	72.60
33	arsenic	As	75	74.91
34	selenium	Se	(74), 76, 77, 78, 80, 82	78.96
35	bromine	Br	79, 81	79.916
36	krypton	Kr	(78), 80, 82, 83, 84, 86	83.7
37	rubidium	Rb	85, 87	85.48
38	strontium	Sr	(84), 86, 87, 88	87.63

COMPLETE LIST OF THE STABLE ISOTOPES OF THE CHEMICAL ELEMENTS

At. No.	Element	Sym.	Isotopes, Mass. No.	At. Wt.
39	yttrium	Yt	89	88.92
40	zirconium	Zr	90, 91, 92, 94, 96	91.22
41	columbium	Cb	93	92.91
42	molybdenum	Mo	92, 94, 95, 96, 97, **98**, 100, 102	96.0
43	technetium	Tc	*99*	97.8
44	ruthenium	Ru	96, 98, 99, 100, 101, **102**, 104	101.7
45	rhodium	Rh	103	102.91
46	palladium	Pd	(102), 104, 105, **106**, 108, 110	106.7
47	silver	Ag	**107**, 109	107.88
48	cadmium	Cd	106, (108), 110, 111, **112**, 113, 114, 116	112.41
49	indium	In	113, **115**	114.76
50	tin	Sn	112, (114), (115), 116, 117, 118, 119, 120, 122, 124	118.70
51	antimony	Sb	121, 123	121.76
52	tellurium	Te	(120), 122, 123, 124, 125, 126, **128**, **130**	127.61
53	iodine	I	127	126.92
54	xenon	Xe	(124), (126), 128, **129**, 130, 131, 132, 134, 136	131.3
55	caesium	Cs	133	132.91
56	barium	Ba	(130), (132), 134, 135, 136, 137, **138**	137.36
57	lanthanum	La	139	138.92
58	cerium	Ce	(136), (138), **140**, 142	140.13
59	praseodymium ...	Pr	141	140.92
60	neodymium	Nd	**142**, **143**, **144**, 145, 146, (148), (150)	144.27
61	prometeum........	Pm		146.0?
62	samarium	Sa	144, 147, 148, 149, 150, **152**, 154	150.43
63	europium	Eu	**151**, 153	152.0
64	gadolinium	Gd	155, **156**, 157, **158**, 160	156.9
65	terbium	Tn	159	159.2
66	dysprosium	Dy	161, 162, 163, **164**	162.46
67	holmium	Ho	165	163.5
68	erbium	Er	**166**, 167, 168, 170	167.64
69	thulium	Tm	169	169.4
70	ytterbium	Yb	171, 172, 173, **174**, 176	173.04
71	lutecium	Lu	175	175.0
72	hafnium	Hf	176, 177, 178, 179, **180**	178.6
73	tantalum	Ta	181	180.88
74	tungsten	W	182, 183, **184**, 186	184.0
75	rhenium	Re	185, **187**	186.31
76	osmium	Os	186, (187), 188, 189, 190, **192**	191.5
77	iridium	Ir	191, **193**	193.1
78	platinum	Pt	(192), 194, **195**, 196, 198	195.23
79	gold	Au	197	197.2
80	mercury	Hg	(196), 198, 199, 200, 201, **202**, 204	200.61

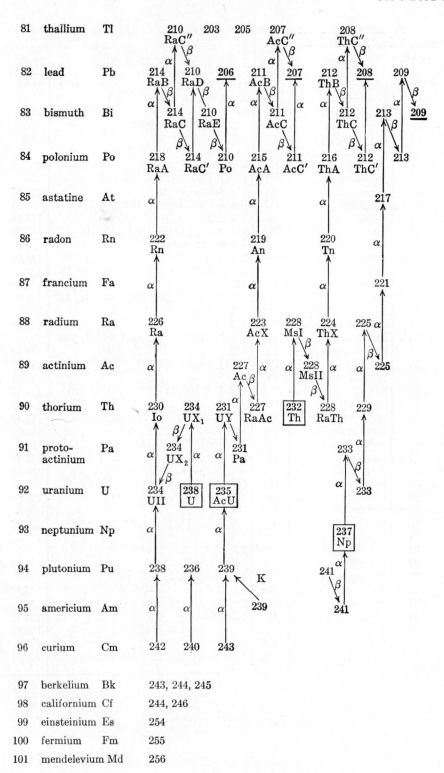

81	thallium	Tl
82	lead	Pb
83	bismuth	Bi
84	polonium	Po
85	astatine	At
86	radon	Rn
87	francium	Fa
88	radium	Ra
89	actinium	Ac
90	thorium	Th
91	proto-actinium	Pa
92	uranium	U
93	neptunium	Np
94	plutonium	Pu
95	americium	Am
96	curium	Cm
97	berkelium	Bk	243, 244, 245
98	californium	Cf	244, 246
99	einsteinium	Es	254
100	fermium	Fm	255
101	mendelevium	Md	256

Appendix III

TABLE OF ATOMIC WEIGHTS FOR ISOTOPES OF THE LIGHT ELEMENTS

s = seconds. m = minutes. hr = hours. d = days. y = years.

Isotope Symbol	Relative Abundance and Half-life		Atomic Weight	Isotope Symbol	Relative Abundance and Half-life		Atomic Weight
$_0n^1$	β^-	10^{-6}s	1.00898	$_9F^{17}$	β^+	70s	17.00749
$_1H^1$	99.98		1.00814	$_9F^{18}$	β^+	112m	18.00667
$_1H^2$	0.02		2.01474	$_9F^{19}$	100		19.00446
$_1H^3$	β^-	31y	3.01700	$_9F^{20}$	β^-	12s	20.00635
$_2He^3$			3.01698	$_{10}Ne^{19}$	β^+		19.00792
$_2He^4$	100		4.00387	$_{10}Ne^{20}$	90		19.99886
$_2He^6$	β^-	0.8s	6.02047	$_{10}Ne^{21}$	0.27		21.00059
$_3Li^6$	7.5		6.01702	$_{10}Ne^{22}$	9.73		21.99827
$_3Li^7$	92.5		7.01822	$_{10}Ne^{23}$	β^-	43s	23.00168
$_3Li^8$	β^-	0.88s	8.02502	$_{11}Na^{21}$	β^+	23s	....
$_4Be^7$	K, γ	43d	7.01915	$_{11}Na^{22}$	β^+, γ	3y	22.00132
$_4Be^8$	2α		8.00785	$_{11}Na^{23}$	100		22.99714
$_4Be^9$	100		9.01504	$_{11}Na^{24}$	β^-, γ	14.8h	23.99865
$_4Be^{10}$	β^-, γ	10^3y	10.01671	$_{11}Na^{25}$	β^-, γ	62s	24.99779
$_5B^{10}$	18.4		10.01611	$_{12}Mg^{23}$	β^+	11.6s	23.00111
$_5B^{11}$	81.6		11.01279	$_{12}Mg^{24}$	77.4		23.99270
$_5B^{12}$	β^-	0.02s	12.01816	$_{12}Mg^{25}$	11.5		24.99381
$_6C^{10}$	β^+	8.8s	10.02060	$_{12}Mg^{26}$	11.1		25.99087
$_6C^{11}$	β^+	20m	11.01492	$_{12}Mg^{27}$	β^-, γ	10.2m	26.99295
$_6C^{12}$	98.9		12.00380	$_{13}Al^{26}$	β^+	7s	25.99619
$_6C^{13}$	1.1		13.00747	$_{13}Al^{27}$	100		26.99014
$_6C^{14}$	β^-	10^3y	14.00768	$_{13}Al^{28}$	B$^-$, γ	2.4m	27.99083
$_7N^{13}$	β^+, γ	9.9m	13.00986	$_{13}Al^{29}$	β^-	6.7m	28.98975
$_7N^{14}$	99.62		14.00751	$_{14}Si^{27}$	β^+	4.9s	26.99525
$_7N^{15}$	0.38		15.00486	$_{14}Si^{28}$	89.6		27.98584
$_7N^{16}$	β^-	8s	16.01074	$_{14}Si^{29}$	6.2		28.98572
$_8O^{15}$	β^+	126s	15.00777	$_{14}Si^{30}$	4.2		29.98331
$_8O^{16}$	99.76		16.00000	$_{14}Si^{31}$	β^-	170m	30.98521
$_8O^{17}$	0.04		17.00453	$_{15}P^{29}$	β^+	4.6s	28.98962
$_8O^{18}$	0.20		18.00487	$_{15}P^{30}$	β^+	2.5m	29.98817
$_8O^{19}$	β^-	31s	19.00948	$_{15}P^{31}$	100		30.98362
				$_{15}P^{32}$	β^-	14.3d	31.98409

Isotope Symbol	Relative Abundance and Half-life		Atomic Weight	Isotope Symbol	Relative Abundance and Half-life	Atomic Weight
$_{16}S^{31}$	β^+	3.2s	30.98886	$_{82}Pb^{208}$		208.04140
$_{16}S^{32}$	95.1		31.98226			
$_{16}S^{33}$	0.74		32.98196	$_{83}Bi^{209}$		209.04550
$_{16}S^{34}$	4.2		33.97877			
$_{16}S^{35}$	β^-	87d	34.98035	$_{84}Po^{218}$		218.07676
$_{16}S^{36}$	0.016		....			
				$_{86}Rn^{222}$		222.08663
$_{17}Cl^{33}$	β^+	2.4s	....			
$_{17}Cl^{34}$	β^+	33m	33.98100	$_{88}Ra^{226}$		226.09574
$_{17}Cl^{35}$	75.4		34.98018			
$_{17}Cl^{36}$	β^+, K, β^-		35.97996	$_{90}Th^{232}$		232.11034
$_{17}Cl^{37}$	24.6		36.97762	$_{92}U^{234}$		234.11379
$_{17}Cl^{38}$	β^-, γ	33m	37.98004	$_{92}U^{235}$		235.11704
				$_{92}U^{238}$		238.12869
$_{18}Ar^{35}$	β^+	1.9s	....			
$_{18}Ar^{36}$	0.31		35.97893	$_{93}Np^{237}$		237.12158
$_{18}Ar^{37}$			36.97850			
$_{18}Ar^{38}$	0.06		37.97488	$_{94}Pu^{239}$		239.12653
$_{18}Ar^{39}$	β^-	4m	....			
$_{18}Ar^{40}$	91.63		39.97510	$_{98}Cf^{244}$		244.14211
$_{18}Ar^{41}$	β^-, γ	110m	40.97776			

Appendix IV

VALUES OF THE GENERAL PHYSICAL CONSTANTS (AFTER DU MOND)

Planck's constant of action.................... $h = 6.6238 \times 10^{-34}$ joule sec

Electronic charge............................ $e = 1.6019 \times 10^{-19}$ coulombs

Electronic charge............................ $e = 4.8022 \times 10^{-10}$ e.s.u.

Specific electronic charge..................... $e/m = 1.7589 \times 10^{11}$ coulombs/kg

Specific proton charge........................ $e/M_p = 9.5795 \times 10^{7}$ coulombs/kg

Electronic mass.............................. $m = 9.1072 \times 10^{-31}$ kg

Mass of atom of unit atomic weight............ $M = 1.6600 \times 10^{-27}$ kg

Mass of proton.............................. $M_p = 1.6722 \times 10^{-27}$ kg

Ratio mass proton to mass electron............ $M_p/m = 1836.1$

Wien's displacement-law constant.............. $C = 0.28976$ cm deg.

Velocity of light............................ $c = 299,790$ km/sec

$$c^2 = 8.9874 \times 10^{10} \text{ km}^2/\text{sec}^2$$

Appendix V

Periodic Table of the Elements

n+1	Sub Shells	1	2	3	4	5	6	7	8	9	10	11	12	13	14
1	1s	1.0080 H 1	4.003 He 2												
2	2s	6.940 Li 3	9.013 Be 4												
3	2p	10.82 B 5	12.011 C 6	14.008 N 7	16 O 8	19.00 F 9	20.183 Ne 10								
	3s	22.991 Na 11	24.32 Mg 12												
4	3p	26.98 Al 13	28.09 Si 14	30.975 P 15	32.066 S 16	35.457 Cl 17	39.944 Ar 18								
	4s	39.100 K 19	40.08 Ca 20												
5	3d	44.96 Sc 21	47.90 Ti 22	50.95 V 23	52.01 Cr 24	54.94 Mn 25	55.85 Fe 26	58.94 Co 27	58.69 Ni 28	63.54 Cu 29	65.38 Zn 30				
	4p	69.72 Ga 31	72.60 Ge 32	74.91 As 33	78.96 Se 34	79.916 Br 35	83.80 Kr 36								
	5s	85.48 Rb 37	87.63 Sr 38												
6	4d	88.92 Y 39	91.22 Zr 40	92.91 Nb 41	95.95 Mo 42	(99) Tc 43	101.1 Ru 44	102.91 Rh 45	106.7 Pd 46	107.880 Ag 47	112.41 Cd 48				
	5p	114.76 In 49	118.70 Sn 50	121.76 Sb 51	127.61 Te 52	126.91 I 53	131.3 Xe 54								
	6s	132.91 Cs 55	137.36 Ba 56												
7	4f	138.92 La 57	140.13 Ce 58	140.92 Pr 59	144.27 Nd 60	(145) Pm 61	150.43 Sm 62	152.0 Eu 63	156.9 Gd 64	158.93 Tb 65	162.46 Dy 66	164.94 Ho 67	167.2 Er 68	168.94 Tm 69	173.04 Yb 70
	5d	174.99 Lu 71	178.6 Hf 72	180.95 Ta 73	183.92 W 74	186.31 Re 75	190.2 Os 76	192.2 Ir 77	195.23 Pt 78	197.0 Au 79	200.61 Hg 80				
	6p	204.39 Tl 81	207.21 Pb 82	209.00 Bi 83	210 Po 84	(210) At 85	222 Rn 86								
	7s	(223) Fr 87	226.05 Ra 88												
8	5f	227 Ac 89	232.05 Th 90	231 Pa 91	238.07 U 92	(237) Np 93	(242) Pu 94	(243) Am 95	(245) Cm 96	(245) Bk 97	(248) Cf 98	(253) Es 99	(254) Fm 100	(256) Md 101	102
	6d	103	104	105	106	107	108	109	110	111	112				

Glossary

Absolute temperature scale. Any temperature scale whose zero is the absolute zero of temperature, e.g., $-273.16°C$.

Absolute zero. The temperature calculated from the limiting value of the coefficient of expansion of various real gases $(-273.16°C)$.

Absorption coefficient. A constant that specifies the relative absorption of radiation per unit thickness of absorber.

Acceleration. The time rate of change of velocity is called the acceleration.

Acceleration due to gravity. This is the acceleration with which a body would fall in the absence of all other disturbing forces, such as those due to friction.

Accommodation, Ocular. Sharp focussing of the eye for objects at different distances is brought about by changes in the tension of the ciliary muscles which control the shape of the crystalline lens.

Adhesion. The interacting forces between unlike kinds of molecules that holds matter together. Sometimes refers to intermolecular forces between the closely contiguous surfaces of adjacent bodies.

Adiabatic compression. Compression without exchange of heat between the compressed system and its surroundings.

Adiabatic expansion. Expansion without gain or loss of heat from outside the substance or system.

Alpha particle. A positively charged particle emitted from a nucleus and composed of two protons and two neutrons. A helium nucleus.

Ampere. A unit of electric current. The flow of charge per unit time.

Amplitude. The crest or maximum value of a periodic wave or motion.

Angle of uniform slip. The angle at which an object slides down an inclined plane at constant speed.

Angstrom. A unit of length usually used for specifying the wave lengths of electromagnetic radiation and the sizes of atoms. $1 \text{ A} = 10^{-8}$ cm.

Armature. The rotating part of an electrical motor.

Atmospheric pressure. The force per unit area exerted by the atmosphere.

Atomic accelerator. A device for accelerating charged atomic particles to high speeds.

Atomic mass unit. A unit of mass equal to one-sixteenth the mass of the oxygen—16 isotope. $1 \text{ amu} = 1.66 \times 10^{-27}$ Kg.

Atomic number. The number of protons

in the atomic nucleus, or the positive charge of the nucleus, expressed in units of the electronic charge **e**. Usually designated by the symbol **Z**.

Atomic weight. The weight of an atom of any element specified with respect to the oxygen—16 isotope taken as 16.0000.

Attitude. Applied to flight. The angle between a horizontal plane and the line through the center axis of an airplane in flight.

Audiogram. A graph showing hearing loss as a function of frequency.

Back emf. The counter electromotive force induced in a solenoid, or coil, by the changing current in the winding.

Ballistics. A branch of science dealing with the measurement of shell velocities from guns, and their effects upon targets.

Barometer. An instrument for measuring the pressure of the atmosphere.

Beat frequency. When two signals of different frequency come together, they reinforce each other at regular intervals. The reinforcement frequency, given by the difference of the two frequencies, is called the beat frequency.

Bel. A dimensionless unit for expressing the ratio of two values of power usually applied to sound. The number of bels is the logarithm to the base 10 of the power ratio.

Bernoulli's principle (or theorem). A law concerning pressure, velocity, and energy in the steady flow of a fluid regarded as incompressible.

Beta ray, or beta particle. A negative electron or positive electron emitted from a nucleus undergoing β disintegration.

Black body. An ideal body which would absorb all and reflect none of the radiation falling upon it.

Bohr-Stoner scheme. A systematic order in which electron shells are filled in the building up of the elements of the periodic table.

Boiling point. The normal boiling point of a liquid is the temperature at which its saturated vapor pressure is equal to normal atmospheric pressure.

Brachistochrone. The cycloidal path along which a body will slide from one point to another under the influence of gravity in the least time, friction being neglected.

Brightness. A sensory response of the eyes to the amount of light appearing to come from a given area. Corresponds to the photometric quantity called luminance.

British thermal unit. The energy required to raise the temperature of one pound of water one degree Farenheit. Abbreviated BTU.

Brownian motion. The irregular and random motion of small particles suspended in a fluid, discovered in 1827 by Robert Brown.

Calorie. The amount of heat required to raise the temperature of one gram of water one degree centigrade. 1 calorie = 4.1840 joules.

Calorimetry. A term applied to the process of measuring quantities of heat under planned laboratory conditions.

Canal rays. The positively charged particles escaping through holes in the cathode of a discharge tube.

Candle power. A unit of luminous intensity, based originally upon the total light given out by the flame of a candle of specified construction.

Capacitance. The ratio of the electric charge given a body to the resultant change in potential produced.

Capacitive reactance. The impedance offered by a capacitor to a flow of alternating current through a circuit.

Capillarity. The phenomena which are caused by surface tension and occur in fine bore tubes or channels.

Carnot cycle. An ideal cycle of four reversible changes in a substance, involved in the running of a heat engine.

Cathode rays. The term applied to the electrons emitted by the cathode of a gas discharge tube.

Center of gravity. The point through which the resultant force of gravity acts regardless of how the body is oriented. Same as the center of mass.

Center of mass. The point about which the sum of the mass moments of all the individual masses constituting the body is zero.

Centrifugal force. A radically outward force experienced by an observer in a reference frame rotating with respect to an inertial frame. The reaction force to centripetal force.

Centripetal force. The inward force on a body causing it to move in a circular path.

Čerenkov radiation. The electromagnetic radiation arising from an atomic particle traveling through matter with a velocity greater than the velocity of light in that medium.

Chain reaction. A self-sustaining reaction in which the agent starting the reaction produces a similar agent which in turn causes a like reaction.

Change of state. Transformation from one to another of the three states of matter: solid, liquid, and gas.

Charge. A quantity of electricity, measured in coulombs or related units.

Chladni sand figures. Standing wave patterns formed on a flat metal plate or drum head by grains of sand.

Chord. The simultaneous sounding of two or more notes, each of which forms a concordant interval with the others, constitutes a chord.

Chromatic scale. A musical scale based upon the diatonic scale, and containing sharps and flats.

Coaxial cable. A double conductor in which one conductor surrounds the other, the two being coaxial and separated by insulating material as a dielectric.

Coefficient of friction. A number specifying the ratio between the force required to move a body along a horizontal plane and the normal force between the body and the plane.

Coefficient of restitution. A number expressing the ratio of the velocity of separation to the velocity of approach, of two bodies in collision, and moving along the same straight line.

Cohesion. The interacting forces between like kinds of molecules that holds matter together. Sometimes refers to intermolecular forces acting throughout the interior of a substance.

Commutator. The ring of copper bars on the shaft of an electric motor or generator used to conduct current to or from the rotating armature.

Compton electrons. Electrons that recoil from a collision with a high-frequency photon.

Concordance. Two or more musical notes that sound harmonious to the ear.

Consonance. A combination of musical tones giving a sense of repose, or harmony.

Constant acceleration. A body is said to move with constant acceleration when its velocity changes by equal amounts each second.

Continuous emission spectrum. A spectrum of light in which all wave lengths over a considerable range of wave lengths are present.

Cosmic ray. The highly penetrating radiation passing down through the earth's atmosphere, and produced by high-energy radiation entering from outer space.

Cosmic-ray shower. A shower of cosmic ray particles and photons initiated by a source of high energy.

Coulomb. A unit of electric charge belonging to the practical as well as the mks system of units.

Critical angle. The minimum angle at which light can be totally reflected from the boundary separating two optical media.

Current. Electric current is a measure of the rate of flow of electrical charge from one point to another.

Damped vibrations. Vibrations of decreasing amplitude, usually caused by resistance or friction.

Dead time (resolving time). The short time interval during which a counter is insensitive as a detector, immediately following its detection of a single atomic event.

De Broglie waves. The waves associated with moving atomic particles. The wave length is given by $\lambda = h/mv$.

Decibel. The decibel is one-tenth of a bel. Usually used to express the energy of sound waves.

Declination. The angle specifying the difference between the needle of a magnetic compass and true north.

Density. The ratio of the mass of a homogeneous body to its volume.

Dew point. The temperature at which the content of water vapor in the atmosphere is sufficient to saturate the air with water vapor.

Dewar flask (thermos bottle). A double-walled flask or bottle designed to minimize the flow of heat in or out of the innermost container. Usually made of glass.

Dielectric constant. The ratio between the permittivity of a given dielectric and the permittivity of free space.

Diffraction grating. An optical device used to disperse electromagnetic radiation into a wave-length spectrum, and composed of an optical surface upon which thousands of equally spaced lines or grooves have been ruled.

Discordant. Two or more musical notes that are not harmonious or concordant.

Disintegration. The transformation of one atomic nucleus into another as the result of natural radioactivity or atomic collisions.

Dispersion of light. The spreading out into a spectrum of the different wave lengths of light.

Dissonant interval. A musical interval between two tones that do not harmonize, or are discordant.

Distance of most distinct vision. The shortest distance at which the average normal eye can accommodate and see an object, usually taken to be 25 cm, or 10 inches.

Doppler effect. The change in pitch and frequency of waves produced by the motions of the source, receiver, or both.

Double refraction. When a ray of light enters certain kinds of crystals such as calcite and quartz, it is refracted into two rays instead of the normal single ray.

Dyad. The musical interval between any two notes.

Dynamics. That branch of mechanics dealing with the motions of bodies under the influence of forces.

Dyne. The unit of force in the cgs system of units.

Dyne centimeter. A unit of mechanical work in the cgs system called the erg.

Edge tones. The tones produced by the splitting of an air-jet by a sharp edge located in the jet.

Efficiency. The ratio of the useful output of a machine and the input power, or energy.

Electrode. Any electrical conductor used as a terminal to or from which electrons or ions flow.

Electrolyte. Any substance whose solutions have the property of conducting an electric current.

Electromotive force (emf). The electric potential difference between the terminals of any device used as a source of electrical energy.

Electron gun. A metal structure of electrodes which produces a beam of electrons.

Electron lens. An electrode arrangement, or conductor arrangement, that has a focusing action on a beam of electrons.

Electron microscope. A microscope in which

a stream of electrons function in the same way as rays of light do in an ordinary microscope.

Electron optics. The control of the motions of electrons by means of electric fields, and their use in diffraction phenomena associated with crystals.

Electron shells. The energy states of an atom having the same principal quantum number.

Emission spectrum. The wave-length array of light emitted by a light source, usually produced by a prism or diffraction grating.

Equal-tempered scale. A series of notes produced by a division of the octave into twelve equal intervals.

Erg. The cgs unit of work and energy. 1 erg = 1 dyne centimeter.

Extraordinary ray. The ray of light produced in the double refraction by crystals, and not obeying Snell's law.

Fahrenheit temperature scale. A temperature scale devised by Fahrenheit in which the freezing point of water is 32 degrees, and the boiling point is 212 degrees.

Farad. A unit of electrical capacitance.

Faraday dark space. The nonluminous region between the positive column and the negative glow in a gas discharge tube.

Ferromagnetism. The property of some materials that gives them very high permeabilities.

Fifth. The musical interval between two notes whose frequency ratio is 3 to 2.

First-order spectrum. Usually applies to the diffraction and interference of light from a diffraction grating where the path differences between successive grooves are equal to one wave length.

Fission. The splitting up of an atomic nucleus into two nearly equal parts.

Fluid friction. The resistance offered by a fluid to the motion of objects through it, or to the motion of a fluid around or through objects.

Fluorescence. The process of emission of electromagnetic radiation by a substance as the result of the absorption of some other radiation.

Focal plane. A plane normal to the optic axis of a lens and passing through a focus of that lens.

Foot-candle. A unit of illuminance expressing the amount of light falling on a surface. The illumination of a surface one foot from a standard candle.

Foot-pound. A unit of work commonly used by engineers.

Force moment (see moment of a force). The product of the magnitude of a force and the perpendicular distance from the line of action of the force to a point which is the center of the rotation induced by that force.

Fourth. A musical interval between two notes whose frequency ratio is 4:3.

Fraunhofer lines. The dark absorption lines as seen in the solar spectrum.

Friction head. The pressure difference between two points in a uniform pipe through which a fluid is flowing.

Fusion. A change from the solid to the liquid state of matter.

Fusion, nuclear. The combination of two atomic nuclei to form a heavier nucleus, with the release of energy.

Galvanometer. An instrument for measuring very small electric currents.

Gamma rays. A quantum of electromagnetic radiation emitted by a nucleus as a result of a quantum transition between two energy levels of a nucleus.

Geiger counter. A device for counting ionization events of an atomic nature.

Half life. The time required for the disintegration of one-half the atoms of a sample of radioactive substance.

Halo. A faint colored ring seen about a light source as viewed through fog or clouds.

Hard X rays. X rays of very high frequency and short wave length, having great penetrating power.

Harmonics. Frenquencies that are whole number multiples of some one basic or fundamental frequency.

Harmony. Consists of a simultaneous sounding of several notes like a chord, followed by other similar combinations of notes.

Heat of fusion. The increase of heat content when units mass of a solid is converted into a liquid at its melting point without a change of temperature.

Heat transfer. The transport of heat from one place to another.

Helmholtz coils. Two identical coils placed apart a fixed distance equal to their radii and used for producing uniform magnetic fields.

Hertzian dipole. Two straight rods of equal length, placed end to end and used as a source antenna for electromagnetic waves in the radio range.

Hooke's law. The law relating small deformations of elastic bodies to the applied stress.

Horsepower. Historically, the rate at which a horse can do work. Defined as 33,000 foot pounds per minute.

Humidity, absolute. The mass of water vapor in a specified volume of air.

Humidity, relative. The percentage of the actual water vapor contained in the atmosphere to the maximum possible water vapor the same volume of air could contain at the same temperature.

Hypermetropia. A condition of the eye in which distant objects are seen more clearly defined than nearby objects.

Index of refraction. The velocity of radiation in vacuo divided by the velocity of the same radiation in a specified medium.

Induced current. A current made to flow through a conducing circuit by changing the total magnetic flux linking through that circuit.

Induced radioactivity. Radioactivity resulting from nuclear reactions.

Inductance. The property of an electrical conductor, often in the shape of a coil of wire, that sets up a back emf due to any change in current through the conductor.

Inductive reactance. The apparent resistance of an electrical conductor due to the flow of an alternating current through that conductor.

Infrared radiation. A range of wave lengths of electromagnetic radiation immediately beyond the red end of the visible spectrum.

Interference. The variation of wave amplitude with distance or time, caused by the superposition of two or more waves.

Interpolation. A process by which an appropriate value of a function is placed between two experimentally determined, or known, values of that function.

Intonation. The act of sounding notes in pitch with a musical scale.

Ionization. A process by which ions are formed. Frequently refers to the removal of an electron from an atom or molecule.

Isobar. One or two or more nuclides having the same number of nucleons in their nuclei and therefore having the same mass numbers.

Isoclinic line. A line, on a map or chart of the earth's surface, drawn through points having equal values of the declination of a magnetic compass.

Isomer. One or two or more nuclides which have the same mass number and atomic number, but differ in energy and behavior.

Isothermal compression. Compression during which the temperature remains constant.

Isothermal expansion. Expansion during which the temperature remains constant.

Isotone. One or two or more nuclides having the same number of neutrons in their nuclei.

Isotope. One or two or more nuclides having the same atomic number, hence constituting the same element, but differing in mass number.

Joule. A unit of energy or work in the mks system of units; abbreviation, J.

Kelvin temperature scale. A temperature scale based upon the efficiency of a reversible heat engine as specified by Carnot's cycle. Absolute zero of scale is at $-273.16°C$.

Keynote. The tonic, or key, of a musical scale as sounded or written.

Kilowatt. A unit of power equivalent to 1000 watts, or 1.34 horsepower.

Kinematics. The quantitative description of motion without reference to forces or bodies of matter.

Kirchhoff's laws. Laws of electrical networks carrying steady currents, one concerned with current flow in and out of any junction, and the other concerned with the voltages across the different elements of any closed circuit.

Knot. A nautical unit of speed equal to 1.152 mi/hr.

Laminar flow. The flow of a fluid in which the relative order of imaginary layers of the fluid are held intact during motion around an object.

Levitation. The phenomenon of lifting heavy objects in the air without material support.

eyden jar. An electrical capacitor consisting of a glass jar coated, inside and out, with a thin conducting layer.

Line absorption spectra. A spectrum showing dark lines on a continuous emission spectrum.

Line emission spectra. A spectrum showing bright lines at different wave lengths.

Longitudinal wave. A wave in which the direction of displacement at each point of the medium is normal to the wave front.

Luminance. Refers to the amount of light emitted by the unit surface of any given surface.

Mach number. The ratio of the speed of an object to the speed of sound in the undisturbed medium in which the object is moving.

Magnetic equator. An imaginary line around the earth's surface where the earth's magnetic field is everywhere parallel to the surface.

Magnetic flux. The number of magnetic lines of induction through any given area taken normal to the magnetic induction.

Magnetic induction. The term applied to that property of a magnetic field that specifies its strength or intensity.

Magnetic lens. A arrangement of coils or magnets so constructed that the magnetic fields they produce have a focusing effect upon a beam of electrically charged particles.

Magnifying power. In an optical instrument, the ratio of the apparent size of an object as seen through the instrument to the apparent size of the same object as seen without the instrument.

Major third. A musical interval between two notes whose frequencies have the ratio 5:4.

Major tone. A musical interval between two notes whose frequencies have the ratio 9:8.

Mass. The physical measure of the inertia of a body.

Mass moment. The product of a mass and the perpendicular distance from the center of the mass to the axis about which the mass may rotate.

Mass number. The whole number nearest in value to the atomic mass when that quantity is expressed in atomic mass units.

Mechanical equivalent of heat. A quantitative measure, or constant, expressing the equivalence of mechanical energy and heat energy.

Melody. A pleasant succession of musical notes that conveys the idea of motion that should go on and on.

Melting point. The temperature at which the solid and liquid states of a substance are in thermodynamic equilibrium.

Meson. An elementary particle having a rest mass intermediate between the mass of the electron and the mass of the proton.

Microfarad. A unit of electrical capacitance equal to one-millionth of one farad. Abbreviated μf. $1f = 10^6 \ \mu$f.

Micromicrofarad. A unit of electrical capacitance equal to one-millionth of one-millionth of one farad. Abbreviated $\mu\mu$f. $1f = 10^{12} \ \mu\mu$f.

Microwave. An electromagnetic wave having a wave length in the microwave region.

Middle octave. That octave of the musical scale having middle C as its keynote.

Milliameter. An instrument that enables the experimentor to measure electric currents to thousandths of an ampere.

Millibar. The unit of pressure used in meteorology, which is $\frac{1}{1000}$ part of a bar. A bar is one million dynes per/cm².

Millihenry. A unit of electrical inductance equal to one-thousandth of one henry. Abbreviated mh. $1h = 1000$ mh.

Minor tone. A musical interval between two notes whose frequencies have the ratio of 10:9.

Moment of inertia. A quantitative property exhibited by all solid bodies representing their resistance offered to rotation about a fixed axis.

Myopia. Nearsightedness. An eye condition in which distant objects are brought to a focus in front of the retina, whereas nearby objects are more clearly seen.

Natural frequency. Any frequency to which an object will respond and vibrate when that frequency is impressed upon it.

Negative glow. The luminous region around the negative terminal in a gaseous discharge tube.

Neutron. A neutral elementary particle of mass number 1, and a common constituent of all nuclei except hydrogen mass 1.

Nodes. The points, lines, or surfaces in a standing wave system in which the amplitude of the waves is a minimum.

Normal state. The state of an atom in which all electrons are in their lowest possible energy states, or the state of a nucleus in which all nucleons are in their lowest possible energy states.

Nuclear disintegration. Any transformation or change involving atomic nuclei.

Nucleons. A constituent particle of the nucleus of the atom.

Octave. The musical interval between two notes whose frequencies have the ratio 2:1.

Orbiting velocity. Any velocity sufficient to cause an object to complete an orbit around another astronomical body.

Ordinary ray. That ray of light, produced in the double refraction of light by crystals, obeying Snell's law.

Oscillator. A device for producing alternating current, the output frequency of which is determined by the characteristics of the device.

Oscilloscope. A cathode-ray device used to produce a visible trace, which is a time graph of any impressed electrical signal.

Overtones. A component of a complex sound having a frequency higher than that of the fundamental frequency.

Pauli exclusion principle. The law that permits no more than one atomic particle of any given kind to occupy a particular state of an atom or nucleus.

Percent error. The difference in percent between a determined value of any given quantity and the generally accepted value of that quantity.

Permeability. A constant giving the ratio of the magnetic induction to the corresponding magnetizing force.

Permittivity. A constant representing a property of a medium affecting the coulomb forces between charged particles located in that medium.

Photoelectric cell. An electronic vacuum tube that contains a photocathode and has an output current depending at every instant on the intensity of the light falling on the photocathode.

Photoelectrons. Ordinary electrons emitted from a material by the action of the photoelectric effect.

Photometry. A laboratory measurement procedure for determining the luminous intensity of a source of light or the illumination falling on a surface.

Photomultiplier tube. An electronic vacuum tube in which the initial photoelectric emission is multiplied many times before extraction at the anode by means of secondary electron emission.

Photon. The term applied to the particle aspect of an electromagnetic wave, frequently called a quantum.

Pile. A nuclear reactor employing a source of nuclear energy, such as uranium, and a moderator, such as carbon, arranged in a suitable configuration minimizing the loss or escape of neutrons.

Pitch. A sensory perception of the frequency of sound waves being heard in relation to some musical scale.

Planck's constant. A universal constant (h) given by the ratio of the energy of a light quantum and its frequency.

Plane-polarized light. A beam of light in which the electric vector of all the waves is in the same plane.

Plateau. The horizontal flat part of the count-rate graph of a Geiger counter.

Polar graph. A graph in which the magnitude of any given quantity is plotted radially outward from a common point and at angles for which the magnitude is determined.

Polarizing angle. The angle at which a beam of incident light and the smooth surface of a dielectric, like glass or water, will be plane polarized.

Polaroid. A commercial product in the form of a thin flat lamina that permits the transmission of light vibrating in one plane only.

Positive column. The luminous glow of an electrical discharge extending from the positive terminal to the Faraday dark space near the negative terminal.

Positive rays. A stream of positively charged atoms or molecules, produced in an electrical discharge tube with suitable electrodes and apertures.

Positron. A particle having the mass of an electron and a positive charge equal to the negative charge of an electron.

Potential barrier. A region around and close to an atomic nucleus tending to prevent charged particles from entering.

Potential divider. A slide-wire resistance arrangement for obtaining any voltage between zero and the maximum voltage of the accompanying source.

Potential energy. The energy a body has by virtue of its position or state, energy that can be utilized at some later time.

Potentiometer. An instrument used for the measurement or comparison of potential differences and based upon the law of potential drops.

Pound. The unit of force used in civil life and by engineers.

Power. The time rate at which energy is developed or expended. Usually measured in watts, kilowatts, or horsepower.

Power factor. The factor $\cos \theta$ in alternating-current networks in which θ is the phase difference between the voltage E and the current I.

Presbyopia. A defect of vision associated with old age and a form of farsightedness.

Pressure. The force per unit area exerted on any given surface. (Not a vector quantity.)

Pressure head. The liquid pressure required to set a fluid stream into motion.

Primary colors. Colors which when mixed together in proper proportions produce other desired colors.

Principal foci. The points on the axis of an optical system at which parallel incoming light, parallel to the principal axis, comes to a focus.

Proton gun. A vacuum tube with electrodes properly designed to produce a stream of protons.

Pythagorean theorem. The geometrical relation for any right triangle which says that the square on the hypotenuse equals the sum of the squares on the other two sides.

Quantum. The term applied to the particle aspect of an electromagnetic wave and often called a photon.

Quantum number. A number assigned to the variously allowed quantized states of an atom or nucleus.

Radian. A unit of angular measure in which the arc is equal to the radius. $360° = 2\pi$ radians.

Radioactivity. Spontaneous nuclear disintegration with the emission of particles or photons.

Range. The distance a particle will penetrate a given substance before its kinetic energy is reduced to a value below which it can no longer produce ionization.

Rankine temperature scale. A temperature scale based upon the Fahrenheit system so that $0°$ Rankine $= -459.69°F$, which is absolute zero.

Reactance. The resistance an electrical circuit offers to a flow of alternating current.

Reaction force. The force equal in magnitude and opposite in direction to any action force.

Real image. An optical image that can be formed in focus on a screen.

Rectifier. A device that permits current to flow through it in one direction only, and is used to change alternating current into direct current.

Rectilinear. In a straight line. Usually applied to the motion of a particle or ray of light.

Refraction. The bending of a ray of light as it crosses the boundary separating two different optical media.

Refractive index. The ratio of the velocity of light in a vacuum to the velocity of light in a medium.

Regelation. The process by which ice melts under increased pressure and freezes again when the pressure is reduced.

Resilience. The property of a body which measures the extent to which energy may be stored by elastic deformation.

Resistivity. A constant specifying the electrical resistance of a substance of unit length and cross section.

Resistor. An electrical conductor that offers retardation forces on the flow of charge through it.

Resolution time. (*See* dead time.)

Resonance. The response of a system to impressed waves or vibrations having the same frequency as the natural frequency of that system.

Rheostat. A resistor with a sliding contact, which when connected to an electric circuit enables the resistance to be altered.

Rolling friction. The frictional force exerted on a body tending to retard its rolling motion.

Root-mean-square. The square root of the average of the square of a quantity, e.g., $\sqrt{\overline{A^2}}$.

Scalar. A quantity which has magnitude only, as distinguished from a vector, which also has direction.

Scattering. The change in direction of particles or photons attributed to collision with other particles.

Scintillation. A flash of light produced in a fluor by an ionizing event.

Secondary emission. A process in which some kind of particles or photons, when they encounter some form of matter, gives rise to additional emission of the same kind or of a different character.

Self-inductance. The ratio of the magnetic flux linking a circuit to the flux-producing current in that circuit.

Semilog graph. A graph in which one coordinate is a logarithmic scale and the other is a uniform scale.

Semitone. A musical interval between two notes whose frequencies have the ratio 16:15.

Shock wave. A wave in which an abrupt finite change takes place in pressure and particle velocity.

Sidereal time. The clock time used by astronomers and based upon the apparent motions of the fixed stars rather than the sun.

Simple harmonic motion. Motion equivalent to that of the projection on any diameter of a point moving in a circle with uniform speed.

Sliding friction. The tangential force required to sustain the motion of a sliding object without acceleration.

Soft X rays. X rays in the longer wave-length region which do not have great penetrating power.

Solenoid. A coil consisting of one or more layers of wire windings.

Specific gravity. The ratio of the mass of a homogeneous substance to the mass of an equal volume of water.

Specific heat. The ratio of the heat needed to raise the temperature of a body through a given temperature range to the heat required to raise an equal mass of water through the same temperature range.

Spectrograph. An optical instrument by which the light from a source can be spread out into a wave-length array and photographed.

Spectroscope. An optical instrument by which the light from a source can be spread out into a wave-length array and observed with the eye.

Spherical aberration. The defects in the image formed on the principal axis of a lens or optical system due to the spherical shape of the lens or mirror surfaces.

Standard atmospheric pressure. A pressure equivalent to that exerted by a column of mercury at 0°C and 76 cm high.

Standing waves. A wave disturbance which is not progressive but is produced by the superposition of two or more waves traveling in opposite directions.

Strain. The deformation produced in a solid as a result of stress.

Stress. The force per unit area acting on a solid.

Supersonic. (A) A speed greater than the speed of sound. (B) A frequency higher than the ear can hear.

Surface tension. The apparent tension on the surface of a liquid tending to reduce the surface area to a minimum.

Tacking. A procedure in sailing a boat against the wind.

Terminal velocity. The limiting speed of a freely falling body when the downward force due to gravity equals the upward force of air friction.

Tetrad. Four musical notes forming a chord.

Thermal capacity. The amount of heat to raise unit mass of a substance one degree in temperature (commonly called the specific heat).

Thermal conductivity. The ability of a substance to conduct heat from one region to another.

Thermal expansion. The expansion of a substance due to a change in temperature.

Thermodynamics. That branch of the theory of heat dealing with molecular motions, the flow of heat energy, pressure and volume, entropy, etc.

Thermocouple. A device consisting of two metals, one of whose junctions is kept at a fixed temperature, while the other is changed to produce an electromotive force.

Thermopile. A number of thermal junctions connected in series, often used to measure heat or temperature.

Thermostat. An apparatus designed to maintain constant temperature at any given place.

Time of flight. The total time required for a projectile to return to the same horizontal level from which it was initially projected.

Torque. Sometimes called force moment, it is the product of a force and its perpendular distance from an axis about which it may rotate.

Total reflection. The reflection of all the light falling on the boundary separating two optical media.

Transmutation. The conversion of one chemical element into another.

Transverse waves. Waves in which the displacement of the wave is perpendicular to the direction of propagation and confined to a plane parallel to that direction.

Triode. A three-electrode electron tube containing an anode, cathode, and a control electrode.

Turbo-jet. A heat engine combining the principles and elements of turbines and exhaust jets.

Turbulent flow. The rapid flow of a fluid in which adjacent fluid layers are greatly distorted and eddy currents prevail.

Ultraviolet radiation. A range of wave lengths of electromagnetic radiation immediately beyond the violet end of the visible spectrum.

Uniform acceleration. (*See* constant acceleration.)

Vector. A measurable quantity having both magnitude and direction.

Virtual image. An image that can be seen by the eye but cannot be formed on a screen.

Viscosity. The phenomenon of the generation of stresses in a fluid resulting from the distortion of fluid elements due to flow.

Watt. A unit of power given by the rate at which energy is converted or consumed per second.

Wave equation. An equation relating the three quantities of wave velocity, frequency, and wave length. $V = f\lambda$.

Wave guide. A hollow metallic conductor used to guide microwaves from one point to another.

Wave length. The distance between corresponding points on two consecutive waves.

Weight-density. The ratio of the weight of a homogeneous body to its volume.

Wet-bulb thermometer. An ordinary thermometer with a water-soaked wick around its bulb.

Wheatstone bridge. One of the simplest and best-known networks of electrical conductors and a meter for measuring electrical resistance.

Work. The product of force times the distance through which the force acts.

Young's modulus. The elastic constant relating the various factors involved in the stretching or compressing of a solid.

Supplementary Problems

MECHANICS

Lesson 1

1. A truck is driven 6¼ mi in 9 min. How far would it travel in 1 hr, moving at the same average speed?

2. Two homing pigeons are released at the same place at the same instant, and each flies to his home coop. One flies due east at 40 mi/hr and the other flies due north at 30 mi/hr. If there is no wind, how far apart are the birds 2 hr after the start?

3. Two motorboats leave the same starting point in still water at the same instant. One boat travels due east at 5 mi/hr and the other travels 60° north of east at 10 mi/hr. How far apart are the boats ½ hr after the start?

4. A man sets out to walk a total distance of 5 mi. He walks the first 3½ mi in 50 min. If he then reduces his average speed to ¾ of its original value, how long will it take him to walk the remainder of his journey?

5. A car driven at 50 mi/hr overtakes and passes a truck that is driven at 35 mi/hr. How far apart will these vehicles be 10 min later if each one continues to travel without change of speed?

Lesson 3

1. An automobile starts from rest and accelerates uniformly to a velocity of 40 ft/sec in traveling 200 ft along a level road. Find the velocity of the automobile ½ sec after starting.

2. Car A starts from rest and accelerates at the rate of 4 ft/sec² for a distance of 50 ft along a level highway. Car B travels with constant velocity and covers the same distance in the same time as car A. Find the velocity of car B.

3. A car starting from rest accelerates to a speed of 40 ft/sec in 10 sec; then the brakes are applied, bringing it to rest in 2 sec. Calculate the total distance the car travels.

4. A block starts from rest at the top of an inclined plane and slides to the bottom with constant acceleration. If its velocity is 5 m/sec when it is halfway down the incline, with what velocity does the block reach the bottom?

Lesson 5

1. A man paddled a canoe across a river and back, heading straight across the stream both ways. He made the complete journey in 8.5 min and landed 1500 ft downstream from his starting point. Find the velocity of the water.

Lesson 7

1. Through what height does an object fall in acquiring a speed of 50 m/sec?

2. A baseball thrown straight up from the ground starts to fall from a height of 50 ft. How fast is it falling when it is 20 ft above the ground?

3. A heavy object is dropped from an elevated point and falls to the ground. If it falls halfway down in 2 sec, how long does it take to fall the rest of the way?

4.* A brick dropped from a high building to the ground covers the last 50 ft of its fall in ½ sec. How high above the ground was it dropped?

Lesson 10

1. A golf ball is driven upward at an angle of 15° and strikes level ground at a point 200 yd away. How high does it rise in its flight?

2. Calculate the range of a projectile which is fired at an elevation angle of 30° and reaches a maximum height of 1000 m.

3. An airplane flying horizontally at 200 mi/hr drops a package to the ground 400 ft below. How far does the package travel horizontally while it is on the way down?

4. The time of flight for a ball thrown straight upward with a particular speed is 5 sec. Find its time of flight when thrown with the same speed at an elevation angle of 60°.

5.* Two hose streams are adjusted to have the same range. One stream has an elevation angle of 30° and reaches a maximum height of 10 ft. What is the maximum height of the other stream if its elevation angle is 45°?

Lesson 12

1. What steady force is required to accelerate an automobile of mass 1500 kg so that it attains a speed of 44 km/hr in 10 sec, starting from rest?

2. Suppose that you are driving along a level road, towing a 2000-lb car behind you, and you observe that your speedometer reading goes up from 15 to 30 mi/hr in 6 sec. Calculate the force acting on the towed car during this period.

3. An automobile that weighs 2400 lb is being pushed along a level road. If the automobile acquires a speed of 15 mi/hr in 5 sec, starting from rest, what force is acting upon it?

4. The standard baseball weighs 5/16 lb. If a ball is moving with a velocity of 100 ft/sec, what force must the catcher exert upon it in order to stop it in a distance of 3 ft?

5. A train starts from rest, and 15 sec later its speed is 30 mi/hr. What force acts upon a 200-lb passenger because of this acceleration?

Lesson 14

1. If an earth satellite weighs 50 lb at the surface of the earth, what would it weigh in an orbit at an altitude of 300 mi?

2. If a man weighs 175 lb on the surface of the earth, what would he weigh on the surface of the moon?

3.* Imagine a spaceship traveling from the earth to the moon. As its journey continues, the attraction of the earth gets weaker and the attraction of the moon gets stronger. At a certain position the ship will equally be attracted by the earth and the moon.

* Challenging problems for the abler student.

How far will the ship then be from the center of the earth? Assume that the ship will be on a straight line joining the earth and moon.

Lesson 15

1. A packing case is to be pulled along the floor, and for this purpose a resultant force of 100 lb in the forward direction is needed. This resultant is provided by two forces applied in the general manner shown in Fig. C on page 74. One force is directed 20° from the forward direction, and its magnitude is 50 lb. The other force is directed 25° from the forward direction. Calculate its magnitude.

2. Three ropes are tied together at point O. From this point rope A extends vertically downward, rope B is directed upward and to the left at 75° with the horizontal, and rope C extends horizontally to the right. Rope A supports a load of 500 lb. Calculate the pull on each of the other ropes.

3. In a particular experiment a block accelerating down an inclined plane is acted on by two forces: (1) the earth pulls vertically downward upon it with a force of 5 newtons and (2) the plane pushes upon it with a force of 4.33 newtons upward and toward the right at 30° from the vertical. Calculate the force (magnitude and direction) required to produce equilibrium.

Lesson 17

1. A sled is pushed along level snow by an applied force of 6 lb directed 30° downward from the horizontal. Calculate the vertical and horizontal components of the applied force.

2. A push applied downward at 20° with the horizontal has a horizontal component of 22.5 newtons. Compute the vertical component of the push.

3. A guy wire 40 ft long is fastened to the top of a pole and anchored in the ground at a point 20 ft from the base of the pole. If the guy wire is under a tension of 240 lb, what horizontal pull does it exert upon the pole?

4. A 50-lb block is placed on a frictionless inclined plane that makes an angle of 30° with the horizontal. (a) Resolve the weight of the block into two components, parallel to the plane and perpendicular to the plane, respectively. (b) What force applied to the block parallel to the plane will keep the block in equilibrium?

Lesson 19

1. If a door can just be opened by a horizontal push of 2 lb applied perpendicularly to the door at the edge near the knob, what push is needed if applied at the center of the door?

2. Assume that a bicycle pedal is attached to the end of a crank 6 in. long and that a boy's foot presses vertically downward upon it with a constant force of 10 lb. Calculate the torque when the crank is (a) horizontal and (b) at an angle of 30° below the horizontal.

3. A uniform plank 10 ft long is pivoted at its midpoint. A 100-lb boy sits halfway between the pivot and one end, and at that end the plank rests on a platform scale. What should the scale reading be?

4. Use a sheet of thin paper and carefully trace the directions of the four forces shown in Fig. D on page 84. Then draw them carefully to scale in their exact directions and show that they form a closed polygon. If they do not, by how many pounds does the polygon fail to close?

Lesson 21

1. A piece of thin plywood is cut in the shape of an L, like a carpenter's square. The short arm is 1½ ft long and the long arm is 3 ft long, each measured on the center

MECHANICS

line. Make a sketch to scale and label it as follows: *O* is the point where the two arms meet, *OS* is the short arm, *OL* is the long arm, *A* is the midpoint of *OS,* and *B* is the midpoint of *OL.* Locate the center of gravity of the L-shaped "square."

2. Suppose the L-shaped "square" of the preceding problem to be pivoted at *O* and free to swing in a vertical plane. Make a diagram showing the position in which it would come to rest. For the rest position, measure and record the angle between the long arm *OL* and the vertical.

3. A square sheet of metal measures 16 in. along each edge. How far is the center of gravity shifted by folding one edge over so that it coincides with the center line of the original sheet?

4.* Calculate the location of the center of mass of the earth-moon system. See page 70.

5.* A croquet mallet has a cylindrical head 2½ in. in diameter that weighs 0.9 lb, and a handle that projects 24 in. from the head; the handle is a uniform cylinder and weighs ¼ lb. Locate the center of gravity of the mallet and state how far it is located from the free end of the handle.

Lesson 23

1. A picture weighing 2 lb hangs from a nail in the wall by a cord fastened to the two top corners of the frame. Find the tension in the cord if it makes an angle of 30° with the top edge of the frame.

2. A uniform board 10 ft long and weighing 30 lb is suspended by two vertical ropes, one at each end, and serves as a scaffold for a painter to stand upon. If the painter weighs 140 lb, what is the tension in each rope when he stands 2 ft from the left end?

3. A 4200-lb truck has a 140-in. wheelbase. If the front tires press against the ground with a joint force of 1800 lb, find (a) the joint force with which the rear tires press against the ground and (b) the horizontal location of the center of gravity of the truck.

4.* A uniform ladder 10 ft long and weighing 100 lb leans against a smooth wall and makes an angle of 60° with the horizontal. A 160-lb man is standing on the ladder at a point 6 ft from its base. Find all forces on the ladder. Assume the force of the wall on the top end of the ladder is horizontal.

Lesson 24

1. A heavy box weighing 76 lb requires a horizontal force of 28 lb to pull it across the floor. Suppose that at an instant when the box has acquired a velocity of 7 ft/sec, the applied force of 28 lb is discontinued, allowing the box to come to rest. How far will the box slide after the force is stopped?

2. A force of 50 newtons is applied to a mass of 20 kg, 10 newtons being used to oppose friction. Find (a) the acceleration and (b) the speed acquired at the end of 5 sec.

3. A force of 550 gm-wt is found necessary to pull a 1-kg steel block at constant speed across an oak table top. If this block is placed on an inclined oak board, at what angle of inclination will the block slide down at constant speed?

4. What horizontal force is required to accelerate a 2400-lb car from standstill to a speed of 40 ft/sec in 10 sec on level concrete pavement? Include friction.

Lesson 27

1. A rowboat is pulled behind a cabin cruiser by a rope inclined at an angle of 35° with the horizontal. The tension in the rope is 45 lb. How much work is done in pulling the rowboat for ¼ mi?

2. How much work is done on a 4-ton elevator which is accelerating upward for 5 sec while the speed increases at a constant rate from 0 to 15 ft/sec?

3. A driver, in bringing a car to a stop, skids on all four tires. If the car weighs 3300 lb and is traveling at 45 mi/hr when it is brought to a stop, what is the amount of energy wasted in friction?

4.* A 200-lb block of iron is drawn 20 ft along a concrete floor. This is done by tying a rope to the block and pulling on the rope. The rope extends upward at 30° with the floor and is pulled with a constant force of 60 lb. Calculate (a) the normal force between the block and the floor, (b) the amount of work done, and (c) the energy wasted in opposing friction.

5. A canal boat is being pulled by two ropes making an angle of 45° with each other. The forces are 150 lb and 175 lb, respectively. The boat is being moved 100 ft along the direction of the resultant force. Calculate the amount of work done upon it (a) by the 150-lb force and (b) by the 175-lb force.

Lesson 29

1. A block slides down a plank 3 m long, one end of which is raised 1 m above the other. The sliding surfaces are greased, and friction may be neglected. Under these circumstances the potential energy of the block at the top of the incline is equal to its kinetic energy at the bottom. Write this statement in the form of an equation and solve for the velocity of the block upon reaching the bottom.

2. A block sliding down an inclined plane reaches the bottom with 30 ft-lb of kinetic energy. If the block weighs 5 lb, with what velocity did it reach the bottom? (*Note:* Mass must be in slugs.)

3. A car weighing 2400 lb is driven at 45 mi/hr. If its kinetic energy could be used to raise the car upward from the earth's surface, through what height would the car be raised?

4. A constant horizontal force of 25 lb acts for a distance of 20 ft on a 500-lb midget racing car. Through what height would a 20-lb weight have to fall to acquire the same amount of kinetic energy as the midget racing car?

5. A train that weighs 100 tons is drawn along a level track at a constant velocity of 60 mi/hr. Assume that the train is acted upon by a backward force of friction of 1450 lb and calculate the power required to pull it.

6. An automobile weighing 3200 lb and moving with a velocity of 45 mi/hr (i.e., 66 ft/sec) is brought to rest in a distance of 200 ft. Calculate the number of horsepower expended in stopping the automobile.

Lesson 31

1. A block starts from rest and slides down a plane that is inclined at 30° with the horizontal. Assume the plane to be frictionless. When the block is halfway down the incline, how does its potential energy (with respect to the base) compare with its kinetic energy?

2. A simple pendulum 1 m long has a 1-kg bob. Raise the bob until the string is horizontal and then release. Find (a) the kinetic energy of the bob at an instant when the string is at 45° with the vertical and (b) its velocity at the same instant.

3.* An oak box weighing 100 lb is pulled 12 ft up an oak plank by a force of 80 lb. The plank makes an angle of 30° with the horizontal. What is the work done on the box? Subtract the potential energy and the stored energy from the work done, thus finding the kinetic energy of the box at the top of the incline.

4.* An oak block of a mass of 2 kg starts from rest and slides down an oak plank 5 m long, one end of which is 3 m higher than the other. Find (a) the potential energy of the block at the top of the incline, (b) the energy wasted in opposing friction on the way down, and (c) by subtraction, the kinetic energy of the block at the bottom of the incline.

Lesson 32

1. Two steel blocks slide toward each other on a smooth horizontal surface and collide head on. One block weighs 8 lb and moves toward the right at 10 ft/sec; the other weighs 2 lb and moves toward the left at 5 ft/sec. After the collision, suppose that the 8-lb block moves toward the right at 4 ft/sec and calculate the velocity of the 2-lb block.

2.* A lead block of 100-gm mass is moving at 5 m/sec behind a second lead block moving in the same direction at 2 m/sec. The blocks collide, and after the collision they move without change of direction but both have the same velocity: 3 m/sec. (a) What was the mass of the second block? (b) Out of the total kinetic energy that the blocks possessed initially, what per cent was wasted in heat?

3.* A steel ball that weighs 3 lb is suspended by a vertical cord 2 ft long so that it hangs just in contact with one side of a 6-lb steel block at rest on a smooth horizontal plane. Next, the ball is pulled away until the cord is at 60° with the vertical, whereupon it is released and swings as a pendulum. Use the principle of conservation of energy to find (a) its velocity just before it strikes the block. Then apply the principle of conservation of momentum and also the principle of conservation of energy to the collision between the ball and the block, considering this as an elastic collision. From the resulting equations find (b) the velocity of the block and that of the ball after collision.

4.* A wood block of mass 3 kg is moving along a horizontal surface at a speed of 10 m/sec in the X direction. A 30-gm bullet is shot into the block along the Y direction (at right angles to the motion of the block) with a velocity of 600 m/sec and becomes embedded in the block. Apply the law of conservation of momentum to the Y direction and determine (a) the momentum of the block (including the bullet) in the Y direction after impact. Then find (b) the velocity of the block in the Y direction and (c) the angle through which the path of the block is shifted by the collision.

Lesson 37

1. A wheel and axle is used to lift a weight of 120 lb through a height of 30 ft. If the radius of the wheel is 8 in. and that of the axle is 3 in., calculate (a) the force that must be applied to the wheel rope and (b) the distance through which this force must be exerted.

2. A crowbar 5 ft long and weighing 4 lb per foot of length is used to pry a large stone out of the ground. If the fulcrum is 6 in. from the stone and if the operator pushes vertically downward with a force of 100 lb at the free end of the crowbar, what vertically upward force is exerted on the stone?

3. Two wheel-and-axle combinations are mounted side by side. No. 1 has a mechanical advantage of 4, and No. 2 has a mechanical advantage of 5. The axle rope of No. 1 passes downward to a 200-lb load. The wheel rope of No. 1 passes to the axle of No. 2. The operator pulls on the wheel rope of No. 2 and raises the load at constant speed. Calculate (a) the tension in the rope connecting No. 1 and No. 2, (b) the force exerted by the operator, and (c) the combined mechanical advantage of the two wheel-and-axle combinations.

4. A force of 30 lb is required to raise a 150-lb weight by means of a pulley system. If the weight is raised 6 in. while the force is exerted through 4 ft, calculate (a) the mechanical advantage and (b) the efficiency of the pulley system.

Lesson 39

1. A 2-lb weight is tied to a slender cord and whirled in a horizontal circle of 18-in. radius. Neglecting gravity, what is the highest linear speed at which it can be driven without exceeding the breaking strength of the cord, which is 10 lb?

2. In making an unbanked turn in an automobile, where the necessary centripetal force must be furnished by friction between the rubber tires and the concrete highway, what is the highest speed at which a curve of 100-ft radius can be rounded?

3. When a certain locomotive rounds a particular curve at 40 mi/hr, the outer rail must exert a centripetal force of 36 tons upon it. If it were to round the same curve at 60 mi/hr, what centripetal force would be required?

4. A driver who finds that he can round a curve of 200-ft radius safely with his car going at 45 mi/hr should reduce his speed to what value when he encounters a curve of 50-ft radius? Both curves are unbanked and have concrete pavement.

Lesson 41

1. Compute the moment of inertia of a flywheel which is brought from rest to a speed of 1200 rpm in 20 sec when acted upon by a constant torque of 15 lb ft.

2. An 8-lb emery wheel 1 ft in diameter is making 3600 rpm. Calculate (a) the constant torque that would bring it from rest to its stated speed in 12 sec and (b) the kinetic energy of the wheel at its stated speed.

3. An emery wheel rotates at 2400 rpm and possesses 1580 joules of kinetic energy. At what angular velocity will its kinetic energy be reduced to one-half of the value stated?

4. A uniform disk of 1-m radius and 5-kg mass rotates about its center at 5 rad/sec. Suppose that the disk starts from rest and is acted upon by a constant torque of 1.5 newton meters. In what length of time will the disk reach the speed of 5 rad/sec?

5. A cast-iron sphere having a radius of 0.1 m and a mass of 30 kg is mounted in bearings on a central shaft and given a speed of 240 rpm. Left to itself it comes to rest in 10.1 sec because of friction. Calculate the backward torque due to friction.

Lesson 42

1. A large grindstone is rotating with an angular speed of 360 rpm and its kinetic energy is 1200 joules. Calculate its angular momentum.

2. The armature of a motor when turning at its rated speed has an angular momentum of 300 newton m sec and its kinetic energy is 18,850 joules. From these data calculate its rated speed in revolutions per minute.

3. Suppose that the ball in Fig. B on page 150 is whirling on a frictionless table top and that the string is fastened to a peg at the center of the circle, so that as the ball revolves, the string winds around the peg and the circle gets smaller. If the ball is set into motion at 70 cm/sec in a circle of 12-cm radius, what is its linear velocity when the radius is reduced to 6 cm?

4.* In the apparatus shown in Fig. C on page 150 suppose that each of the masses m m weighs 2 lb and that initially they are rotating in a circle of 8-in. radius at the rate of 2 rev/sec. When the ring is pulled up, if the radius of the circle is reduced to 5 in., what is the angular velocity of the masses? Consider each of the masses to be concentrated, as in part e of Fig. D on page 147.

PROPERTIES OF MATTER

Lesson 1

1. An iron wire 200 cm long hangs vertically from the ceiling and to its lower end a copper wire 300 cm long is securely fastened. Each wire has a cross-sectional area of 0.0125 cm². When a mass of 5 kg is suspended from the lower end of the wire combination, what total elongation is produced?

2. A load weighing 1000 lb is supported from above by two wires, *A* and *B*. Wire *A* is 20 ft long and makes an angle of 30° with the horizontal. Wire *B* is 14.14 ft long and makes an angle of 45° with the horizontal. Each wire is of iron and has a cross-sectional area of 0.08 in.^{2} Calculate the elongation of wire *A*.

3. A copper wire and a brass wire hang vertically, and each supports a load at the lower end. The copper wire is 4 m long. If the wires have the same cross-sectional area and support equal loads, how long should the brass wire be in order that both wires shall stretch by the same amount?

4. In the crane problem illustrated in Fig. A on page 92, suppose the tie rope to consist of a brass wire having a length of 6.22 ft and a cross-sectional area of 0.003 in.^{2} Calculate the elongation of the tie rope under the load conditions described.

Lesson 3

1. A timber beam 10 ft long, 6 in. wide, and 2 in. thick is supported at the ends and loaded at the middle as in Fig. A on page 166. For a load of 500 lb the central bending displacement is 3 in. Suppose the beam were laid like a floor beam, with the 6-in. sides vertical and the 2-in. sides horizontal, and calculate the central bending displacement for the same 500-lb load.

2. A uniform strip of metal 50 cm long, 5 cm wide, and 1 cm thick is supported at both ends and loaded at the middle as in Fig. A on page 166. The load has a mass of 40 kg and causes a bending displacement of 0.2 cm at the middle of the strip. From these data calculate Young's modulus for the material of the strip.

3. An ivory ball is dropped from a height of 72 in. onto the smooth surface of a heavy anvil. The energy of the ball on rebound is what fraction of its energy before it strikes the anvil? The coefficient of restitution is 0.60.

4. A smooth, heavy iron plate is mounted vertically on a wall. Directly above the plate a cord is fastened to the wall, and to this cord is attached an ivory ball with a coefficient of restitution of 0.60. Starting with the cord horizontal, the ball is released as a pendulum and strikes the plate; through what angle will the cord swing on the rebound?

5.* An ivory ball of a mass of 100 gm and moving with a speed of 300 cm/sec collides head-on with another ivory ball of the same mass and size, moving with equal speed in the opposite direction. Take the coefficient of restitution as 0.6 and find the velocity of each ball after collision.

Lesson 4

1. The pressure within a water main is 75 lb/in.^{2} higher than that outside. What height of water in a standpipe would be needed to furnish the same pressure? Take the weight of 1 in.^{3} of water to be 0.036 lb.

2. If 1 in.^{3} of water weighs 0.036 lb and 1 in.^{3} of mercury weighs 0.50 lb, at what depth below the surface of water would the liquid pressure be the same as that at a depth of 30 in. below the surface of mercury?

3. An open-top cubical tank measuring 4 ft along each edge is level full of water. Given that 1 in.^{3} of water weighs 0.036 lb, calculate (a) the water pressure at the bottom of the tank and (b) the total force on the bottom due to the water.

4. The areas of the pistons in a hydraulic press are 1600 in.^{2} and 4 in.^{2}, respectively. Assume that this press is filled with water. There is a 2-ton automobile exerting pressure on the large piston. Calculate the total pressure at a point within the water 5 ft below the large piston. Include the pressure due to the water above the point (1 in.^{3} of water weighs 0.036 lb) but neglect the weight of the piston.

Lesson 6

1. A wood plank floating on water projects 2.5 cm above the surface. If the plank is 7.5 cm thick, what is the density of the wood?

2. A cubical block of wood measuring 10 cm along each edge floats with 2.5 cm projecting above the surface when placed in water, and it floats with 1.67 cm projecting when placed in oil. Find (a) the density of the wood and (b) the density of the oil.

3. A block of pine wood 2 ft long, 6 in. wide, and 4 in. thick is floating on water. A 3-lb metal weight is carefully placed upon it. The wood block then floats with 1 in. projecting above the liquid surface. From these data calculate the weight density of the wood.

4. A test tube, open at one end, has a length of 30 cm, a diameter of 2 cm, and a mass of 20 gm. In the tube is placed some lead shot, of mass 60 gm, so that it will float upright in water. Calculate how far above the water surface it will project when so floating.

Lesson 8

1. Carbon tetrachloride at 20°C is found to rise to a height of 4.6 cm in a glass capillary tube that has a bore diameter of 0.15 mm. Take the density of carbon tetrachloride to be 1.6 gm/cm³ and calculate the coefficient of surface tension of this liquid.

2. A thin wire formed into a circular loop is placed in a horizontal plane beneath the surface of a liquid under test, and the force necessary to pull it upward through the surface is measured. If the loop has a radius of 1 cm and if the force, in addition to the weight of the loop, is 465 dynes, calculate the coefficient of surface tension of the liquid.

3. A liquid of density 1.26 gm/cm³ rises to a height of 8.16 cm in a glass capillary tube having a bore diameter of 0.25 mm. If this liquid were tested as shown in Fig. D on page 181, how much force would be needed to pull a U-shaped wire 3.5 cm long through the liquid surface?

4. A force of 150 dynes is required to pull a U-shaped wire 3 cm long out of a certain liquid and break the film as shown in Fig. D on page 181. If the liquid has a density of 0.87 gm/cm³, to what height will it rise in a glass capillary tube having a bore diameter of 0.2 mm?

Lesson 9

1. At an altitude of 10 kilometers above sea level, the average value of atmospheric pressure is reported to be 210 mm of mercury. What would a water barometer read (in feet and inches) at the same altitude?

2. Assume a mercury barometer reading to drop 1 cm from normal and calculate the drop of a water barometer for the same lowering of atmospheric pressure.

3. The cylinder and piston in Fig. G on page 187 have an internal diameter of 6 in. What maximum load can be lifted by the piston as the cylinder is evacuated? Assume the atmospheric pressure to be 15 lb/in.² and that the cylinder is to be evacuated only enough to lower the pressure within it to one-third of its normal value.

4. When the mercury column in a barometer at sea level is 30 in. high, what is the average density of the air above sea level? Assume that the atmosphere extends to a height of 600 mi, and express the result in grams per cubic centimeter.

5. Atmospheric pressure decreases, for moderate heights, about 1 in. for each 1000 ft of elevation. Suppose you had an aneroid barometer calibrated in inches and wanted to use it as an altimeter. You might cover the barometer scale with blank paper and mark it "altitude, thousands of feet," and then replace the 30-in. mark with "0"

(zero), taking 30 in. to be standard pressure at zero altitude or sea level. With what numbers would you replace the 29-, 28-, and 27-in. marks?

Lesson 11

1. A cylindrical tank 80 ft high and full of water develops a hole in its side 16 ft below the top. A second hole develops vertically below the first hole, from which water strikes the ground at the same point as water from the first hole. How far up from the base is the lower hole located?

2. An open-top tank 3 m deep is kept level full of water, while a steady stream flows out through an orifice in the side wall at a point ½ m from the bottom of the tank. At the orifice the stream enters an elbow with the open end pointed upward. Calculate the height above the orifice to which the issuing stream will rise.

3. A main 6 in. in diameter branches into two pipes each 4 in. in diameter. The piping system is horizontal and full of flowing water. Assume the velocity in the 6-in. main to be 2 ft/sec. Calculate the velocity in the 4-in. pipes.

4. Water flows with a velocity of 2 m/sec in a pipe 4 cm² in cross section. Calculate the kinetic energy of the water contained in a 10-meter length of the pipe.

Lesson 14

1. A mass of 0.5 kg suspended from a coiled spring stretches the spring 5 cm. Next, another mass is added, stretching the spring 15 cm more. When the entire mass is set vibrating up and down, what will be its period of vibration?

2. A certain spring pendulum vibrates with a period of 0.6 sec. If the load carried by the spring is replaced by one having three times the mass, what will then be the period?

3. A mass of 50 gm hangs from the lower end of a coil spring. The spring constant is 2000 dynes/cm. Calculate the length of a simple pendulum that will have the same period as this coil spring.

4. A piano string vibrating with a period of 0.00391 sec sends out a sound wave that has a velocity of 1100 ft/sec. Find the frequency and and the wave length.

HEAT

Lesson 1

1. At what temperature do the Centigrade and Fahrenheit scales have the same reading?

2. If the temperature of a fever patient is 5° above normal as measured on the Fahrenheit scale, how much above normal would it be as measured on the Centigrade scale?

3. The temperature of "dry ice" is $-78°C$. Express this temperature on the Fahrenheit scale.

4. The linear coefficient of thermal expansion of tin is 15×10^{-6} per °F. Find the value of this constant per °C.

5. A rectangular frame made from aluminum strips is exactly 18 in. high and 27 in. wide. If these dimensions were measured at 10°C and the temperature then rose to 40°C, calculate (a) the height and width of the frame at the higher temperature and (b) the increase that took place in the area of the frame.

6. A brass rod at 20°C is to be heated until its length is increased by 1 per cent. To what value should its temperature be raised?

7.* A steel tape measure 100 ft long is standardized to be used at 72°F. Calculate what stretching force applied to the tape will make its readings correct when used at a temperature of 0°F. Assume the tape to be ½ in. wide and 1/64 in. thick, and take Young's modulus from the table on page 164.

Lesson 3

1. How many British thermal units must be supplied to 1 lb of water at its freezing point in order to raise it to its boiling point and then vaporize it? See Fig. B on page 216.

2. How many grams of iron would give off enough heat in cooling from 400°C to 40°C to raise the temperature of 200 gm of water from 20°C to 40°C?

3. The iron rim of a wagon wheel has an internal diameter of 1.0 m when the temperature is 150°C. If the rim is 10 cm wide and 0.5 cm thick, how much heat does it give off in cooling from 150°C to 25°C?

4. A copper can of mass 70 gm contains 400 gm of water at 20°C. How many grams of water at 50°C should be added to produce a final temperature of 30°C for the mixture?

5. A 150-gm sample of an alloy under test is heated to 200°C and dropped into a 30-gm copper can containing 300 gm of water, all at 16°C. If the final temperature of the mixture is 24°C, what is the specific heat of the alloy?

Lesson 4

1. What is the rate of heat conduction through a copper rod 18 cm long and having a cross-sectional area of 3 cm² when one end is maintained at 90°C and the other end at 5°C? Express the result in calories per second.

2. To measure the thermal conductivity of steel, a steel rod, covered with heat insulation, was heated at one end and cooled at the other. After steady conditions were established, the following readings were taken: temperature of hot end, 60°C; temperature of cold end, 10°C; rate of heat flow, 1.2 cal/sec. The rod had a length of 15 cm and a diameter of 2 cm. From these data calculate the thermal conductivity of the sample.

3.* In engineering work dealing with heat conduction through walls, the amount of heat H is commonly expressed in British thermal units, the length of the heat path L in inches, its cross-sectional area A in square feet, the time interval of flow T in hours, and the temperature difference $t_2 - t_1$ in Fahrenheit degrees. Express the thermal conductivity of wood in the unit Btu in./hr ft² F°.

4.* A laboratory oven is to be kept at a constant temperature by operating an electric lamp continuously inside the oven to offset heat lost by conduction through its walls. The oven is constructed of fiber board which has a thermal conductivity of 0.00012 cal cm/sec cm² C°. The surface of the oven is 18,600 cm² and the walls are 2.5 cm thick. The inside temperature is to be maintained at 37°C and the surrounding temperature may be taken as 21°C. Calculate the wattage of the electric lamp needed to offset heat conduction losses.

Lesson 6

1. Under certain conditions a blackened copper sphere radiates 500 cal of heat per min to its surroundings and at the same time absorbs 420 cal of heat per min from its surroundings. If the sphere has a mass of 150 gm, at what rate is its temperature falling?

2. If the temperature of the ball in the preceding problem is 665°K, what is the temperature of the surroundings?

3. A certain black body when heated to a temperature of 500°K radiates 5 cal of heat per second to its surroundings. At what temperature will the heat radiation be doubled?

4. A black body at a temperature of 300°K is placed in a blackened enclosure which is also at a temperature of 300°K. At what rate is the body radiating heat to the surroundings?

5. A polished steel sphere having a surface area of 50 cm² is placed in a blackened enclosure, the walls of which are maintained at 700°K. (a) How many calories of radiant heat fall upon the sphere every second? (b) About how many of these calories are absorbed?

6.* A blackened copper ball is heated to a temperature of 127°C. The ball has a radius of 1 cm, a surface area of 12.56 cm², and a volume of 4.187 cm³. (a) How many calories of heat are radiated from the ball per second? (b) Use the same method and find how many calories of heat are radiated from the surroundings to the ball per second, assuming that the surroundings are at a temperature of 27°C. (c) By subtraction, what is the net loss of heat per second by the ball? (d) At what rate in degrees per second is the temperature of the ball falling?

Lesson 8

1. The temperature in a room is 25°C and the relative humidity is 35 per cent. If the room is 4 m wide, 5 m long, and 3 m high, how many grams of water vapor does it contain?

2. The dew point in a room is found to be 10°C. (a) What is the absolute humidity in the room? (b) If the room temperature is 20°C, what is the relative humidity? (c) If the room temperature should drop to 5°C, how much water vapor would condense?

3. Some air at 25°C occupies a volume of 400 m³, the relative humidity being 30 per cent. Some more air, also at 25°C, occupies a volume of 600 m³, the relative humidity being 50 per cent. If these volumes of air are allowed to mix, what is the relative humidity of the combination?

4. A room has a volume of 1000 m³ and contains air at 25°C, the relative humidity being 10 per cent. One-fifth of this air is withdrawn and replaced by an equal volume of saturated air at 15°C. Calculate the resulting absolute humidity.

Lesson 9

1. Given some water at a temperature of 50°C and at a pressure of 100 cm of mercury. Refer to Fig. B on page 234 and calculate (a) the value to which the pressure must be lowered to make the water boil at its present temperature of 50°C and (b) the value to which the temperature must be raised to make it boil at its present pressure of 100 cm of mercury.

Lesson 11

1. A trunk weighing 100 lb is pulled 20 ft across the floor. If the coefficient of sliding friction is 0.50, calculate the amount of heat produced in opposing friction.

2. An automobile weighing 3200 lb and moving with a velocity of 45 mi/hr (i.e., 66 ft/sec) is brought to rest in a distance of 200 ft. How much heat was produced in the brakes while the automobile was coming to rest?

3. Because of air friction, raindrops fall with constant speed and also become heated. Neglect heat radiated to the surroundings and calculate the rise in temperature of a raindrop in falling 1000 ft at constant speed.

4. A quantity of nitrogen occupies a volume of 20 ft³ at a pressure of 40 lb/in.² and a temperature of 90°C. What volume will it occupy when its pressure is increased to 70 lb/in.² and its temperature raised to 180°C?

5.* A cylinder similar to that in Fig. E on page 241 contains 1 ft³ of nitrogen at a pressure of 15 lb/in.² and a temperature of 27°C. At first, heat is applied and the gas expands at constant pressure, its temperature rising to 527°C. Next, the piston is pushed inward, compressing the gas into a volume of 0.75 ft³. This process of compression is carried out so slowly that the heat produced by compression escapes through the cylinder walls, so this step may be considered to take place at constant temperature. Finally the piston is blocked in position and the cylinder is cooled, lowering the temperature of the gas to 327°C at constant volume. Find the final pressure of the nitrogen.

SOUND

Lesson 1

1. How much longer will it take sound to travel 1000 ft through air at 0°C than to travel an equal distance through water?

2. A sound wave sent by a ship to the bottom of the ocean returns after 2.15 sec. Calculate the depth of the ocean at the place of measurement.

3. A steel pipe is struck a heavy blow at a distance point. An observer near the pipe hears two sounds, one through the pipe and the other through the air. If the time interval between the sounds is 3¼ sec, how far away from the observer was the pipe struck? Take the air temperature to be 20°C.

4. A card is held against the teeth of a rotating wheel, as shown on page 260. The wheel has 50 teeth and is driven by a variable-speed motor. How fast should it be driven for the vibrating card to produce a tone having the pitch of middle C, 264 vib/sec?

5. A missile of Mach No. 2 is in a region where the temperature is 175°F. What is its velocity in miles per hour?

Lesson 3

1. Two violin strings sounded together produce 50 beats in 15 sec. One string has a frequency of 440 vib/sec; find two possible frequencies for the other string.

2. An organist having no note on his instrument of pitch lower than 33.0 vib/sec is able to produce a beat note having one-half the frequency just stated. To obtain this result, he sounds the note of 33.0 vib/sec simultaneously with another note. What is the frequency of the other note?

3. An observer on a north-bound train hears the whistle of a south-bound train which approaches and passes him. The north-bound train is moving at 45 mi/hr and the south-bound train is moving at 60 mi/hr. The whistle has a frequency of 350 vib/sec. What is the observed pitch (a) while the whistle is approaching the observer and (b) after it has passed the observer? Take the velocity of sound as 1100 ft/sec.

4. A freight train moving at 20 ft/sec sounds its whistle of 400 vib/sec. What frequency is heard by a trainman running forward on the train at 10 ft/sec?

Lesson 4

1. A copper wire 3 m long and 2 sq mm in cross-sectional area hangs from the ceiling. A 2-kg mass is suspended from the lower end. Calculate the frequency with which the wire would vibrate if it was plucked.

2. A wire of mass 0.5 gm is stretched between two supports 1 m apart. Calculate the stretching force in the wire if a transverse wave set up in it travels from end to end in 0.0025 sec.

3. A string is stretched with a force of 60 newtons between supports 0.4 meter apart. If the mass of the string is 3×10^{-4} kg, what is the frequency of vibration of the third harmonic?

4. A slender wire stretched with a force of 100 newtons vibrates with a frequency of 250 vib/sec. If the stretching force were reduced to 90 newtons, what would be the new value of the frequency?

Lesson 6

1. Two organ pipes, each closed at one end, are sounded together. The pipes are 48 and 50 in. long, respectively, and each is vibrating in its fundamental mode. Calculate the number of beats produced per minute.

2. Find the length of an air column open at both ends that will vibrate in resonance with an air column 3 ft long open at one end.

3. Calculate the length of a pipe open at one end in which the air column will vibrate with the same frequency as a stretched wire whose mass is 0.08 gm/cm length and along which waves travel at 50 m/sec. Take the length of the wire to be 25 cm and assume that both sounding bodies vibrate in the fundamental mode.

4. Tuning forks are often mounted on resonator boxes as shown in Fig. B on page 263. Calculate the length of such a resonator box for a tuning fork with a frequency of 264 vib/sec.

5. Calculate the frequency with which impulses should be applied to the air column within a chimney 50 ft tall to set it vibrating in its fundamental mode. Assume that the chimney is closed at the base and open at the top, and take the velocity of sound in air to be 1100 ft/sec.

6. (a) Use the equation $V = \sqrt{K\dfrac{p}{\rho}}$ to calculate the speed of sound in air at a pressure of 76 cm of mercury and a temperature of 0°C. The density of air under these conditions is 0.00129 gm/cm³. (b) Modify the result found in (a) to find the speed at 20°C. Each degree centigrade rise in temperature increases the speed in air by 61 cm/sec.

Lesson 8

1. A source emits sound energy at the rate of 10 watts. Assume the radiation to be uniform in all directions and calculate the intensity of the sound (a) at a distance of 850 cm from the source and (b) at a distance of 600 cm from the source.

2. In the preceding problem, if an observer starts at 850 cm from the source and moves to the position 600 cm from the source, what increase of sound level does he encounter?

3. An observer moves from a point 20 ft away from a sounding source to a new position 10 ft from the source. (a) How does the sound intensity at the new position compare with that at his earlier position? (b) What approximate increase of sound level occurred in moving to the new position?

4. For a sound level of 120 db, at what rate in ft-lb per minute is energy wasted as sound through a square foot of area taken normal to the direction of the wave?

LIGHT

Lesson 1

1. A pinhole camera has photographic film 4 in. high mounted 6 in. behind the pinhole. To take a picture of a building 90 ft high and get it all on the film, how far from the building should the camera be located?

2. Even with its amazing speed, light from the nearest star travels about 3½ years to reach the earth. How far away is the star, in millions of miles?

3. How far does light travel in 1 microsecond?

4. Light travels through water at ¾ of its velocity in air, and it travels through carbon disulfide at 8/13 of its velocity in air. How far will light travel through water in the time that it travels 32 cm through carbon disulfide?

Lesson 2

1. What thickness of water will light pass through in the same time that it takes to pass through a glass slab 1 in. thick?

2. Light passes through a certain slab of glass in 10^{-4} microsecond. Find the time in which it will pass through an equal thickness of water.

3. If a lamp suspended 20 ft above the ground is rated 600 candle power, will the illuminance on the ground be greater than the illuminance of 1.2 ft-candles coming from a light of 750 candle power suspended 25 ft above the ground?

4. Calculate how high above the table top a 60-watt lamp with an efficiency of 1.1 candles per watt should be located to produce the same illuminance as a 100-watt lamp located 3 ft above a table top with an efficiency of 1.27 candles per watt.

5. A 60-watt lamp and a 75-watt lamp are located 6 ft apart, and a photometer screen placed between them is equally illuminated when it is 2.79 ft from the 60-watt lamp. If the efficiency of the 60-watt lamp is 1.1 candles/watt, what is the efficiency of the 75-watt lamp?

Lesson 4

1. In Fig. C on page 310 let the parallel mirrors MN be 10 cm apart and the object 2 cm from M. Calculate the distance between the two images marked 3.

2. A man stands at the center of a square room measuring 12 ft along each edge. He faces the north wall, centered on which there is a plane mirror. How wide must the mirror be in order that the man can see the entire width of the south wall in it by reflection?

3. In Fig. D on page 311, if the object O is 4 cm from mirror M and 3 cm from mirror N, what is the radius of the circle on which its images are located?

4.* A ray of light strikes a plane mirror as in Fig. A on page 309, except that the angle of incidence is 30°. If the mirror is rotated through an angle of 10° about an axis perpendicular to the page, through what angle is the reflected ray rotated?

Lesson 6

1. An object 3 cm high located 40 cm in front of a concave mirror of 20-cm radius is moved 10 cm nearer the vertex of the mirror. What change takes place in (a) the image distance and (b) the image height?

2. An object 3 cm high and located 60 cm in front of a concave mirror of 30-cm radius is moved to a point 7.5 cm in front of the mirror. Calculate what change takes place in (a) the image distance, (b) the image height, and (c) the nature of the image.

3. Where should an object be placed with respect to a concave mirror in order to form an image at the center of curvature C?

4. A convex mirror has a focal length of 20 cm. Where should an object be placed to form an image ¼ as high as the object?

Lesson 7

1. A ray of light is incident upon a glass surface as in Fig. A on page 318. It is found that when the angle of incidence is 60°, the reflected ray at the surface is at right angles with the refracted ray within the glass. Calculate the refractive index of the glass.

2. Light is incident upon a glass surface at an angle of 50°, and the angle of refraction is 27°. If the angle of incidence is changed to 40°, what is the new angle of refraction?

3. Light passes through a 60° prism as shown in Fig. E on page 320, except that the ray passes symmetrically through the prism so that within the prism the ray is

parallel to the base. If the angle of incidence at the first face is 50°, what is the refractive index of the glass?

4.* A ray of light passes through two slabs of glass, each 1 in. thick. The slabs are separated by a layer of air of negligible thickness. The upper slab is of crown glass and has a refractive index of 1.5. The lower slab is of flint glass and has a refractive index of 1.75. If the ray is incident at 60° on the upper slab, what is the total lateral displacement produced by the combination?

Lesson 9

1. In Fig. G on page 326 calculate (a) the focal length of the lens and (b) the height of each image, taking the height of the object as 1 cm.

2. An object is placed 60 cm in front of a converging lens and its image is located 40 cm behind the lens. If the object is moved 12 cm farther away from the lens, where will the image be located?

3. A converging lens is placed 80 cm away from an object and forms an image 50 cm behind the lens. In order to get a larger image the lens is moved 30 cm nearer the object. (a) How far from the lens will the image then be and (b) how will this image compare in height with the one obtained before the lens was moved?

4. Two converging lenses are placed 100 cm apart with their axes along the same line. Each has a focal length of 20 cm. An object 5 cm high is located 40 cm in front of the first lens and its image serves as the object for the second lens. (a) How far behind the second lens is the final image formed and (b) what is the height of the final image?

Lesson 11

1. When a beam of light within a water solution of sodium chloride approaches the surface at an angle of incidence greater than 47.4°, no light is refracted out into the air. If a beam of light in air approaches the surface of the same solution at an angle of incidence of 47.4°, what is the angle of refraction within the solution?

2. When a beam of light traveling in amber approaches the surface at an angle of incidence greater than 40.2°, no light is refracted out into the air. If the angle of incidence within the amber is 30°, what is the angle of refraction for the ray that enters the air?

3. A ray of light incident on a glass surface at an angle of 45° is deviated through an angle of 18°. Find the value of the critical angle of the glass.

4. When white light travels in dense flint glass, how much faster do the rays of red light move then those of violet? See Table 1 on page 331.

Lesson 14

1. An object 6 ft high is photographed by a camera having a lens of 4-in. focal length. If the object is 15 ft in front of the camera, how high is the image in the photograph?

2. In the telescope shown in Fig. E on page 340, assume that an image of a distant object is formed 100 cm behind the objective lens and that this image serves as an object for the eyepiece. If the eyepiece has a focal length of 8 cm, what is the magnifying power of the telescope?

3. A projection lantern uses a converging lens. The film to be projected is placed behind the lens and is brightly illuminated by a concealed lamp, and the enlarged image appears as a picture on a screen in front of the lens. If the film measures 2¼ cm by 3 cm and the screen is 5 m from the projection lens of 15-cm focal length, what is the size of the picture?

4. The simple magnifying glass is a converging lens of short focus. With the object at the focus of the lens, the eye is brought near the lens and accommodated for infinite

distance. The image is magnified, erect, and virtual, and the magnification becomes $M = 10$ in./f where f is the focal length of the lens in inches. Calculate the magnifying power of a magnifying glass of 2.5-cm focal length.

Lesson 16

1. Violet light of wave length 4×10^{-5} cm falls on a double slit, and interference fringes are formed 2 m away on a white screen. How far apart would the interference fringes be?

2. Suppose Fig. E on page 344 to be the exact size of the interference pattern produced by a double slit with a spacing of 0.8 mm, using light of wave length 0.000066 cm, and calculate the distance between the double slit and the screen.

3. When a double slit with a spacing of 1 mm is illuminated by light from glowing sodium vapor and the interference pattern is measured on a screen 2 m away, it is found that the distance along the screen from the central fringe to the seventeenth fringe on either side is 2 cm. From these data, calculate the wave length of the light emitted by glowing sodium vapor.

4. Light of wave length 0.000046 cm is used to illuminate a double slit, and the spacing between adjacent fringes is measured on a screen 3 m away. Using the same double slit with light of wave length 0.000061 cm, how far away from the double slit should the screen be located to produce the same spacing between adjacent fringes?

Lesson 17

1. When light strikes the flat surface of ice at an angle of incidence of 52.6°, the ray reflected at the surface is plane polarized. If the angle of incidence is changed to 45°, find the angle of refraction.

2. When light strikes the surface of carbon disulfide at an angle of incidence of 45°, the angle of refraction is 25.7°. What should be the angle of incidence in order that the ray reflected at the surface shall be plane polarized?

3. If the polarizing angle for a specimen of flint glass is 58.8°, what is the velocity of light in the specimen?

4. The critical angle of total reflection for benzene is 41.9°. Calculate the polarizing angle for this liquid.

Lesson 18

1. Find the length of a light wave for which the scattering would be double the scattering of light with a wave length of 6×10^{-5} cm.

2. Find the length of a light wave for which the scattering would be one-half the scattering of light waves with a wave length of 6×10^{-5} cm.

3. The waves used in radio broadcasting are of the same character as light waves but much longer. Typical values for wave length may be taken as 4×10^4 cm for the radio wave and 6×10^{-5} cm for the light wave. For every 10 radio waves that are scattered, how many light waves would be scattered?

4. X rays are like light waves except that their wave length is shorter. Typical wave lengths may be taken as 10^{-8} cm for the X rays and 6×10^{-5} cm for the light waves. For every 10 light waves that are scattered, how many X rays would be scattered?

ELECTRICITY AND MAGNETISM

Lesson 2

1. Calculate the force of repulsion between two electrons 1 mm apart.

2. Two positive charges 4 cm apart repel each other with a force of 0.9 newton. One

of the charges is known to be four times as large as the other. Find the magnitude of each charge.

3.* Two charges, each of -2×10^{-7} coulomb, are located at two corners of a triangle that measures 10 cm along each side. At the third corner is a charge of $+3 \times 10^{-7}$ coulomb. Find the resultant force that the two negative charges exert upon the positive charge and show its direction on a diagram drawn to scale.

4.* Two positive charges A and B are located 12 cm apart. Charge $A = 5 \times 10^{-8}$ coulomb and charge $B = 20 \times 10^{-8}$ coulomb. A third positive charge C is free to move along the line joining A and B. At what point on this line will charge C come to rest?

5.* Given three electric charges A, B, and C, of which A is known to be $+6 \times 10^{-8}$ coulomb. A and B placed 10 cm apart repel each other with a force of 0.00540 newton. A and C placed 10 cm apart attract each other with a force of 0.00648 newton. What force will B and C exert upon each other when placed 10 cm apart?

Lesson 3

1. How many coulombs of electricity pass through a flatiron in which a current of 5 amp flows for 30 min?

2. A battery which is passing electricity at a steady rate through an electric circuit drives 60 coulombs around the circuit in 2 min. What current is the battery supplying?

3. In charging a storage battery a current of 12 amp is passed through the battery for 2 hr. How many coulombs of electricity are supplied to the battery?

4. What current flowing for 5 sec will represent the same quantity of electricity as 0.01 amp flowing for 1 hr?

Lesson 5

1. A battery supplies a potential difference of 18 volts to a 4-Ω relay, a 6-Ω gong, and a 25-Ω resistor, all connected in series. If the remainder of the circuit has a resistance of 1 Ω, what is (a) the current in the circuit and (b) the voltage across the relay?

2. A battery lamp of 1.5-Ω resistance is to be lighted on a 110-volt circuit. How much resistance must be placed in series with the lamp in order that the voltage across the lamp shall not exceed 6 volts?

3. A 10-Ω coil of wire was designed to carry 2 amp safely. If this coil is to be connected across a 48-volt battery, how much resistance should be used in series with it in order that the current shall not exceed 2 amp?

4. To measure a high resistance a 15,000-Ω voltmeter is connected in series with it across a 115-volt supply line. If the voltmeter reading is 8.3 volts, what is the value of the high resistance?

Lesson 7

1. How many lamps each having a resistance of 220 Ω can be connected in parallel across a 110-volt supply line without drawing more than 6 amp from the line?

2. A certain current divides through two parallel branches having resistances of 6 Ω and 18 Ω, respectively, the potential difference across the parallel group being 54 volts. Find (a) the current in each branch and (b) that in the main line.

3. Four equal resistors draw a total current of 8 amp when connected in parallel across a 120-volt line. If these resistors were disconnected and placed all in series across the same line, how much current would they draw?

4.* A battery has an emf of 30 volts and an internal resistance of 0.5 Ω. It is connected to a load composed of two resistors of 5 Ω and 20 Ω, respectively, joined in parallel.

Calculate (a) the current supplied by the battery, (b) the potential difference across the battery, and (c) the current in the 5-Ω resistor.

Lesson 8

1. A spherical conductor of radius 3 cm has a charge of -15×10^{-7} coulomb. Consider a point on the surface of the sphere and find (a) the potential at this point and (b) the electric field intensity at this point.

2. Two spherical conductors carrying positive charges of 8×10^{-8} coulomb and 12×10^{-8} coulomb, respectively, are located 20 cm apart. Calculate (a) the potential at a point midway between the charges and (b) the electric field intensity at the same point.

3.* A metal sphere 4 cm in diameter has a positive charge of 5×10^{-8} coulomb. Point A is 30 cm from the center of the sphere and point B is 10 cm from the center of the sphere. Calculate the work done in carrying a positive charge of 2×10^{-8} coulomb (a) from A to B and (b) from B to the surface of the sphere.

4.* A pair of horizontal parallel plates are spaced 0.5 cm apart in air, and a droplet of oil charged with 2 electrons (3.204×10^{-19} coulomb) is introduced into the space between them. If the droplet weighs 8×10^{-15} newton, what potential difference must be applied to the plates in order to hold the droplet at rest?

Lesson 10

1. A large sheet of amber 2 mm thick is placed between a pair of metal plates measuring 20 cm by 30 cm. If the capacitor thus formed has a capacitance of 0.00075 μf, what is the dielectric constant of amber?

2.* Two capacitors of 4 μf and 12 μf, respectively, are connected in series. Two other capacitors of 1 μf and 5 μf, respectively, are connected in parallel. These two groups are connected in series across a 30-volt battery. Find (a) the voltage across the 1-μf capacitor and (b) the charge stored in the 5-μf capacitor.

3.* Two metal plates, each having an area of 800 cm², are parallel to each other and 5 mm apart. The plates are vertical and dip into petroleum so that half of their area is immersed. Calculate the capacitance of the capacitor thus formed.

4.* A 5-μf capacitor is charged from a 6-volt battery, which is then removed. (a) What is the charge on the capacitor? This capacitor is next connected in parallel with a 10-μf capacitor, previously uncharged, care being taken that no charge escapes. (b) What is the capacitance of the parallel combination? (c) What is the potential difference across the parallel combination? What is the final charge (d) on the 5-μf capacitor and (e) on the 10-μf capacitor?

Lesson 15

1. Three hot plates of 4 Ω, 5 Ω, and 20 Ω, respectively, are connected in parallel to a 48-volt battery. Calculate the total quantity of heat generated in 1 min by these hot plates.

2. An electric heater has two heating elements: their resistances are 20 Ω and 30 Ω, respectively, and they can be used (a) singly, (b) in series, or (c) in parallel. For each of these connections, how much heat will be generated in 1 min with the heater connected to a 120-volt circuit?

3. A trunk weighing 100 lb is pulled 20 ft across the floor. The coefficient of sliding friction is 0.50. Calculate the resistance of an electric heater carrying a current of 3 amp that would produce the same amount of heat in 1 sec as that expended in friction in pulling the trunk across the floor.

4.* A copper calorimeter of 75-gm mass contains 500 cm³ of water and 100 gm of ice, all at 0°C. A 20-Ω immersion heater is placed in the water and connected across a 120-volt line. How long will it take to melt the ice and raise the temperature of the calorimeter and its contents to 70°C?

Lesson 17

1. The moving coil of a millivoltmeter has a resistance of 5 Ω and deflects full scale when carrying a current of 0.01 amp. What shunt resistance connected across this instrument would make it into an ammeter with a full-scale deflection of 15 amp?

2. If the shunt is removed from the instrument in the preceding problem, what resistance connected in series with the coil will make the instrument into a voltmeter with a full-scale deflection of 15 volts?

3. Given a voltmeter having a resistance of 1500 Ω and a full-scale deflection of 15 volts, calculate the resistance needed to connect in series with this instrument to have it deflect full scale for 150 volts.

4. A galvanometer under test is found to deflect 10 divisions on its scale when 250 microvolts are applied to it. How many divisions will it deflect when connected in series with a 1.5-volt dry cell and a resistance of 1,000,000 Ω? The resistance of the galvanometer is 400 Ω.

Lesson 18

1. Two long, straight wires are stretched parallel to each other, 20 cm apart. Wire No. 1 carries 50 amp and wire No. 2 carries 30 amp, the current flowing in the same direction in both wires. At what place between the wires will the magnetic induction due to one of the currents just neutralize the magnetic induction due to the other?

2. Refer to the preceding problem and calculate the force which each of the wires exerts upon the other per meter of length.

3. A flat coil of 50 turns has a diameter of 4 in. and carries an electron current of 15 amp. This coil is placed on a table top. A second flat coil is then placed on the table top concentric with the first. The second coil has 75 turns of 6-in. radius, and its current, 25 amp, is in the same direction as that in the first coil. Find the magnetic induction at the common center of the coils.

4. A small metal sphere charged with 5×10^{-6} coulomb of electricity is whirled around in a horizontal circle of 20-cm radius. If the moving charge makes 15 rev/sec, what magnetic induction does it produce at the center of the circle?

5. A positively charged particle is shot with a speed of 2×10^7 m/sec through a region where the magnetic induction is 0.03 w/m². The particle is found to experience a force of 9.6×10^{-14} newton. If the particle moves along a direction that makes an angle of 30° with the magnetic field, what is the charge of the particle?

Lesson 20

1. To measure the magnetic induction of a magnetic field, a conductor is moved through the field as shown in Fig. C on page 422, and the emf generated in the wire is measured. If the wire is 0.6 m long and is moved at a speed of 5 m/sec, and if the emf is 2 volts, what is the magnetic induction?

2.* When an electron is shot horizontally into the magnetic field represented in Fig. C on page 422, it begins to move around a circle, showing that the magnetic force $F = QvB$ serves as the centripetal force necessary for circular motion. If the electron has a velocity of 3.25×10^5 m/sec and the flux density is 2×10^{-5} w/m², what is the radius of the circular path? The electron has a mass of 9.11×10^{-31} kg and a charge of 1.60×10^{-19} coulomb.

3.* If Fig. E on page 423 is taken to represent a coil of 20 turns each measuring 4 cm by 10 cm, and if the coil is rotated in a magnetic field where the magnetic induction is 1.2 w/m², (a) at what speed in revolutions per minute must the coil be driven in order that it may set up a root mean square voltage of 4 volts? (b) How many cycles will be generated per second?

4.* An electron is shot horizontally into a region where there is a vertical electric field, as shown in Fig. E on page 389, and also a horizontal magnetic field as shown in Fig. C on page 422. The electron experiences an upward force due to the presence of the electric field and a downward force because of its motion in the magnetic field. Suppose the electrical field intensity is 5×10^5 newtons/coulomb and the magnetic induction is 0.2 w/m². Find how fast the electron must be moving in order that the electric force acting upon it shall just neutralize the magnetic force.

Lesson 22

1. In Fig. H on page 430 suppose that the step-up transformer has 800 primary turns, the step-down transformer at the substation has 100,000 primary turns, and the step-down transformer near the consumer has 900 primary turns. Calculate the number of secondary turns on each transformer.

2. A transformer designed to step the voltage down from 2400 volts to 120 volts is rated 25 kva (25,000 volt-amp). Suppose the transformer to be carrying full load, and calculate (a) the primary current and (b) the secondary current.

3. A 10:1 step-down transformer supplied by a 2400-volt primary circuit is connected to a load which uses 7.5 kilowatts. Assume the transformer to be 100 per cent efficient and calculate its primary current.

4. A transformer draws a primary current of 7.57 amp from its supply circuit, and its secondary coil delivers 50 kilowatts at 1100 volts (rms) to the load. The transformer is designed to induce a peak voltage of 3.2 volts/turn in its windings. Assume an efficiency of 100 per cent and calculate the number of turns on the primary coil.

Lesson 23

1. A round iron bar 4 cm in diameter and 20 cm long is wound with copper wire to form a solenoid. The iron has a permeability of 12.57×10^{-4} w/amp-m, and the inductance is 0.45 h. A 6-volt 60-cycle transformer is used to supply current to the solenoid. Consider the resistance to be negligible and calculate the current in the circuit.

2. A 120-volt a.c. generator passes a current of 2.4 amp through a circuit composed of resistance, inductance, and capacitance, all in series. Take the resistance to be 40 Ω and the capacitive reactance 20 Ω, and calculate the value of the inductive reactance.

3. An inductance is connected in series with a capacitance of 20 μf across a 110-volt 60-cycle supply line. The resistance of the circuit is 10 Ω, and the inductance has a value such that the inductive reactance is just equal to the capacitive reactance. Calculate (a) the inductance and (b) the current in the circuit.

4. An inductive reactance of 5 Ω and a resistance of 12 Ω are connected in series across a 130-volt a.c. line. Calculate (a) the phase angle by which the current lags the voltage, (b) the power factor of the circuit, and (c) the power delivered to the circuit.

ATOMIC PHYSICS

Lesson 2

1. If an electron having a velocity of 2×10^7 m/sec moves in a circular path of 10-cm radius when it enters an electric field, what is the intensity of the field?

2. Electrons entering a uniform magnetic field in a direction at right angles to the lines of induction where $B = 4 \times 10^{-4}$ w/m² have a velocity of 6.5×10^8 cm/sec. These

electrons take a circular path of definite radius. Calculate the intensity of an electric field such that in the electric field alone the electrons would take a circular path having the same radius.

3. In Thomson's apparatus shown in Fig. A on page 448, suppose the electrons to have a velocity of 10^9 cm/sec. Calculate (a) the voltage impressed upon the $+$ and $-$ high-voltage terminals and (b) the work done upon each electron to give it the stated velocity.

4. A droplet of oil is admitted into the region between two parallel charged plates, as shown in Fig. D on page 450. The plates are 12 cm in diameter, spaced 0.44 cm apart, and are maintained at a potential difference of 220 volts. By how much will the upward force on the droplet be increased if it acquires 2 electrons?

Lesson 3

1. Take the atomic weight of hydrogen to be 1.01 and that of carbon to be 12.00 and calculate the (approximate) mass in grams of one molecule of benzine. See Fig. A on page 155.

2. From the atomic weights listed in Appendix II calculate the number of molecules in 1 gm of water. See Fig. A on page 155.

3. An element is composed of two isotopes with masses of 63 and 65 atomic mass units. If the first of these has an abundance of 71.5%, calculate (a) the abundance of the other isotope and (b) the atomic weight of the element.

4.* Silver is composed of two isotopes with masses of 107 and 109 atomic mass units. Calculate the relative abundance of these two isotopes to give 107.88 as the atomic weight of silver.

Lesson 8

1. The half life of polonium is known to be 140 days. In what length of time would the activity of polonium be reduced to approximately 0.001 of its initial value?

2. If, at a particular time, a specimen contains 0.001 gm of polonium, how much polonium does it contain (a) 140 days later and (b) 140 days earlier?

ELECTRONICS

Lesson 1

1. Calculate the inductance to use with a capacitance of 0.03 μf to emit electromagnetic waves having a frequency of 5×10^8/sec.

2.* Two capacitors rated 4 μf and 12 μf, respectively, are joined in series, and a capacitor of unknown capacitance is connected in parallel with this combination. The group of capacitors is connected across a 5-μh inductor, and the oscillating circuit is found to have a frequency of 22.5 kilocycles/sec. What is the capacitance of the unknown capacitor?

Lesson 5

1. Make a diagram showing how to use a photoelectric cell to tell when a bowler steps over the foul line.

2. Find the ratio of the energy in a quantum of violet light to that in a quantum of red light. Use wave lengths tabulated on page 331.

3. If tests are made in which light of different wave lengths is caused to strike the surface of sodium, what is the limiting wave length above which no electrons would be liberated from the surface? The work function of sodium is 3.65×10^{-19} joule.

4. The work function of a metal must be less than a certain limiting value if the surface is to release electrons when illuminated by a particular color of light. Calculate such a limiting value for the work function of a metal when illuminated by green light having a wave length of 54.61×10^{-6} cm.

5.* Light of wave length 0.0000393 cm strikes the surface of sodium, which has a work function of 3.65×10^{-19} joule. Calculate the greatest velocity with which electrons leave the surface when it is illuminated in this manner.

Lesson 7

1. What is the cut-off frequency for a wave guide that has a rectangular cross section measuring 2 cm by 4 cm?

2. Calculate the wider dimension of a rectangular wave guide used for transmitting waves having a frequency of 2000 Mc/sec.

3. Each scanned picture in TV requires 325 lines, and 30 pictures per second are used. Assume the picture to be 18 in. wide and calculate the speed with which the reproducing spot moves across the fluorescent screen. Neglect the time occupied in jumping back to start the next line.

4. In the pulsed system of radar ranging, if the time interval between a transmitted pulse and its echo is 7.5×10^{-5} sec, how far away is the object from which the wave was reflected?

5. To compare the scattering of light waves and radar waves, suppose the radar wave to have a frequency of 30,000 Mc/sec and find how many waves of green light will be scattered for every 10 radar waves scattered. Take the wave length of green light to be 5300×10^{-8} cm.

QUANTUM OPTICS

Lesson 1

1. Given that the radius of the innermost orbit of the hydrogen atom as 5.28×10^{-11} m, use the equation $r = \dfrac{n^2 h^2}{4\pi^2 m e^2 k}$ and note that the quantities are all constant except r and n. Write down by inspection the radii of the second and third orbits.

2.* Use the equation $r = \dfrac{n^2 h^2}{4\pi^2 m e^2 k}$ and show by calculation that the radius of the innermost orbit in the hydrogen atom is 5.28×10^{-11} m.

3. Knowing the radii of the orbits in the hydrogen atom, use the equation $F = k \dfrac{QQ'}{d^2}$ and find the attractive force between the nucleus of the hydrogen atom and an electron revolving in the innermost orbit.

4. From the equation $mvr = n \dfrac{h}{2\pi}$ find the angular momentum of an electron revolving in the innermost orbit of the hydrogen atom.

5.* Use the result of Problem 6 on page 514 and compute the kinetic energy of the electron in the hydrogen atom when it is revolving in its innermost orbit.

Lesson 2

1. Imagine the hydrogen atom in its normal state to be magnified until its electronic orbit is a mile in diameter. What would be the apparent diameter of the nucleus? Take its true diameter to be 10^{-12} cm.

2. The equation $r = \dfrac{n^2 h^2}{4\pi^2 m e^2 k}$ was used for the hydrogen atom, but it may be used for other atoms by recognizing that the term e^2 represents the product of the charge of the nucleus and the charge of the electron. Show by analysis of this equation that the radius of the innermost orbit in the helium atom will be one-half of the radius of the innermost orbit in the hydrogen atom. What is this radius for helium?

3. Calculate the charge on the nucleus of the helium atom, and from the equation $F = k\dfrac{QQ'}{d^2}$ get the force of attraction between the helium nucleus and an electron in its innermost orbit, using the radius found in the preceding problem.

4. Calculate (a) the radius of the innermost orbit in the lithium atom and (b) the force of attraction between the nucleus and an electron in this orbit.

Lesson 3

1. Calculate the energy of a quantum of X rays having a wave length of 7×10^{-11} m.

2. If X rays are caused to shine upon a metal surface, the work function of the metal must not exceed a certain limiting value if photoelectrons are to be ejected. Calculate this limiting value for a metal exposed to the X rays of the preceding problem.

3. If the momentum of an X-ray photon is 9×10^{-24} kg m/sec², what is the wave length of the X rays?

4. Calculate the velocity of an electron for which the De Broglie wave length is 5×10^{-12} m.

Lesson 4

1. An electron moving with a velocity of 5×10^4 m/sec enters a medium in which its velocity is reduced to 3×10^4 m/sec. If the electron meets the boundary between the two mediums at an angle of incidence of 30°, what is the angle of refraction?

2. An electron moving with a velocity v enters an electric field at an angle of incidence of 45°. If the path of the electron is deviated 15° toward the normal upon entering the field, what is the velocity of the electron in the field?

3. An electron enters an electric field at an angle of incidence of 60° and is deviated so that the angle of refraction is 30°. What is its velocity before entering the field if its velocity in the field is 1/10 of the velocity of light?

4. Suppose that an electron enters the region between a pair of parallel charged plates with a velocity of 4×10^5 m/sec, and it is found that within the field the angle of refraction is 20° and the velocity of the electron is 5×10^5 m/sec. What is the angle of incidence of the electron upon entering the field?

NUCLEAR PHYSICS

Lesson 1

1. In a recent survey the average electrical energy used daily in a large city was found to be about 40×10^6 kilowatt-hours. If it were possible to obtain this energy by the annihilation of matter, how much matter would have to be completely annihilated?

2. Calculate the mass of the chlorine isotope $_{17}Cl^{35}$ and express the result (a) in atomic mass units and (b) in kilograms.

3. How many electron volts of energy would be liberated by the annihilation of an α particle?

4. Convert an energy of 1 Mev to foot-pounds.

Lesson 5

1. Complete the following disintegration reaction: $_1H^2 + _8O^{16} \rightarrow _7N^{14} + ?$ Calculate the amount of mass annihilated. Follow the method used on page 546 and express the results in kilograms.

2. Write down the disintegration equation when nitrogen-14 is bombarded by deuterons. Calculate the amount of mass annihilated in the disintegration, expressing the result in kilograms.

3. Consider the disintegration represented in the equation $_2He^4 + _4Be^9 = _6C^{12} + _0n^1$. Follow the method described on page 546 to calculate the amount of energy liberated.

4. Radioactive sulfur-35 is produced by the neutron bombardment of chlorine-35. Calculate the energy liberated in the disintegration.

Lesson 6

1. If two protons and two neutrons were combined to form a helium-4 nucleus, what percentage of their original mass would be annihilated?

2. Calculate the amount of energy needed to remove a neutron from the nucleus of argon-38.

3. How much energy would be required to break up an oxygen-16 nucleus into individual protons and neutrons?

4. How much energy in Mev is needed to separate a beryllium-8 nucleus into four deuterons?

Index